ANNUAL REVIEW OF PHYSIOLOGY

ANNUAL REVIEW OF PHYSIOLOGY

JULIUS H. COMROE, JR., *Editor*
University of California Medical Center, San Francisco

ARTHUR C. GIESE, *Associate Editor*
Stanford University

RALPH R. SONNENSCHEIN, *Associate Editor*
University of California, Los Angeles

VOLUME 34

1972
ANNUAL REVIEWS INC.
4139 EL CAMINO WAY
PALO ALTO, CALIFORNIA 94306, USA

ANNUAL REVIEWS INC.
PALO ALTO, CALIFORNIA, USA

© 1972 BY ANNUAL REVIEWS INC.
ALL RIGHTS RESERVED

Standard Book Number 8243–0334–2
Library of Congress Catalog Card Number 39–15404

FOREIGN AGENCY

Maruzen Company, Limited
6 Tori-Nichome, Nihonbashi
Tokyo

PRINTED AND BOUND IN THE UNITED STATES OF AMERICA
BY GEORGE BANTA COMPANY, INC.

PREFACE

Victor E. Hall, Associate Editor of the *Annual Review of Physiology* for its first eight volumes and Editor for the next twenty-five, retired in 1971. We wish to express our deep appreciation to Dr. Hall, on behalf of physiological scientists throughout the world, for initiating this venture, enlarging its scope, and continuously increasing its usefulness over the past three decades. His fine touch as Editor was evident in the progressively improved style and content of the *Annual Review;* he furthermore instituted one of the most valuable aspects of the *Review*—the prefatory chapters of personal reminiscences by senior physiologists whose words can be of interest and inspiration to all their successors. The practice of including such chapters has since been adopted by several other *Annual Reviews.*

During this period, the number of physiological investigations reported each year became so large that an annual review could no longer *list* all of them let alone mention their principal findings or comment critically on them. And so the *Annual Review* changed its policy from trying to achieve an all-inclusive, annotated, organized bibliography year by year to attempting to be selective: reviewers were asked to discuss those articles most likely to advance physiological science, to evaluate conflicting reports on important issues, to synthesize knowledge from many fields into unifying new concepts, and to point out areas of ignorance that might be clarified by modern experimental approaches. This policy, which will be continued by the new Editor, changes the role of the author of each chapter from that of an observer, recorder, and commentator to that of a statesman in physiological science. It places an additional responsibility on the authors of *Annual Reviews* but we believe that the gratitude of our readers will repay them. To avoid the loss to physiologists of the valuable report that is unappreciated and therefore uncited by the reviewer, the *Annual Review of Physiology* will continue to make available to readers more complete bibliographies than the list of reports cited at the end of each review and will continue to call to the attention of readers more complete reviews that appear elsewhere.

In June of this year, a new *Annual Review* will appear—in Biophysics and Bioengineering—under the Editorship of Dr. Manual Morales. This new *Review* reflects the tremendous growth of knowledge in the physiological sciences. As a "cross-over" volume, it will assist many physiologists, cell biologists, geneticists, biochemists, molecular biologists, biophysicists, and bioengineers to maintain their broad interests as well as more specialized ones. Volume one of still another new *Annual Review*—of anthropology—will appear in the fall of this year. For these and many other constructive ideas that help to maintain the role of Annual Reviews in assisting the scientific community, we thank a distinguished Board of Directors.

Last November, the new home of Annual Reviews in Palo Alto was re-dedicated as the J. Murray Luck Building to honor the man who conceived Annual Reviews and charted their course as Editor-in-Chief for many years; Dr. Luck was also the first Editor of the *Annual Review of Physiology*.

We acknowledge the valuable editorial assistance of Christina Smillie and the continued fine work of the Banta Press.

JHC
ACG
RRS

CONTENTS

ERRATA

Volume 33 (1971)—Actions of Vertebrate Sex Hormones, by H. G. Williams-Ashman and A. H. Reddi

page 50 line 44: new *should read* next
page 56 line 13: secretary *should read* secretory
page 76 reference 182: 69:153–64 *should read* 62:153–64
page 77 reference 201: 5:420–31 *should read* 5:428–31
page 78 reference 259: 114:59–60 *should read* 114:59–60P
page 79 reference 291: 1968. *J. Pharmacol. Exp. Ther.* 162:362–71
    should read 1969. *Steroids* 13:155–61

REPRINTS

The conspicuous number (1071 to 1086) aligned in the margin with the title of each review in this volume is a key for use in the ordering of reprints.

The sale of reprints from all *Annual Reviews* volumes was initiated in July 1970. Reprints of most articles published in the *Annual Reviews of Physiology and Microbiology* from 1968 to 1970 and the *Annual Reviews of Biochemistry and Psychology* from 1961 to 1970 are now maintained in inventory.

Available reprints are priced at the uniform rate of $1 each postpaid. Payment must accompany orders less than $10. The following discounts will be given for large orders: $5–9, 10 percent; $10–$24, 20 percent; $25 and over, 30 percent. All remittances are to be made payable to Annual Reviews Inc. in US dollars. California orders are subject to sales tax. One-day service is given on items in stock.

For orders of 100 or more, any *Annual Reviews* article will be specially printed and shipped within 6 weeks. Reprints that are out of stock may also be purchased from the Institute for Scientific Information, 325 Chestnut Street, Philadelphia, Pa. 19106. Direct inquiries to the Annual Reviews Inc. reprint department.

The sale of reprints of articles published in the *Reviews* has been expanded in the belief that reprints as individual copies, as sets covering stated topics, and in quantity for classroom use will have a special appeal to students and teachers.

Ragnar Granit

DISCOVERY AND UNDERSTANDING

Ragnar Granit

The Nobel Institute for Neurophysiology, Karolinska Institutet, Stockholm, Sweden

In asking me to write an introduction to these review articles the Editors have generously given me a free hand. They may nevertheless have expected me to write something about my research —its background in contemporary work and in my own upbringing. If this was the idea, it did not appeal to me in the least. The reason for this was that anyone interested in this kind of information can have it in the books I have already written (see especially 6, 7, 9). To some extent these books not only report my work but also illustrate my considerable delight in tracing the history of the ideas that they have propounded. As to my personal attitude to our science, it emerges in my book on Sherrington (8); nobody can write a book concerned with values and evaluation without exposing his own values rather fully.

Grappling with the necessity of supplying something of general interest, I remembered the frame of mind in which I had spent the early spring 1941 after a bicycle accident that crushed one knee. Reading could not then fill all my time; besides, it compounded the constraint I felt, being confined to intake alone, while all the time the creative urge demanded release in some form of output. In this predicament I recalled an early lecture of mine to an academic student body under the heading "Talented youngster looking for a teacher," and this put me to writing a collection of essays, *Ung mans väg till Minerva* (5) (Young man's way to Minerva) which was published that autumn.

My book preceded Cannon's *The Way of an Investigator* (4) by a few years. When his work appeared I read it eagerly and found a great deal of overlap, both in its point of view and in its emphasis. Far more has since been written on the same subject—more systematic, better documented books covering the whole field (e.g. Beveridge 3). Thus, it was with feelings of anxiety that I looked up my old work. Rereading it now and musing over it, I found it, indeed, a book by a younger man than my present self, written for young men fired by enthusiasm for a life devoted to science. The tutor, slightly older than his listeners, speaks to them about the courting of Minerva: he tells them of her apparent fickleness and real austerity, of her views on ambition and success, and of much else, not forgetting to mention the radiance of her smile on the rare occasions when she bestows it. There was about these essays an air of intimacy nurtured by convalescence.

1

I have been asked by a publisher to translate them into English but do not trust myself to render into another language something that depended so much on its style of presentation.

Now, thirty years later, I return to such matters in a mood of detachment. Many people regard detachment as one of the great virtues. But it is probably not conducive to scientific creativity of the kind that was life itself to the young author of "Minerva." Passion is a better word for describing that attitude. Young people are out for themselves, to make discoveries, to see something that others have not seen. They may be satisfied with a modicum of analysis because there is always something round the corner to look at—perhaps something new and quite unexpected, exciting and important, at any rate a temptation hard to resist. Later in life one may feel it less compelling to discover something. Rather does one prefer to learn to understand a little of Nature's ways in a wider context. Then, detachment comes in handy. One realizes that it really is a great virtue: the virtue of those who have to weigh and judge. In this state of mind, I have decided to offer some comments on discovery and understanding. In the main I shall restrict myself to experimental biology.

By "discovery" we mean in the first instance an experimental result that is new. In a more trivial sense most results are new just as they always impart "knowledge" of some sort. For practical purposes I tend to ask myself when reading a paper: is this knowledge, or real knowledge? Similarly one may ask: is this result new, or really new? In the latter case it is a discovery, and a discovery tends to break the carapace of dogma around an established view, just as a bombardment with heavy particles tends to scatter the nucleus of an atom. In this type of discovery there is an element of unexpectedness. One of the best known examples is Röntgen's discovery of the rays that in many languages bear his name, a discovery that came as a surprise to him and to the rest of the scientific world.

There is a second and equally fundamental type of discovery: the delivery of experimental evidence for a view that is probable, yet not established, because such evidence as there is has not yet excluded alternative possibilities. An example of the latter type is the theory of chemical transmission at synapses, suggested by T. R. Elliot in 1905, but not proved until very much later (Loewi, Dale). This is the most common type of discovery: confirmation by evidence of one theory from a number of alternative hypotheses.

Either type of discovery, to deserve the term, must have far-reaching consequences, as the cases illustrated here indeed have had. Unless this criterion is satisfied, we are not willing to use a grand word like "discovery" instead of speaking modestly of a new result, more or less interesting, as the case may be.

The experimenter himself may not always understand what he has seen, though realizing that it is something quite new and probably very important. Thus, for instance, when Frithiof Holmgren in 1865 put one electrode on the cornea and another on the cut end of the optic nerve, he recorded a response to onset and cessation of illumination. This he held to be Du Bois-Reymond's "negative variation," that is, the action currents of the optic nerve fibres. These were what he had been looking for and therefore expected to find. Six years later, Holmgren started shifting his electrodes around the bulb and soon understood that the distribution of current he obtained required that the response had to originate in the retina itself. Dewar and M'Kendrick independently rediscovered the electroretinogram on the equally false supposition that a retina would display the photoelectric effect, at that time recently discovered by Willoughby Smith. In both cases the electroretinogram was the unexpected result of something expected. It was an important discovery, the first evidence for an electrochemical process generated by stimulation of a sense organ: evidence that something objective connected a physically defined stimulus to a sensory experience. Quite rightly Holmgren titled his first paper (in translation) "Method for objectivating the effect of an impression of light on the retina." It also satisfies the criterion that a discovery should have far-reaching consequences. I was myself concerned with three of them: the discovery of inhibition in the retina, the demonstration that an important component of light adaptation and dark adaptation was electrical in origin and not due to photopigments alone, and the development of the theory that generator potentials stimulate sensory nerves to discharge. Subsequent workers in this field could easily extend the list, if further proof of its importance should be required.

Quite interesting is the period of latency between the discovery of the electroretinogram and an elementary understanding of what it meant. In the present context the latency serves to emphasize that "discovery" and "understanding" really are different concepts and are not arbitrarily differentiated. There is in discovery a quality of uniqueness tied to a particular moment in time, while understanding goes on and on from level to level of penetration and insight and thus is a process that lasts for years, in many cases for the discoverer's lifetime.

The young scientist often seems to share with the layman the view that scientific progress can be looked upon as one long string of pearls made up of bright discoveries. This standpoint is reflected in the will of Alfred Nobel whose mind was that of an inventor, always loaded with good ideas for application. His great Awards in science presuppose definable discoveries. The following are his own formulations from his will: "The most important discovery or invention within the field of physics," "The most important discovery within the domain of physiology or medicine," "The most important chemical discovery or improvement." Only in chemistry, of which he had first-hand experience as an inventor of smokeless powder and dynamite, did he allow that a Nobel prize could also be given for an "improvement." It is well known that one of his major contributions to the invention of dynamite was in the nature of an improvement: he made the use of dynamite nearly foolproof by adding kieselguhr to the original "blasting oil" (nitroglycerol) that had proved so dangerous in practice. This finding may have made him realize that there are inventions and discoveries which have to be improved before their significance can be established. One should thread warily through these subtle distinctions. I can think of Nobel Prizes in Chemistry that have been given for "improvements" but do not remember ever in 27 years of Academy voting having heard any citation legitimized by this term.

It is easy to understand the emphasis, or rather overemphasis, on discovery as the real goal of scientific endeavour. By the definition used here, a discovery has important consequences and initiates a fresh line of development. It catches the eye and, in the present age, is pushed into the limelight by various journals devoted to the popularization of science—sometimes even by newspapers. In my youth we were much impressed by a philosopher at the University of Lund, Hans Larsson (who, I believe, wrote only in Swedish). I remember a thesis of his to the effect that in our thinking we try to reach points commanding a view. In science, discoveries often serve as viewing towers of this kind. The discoverer himself may not always climb to the top of his own tower. Others make haste to reach it, outpacing him. In the end many people are there, most of them trying to do much the same thing. The discoverer himself should be excused if he is possessed by a desire to find a peaceful retreat where he can do something else and quietly erect another lookout.

A systematic classification of types of discovery cannot be attempted here but some comments should be made. There are, for example, the discoveries that ride on the wave of a technical advance. At the time it became possible to stimulate nerves electrically, it became possible to discover any number of new and important mechanisms of nervous control. Small wonder that the great German physiologist Karl Ludwig could say to his pupils: "wer nur arbeitet, findet immer etwas."[1] Equally optimistic was Helmholtz when, as professor of physiology at Heidelberg, he said that it was merely necessary to take a deep dig with the spade in order to find something new and interesting. Transferring these amiable opinions of Ludwig and Helmholtz recorded by their pupil Frithiof Holmgren to the present age, one would, for example, expect every one of the large and busy brotherhood of neurophysiologists to turn out discoveries. But is this so? The question is rhetorical.

Today there is a much shorter period of skimming the cream off a new technique than there was in the 1860s. It is not uncommon to find that those workers who depend very largely on a specific technical innovation, soon become sterile even though they themselves may have had an honorable share in the development of the technique they are using.

Those who start with a problem and develop the technique for solving it

---

[1] "He who but works will always find something."

can in the long run look forward to better prospects. As an example one might take Erlanger and Gasser's use of the newborn cathode ray to measure conduction velocities of the component fibers of nerve trunks. On the basis of W. Thompson's formula for electrical cable conduction, Göthlin had made calculations in 1907 leading to the theory that conduction velocity in thick nerve fibers would be greater than in thin ones. Some fifteen years later Erlanger and Gasser, realizing that amplification made it possible to use the inertia-less cathode ray for tackling this question, took the trouble to overcome the deficiencies with which the early cathode ray tubes were afflicted and, as we all know, solved the problem of conduction velocity in nerve fibers of different diameter.

This is an interesting example of a rather common type of discovery, the one in which it is realized at the outset that something definite can be discovered, provided that the required technical solution can be managed. It presupposes that the experimenter knows how to formulate a well defined question and realizes what kind of obstacles prevented earlier workers from answering it. In the case of Erlanger and Gasser the basic result could hardly be called unexpected. Nevertheless most neurophysiologists are willing to classify their result as an important discovery, some perhaps merely because it had far-reaching consequences in physiological experimentation. I do so with a further motivation: many things can be predicted with a fair degree of probability, and in all good laboratories a number of such predictions, some passing fancies, others quite significant, are floating about. My respect and admiration goes to the people who reformulate such notions into experimental propositions and do the hard work required for testing them. These people are the real discoverers. The other day I saw in a student journal from the Royal Technical University of Stockholm my viewpoint expressed in a modern version: "It is easy enough to say Hallelujah, but go and do it!"

The sterilizing effect of a technique stabilized into a routine was briefly alluded to above. What then happens is that those adept in the routine easily turn into great producers of small things. Of course rejuvenation is possible. A good example is the technique of tissue culture which was for a long time in that particular state of aimless delivery but has since recovered its significance. In my own field of neurophysiology it seems that the technique of evoked mass potentials is balancing on a rather thin edge of functional relevance, all the time running the risk of becoming merely an accessory to anatomy. While this itself is a respectable science, physiology should have different aims in order to remain respectable in its own sphere. There should not be too many people within a field who care merely for the technically soluble and not for what is worth solving. However, this tempting subject will not be pursued now. Most workers, as they grow older, realize that some kind of borderline exists between those who are interested in a technique as an instrument for producing papers justifying grants, and those who see it as a possible way of furthering long-range projects.

"I have to admit," said Helmholtz in his *Vorträge und Reden*, "that those fields of study have steadily grown more pleasant for me in which one is not constrained to resort to happy coincidences and fancies" (my translation). With that basic attitude to a life in the field of science there is no alternative available than to try to realize some fundamental ideas about biological structures and their functions, that is, to promote understanding. Gradually understanding will ripen into insight. It cannot be denied that for some time "happy coincidences and fancies" may have a value that they otherwise would not possess, when fresh possibilities are opened up by a new technique. But will this inspiration last into one's old age? I daresay Helmholtz was right when he advocated working from a basis of understanding.

This attitude toward scientific work has the advantage of permitting the experimenters to devote themselves quietly to their labors without filling various journals with preliminary notes to obtain minor priorities. A disadvantage is of course the practical difficulty of persuading various foundations and research councils that their work is of some importance in a world such as ours is at present. The judgment required to appreciate the mode of progress I am advocating may not always be at hand. There is a well-known example in Fulton's biography of Harvey Cushing: After a visit to Sherrington in Liverpool in 1901 Cushing wrote in his diary: "As far as I can see, the reason why he is so much quoted is not that he has done especially big things but that his predecessors have done them all so poorly before." Sherrington, as we all know, had a good long-range program, and Cushing was no fool. One can only conclude that it can be very difficult to make others even understand the aims of long-range programs—much less support them.

There are so many instances of discoveries having led to major advances that one is compelled to ask whether it is at all possible to make a really important contribution to experimental biology without the support of a striking discovery. Sherrington's life and work throw light on this question. Most neurophysiologists would not hesitate to call him one of the leading pioneers in their field. Yet he never made any discovery. In a systematic and skillful way he made use of known reflex types to illustrate his ideas on synaptic action and spinal cord functions. Reciprocal innervation was known before Sherrington took it up, decerebrate rigidity had been described, many other reflexes were known, inhibition had been discovered, spinal shock was familiar—at least to the group around Goltz in Strasbourg, and the general problem of muscular reception had been formulated. What Sherrington did was to supply the necessary element of "understanding," not, of course, by sitting at his writing desk, but by active experimentation around a set of gradually ripening ideas which he corrected and improved in that manner. This went on for years—a life time, to be precise. Ultimately a degree of conceptual accuracy was reached in his definition of synaptic excitation and inhibition that could serve as a basis for the development that has taken place in the last thirty years. His concepts are still with us, now fully incorporated in our present approach to these problems.

The insight Sherrington ultimately reached can of course be called a "discovery," but to do so is contrary to usage. Within the experimental sciences the term "discovery" is not applied to theories acquired in this manner, even though the experimenter himself may feel that he has had his moments of insight coming like flashes of discovery after some time of experimentation.

Another example illustrating slow ripening of fundamental insight is provided by Darwin's life and labors. Back in England after the long cruise in the Beagle he went to work. "My first note-book," he said, "was opened in July 1837. I worked on true Baconian principles, and without any theory collected facts on a wholesale scale, more especially with respect to domesticated productions, by printed enquiries, by conversation with skillful breeders and gardeners, and by extensive reading.—I soon perceived that selection was the keystone of man's success in making useful races of animals and plants. But how selection could be applied to organisms living in a state of nature remained for some time a mystery to me" (1). Malthus' *Essay on Population*, a book still quite readable, gave him a "theory by which to work," because, he says, he was "well prepared to appreciate the struggle for existence" which would tend to preserve favorable variations, and tend to destroy unfavorable ones.

Darwin described flashes of insight in his work—as all scientists could do—but essentially it was twenty years of hard labor scrutinizing the evidence for his thoughts that in the end brought clarity. In 1858 he published a preliminary note together with Wallace who had independently arrived at similar conclusions; in 1859 appeared his *Origin of Species*. The idea of evolution was by no means new. His granddaughter Nora Barlow emphasizes that "to Charles Darwin it was the body of evidence supporting evolutionary theory that mattered, and that he knew was his own contribution" (2).

With some justification one can say that today the long, narrow and winding road to real knowledge has become harder to follow. In the face of innumerable distractions it has become increasingly difficult for the individual worker to preserve his identity. This, however, is necessary if he intends to grow and ripen within any branch of science. The point I want to make is that what we read, what we actively remember, and what we ourselves contribute to our fields of interests very gradually build up living and creative structures within us. We do not know how the brain does it, no more than we know how the world of sight gradually becomes upright again when for a while we have carried inverting spectacles. Our knowledge of the workings of our mind is of the scantiest. We simply have to admit that the brain is designed that way.

By "keeping track of one's identity" I mean cultivating the talents of listening to the workings of one's own mind, separating minor diversions from main lines of thought, and gratefully accepting what the secret process of automatic creation delivers. I can well understand that many people do not think much of this notion and prefer to regard it as one of my personal

idosyncracies. Others who late in life look over their own activities, are sure
to find at least something that looks like a main line of personal identity in
the choice of their labors. Up to this point many colleagues are perhaps willing to agree. But a little more than that is meant when I maintain that an
active brain is self-fertile in the manner described. I am convinced that if
one can take care of one's identity, it, in turn, will take care of one's scientific
development.

I am emphasizing all this so strongly because there are today so many
distractions preventing scientists from enjoying the quietude and balance
required for contact with their own creative life. The cities and the universities are becoming more restless, and the "organization men" with their
meddlesome paper work of questionnaires and regulations tend to increase
in number while the number of teachers relative to students decreases. This
development tends to breed a clientele of anti-scientific undergraduates de-
manding more and more of the universities and less and less of themselves.
The research workers withdraw into separate research institutes—furthering
the deterioration of standards in teaching and in intellectual idealism in the
faculties of our ancient sites of learning. Science does indeed need a number
of pure research institutes, but university faculties left to themselves and
engaged wholly in teaching can hardly be called universities; these should
be capable of living up to the true "idea of a university" in the sense that it
once was defined by Cardinal Newman in his well known book.

In all creative work there is need for a good deal of time for exercising
the talent of listening to oneself, often more profitable than listening to
others or, at any rate, an important supplement to the life of symposia and
congresses. Perhaps this latter kind of life is also overdone in the present age.
There are so many of these meetings nowadays that people can keep on
drifting round the world and soon be pumped dry of what is easier to empty
than to refill.

My plea for a measure of "self-contact" is really that of the poet and
essayist Abraham Cowley (1618–1667) who said that the prime minister
has not as much to attend to in the way of public affairs as a wise man has
in his solitude. If there are those who experience nothing when trying to
listen to themselves, this need not always indicate congenital defects. They
may have been badly trained or may have been too lazy to absorb the
knowledge and experiences that the brain needs for doing its part of the
job.

Against this background one can raise the question of whether all creative originality in science is necessarily inborn or whether there also exists
an acquired variety of this valuable property. I suppose most people share
my view that great originality in creative work is part of a man's inheritance.
But after half a century of scientific activity I have had the opportunity to
observe the development of many contemporary as well as younger colleagues. I feel that a perusal of these experiences—without mentioning any

names—might suggest an answer to this question or at least provide an opinion. It seems then that some of those who as young men did not show much promise of originality, although quite capable of the necessary intellectual effort, later have given original contributions to our science. How should this observation be interpreted? Obviously I may have been mistaken. On the other hand, one does not often make mistakes about real originality—quite apart from the fact that real originality often insists upon being recognized. I do not believe that the category of people of whom I am now speaking were wrongly assessed at an earlier date. Rather it is my conviction that these are the very people who without difficulties have managed to explore their own mental resources so as to make profitable use of them. They have had the capacity for listening quietly to their own minds and to the good advice of others, and in this way have grown, blossomed, and born fruit.

These conclusions will appear more evident if one considers progress within any individual branch of science. It is well known that in each phase of development the same ideas turn up in many laboratories of the scientifically active world. It is hardly necessary to add examples, as two good ones have already been provided: Holmgren with Dewar and M'Kendrick, and Darwin with Wallace. Even Newton himself said that he had stood on the shoulders of a giant. At the time when I regularly followed the scrutiny of proposals for Nobel prizes (requiring careful study of priorities), there were many opportunities to observe independent but overlapping discoveries as the bases of proposals from different sources. This is by no means surprising. Why should not well trained people who have read much the same lot of papers and monographs come to similar conclusions about the next step in a logical sequence? Since it is often difficult to foresee what each step implies for subsequent steps, parallel conclusions may in a number of instances lead to quite original contributions based on knowledge and perseverance.

In the last instance the front line of research is created by minds whose combined effort more or less perfectly represents the inner logic characteristic of a particular period. Many professional scientists have good intuitive contact with the broad lines of this development. This is expressed in the saying that something reflects the "characteristic note of the age." The original part of what is called "originality" is a capacity for understanding, intuitively as well as logically, what is an important step forward within any specific branch of science. A creative scientist has more numerous, better developed and more precise contacts with the characteristic note of his age, and can therefore, if health and perserverance do not fail him, make greater contributions than others.

I think I have said enough in defense of my thesis that acquired originality exists. Such acquisition requires intense work—preferably within one particular sphere of problems—and, obviously, enough talent to support a reasonable rate of intake. I have always believed that in most cases people have enough talent for handling research, at least when working with a team, and that failures should be accounted for by other factors which I need not enumerate in this connection.

All this implies that, in the present era of rapid communication by many channels, the individual scientist has but a share in the process of scientific discovery and understanding: even if he abandons his field of research, its development will continue, though perhaps in a slightly different way or at a slower pace.

From this standpoint it is profitable to contemplate the disturbing and often pathological quarrels concerned with the ownership of ideas. Ideas, notions, and suggestions are often thrown out in passing at meetings or in laboratory discussions and may sometimes fall on fertile ground. Who then is the owner? The one who made the suggestion may or may not have intended to make anything out of it. Again I maintain that the only definable ownership belongs to the man who develops the idea experimentally, or propounds it as a definite and well-formulated hypothesis capable of being tested.

Fights about priorities are never as violent as when a discovery is at stake. This is well known, and, if I mention such matters briefly, it is merely to point out the dangers of too much emphasis on the need for making a discovery, and to contrast it against the more peaceful life of development of understanding—without looking askance at "discovery" and what it may bring in its trail in the way of specific rewards.

I began by comparing the efforts of young men with those of men old enough not to be called young and by trying to show with the aid of two famous examples that it is by no means necessary to make any discoveries at all to do extremely well in science. It is not my intention to undervalue discoveries, but only to emphasize that it is really understanding that scientists are after, even when they are making discoveries. These are or can be of little interest as long as they are mere facts. They have to be understood, at least in a general way, and such understanding implies placing them into a structural whole where they illuminate a relevant step forward or solidify known ideas within it.

Since understanding or insight is the real goal of our labors, why make so much noise about discoveries? Why indeed? Perhaps because they provide instantaneous excitement—releasing the "eureka," whose echo we hear reflected across the centuries, and because they offer the immediate rewards found in the appreciation of colleagues, laymen, and donors. The alternative, the slow development of a world of conceptual understanding in the manner of a Darwin or a Sherrington is of course far more difficult to follow. If it is worth a great deal to have some good ideas when one wants to make a discovery, then it is an absolute necessity to have them if one intends to take that long road whose ultimate goal is to reveal fundamental principles guiding the development of knowledge in any field.

This second variant of scientific endeavour does not always suit the impatient passion of the young, ruled by an ambition which craves immediate satisfaction, but a little later in life it provides feelings of assurance and satisfaction in one's work. The pleasure of living to see a synthesis mature after years of labor helps the worker to maintain a more generous attitude toward the results of others and also to mention more freely the names of colleagues whose findings have contributed to the understanding ultimately achieved. Work becomes less competitive and the atmosphere of a laboratory friendlier. Such an attitude is particularly valuable in research institutes where people have to defend themselves by delivering results and have no chance of escaping into teaching or administration. The long-range program protects the individual worker and fosters insight of the kind that makes disputes about "intellectual ownership" meaningless.

LITERATURE CITED

1. Barlow, N., Ed. 1958. *The Autobiography of Charles Darwin*, London: Collins, p. 119–120.
2. Ibid. p. 157.
3. Beveridge, W. I. B. 1961. *The Art of Scientific Investigation.* London: Heinemann.
4. Cannon, W. B. 1945. *The Way of an Investigator.* New York: Norton.
5. Granit, R. 1941. *Ung Mans Väg till Minerva.* Stockholm: Nordstedt.
6. Granit, R. 1947. *Sensory Mechanisms of the Retina.* London: Oxford Univ. Press.
7. Granit, R. 1955. *Receptors and Sensory Perception.* New Haven: Yale Univ. Press.
8. Granit, R. 1966. *Sherrington. An Appraisal.* London: Nelson.
9. Granit, R. 1970. *The Basis of Motor Control.* London, New York: Academic.

CIRCULATION: OVERALL REGULATION 1072

ARTHUR C. GUYTON, THOMAS G. COLEMAN, AND HARRIS J. GRANGER[1,2]

The Department of Physiology and Biophysics, University of Mississippi
School of Medicine, Jackson, Mississippi

This article is an experiment, one undertaken primarily because of the long-term belief of Dr. Victor Hall, Editor of the *Annual Review of Physiology* for many years, that physiology is, or at least should be, an analytical subject, and that a method not utilized to its fullest advantage for organizing review material is the systems analysis. Furthermore, one of the most likely areas in physiology for which a systems analysis could be of value would be in a discussion of circulatory regulation. Therefore, this article was undertaken directly at the request of the editors of the *Annual Review of Physiology* to attempt the welding together of a systems analysis of circulatory regulation with a review of the current literature in this field.

The systems analysis of circulatory regulation developed for this article is based on earlier, much less extensive analyses (Guyton & Coleman 1, 2); it is illustrated in Figure 1. This analysis is comprised of 354 blocks, each of which represents one or more mathematical equations describing some physiological facet of circulatory function. In general, each of the functional blocks has been the subject of research investigation by one or many investigators, but the analysis is based on cumulative knowledge of the circulation rather than simply on current literature. Therefore, the analysis presented here is not a review of the current literature but is a framework to show how the different regulations operate together in the overall system. Later in this review we will attempt to show some of the voids still present in our knowledge of circulatory regulation (which is perhaps the most important value of performing systems analyses), and we will discuss the current research that is attempting to fill these voids.

A criticism that has often been made against systems analyses, and very justly so, is that they are usually designed to explain specific phenomena. Therefore, they too often are based on such bizarre concepts of function that they not only fail to give correct predictions (other than the specific ones for which they are designed) but, indeed, often give exactly reverse predic-

[1] Preparation of this article and personal work referred to in it were supported by grants from the USPHS and the American Heart Association.

[2] The authors wish to acknowledge, with deepest thanks, the kindness and helpfulness of Mr. Ronnie Darby and Dr. Fred Sias for their suggestions and for many of the computing techniques used in this project.

tions. Therefore, the analysis of Figure 1 was based almost entirely on actual experimental data, and it has been tested in computer simulations to see whether or not it can predict the animal or human results of many different types of circulatory stresses induced either experimentally or as the result of clinical abnormalities. Figures 2 through 5 present simulations of some of these experiments or clinical conditions. They will be described later in the article.

BRIEF DESCRIPTION OF THE SYSTEMS ANALYSIS

For someone familiar with the principles of systems analysis, most of the present analysis can be understood by studying Figure 1 and its legend, which includes (a) definitions of the symbols used in the systems analysis and (b) units used in the analysis. However, the following brief description will give other helpful information for understanding the overall function of the analysis.

As illustrated in Figure 1, the analysis is divided into 18 different major systems that enter into circulatory control. Within each of these major systems are often several subsystems. The systems, their block numbers, and brief discussions of their components are given in the following few paragraphs.

1. *Circulatory dynamics (blocks 1 through 60).*—Blocks 1 through 33 represent the pathway of blood flow around the circulation, beginning with aortic pressure (PA) and returning to excess filling volume of the aorta (VAE) above that value which can be held by the aorta at zero pressure. The circuit is divided into five different volume segments: the aorta, the veins, the right atrium, the pulmonary arteries, and the combination of pulmonary veins and left atrium. Flow from each of these respective segments to the next segment is calculated by dividing pressure difference by resistance; the volumes are integrated with respect to time; and the volume of filling in each segment determines the pressure in that segment.

Other blocks in the circulatory dynamics portion of the analysis are: blocks 34 through 38 to calculate the resistances to blood flow respectively through the muscle vasculature and through the non-muscle, non-renal vasculature; blocks 39 through 43 to calculate venous resistance; block 44 to calculate the resistance between the large veins and the right atrium; blocks 45 through 48 to calculate the interaction of left ventricular function on right ventricular function; blocks 49 through 51 to calculate the effects of right ventricular muscle strength, autonomic stimulation, hypertrophy of the heart, deterioration of the heart, and pulmonary arterial pressure on the output of the right ventricle; blocks 52 through 57 to calculate pulmonary resistances; blocks 29, 58, and 59 to calculate the effects of sympathetic stimulation, cardiac deterioration, cardiac hypertrophy, left ventricular muscle strength, and the loading effect of aortic pressure on the output of the left ventricle; and block 60 to calculate the change in filling of the vascular system as the blood volume changes.

2. *Vascular stress relaxation (blocks 61 through 65).*—The control factors of stress relaxation are the sensitivity of the mechanism, set by the value SR, and the excess volume of blood in the veins (VVE). The output of this circuit is additional vascular volume that is added to that of the circulatory circuit ($VV7$).

3. *Capillary membrane dynamics (blocks 66 through 82).*—Blocks 66 and 67 calcu-

late capillary pressure. Blocks 68 and 69 calculate fluid leakage from the capillaries, and blocks 70 through 72 calculate the rate of change of fluid volume in the plasma, plasma volume, and blood volume. Blocks 73 through 76 calculate loss of protein from the capillaries, including the "stretched pore phenomenon." Blocks 77 and 78 calculate hepatic formation of protein, and blocks 79 through 82 calculate total plasma protein and plasma colloid osmotic pressure.

4. *Tissue fluids, pressures, and gel (blocks 83 through 113).*—Blocks 83 through 85 calculate total tissue fluid volume and total tissue pressure. Blocks 86 through 88 calculate free interstitial fluid volume, solid tissue pressure, and pressure of the free interstitial fluid. Blocks 89 through 92 calculate recoil effects of the gel reticulum (PRM) and the pressure caused by this (PGH). Blocks 93 through 99 calculate the balance of pressures at the interface between free interstitial fluid and fluid in the gel phase of the tissue fluids. Blocks 100 and 101 calculate gel volume. Blocks 102 through 105 calculate free interstitial fluid protein, its concentration, and its colloid osmotic pressure. Blocks 106 through 108 calculate lymph flow and return of protein in lymph to the circulation. Blocks 109 through 113 calculate transfer of protein into or out of the tissue gel, total protein in tissue gel, and concentration of protein in tissue gel.

5. *Electrolytes and cell water (blocks 114 through 135).*—Blocks 114 and 115 calculate extracellular fluid volume and total body water. Blocks 116 through 119 calculate accumulation of sodium in the extracellular fluids and concentration of sodium. Blocks 120 through 126 calculate extracellular fluid potassium, quantity and concentration, and also rate of potassium excretion by the kidney. Blocks 127 through 132 calculate accumulation of potassium in the cells and its intracellular concentration. Blocks 133 through 135 calculate transfer of fluid through the cell membrane and also intracellular fluid volume.

6. *Pulmonary dynamics and fluids (blocks 136 through 152).*—Blocks 136 through 138 calculate pulmonary capillary pressure. Blocks 139 through 143 calculate volume of pulmonary free fluid and pressure of the free fluid in the interstitial spaces. Blocks 144 and 145 calculate rate of pulmonary lymph flow. Blocks 146 through 151 calculate protein accumulation in the free fluid of the lungs, total protein, and its colloid osmotic pressure. Block 152 calculates rate of protein return in the pulmonary lymph.

7. *Angiotensin control (blocks 153 through 163).*—Block 153 calculates control of angiotensin formation as a function of renal blood flow. Blocks 154 and 155 calculate the effect of sodium concentration on angiotensin formation. Blocks 156 through 163 calculate first, angiotensin concentration (ANC) and then the angiotensin effect on other functions of the body [called "angiotensin multiplier" (ANM)] and expressed as a ratio of normal function.

8. *Aldosterone control (blocks 164 through 174).*—Blocks 164 through 167 calculate the effects of arterial pressure, potassium to sodium ratio, and angiotensin on aldosterone secretion rate. Blocks 168 through 170 calculate the accumulation of aldosterone in the tissues and its concentration. Blocks 171 through 174 calculate the "aldosterone multiplier" (AM) which represents the functional effect of aldosterone in the body in proportion to its normal effect.

9. *Antidiuretic hormone control (blocks 175 through 189).*—Blocks 175 through 182 calculate the total effect on antidiuretic hormone secretion of extracellular ion concentration (represented by CNA), of right atrial pressure, and of autonomic stimulation. Blocks 183 through 189 calculate the rate of secretion of antidiuretic hormone and antidiuretic hormone multiplier expressed as the functional effect of antidiuretic hormone in ratio to its normal effect.

10. *Thirst and drinking (blocks 190 through 194).*—Blocks 190 and 191 calculate the effect of central nervous system stimulation on thirst and drinking, assuming that the same drives that affect thirst and drinking also affect the secretion of antidiuretic hormone. Blocks 192 and 193 calculate the effect of tissue ischemia (hypoperfusion states) on salt and water intake. These combine together in block 194 to control overall thirst and drinking.

11. *Kidney dynamics and excretion (blocks 195 through 222).*—Blocks 195 through 200 calculate renal resistances and the effects of autonomic stimulation and blood viscosity on these. Blocks 201 through 207 calculate the effects of arterial pressure, renal resistances, and plasma colloid osmotic pressure on glomerular pressure, filtration pressure, glomerular filtration rate, and renal blood flow. Blocks 208 through 211 represent feedback control of afferent arteriolar resistance in response to flow of fluid through the tubular system (presumably acting through the macula densa and juxtaglomerular apparatus). Blocks 212 through 217 calculate the effects of glomerular filtration rate, degree of renal damage (REK), antidiuretic hormone, and aldosterone on tubular reabsorption. Block 218 subtracts tubular reabsorption from glomerular filtration rate to calculate rate of urine output. Blocks 219 through 222 calculate the effects of rate of urinary output, aldosterone secretion, and natriuretic factor on sodium excretion.

12. *Muscle blood flow control and Po_2 (blocks 223 through 254).*—Blocks 223 and 224 calculate the effect of pulmonary free fluid on arterial oxygen saturation. Blocks 225 through 232 calculate the effects of hematocrit, arterial oxygen saturation, and muscle blood flow on concentration of oxygen in arterial blood, concentration in the muscle venous blood, and muscle venous Po_2. Blocks 233 through 237 calculate diffusion rate of oxygen from the capillaries into the muscle cells. Blocks 238 through 240 calculate accumulation of oxygen in muscle cells and the muscle cell Po_2. Blocks 241 through 244 calculate the effect of muscle cell Po_2 on rate of oxygen consumption by the cells. Blocks 245 through 247 calculate the effects of autonomic stimulation on muscle cell utilization of oxygen. Block 248 calculates the rate of oxygen utilization by the muscle cells of the body. Blocks 249 through 254 calculate the vasodilating effect (AMM) of muscle capillary Po_2 (PVO).

13. *Non-muscle oxygen delivery (blocks 255 through 272).*—Blocks 255 through 261 calculate the effects of arterial oxygen concentration, non-muscle non-renal blood flow, and hematocrit, on non-muscle, non-renal venous oxygen concentration and venous oxygen Po_2. Blocks 262 through 265 calculate the effect of capillary Po_2 (POV) and cell Po_2 (POT) on diffusion of oxygen from the capillaries to the cells. Blocks 266 through 270 calculate the effect of cell Po_2, autonomic stimulation, and basic rate of oxygen consumption by the tissues on the actual rate of oxygen consumption by the tissues. Blocks 271 and 272 calculate the accumulation of oxygen in the cells and the cell Po_2.

14. *Non-muscle, non-renal local blood flow control—autoregulation (blocks 273 through 290).*—Blocks 273 through 278 calculate the effect of capillary Po_2 (POV) on rapid autoregulation of blood flow (ARI), with a time constant of one minute ($A1K$). Blocks 279 through 283 calculate the time course and the degree of intermediate autoregulation, with a time constant of 20 minutes. Blocks 284 through 289 calculate the effect of long-term vascular changes (for instance, changes in vascularity) on local blood flow control, with a time constant of 11,520 minutes. Block 290 calculates the overall effect of short, intermediate, and long-term local blood flow controls on nonmuscle, non-renal, vascular resistance (ARM).

15. *Autonomic control (blocks 291 through 320).*—Blocks 291 and 292 calculate the effects of arterial pressure and non-muscle, non-renal Po_2 on autonomic function. Blocks 293 through 297 calculate the effects of exercise and of muscle metabolism on autonomic function. And block 298 sums these effects with those of arterial pressure and non-muscle Po_2. Block 299 calculates chemoreceptor output. Blocks 300 through 305 calculate baroreceptor output, including baroreceptor adaptation. Block 306 calculates the output resulting from ischemia of the CNS. Blocks 307 through 311 calculate the summation of total autonomic output expressed as a positive effect for sympathetic output and negative effect for parasympathetic output, and with a time constant of approximately 10 seconds controlled by *Z8*. Blocks 312 and 313 calculate the effects of autonomic stimulation on vascular compliance. Blocks 314 and 315 calculate the effects of autonomic stimulation on the heart. Blocks 316 and 317 calculate the effects of autonomic stimulation on peripheral arteriolar vasoconstriction. Blocks 318 through 320 calculate the effects of autonomic stimulation on venous vasoconstriction.

16. *Heart rate and stroke volume (blocks 321 through 328).*—Blocks 321 through 323 calculate the effects of autonomic stimulation and right atrial pressure on heart rate. Blocks 324 through 326 calculate the effects of cardiac deterioration on heart rate, and block 327 calculates heart rate itself. Block 328 calculates stroke volume output.

17. *Red cells and viscosity (blocks 329 through 339).*—Blocks 329 through 333 calculate the effect of tissue Po_2 on the rate of red blood cell production, and also calculates red cell destruction, accumulation of red cells in the blood, and red cell volume. Blocks 334 and 335 calculate hematocrit. Blocks 336 through 339 calculate blood viscosity expressed in terms of ratio to that of normal blood.

18. *Heart hypertrophy or deterioration (blocks 340 through 253).*—Blocks 340 through 344 calculate the effect of systemic arterial pressure and basic strength of the left ventricular muscle on hypertrophy of the left ventricle with a time constant of 57,600 minutes. Blocks 345 through 349 calculate the effects of pulmonary arterial pressure and basic strength of the right ventricular muscle on right ventricular hypertrophy, with a time constant of 57,600 minutes. Blocks 350 through 352 calculate the effect of diminished tissue Po_2 on deterioration of the heart.

Overall comment on the systems analysis.—An important factor that allows a systems analysis such as this to predict actual function with good accuracy is the extreme stability of the actual circulatory control system. Because of this stability, the function of any single block, or of any single control mechanism, can be in error as much as $\pm 50\%$ (sometimes even more than this) without significantly affecting the overall output of the system. To give an example, simulated removal of $\frac{3}{4}$ of the mass of the kidneys, thereby depressing all renal functions to $\frac{1}{4}$ normal, causes less than 1% change in body fluid volumes (after all compensations have taken place) and causes only 7 mm Hg rise in arterial pressure. Obviously, the goal of the systems analysis is to be as accurate as possible, but another byproduct of such an analysis is to demonstrate the beauty of the built-in compensations when any one or even a significant combination of its parts is functioning very abnormally. If it were not for the extreme stability of the overall circulatory control system, we would have to know far more basic physiology to make such a systems analysis as this work.

Solution of the systems analysis on a computer.—To simulate overall function of the circulatory system, and particularly to simulate dynamic changes in circulatory function when a stress is introduced into the circulatory system, one can solve the systems analysis of Figure 1 on any computer that is large enough to handle it. The solution requires 16K words of memory for solution in the FORTRAN language on the PDP–9 computer (others may require more). One of the principal problems in such a solution is the fact that some of the control and hemodynamic systems operate with very short time constants (as low as 0.005 min for some points in the hemodynamic circuit) while others operate with tremendously long time constants (as high as 57,600 min for the hypertrophy effect on the effect of the ventricles). In an iterative solution of the analysis without using special computational techniques, the time for computation on the computer could be as great as 100 times real time. However, by computing the rapid time constant factors until equilibrium is reached and then computing the slower time constant factors, it is possible to speed the solution to almost 1/1000 real time.

SIMULATION OF THE EFFECTS OF SPECIFIC CIRCULATORY STRESSES ON CIRCULATORY CONTROL

Simulation of the development of hypertension in a salt loaded, renal deficient patient.—Figure 2 illustrates a cathode ray display of the sequential events during development of hypertension in a simulated patient who was subjected to two abnormalities. Firstly, renal mass was decreased to 0.3 normal and, secondly, the salt load was increased to 5 times normal. These changes were made at the point where the curves begin to break. The curves illustrate the simulated effects, from top to bottom, on extracellular fluid volume, blood volume, degree of sympathetic stimulation, cardiac output, total peripheral resistance, arterial pressure, and urinary output. The time period for the abscissa was two weeks. Note that the instantaneous change was a decrease in urinary output to 0.3 normal. This was followed by slight increases in extracellular fluid volume and blood volume and a simultaneous increase in cardiac output, with less increase in arterial pressure. The increase in arterial pressure that did occur initiated a baroreceptor reflex with resultant depression of sympathetic activity. This decreased sympathetic activity, combined with the vascular stretching effect of the elevated arterial pressure dilated the peripheral blood vessels so that the total peripheral resistance fell below normal for the first few days. Therefore, all the initial increase in arterial pressure was caused by increased cardiac output and not by increased total peripheral resistance.

For the first few days of the simulated experiment, the cardiac output continued to rise, while total peripheral resistance remained below normal. However, at the end of two days the total peripheral resistance returned to normal. By this time the arterial pressure had already risen to approxi-

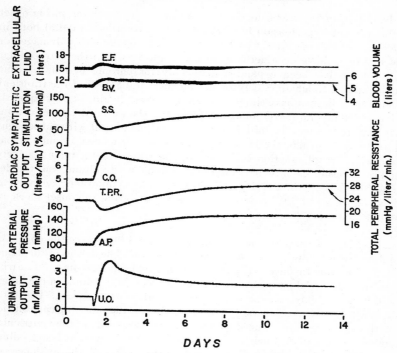

FIGURE 2. Simulation of changes in circulatory function at the onset of hypertension caused by reduction of renal mass to ⅓ normal and simultaneous increase in salt intake to five times normal. The changes were made at the point where the curves begin to break.

mately 2/3 as high as it would rise by the end of the experiment. During the subsequent days the cardiac output fell toward normal, while total peripheral resistance rose progressively and became the factor that eventually maintained the elevated arterial pressure. In the systems analysis, this shift from increased cardiac output to increased total peripheral resistance was caused by two factors: adaptation of the baroreceptors and long-term control of local blood flow in which excess blood flow through the tissues cause progressive constriction of the blood vessels until the flow returns to normal. Two other significant events were: (a) the initial overshoot in blood volume and extracellular fluid volume with return of both of these almost to normal by the end of ten days to two weeks, and (b) the increase in urinary output to considerably above normal, despite decrease in renal mass, caused by the effect of the high salt intake on the thirst mechanism.

This test of the circulatory systems analysis was performed because all of the details of the transient changes in circulatory function during onset of this type of hypertension have recently been recorded in detail both in experimental animals and in patients whose kidneys are either damaged or whose kidneys have been actually removed and in whom the extracellular fluid volume has been expanded artificially for chronic periods of time (Ledingham 3, Coleman & Guyton 4, Coleman et al 5). All of the transient effects shown in the above simulation actually occur in almost exact quantitative and temporal correspondence, including the initial decrease in total peripheral resistance, the initial increase in cardiac output with subsequent return toward normal, the high urine output in salt-loaded animals or patients whose renal function is depressed, the transient but quantitatively small increases in blood volume and extracellular fluid volume, and the decrease in sympathetic activity or increase in parasympathetic activity as evidenced by about 40% reduction in heart rate during the onset phase of the hypertension.

Simulation of congestive heart failure.—Figure 3 illustrates the effects of simulated heart failure over a period of two months. The curves of the figure (listed from top to bottom) show changes in plasma volume, left atrial pressure, right atrial pressure, cardiac output, free fluid volume in the lungs, aortic pressure, extracellular fluid volume, and urinary output. The total time is nine weeks. At the first break in the curves, the pumping capabilities of both ventricles were reduced (reduction of all segments of the ventricular function curves) to 0.3 their normal values, and evidences of heart failure ensued. However, recovery of the heart caused many of the evidences of heart failure to disappear. At each subsequent break in the curves, the pumping capability of the heart was decreased approximately another 30% below its value immediately before the break. Eventually the failure was so severe that the simulated person developed severe congestion in the lungs, low cardiac output, and peripheral edema leading to death.

Note the instantaneous decrease in urinary output at the onset of the first heart attack, with urinary output remaining for about one day at about 300 ml/day, the obligatory level of ouptut, until there was beginning evidence of recovery from the heart attack. Note also the instantaneous marked decrease in both cardiac output and arterial pressure, with recovery within minutes of both of these to levels only 10 to 20% below normal despite the severe reduction in the capability of the pump. These initial effects were followed rapidly by increasing extracellular fluid and plasma volumes, and the initial slight increases in atrial pressures increased still more as fluid volume accumulated. However, during subsequent days, as the heart recovered from the attack, all the abnormal effects returned toward normal.

With subsequent attacks the simulated person went though similar repeated episodes until, finally, recovery was insufficient to return the person to a compensated state. The left atrial pressure became so high that the

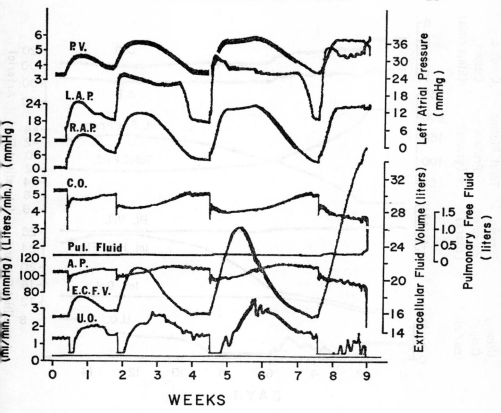

FIGURE 3. Simulation of development of congestive heart failure. At the point where the curves first began to break, the pumping capabilities of both the left and right ventricles were decreased to 0.3 normal. At each of the subsequent breaks in the curves, the pumping capabilities of the ventricles were reduced approximately an additional ⅓ below the pumping capabilities at that time. The heart recovered partially between each of the attacks. Note at the end of the record that free fluid in the lungs increased suddenly during the last few hours of life, and this increase in pulmonary fluid was the immediate cause of death.

volume of free fluid in the lungs began to rise drastically during the last hours of life. Also, not shown in the record, the oxygen saturation of aortic blood fell below the 50% level, and it was at this point that death occurred.

The events simulated in Figure 3 are almost identical with those that occur in actual cases of progressive cardiac failure, with transient episodes

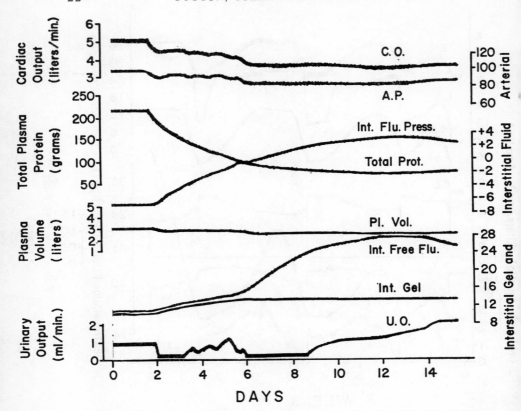

FIGURE 4. Simulation of circulatory changes in nephrosis. At the initial break in the curves, the kidneys began to excrete large amounts of plasma protein, as evidenced by the fall in total circulating plasma protein. Note the tremendous increase in interstitial free fluid when the plasma total protein fell below a critical level. At the end of the record an extremely minute increase in total plasma protein caused marked diuresis and beginning resorption of the edema, a well known characteristic of the disease.

of edema following acute attacks and final entry into a severe stage of congestion and cardiac decompensation, followed by typical pulmonary congestive death.

Simulation of nephrosis.—The principal effect of nephrosis is loss of protein in the urine, which may or may not be associated with significant changes in other functions of the kidneys. Figure 4 illustrates simulated nephrosis in which there was only loss of protein. The different factors displayed in the simulation are (from top to bottom) cardiac output, arterial pressure, total plasma protein, interstitial fluid pressure, plasma volume, total interstitial fluid volume, volume of fluid in interstitial gel, and urine output. Total time is two weeks. Note also that the space between the total fluid volumes and that of the interstitial gel represents the volume of interstitial free fluid. The initial effect, once the state of nephrosis was instituted, was a progressive decrease in total plasma protein, as illustrated by the declining curve in the figure. This was followed soon by slight decreases in both arterial pressure and cardiac output, marked decrease of urinary output while fluid was collecting in both the free and gel portions of the interstitial fluid, slight decrease in plasma volume, and beginning rise in interstitial fluid pressure. The increase in interstitial fluid pressure continued almost in inverse proportion to the decrease in plasma protein. On the other hand, the interstitial fluid volumes increased moderately at first and then did not increase greatly thereafter until a critically low level of plasma protein (about 0.3 the normal level) was reached. At that point, there was an abrupt rise in total interstitial fluid volume. It was at this same time that the interstitial fluid pressure rose from a previously negative (subatmospheric) pressure into the positive pressure range. Furthermore, the increase in total interstitial fluid volume rose abruptly in spite of the fact that the interstitial fluid pressure rose only slightly from that point on. Another very important effect was the character of the fluid in the interstitial spaces. The early increase in interstitial fluid volume was primarily the result of swelling in the interstitial fluid gel, but the abrupt increase in fluid that occurred when the plasma protein concentration reached its critical level for edema formation was an increase in free interstitial fluid volume while the gel fluid volume remained almost constant from this point on. The final important effect in this simulation occurred at the very end when the rate of renal loss of protein was reduced by a factor of approximately 4%. This allowed only a minute increase in protein in the plasma, but even this minute change shifted the equilibrium at the capillary membrane sufficiently to cause beginning reduction of the edema fluid and a high level of diuresis.

Once again the results from the simulation are almost identical with those that occur in patients with nephrosis, including the failure to develop sufficient amounts of edema until the protein concentration falls below a critically low level of about 1/3 normal, the critical value also found in the simulation. When tremendous amounts of fluid do collect it is almost entirely in the free fluid form, which is what the simulation shows. The simulation also shows the typical tendency for nephrotic patients to have a mild degree of circulatory collapse and slightly decreased plasma volumes. Another important feature is the changing level of urinary output, an effect that also occurs in nephrotic patients, with urinary output falling very low during those periods when large amounts of edema are being actively formed and the urinary output becoming great during those periods when edema is being resorbed. Finally, another important point of this simulation is that

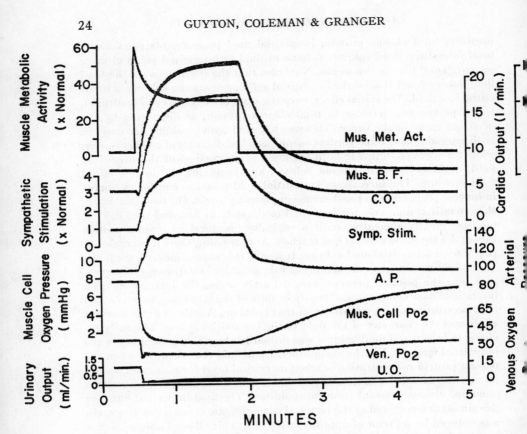

FIGURE 5. Simulation of circulatory dynamics during muscle exercise. At the initial break in the curves the muscles were activated to a level 60 times their normal value, and the degree of activation was returned to normal at the second break in the curves.

essentially all of the known circulatory effects of clinical nephrosis can be simulated without implicating any other damage to the kidneys besides simple loss of protein.

Simulation of circulatory changes during severe muscle exercise.—Figure 5 illustrates simulated changes during extremely severe exercise for a period of 1.5 minutes and for 3 minutes after the exercise was over. Displayed in the record (from top to bottom) are rate of metabolic activity in the muscles, muscle blood flow, cardiac output, degree of sympathetic stimulation, systemic arterial pressure, venous Po_2, muscle intracellular Po_2, and urinary output. The two initial events at the onset of the exercise were: (*a*) instantaneous increase in metabolic activity of all of the muscles in the body to about sixty times their normal resting level, and (b) a subsequent rapid increase in the activity of the sympathetic nervous system (one-half time of about six seconds). These effects are followed within seconds by (a) rapid decreases in muscle cellular Po_2 and venous oxygen, and (b) marked increases in muscle blood flow and cardiac output. The urinary output decreased to about 0.3 ml/minute, or to the obligatory level of urinary output, and arterial pressure rose moderately during the course of the simulated exercise. Despite neurogenic driving of the muscles at the same continuous level, the metabolic activity of the muscles decreased considerably from their peak levels of activity because of development of a metabolic deficit in the muscles. When muscle exercise was abruptly stopped after 1.5 minutes, muscle metabolic activity decreased instantly essentially to normal (or perhaps even a minute amount below normal) but blood flow through the muscles continued at an elevated level for the next several minutes as did also cardiac output and arterial pressure. These effects were evidences of the metabolic deficit of the muscles and occurred during the period that the person was repaying his oxygen debt. Not shown in the curves was the effect on heart rate, which increased during extreme exercise to approximately 170 beats per minute and returned to normal along a curve similar to that for arterial blood pressure, but slightly less rapidly.

Other simulations.—Other simulations that have been performed utilizing this circulatory systems analysis include the effects of other degrees of general heart failure besides those shown in Figure 3, unilateral heart failure of the right or left side, effects of removal of the sympathetic nervous system on circulatory function, effect of infusion of different types of substances (such as saline solution, plasma, or water), effects of vasoconstrictor agents acting on different parts of the circulation, effects of extreme reduction of renal function on circulatory function, and others.

A word of caution and comment.—Despite the fact that the systems analysis of Figure 1 contains 354 blocks and more than 400 mathematical operations, and also despite the fact that the simulation is capable of predicting many if not most major circulatory changes in clinical and experimental conditions, the detailed analyses of the different sectors of circulatory function and control are based on gross functions of the parts. The analysis does not show the minute details of many of the control systems.

Three major values have come from this systems analysis. These are the following:

First, even when the details of the individual control systems of the circulation are simulated in a gross fashion, the overall results of the total systems analysis can still be highly accurate in predicting principal functions of the circulation. In other words, it does not matter from the overall point of view whether the simulation takes into consideration all the details of the individual control systems or whether the simulation utilizes the "black box" approach to these separate controls.

Second, the systems analysis helps to identify the different control systems that are most important from a quantitative point of view in overall control of the circulation.

Third, a systems analysis such as this is very important in identifying inconsistencies between postulated mechanisms from different laboratories. To give an example, prolonged activity of very potent volume receptors operating from the heart should reduce blood volume, but blood volume actually increases in patients with congestive heart failure and very high atrial pressures. On the other hand, volume receptors that act strongly at first but adapt over a period of days would allow consistency between these two phenomena. Thus, a suggested experiment that derives from this inconsistency is to determine whether the volume receptors do indeed adapt. Many other experiments have also been suggested by similar inconsistencies found in other areas of circulatory control.

FUNCTION OF THE DIFFERENT SUBSYSTEMS FOR CIRCULATORY CONTROL

In the following pages we will attempt to use some of the principles that were forthcoming from the systems analysis of the circulatory function to build a logical pattern for circulatory control and to show how current research is adding each day to our understanding of the control mechanisms.

CONTROL OF OXYGEN DELIVERY TO CELLS

We begin our discussion of the logic of circulatory control with the topic of oxygen delivery because so many of the circulatory controls seem to be geared toward this purpose. Most of the physiologic mechanisms for precise control of oxygen delivery to cells are already well known, including (a) changes in oxygen extraction from the blood, (b) changes in capillary density, (c) changes in vascular resistance to local blood flow, (d) changes in cardiac output, (e) changes in respiration, and (f) changes in circulating red blood cell mass and hematocrit.

In recent studies, both Crowell (6) and Halmagyi and co-workers (7, 8) demonstrated that oxygen transport to tissues is at least to some extent flow limited and can become seriously flow limited in hypotensive states such as hemorrhagic shock. Therefore, even a minute decrease of tissue blood flow usually causes at least some decrease of oxygen usage by the tissues. One of the most important local mechanisms to prevent decreased oxygen delivery to tissues when hypotensive states occur is the onset of vasodilatation in response to diminished local tissue oxygenation. The microelectrode studies of intracellular Po_2 by Whalen and co-workers (9) have been especially enlightening for several reasons. First, the time response of their measurements is rapid enough that the records show increases and decreases in intracellular P_{O_2} occurring along with the phasic changes in capillary blood flow. These workers have shown that changing arterial P_{O_2} over very wide ranges has little effect on the intracellular P_{O_2} of many tissues, this effect being caused by increased or decreased shutdown time of capillary flow or by changes in the fraction of total blood flow passing through non-nutrient channels. These concepts are further supported by the work of Duling & Berne (10) who have shown that the P_{O_2} near the functional cells is only about 8 mm Hg instead of the 30 to 40 mm Hg usually regarded as venous P_{O_2}. Also, the P_{O_2} immediately outside the terminal ends of small arterioles was found to be about 21 mm Hg, a value less than the P_{O_2} in the veins, an effect possibly caused by "countercurrent" diffusion of oxygen from arteries to veins. Jones, Crowell & Smith (11), using an implanted capsule method, found similar values for muscle, liver, and cerebral cortex.

In the past it has been believed that the local vasodilator response to oxygen deficiency occurs in some organs but not in others. However, several different studies indicate that the vasodilatation resulting from oxygen deficiency might be a universal phenomenon throughout the systemic circulation rather than an occurrence found only in specific areas. For instance, Granger & Guyton (12) demonstrated that very significant degrees of autoregulation occur in the total systemic circulation following destruction of the central nervous system in the dog. These same effects are almost impossible to demonstrate in the dog with a normal operating nervous system because of sympathetic reflexes at work throughout the body. Although many authors in the past have felt that the liver might not autoregulate, Takeuchi and co-workers (13), studying the isolated perfused liver, have demonstrated a high degree of autoregulation in the hepatic arterial vascular system. Scholtholt & Shiraishi (14), also studying the liver, but in the intact animal, demonstrated that when the animals were artificially ventilated with a gas mixture low in oxygen, the reflex sympathetic stimulation was so great that the animal's arterial pressure rose and blood flow through the liver decreased rather than increased. Costin & Skinner (15) observed this same effect in muscle, but vasodilatation occurred when nerves to the muscle were blocked.

Most of the studies in anemia point toward at least two mechanisms by which anemia increases local blood flow. One of these is by viscosity changes (Schrier and co-workers 16) and the other is by vasodilatation resulting from reduced delivery of oxygen to the tissues (Cropp 17, Housley & Hedworth-Whitty 18). One of the principal reasons for believing that vasodilatation is a component is that breathing pure oxygen reduces the cardiac output approximately 15 percent in an anemic patient. This is approximately the amount that would be expected due to the small additional amount of oxygen dissolved in the blood. As a combined result of both of the effects that occur in anemia, Neill, Oxendine & Moore (19) have shown that the cardiac output increases almost exactly in proportion to the degree of induced anemia in unanesthetized, trained dogs. Furthermore, these effects are unaffected by block of the sympathetic reflexes.

The vasodilatation which occurs in the hypoxic state continues to increase for long periods of time after the initial acute vasodilatation. In their studies on total systemic autoregulation, Granger & Guyton (12) found that the vasodilatation induced by decreased systemic arterial pressure continues to increase on the average for 30 minutes or more. And studies by Cassin and co-workers (20) have shown that capillary counts in relation to the total tissue mass continue to increase for many days or weeks. However, these authors believe that the prolonged increase in local blood flow occurs primarily because of opening of preexisting capillaries rather than because of increased absolute numbers of capillaries.

The systems analysis presented in the first part of this article, in general, follows the principles demonstrated by the results of animal experiments in anemia, hypoxemia, and other related states. However, there remain many unanswered questions. Among the most important of these is the relative importance of diminished oxygen in causing vasodilatation versus other metabolic factors. For instance, it is logical that carbon dioxide released from the tissue cells, because of its mass effect, could easily cause weakness of vascular smooth muscle and thereby cause dilatation. The consensus of opinion in a symposium on autoregulation and local blood flow regulation in 1963 (21) was that carbon dioxide did not have nearly so much effect in most tissues as diminished oxygen, through some workers even then felt that the carbon dioxide factor had been underrated. A recent study by Scholtholt & Shiraishi (14) has again raised this point, because increased arterial carbon dioxide in the arterial blood appears to have far more vasodilating effect on blood flow in the liver and mesenteric vessels than does hypoxia.

It is obvious that much more quantitative information is needed to determine the relative importance of the different vasodilator factors. Also there has been little progress in recent years to determine whether oxygen deficiency causes vasodilatation simply because of lack of enough oxygen for the metabolic machinery to maintain vascular contraction or whether the diminished oxygen causes release of a vasodilator substance from the tissues

.

REGULATION OF CARDIAC OUTPUT

With the work of Frank and Starling at the turn of the century, a concept developed that cardiac output is regulated primarily by peripheral tissues of the body rather than by the heart itself. However, approximately a decade ago it again became fashionable to champion the idea that cardiac output is primarily controlled by the heart and nervous reflexes to the heart. Indeed, this concept still appears in the research literature (Cropp 17). However, two major events have occurred in clinical cardiology which seem to return us mainly to the original concepts of Frank and Starling. First, with the advent of the pacemaker, it has become generally acknowledged that the heart rate can be changed in an otherwise normal heart within wide limits, and still the cardiac output remains controlled at essentially its normal value. Recent studies by Cowley (22) have shown that this is also true in the experimental animal but with an additional proviso: when the input load of venous blood is greatly increased, heart rate then becomes a very important determinant of cardiac output. The second event in clinical cardiology that has provided important conceptual information is transplantation of the heart. Carleton and co-workers (23) and Beck, Barnard & Schrire (24) have shown that even after transplantation of the human heart, the heart functions almost exactly normally even in the absence of innervation.

New measurements of ventricular function curves in normal and abnormal animals (Siegel & Downing 25, Herndon & Sagawa 26, Tsakiris et al 27, Bishop et al 28) have shown that the normal heart has far more capacity to pump higher cardiac outputs than is usually used and that the output of the heart seems normally to be determined mainly by inflow into the heart except when this inflow becomes excessively increased or except when the pumping capacity of the heart itself becomes excessively small. Thus, in heavy exercise a marked increase in heart rate (Hermansen, Ekblom & Saltin 29) and beta receptor stimulation either by the sympathetic nerves or by circulating catecholamines (29a) seem to be among the necessary factors in achieving the very large increases in required cardiac output. At the other extreme, after prolonged periods of acute hemorrhagic shock (Siegal and Downing 25) the heart loses a major share of its cardiac reserve and cardiac function then becomes one of the limiting factors in cardiac output. Likewise, following myocardial infarction (30–34) the heart becomes too weak to pump even the normal load of blood returning to it from the veins. Treatment with different agents such as hyperbaric oxygenation (30), dopamine (31), norepinephrine (32), and under some conditions acetyl-strophanthidin (33) will increase the strength of the heart muscle and cause the cardiac output to return toward normal even though these same agents used in normal animals or persons rarely cause any increase in cardiac output. Also, stiffening of the ischemic myocardium occurs within a few days after an attack of myocardial ischemia (34), and this prevents aneurysmal bulging. This, too, improves the pumping capability of the heart, and the cardiac output in response returns toward normal. Thus, under failing conditions the heart seems to be the limiting factor in cardiac output regulation, while under normal conditions it is mainly peripheral factors that are limiting.

But what are the peripheral factors that are most important for regulation of cardiac output? These appear to fall into two major categories. First, the peripheral resistance and, second, the ratio of blood volume to filling capacity of the circulation (measured as mean circulatory pressure). The first of these is to a great extent controlled by the local needs of the tissues, while the second is determined by a combination of two factors, the blood volume itself and the capacity of the vascular system. However, a very confusing factor enters into the relationship between blood volume and capacity of the circulation, namely, the phenomenon of stress relaxation. Studies on isolated blood vessels throughout the body have demonstrated high degrees of vascular relaxation following prolonged changes in pressure. And recently Prather and co-workers (35) demonstrated that the mean circulatory pressure of animals, a measure of the filling pressure of the circulation, returned to normal within two hours after massive transfusion of blood or dextran solution into dogs even though the total blood volume at that point was still 13 to 32% above normal. If these animals were bled back to normal blood volume at this point in the experiment, the animals actually showed signs of shock. These same principles could explain the results found by Coleman and co-workers (36) during the dialysis of patients for chronic renal failure, namely, a large decrease in arterial pressure and cardiac output following rapid removal of fluid from the patient but return of these factors back toward normal during the ensuing hours.

Again, the overall principles of cardiac output control which emerge from current experiments are the same as those predicted from the systems analysis of circulatory control given in this article. That is, under normal conditions output is controlled mainly by the tissues, each tissue contributing its own control of cardiac output by controlling its proportionate share of venous return. However, under abnormal conditions, such as in very heavy exercise, or in conditions that damage the heart, the heart itself then becomes the dominant factor controlling cardiac output. Note that it is the conditions in which the heart becomes the controller of cardiac output (that is, when the tissues can no longer protect their own nutritional supplies) in which death soon ensues, such as in irreversible shock and in congestive heart failure.

REGULATION OF ARTERIAL PRESSURE HYPERTENSION

Probably the most important contribution thus far made by the systems analysis of circulatory control has been to advance our understanding of the control of arterial pressure. The analysis demonstrates that at least three main factors play extremely important roles in pressure regulation, all of which are already known but the interrelationships of which have not been clear. These factors are (a) control of pressure by autonomic reflexes, (b) control of arterial pressure by changes in body fluid volumes and electrolytes, and (c) control of arterial pressure by the renin-angiotensin-aldosterone mechanism. The autonomic mechanisms will be discussed later; these seem to play their most significant role in short-term regulation of arterial pressure from second to second, minute to minute, and hour to hour, while other factors seem to play the primary role in long-term regulation of arterial pressure. However, the nervous mechanisms can affect the long-term mechanisms also, as will be pointed out.

Two devastating predictions of the systems analysis.—The systems analysis gives two extremely important predictions which were not immediately evident previously; these could change considerably the course of research in the field of blood pressure regulation and in the field of hypertension (Guyton & Coleman 2). These are the following:

1. Changes in total peripheral resistance per se play essentially no role in long-term regulation of arterial pressure.

2. It is impossible to change the arterial pressure chronically from its status quo level without either (a) altering the function of the kidneys in some way to change their output of water and electrolytes or (b) changing the intake of water and electrolytes. That is, some change in body fluid, usually as a result of a change in kidney function, must occur for chronic, long-term hypertension to develop.

These two predictions may be startling in themselves, but already there is support for them both in a large body of information which upon reflection one can readily understand. Relative to peripheral resistance, one need only to remember that opening and closing very large A-V fistulae, which can change the total peripheral resistance as much as 100%, is not associated with a measurable long-term change in arterial pressure (37). Likewise, removal of all four limbs, which increases the total peripheral resistance to as much as 160% of normal, causes no change in arterial pressure.

The second prediction, that the kidney (or changes in water and salt intake) must be involved in any long-term pressure change, derives from the fact that the kidney and mechanisms of water and salt intake operate in an integral control system as follows: As long as the arterial pressure is above normal and all other conditions of the kidney are completely normal, both the systems analysis and isolated kidney experiments show that the kidney will continue to pour out excess amounts of water and salt until the loss of this water and salt reduces the pressure back to the level at which output equals intake. Such an integral control system has infinite gain if allowed adequate time to come to equilibrium—days, weeks, months— which means that theoretically it can override all non-integrative control systems. More will be said about these predictions in subsequent paragraphs.

Role of body fluids and volumes in arterial pressure regulation.—The simulated experiment of Figure 2 illustrated the principles of arterial pressure regulation by changes in fluid volumes or filling pressure of the circulation. The main principles of this simulated experiment have been confirmed by recent experiments from the laboratories of Ledingham (3), Guyton (1, 38), Coleman (4, 5), Bianchi (39), and Ferrario (40), and they are the following: If renal function is altered to cause fluid retention, or if excess water and salt are ingested, the extracellular fluid volume begins to rise, which also increases the blood volume. This increases venous return and therefore increases cardiac output above normal. As a result, arterial pressure rises. However, the baroreceptor reflexes reduce the heart rate and cause peripheral vasodilatation for the first few days to delay the rise in arterial pressure. Secondary to the increase in cardiac output, peripheral autoregulation occurs. That is, excess blood flow through the tissues increases local vascular resistance as a result of (a) acute local vascular constrictor effects and (b) long-term changes in vascular dimensions. These effects were discussed earlier in relation to local blood flow control. Once the pressure has risen to its high level, output from the kidney will have been increased to equal the intake of water and salt, and a new state of equilibrium will have been established. Note particularly that the increase in total peripheral resistance occurs as a secondary phenomenon in the elevation of arterial pressure. Also, the increase in total peripheral resistance is associated with diminished flow through all the tissues of the body, consequently returning cardiac output back toward normal. The increase in resistance is also associated with diminished capillary pressure and reduction of the body fluid volumes toward normal. Therefore, once the equilibrium state has been established, the systems analysis predicts that the cardiac output and body fluid volumes will be so near to normal in the pure fluid volume-caused hypertension that abnormalities can not be measured by usual measuring techniques. Indeed, these are the effects that have been observed by many investigators, including Julius et al (41) and Hampers et al (42).

A confusing point in the above picture has been that some types of experimental renal hypertension do not show the initial transient increase in cardiac output and fluid volumes, and some investigators have, therefore, questioned whether the basic scheme could possibly be true. However, the systems analysis predicts that if there is a simultaneous vasoconstriction in the circulation along with the tendency for water and salt retention, one could actually have decreased fluid volumes and even decreased cardiac outputs and still have hypertension caused by the tendency for water and salt retention (2), a fact that has also been confirmed by measurements in hypertensive patients with high renin activities (Tarazi, Dustan & Frohlich 43). Under these conditions the cardiac output and fluid volumes are greater than those that would have existed had it not been for the tendency for water and salt retention. A further important point is that the final level to which the arterial pressure rises is exactly the same whether or not there is a vasoconstrictor factor (Coleman and Guyton 2). On the other hand, simulating a vasoconstrictor factor in the systems analysis without the fluid retention factor causes a simulated hypertension that lasts for only a day or so, except under the following condition: If the vasoconstrictor factor is also programmed to cause vasoconstriction in the kidney, then the kidney enters into a mode tending to cause fluid retention, and hypertension ensues (2). This points up again the principle discussed earlier that fluid control must be changed from normal for chronic hypertension to be maintained.

Another important conclusion from the analysis is that return of an abnormal kidney to normal will cause return of arterial pressure to normal in a much shorter time than required for the elevation. The reason for this is that high pressure acting on a kidney that has been returned to normal causes extremely rapid loss of water and salt, a fact illustrated by the experiments of Crawford (44) in which release of a balloon clamp on the renal artery of dogs with Goldblatt hypertension caused return of arterial pressure to normal within 24 to 36 hours, associated with very transient and minute negative fluid and salt balance. In studies by Funder et al (45), in which a renal artery clip was removed surgically from Goldblatt hypertensive sheep, the offset events in fluid balance and cardiac output were very slight when measured one day later. The minuteness of the fluid volume changes required to return blood pressure to normal in human essential hypertension during thiazide therapy has also been shown in studies by Tarazi, Dustan & Frohlich (46). Furthermore, in Goldblatt hypertension, the simultaneous vasoconstrictor effect of angiotensin can readily obscure most or all of the fluid volume and cardiac output changes (Bianchi 39) despite their theoretically overriding importance.

Both the old and the new literature (Ueda, Iwai & Yasuda 47) point out the extreme dependence of renal hypertension on salt intake. Yet, it is still questionable whether it is the salt per se or the induced volume changes resulting from this salt intake that causes the hypertension. The systems analysis suggests that it is the volume changes and not the salt, and recent studies by Brown et al (48), de la Riva et al (49), and Davidov et al (50) all support the view that sodium per se is not the factor responsible for the pressure changes. These results also fit with the earlier studies of Langston et al (51) which showed that hypertension frequently occurs in partially nephrectomized, fluid volume loaded animals despite lower than normal sodium plasma concentrations. Most investigators who have believed that sodium per se plays a significant role in the development of hypertension, have believed that the sodium causes this effect by constricting the peripheral vessels. However, the demonstration of the systems analysis that increase in total peripheral resistance without some simultaneous change in the kidney as well will cause only transient hypertension indicates that, even if sodium does cause increased arteriolar resistance in all other tissues of the body besides the kidneys, there would still be no elevated arterial pressure. However, increase in intrarenal resistance as a result of the change in sodium could indeed cause the necessary water and salt retention tendency that is required to cause chronic hypertension.

It has also often been stated that neurogenic hypertension can occur independently of fluid balance changes. However, Herd (52), recognizing the importance of the renal integrative control system for pressure control, recently pointed out that in neurogenic hypertension nervous stimuli to the kidney can cause the necessary tendency for water and salt retention. He also pointed out that this is likely to be a general phenomenon of all neurogenic types of hypertension, the initial stages of the neurogenic hypertension being caused by the temporary hypertensive effect of increased peripheral resistance and the prolonged hypertension being caused by water and salt retention. In further support of this concept, Gill & Casper (53) have demonstrated that sympathetic stimulation causes marked retention of salt.

The final question that is raised by the systems analysis approach is whether the increase in total peripheral resistance found in most hypertensive states is a cause of the hypertension or is the result of the hypertension. Studies by Coleman et al (4, 5), by Ledingham (3), and by Conway (54) have shown that the hypertension, at least the salt loading variety, occurs first, and the increase in total peripheral resistance is a secondary phenomenon. Furthermore, the concept currently advanced is that the long-term change in total peripheral resistance results from actual vascular changes rather than simply from vasoconstriction. This has been borne out by studies of Folkow and his colleagues (55) in which they have shown that the intrinsic resistance of fully dilated tissue vascular beds increases during progressive stages of hypertension in rats that develop the condition spontaneously. Thus, it seems that a basic change in vascular dimensions and not simply a vasoconstrictor effect causes the increased total peripheral resistance in hypertensive states.

Role of the renin-angiotensin system in hypertension.—The principal question being asked today is: Does the renin-angiotensin system play significant role in most types of hypertension? Reasons for this question include the finding of Macdonald and co-workers (56) that Goldblatt hypertension occurs in rabbits equally as well after they have been immunized against angiotensin II as before, which confirms Flasher & Drury's observations (57) of more than 20 years ago that immunizing animals against renin also does not prevent typical Goldblatt nor renal-encapsulation hypertension. Furthermore, Jerums & Doyle (58) have shown that in many hypertensive patients plasma renin is lower than normal and the renin response to sodium deprivation is low. Also, measurements of renin activity in other types of hypertension, such as coarctation of the aorta (Werning et al 59 and Koletsky et al 60) and in a variety of clinical hypertensions including essential hypertension, renal parenchymal disease hypertension, and primary aldosteronism (Dustan, Tarazi & Frohlich 61) are all normal or below normal.

However, there seem to be two major exceptions to the thesis that renin plays no role in hypertension. First, Dustan and co-workers (61) found good correlation between plasma renin activity and the degree of hypertension that occurs in renovascular disease. Furthermore, large numbers of workers have in the past already pointed out the high degree of correlation between the elevated pressure and renin activities in malignant hypertension. A role that has often been suggested for renin in renal hypertension is that renin secreted by one kidney or by a damaged portion of a kidney can pass in the blood stream to the undamaged renal tissue of the same kidney or of the opposite kidney and cause fluid and salt retention. Such a mechanism would elevate the arterial pressure, and the increased arterial pressure would perhaps make the damaged renal tissue become functional once again. Such a mechanism could play an important role in preventing uremia in patients whose renal mass is barely enough to eliminate the end-products of metabolism. With this thought in mind, Fourcade and co-workers (62) studied the possibility that minute doses of angiotensin might indeed cause water and salt retention by normal renal tissue. The studies, however, indicated that greater than physiological levels of angiotensin would be required for this mechanism to function properly under acute conditions. The study did not delineate whether or not such a mechanism could be operative under chronic conditions in which the renin could elicit aldosterone production.

Angiotensin is known to affect arterial pressure in at least several different ways, including vasoconstriction, effects on the kidneys themselves to cause water and salt retention under at least some conditions, stimulatory effect on aldosterone secretion which in turn causes water and salt retention, and enhancing autonomic effects on the circulatory system. Several studies (Fukiyama et al 63, Andersson and Eriksson 64, Scroop and Lowe 65, and Ueda et al 66) have shown, either by infusion into the vertebral arteries or into the third ventricle, that angiotensin can act directly on the brain to cause cardiovascular effects mediated by the autonomic nervous system; the main effect seems to be decreased vagal stimulation of the heart, and a lesser effect is enhancement of sympathetic activity. Fukiyama, McCubbin & Page (63) also demonstrated that the effect will continue for at least a week during continuous infusion of the angiotensin, but the maximum sustained pressure rise that can be achieved in this manner appears to be limited to only 10 to 15 mm Hg. Another effect closely associated with the autonomic effect is the ability of angiotensin to stimulate ADH release causing water retention and thereby affecting circulatory function in still another way (Mouw et al 67).

Several recent studies suggest the possibility that the renin-angiotensin system might play a more important role in acute regulation of arterial pressure than in the causation of chronic hypertension. An open-loop analysis of the renin- angiotensin system by Cowley, Miller & Guyton (68) in dogs in which the obscuring effects of nervous cardiovascular control had been removed by decapitation showed that the renin-angiotensin-vasoconstrictor system of the dog has a feedback gain of approximately 1.6. This means that a sudden decrease in arterial pressure to 50 mm Hg caused by some effect such as hemorrhage would be corrected back to approximately 80 mm Hg by operation of the renin-angiotensin-vasoconstrictor system alone, without aid from any of the other pressure regulating systems. The time for full development of this response is about 10 minutes; therefore, it could be one of the important semiacute blood pressure control mechanisms. Studies by Meyer & Worcel (69) show that administration of anti-angiotensin plasma to rats causes very significant prompt decrease in arterial pressure, which also suggests that the vasoconstrictor effect of normally secreted angiotensin might be a continually important controller of arterial pressure. And, finally, Oparil et al (70) have demonstrated that renin activity can increase in the plasma in a matter of minutes after tilting patients on a tilt table, further supporting the view that this overall mechanism could be a valuable pressure regulator over short periods.

The mechanism of control of renin secretion is still very uncertain, although almost everyone agrees that low plasma sodium and low plasma potassium (71–75) acting directly on the kidney, enhance renin release. Blaine, Davis & Witty (76) have developed an animal preparation in which there is essentially no tubular fluid flow, and the kidneys of these animals still secrete enhanced amounts of renin in response to hyponatremia. On the other hand, Cooke et al (77) in studying renin-release induced by ethacrynic acid have shown that blockage of the ureters, with consequent blockage of tubular flow, prevents the renin release. They conclude that the stimulus for renin release after ethacrynic acid administration is change in sodium concentration in distal tubular fluid, perhaps acting at the macula densa and exerting a feedback effect on the juxta-glomerular cells. Also significant have been two other findings, that of Blair-West and his colleagues (78) that angiotensin has a direct effect on the kidneys themselves to block renin release, and that of Fojas & Schmid (79) that renin release is not greatly increased in response to decreased arterial pressure until the arterial pressure falls so low that the kidney is no longer able to autoregulate its blood flow, thus suggesting that decrease in blood flow might be much more important as a regulator of renin release than is renal intravascular pressure.

Role of aldosterone in hypertension.—The vast literature on hypertension in primary aldosteronism and on DOCA and other types of steroid-induced hypertension leave no doubt that mineralocorticoids can cause hypertension. There seems to be a tacit assumption that this type of hypertension is similar to other types of salt and water retention hypertension. However, the quantitative significance of angiotensin as a primary controller of aldosterone secretion and the mechanism by which these hormones act together in hypertension still remain highly problematical. Several different studies have indicated that Goldblatt hypertension and other renal types of hypertension do not depend on this mechanism. For example, a demonstration by Blair-West and his colleagues (80) shows that Goldblatt hypertension occurs equally well in steroid supported animals whose adrenal glands have been removed as in normal animals, a fact that supports the earlier study of McCaa et al (81) that adrenal secretion of aldosterone can actually be markedly decreased in Goldblatt hypertension rather than increased. These facts also fit with the observation of Bull et al (82) that it is mainly sodium concentration in the body fluids that controls the renin aldosterone system, rather than blood volume or pressure, indicating that the primary function of aldosterone is to control sodium.

The quantitative importance of the different factors that control aldosterone secretion rate is still confusing: many investigators support angiotensin control as the major factor while others support central control by the nervous system and neurohormones. Though little headway has been made in this controversy, a study by Horton (83) has shown that injection of small amounts of adrenocorticotropic hormone is a stronger stimulus in man for the production of aldosterone than is an infusion of angiotensin in amounts that cause hypertension.

CONTROL OF BODY FLUID VOLUMES

One of the important features of the systems analysis presented earlier is the intricate interplay of many factors required for control of body fluid volumes, not merely the concepts of volume receptors, hemodynamic factors, or renal output of fluid taken individually but, rather, the combination of all these factors and still many others. But, first, let us see what has been done recently and then return to the systems analysis.

Antidiuresis, thirst, and salt appetite.—Additional studies confirm that increased atrial transmural pressure elicits a reflex to cause increased water and salt output by the kidneys (84, 85). Johnson, Zehr & Moore (84) also found simultaneous decrease in ADH secretion, but Goetz et al (85) found no change in ADH.

The regulation of thirst and intake of water is closely associated with the regulation of antidiuretic activity, and essentially the same factors affect both of these mechanisms. Stricker's studies (86, 87), for instance, show that both a decrease in plasma volume and an increase in osmolality, the same factors that affect antidiuretic hormone secretion, likewise stimulate thirst. Thus, the two mechanisms complement each other.

Still another factor important to circulatory homeostasis is the appetite for salt. Stricker & Jalowiec's (87) studies point out that osmotic dilution stimulates the salt appetite in rats and that this is probably equally as important a mechanism for repletion of body fluid volumes as are the thirst and antidiuretic mechanisms.

Natriuresis.—The old observation is that extracellular fluid volume expansion, caused in a number of different ways, but particularly by saline infusion, is associated with marked natriuresis. This effect occurs without any plasma expansion (Reyburn & Gilmore 88) but it is highly correlated with the increase in the interstitial fluid volume increase (Higgins 89). Also, the effect is promoted more by changes in sodium load than by changes in volume load per se (Schrier et al 90). Finally, studies of Higgins (91), Stumpe, Lowitz & Ochwadt (92), and Bank et al (93) all demonstrate that there is decreased proximal tubular sodium reabsorption; it is also suggested that this effect might be caused by physical factors in the kidney, especially by increased renal interstitial fluid volume which diminishes the sizes of the tubules and their absorptive capability. Schrier and co-workers (16) have implicated still other physical factors, including decreased blood viscosity and decreased colloid content of the plasma, which can affect pressures and osmotic absorption at different points in the kidneys including in the glomeruli, the peritubular capillaries, and the vasa recta. Schultze, Shapiro & Bricker (94) point out that the phenomenon of increased single nephron natriuresis that occurs when only a few viable nephrons remain exhibits nearly the same effects as those which occur in the saline diuresis phenomenon, and they conclude that the two phenomena might be, at least partially, manifestations of the same mechanism.

Whether or not a natriuretic factor (third factor) actually exists to cause natriuresis following saline loading is still a matter of discussion. Bonjour & Peters (95) were unable to find such a natriuretic factor in cross-circulation experiments. On the other hand, Sealey, Kirshman & Laragh (96) do report a weakly natriuretic factor that is slow to act, that can have an effect for as long as three hours after injection, but that acts only under special conditions. Thus, the significance of the natriuretic factor is still much in doubt.

Renal autoregulation.—At least two studies (92, 97) have pointed out that autoregulation of arterial pressure and of glomerular filtration rate does not prevent tremendous increases in urine output when the arterial pressure increases, an increase in urine output from 6 to 20 fold occurring when the arterial pressure rises from 100 to 200 mm Hg. In animals with diabetes insipidus (Navar, Uther & Baer 97), enough increase in glomerular filtration rate was observed to account for the increase in water loss. On the other hand, the studies of Stumpe, Lowitz & Ochwadt (92) indicated instead that the marked increase in the urine flow rate is caused by decreased sodium and water reabsorption along the loop of Henle. However, in overall circulatory regulation, the important point is simply that increased arterial pressure does indeed cause marked increases in both water and salt output despite autoregulation in the kidney.

The possibility that feedback at the macula densa is the cause of renal autoregulation also still receives attention. Most important has been the observation by Schnermann et al (98) that perfusion of the loop of Henle with Ringer's solution at different rates of flow causes changes in afferent arteriolar resistance, presumably mediated by the juxtaglomerular apparatus. On the other hand, Gagnon and co-workers (99) have shown that maneuvers to block the action of angiotensin on the afferent arteriole do not prevent renal autoregulation, thus indicating that the earlier suggestion of Thurau (100) that feedback at the juxtaglomerular apparatus is effected through intermediation of renin and angiotensin probably is not correct. Therefore, some other type of feedback stimulus might still need to be found.

Role of hemodynamic factors in volume regulation.—Most of the hemodynamic factors that affect renal output of urine are well known and are not
the subject of much research. These factors include increase in renal arterial
pressure, changes in renal resistances caused by nervous factors, changes in
plasma colloid osmotic pressure and changes in blood viscosity. The systems
analysis presented in this article demonstrates particularly that blood viscosity and plasma colloid osmotic pressure could play far greater roles in control
of urinary output than have previously been believed. Studies by Schrier et
al (16) support both of these observations, and Spitzer & Windhager (101)
have shown that increased colloid osmotic pressure can not only decrease
glomerular filtration rate but can also increase reabsorption of water and
salt from the proximal tubules as well. Furthermore, because of the very fine
balance that exists between glomerular filtration rate and tubular absorption, even minute changes in either of these can cause tremendous changes
in urine output. This could explain the extreme sensitivity of diuretic and
natriuretic responses to renal hemodynamic factors and to volume expansion
or saline loading.

Regulation of interstitial fluid volume.—The systems analysis also explains how the interstitial fluid volume can be regulated very precisely. This
subject is reviewed in detail elsewhere by Guyton, Granger & Taylor (102),
but the gist of it is the following: The interstitial fluid exists in two phases,
as free fluid and as fluid imbibed in a gel-like ground substance. Under normal conditions, essentially all of this fluid is in the latter form, with only
minute portions of free fluid. When free fluid increases even slightly, lymphatic flow also increases tremendously (Taylor et al 103) thereby acting
normally as a negative feedback mechanism to prevent any significant increase in free fluid in the tissue spaces. Lymph flow removes protein as well
as water from the tissue spaces, decreasing tissue colloid osmotic pressure
and increasing capillary absorption of fluid. On the other hand, the interstitial fluid gel, because of its imbibition properties, pulls fluid into it from
the free fluid phase. The amount of fluid held in the gel is determined primarily by its imbibition forces, and the quantity of this fluid is relatively
stable—at least this is so for short-term hemodynamic function. In brief, the
lymphatic system (and capillary absorption) normally seem to keep the
interstitial fluid spaces relatively "dry" of free interstitial fluid. Therefore,
the normal volume of interstitial fluid volume is almost entirely that volume
imbibed in the tissue gel. When the normal drying mechanism for the interstitial spaces fails to maintain the dry state, then large quantities of free
fluid begin to collect, and edema ensues.

Reflex Control of the Circulation

Reflex control of the circulation takes last place in this discussion not
because it is unimportant but because most of the current research work is
mainly confirmation of previous studies or is the study of patterns of cardio-

vascular responses following (*a*) vagal afferent stimulation (Oberg & White 104), (*b*) stimulation of the baroreceptor system in man (Beiser et al 105 and Epstein et al 106), and (*c*) chemoreceptor stimulation (Kontos, Vetrovec & Richardson 107).

Several quantitative studies have been performed to determine the overall effectiveness of the baroreceptor system and its mode of action. Allison, Sagawa & Kumada (108) performed an open-loop analysis of the aortic arch barostatic reflex and found that it functions very much the same as the carotid sinus reflex, except that higher arterial pressures are required to excite the system. Hainsworth, Ledsome & Carswell (109) have also studied baroreceptor responses from the aortic arch and compared these with carotid sinus responses. The responses are qualitatively the same, and the experiments indicate that signals from the aortic stretch receptors and from the carotid stretch receptors sum to produce the same types of effects.

Kumada & Sagawa (110) demonstrated that blood volume changes of 10 to 20% cause a 21 to 31% change in impulse traffic in the aortic nerves of the rabbit, this occurring with only a 6% increase in arterial pressure. Therefore they suggest that arterial baroreceptors act as "volume" receptors in the same way as do atrial receptors. However, the study also demonstrates that so-called "volume" receptors cannot be distinguished from pressure receptors.

In view of the great emphasis that has been placed on pulse pressure as a stimulus to the baroreceptors in recent years, perhaps one of the most important recent papers is that of Kumada et al (111) demonstrating that the pulsatile component of the carotid sinus reflex does not improve the reflex response of an animal to hemorrhage. This experiment was performed by preventing the pulses from reaching the carotid sinus area.

A new study has confirmed the concept of resetting of the baroreceptors. Krieger (112) demonstrated that essentially all baroreceptors are reset within 24 to 48 hours in the rat. This study, added to previous studies on resetting of vascular stretch reflexes, indicates that these reflexes exert their effects only during the first few hours to the first few days after pressure changes occur, and that other mechanisms are required for long-term regulation—either chemoreceptors reflexes or the intrinsic controls of the circulatory system itself. Another type of resetting was demonstrated by Alexander & De Cuir (113), who showed that the heart rate in the rabbit, after rising markedly immediately following sinoaortic denervation, returned to normal within two to six days when only one side was denervated and returned 50% toward normal within two to five weeks when both sides were denervated.

CONCLUDING REMARKS

Again it should be repeated that this attempt to combine a systems analysis with a review was a purposeful experiment. A disadvantage has been that a systems analysis in itself requires a tremendous amount of space for explanation, and even then the origins of the different components must unfortunately be omitted, or alternatively they would require an entire book to explain. However, those of us who have made this systems analysis will testify that such a procedure forces one into a pattern of logical thinking and logical organization, whether the results in all instances are correct or not. If the general principles of this systems analysis are correct, and we believe they are, then it seems clear that the field of circulatory physiology is on the verge of changing from the realm of a speculative science to that of an engineering science.

LITERATURE CITED

1. Guyton, A. C., Coleman, T. G. 1967. *Physical Bases of Circulatory Transport: Regulation and Exchange,* ed. E. B. Reeve, A. C. Guyton, 179–201. Philadelphia: Saunders.
2. Guyton, A. C., Coleman, T. G. 1969. Quantitative analysis of the pathophysiology of hypertension. *Circ. Res.* Suppl. 1, 24:1–19
3. Ledingham, J. M. 1971. Blood-pressure regulation in renal failure. *J. Roy. Coll. Physicians London* 5:103–34
4. Coleman, T. G., Guyton, A. C. 1969. Hypertension caused by salt loading in the dog: III. Onset transients of cardiac output and other circulatory variables. *Circ. Res.* 25:153–60
5. Coleman, T. G., Bower, J. D., Langford, H. G., Guyton, A. C. 1970. Regulation of arterial pressure in the anephric state. *Circulation* 42:509–14
6. Crowell, J. W. 1970. Oxygen transport in the hypotensive state. *Fed. Proc.* 29:1848–53
7. Halmagyi, D. F., Goodman, A. H., Neering, I. R. 1969. Hindlimb blood flow and oxygen usage in hemorrhagic shock. *J. Appl. Physiol.* 27:508–13
8. Halmagyi, D. F., Kennedy, M. 1970. Dependence of oxygen consumption on circulation in normovolemic and hypovolemic dogs. *J. Appl. Physiol.* 29:440–43
9. Whalen, W. J. 1971. Intracellular P_{O_2} in heart and skeletal muscle. *Physiologist* 14:69–82
10. Duling, B. R., Berne, R. M. 1970. Longitudinal gradients in periarteriolar oxygen tension. *Circ. Res.* 27:669–78
11. Jones, C. E., Crowell, J. W., Smith, E. E. 1969. Determination of the mean tissue oxygen tensions by implanted perforated capsules. *J. Appl. Physiol.* 26:630–33
12. Granger, H. J., Guyton, A. C. 1969. Autoregulation of the total systemic circulation following destruction of the central nervous system in the dog. *Circ. Res.* 25:379–88
13. Takeuchi, J. et al 1969. Autoregulation between two vascular systems in dog liver. *J. Appl. Physiol.* 27:77–82
14. Scholtholt, J., Shiraishi, T. 1970. The reaction of liver and intestinal blood flow to a general hypoxia, hypocapnia and hypercapnia in the anesthetized dog. *Pfluegers Arch.* 318–185–201
15. Costin, J. C., Skinner, N. S., Jr. 1970. Effects of systemic hypoxemia on vascular resistance in dog skeletal muscle. *Am. J. Physiol.* 218:886–93
16. Schrier, R. W., McDonald, K. M., Wells, R. E., Lauler, D. P. 1970. Influence of hematocrit and colloid on whole blood viscosity during volume expansion. *Am. J. Physiol.* 218:346–52
17. Cropp, G. J. A. 1969. Hemodynamic responses to oxygen breathing in children with severe anemia. *Circulation* 40:493–500
18. Housley, E., Hedworth-Whitty, R. B. 1969. Circulatory effects of breathing oxygen in patients with chronic anaemia. *Clin. Sci.* 37:715–20
19. Neill, W. A., Oxendine, J. M., Moore, S. C. 1969. Acute and chronic cardiovascular adjustments to induced anemia in dogs. *Am. J. Physiol.* 217:710–14
20. Cassin, S., Gilbert, R. D., Bunnell, C. E., Johnson, E. M. 1971. Capillary development during exposure to chronic hypoxia. *Am. J. Physiol.* 220:448–51
21. Johnson, P. C., Ed. 1964. Auto-regulation of blood flow. *Circ. Res.* 15: Suppl. 1, 1–291
22. Cowley, A. W., Jr., Guyton, A. C. 1970. Importance of heart rate for controlling cardiac output under conditions of high venous return. *Fed. Proc.* 29:2
23. Carleton, R. A., Heller, S. J., Najafi, H., Clark, J. G. 1969. Hemodynamic performance of a transplanted human heart. *Circulation* 40:447–52
24. Beck, W., Barnard, C. N., Schrire, V. 1969. Heart rate after cardiac transplantation. *Circulation* 40:437–45
25. Siegel, H. W., Downing, S. E. 1970. Reduction of left ventricular contractility during acute hemorrhagic shock. *Am. J. Physiol.* 218:772–79
26. Herndon, C. W., Sagawa, K. 1969. Combined effects of aortic and right atrial pressures on aortic flow. *Am. J. Physiol.* 217:65–72
27. Tsakiris, A. G., Donald, D. E., Rutishauser, W. J., Banchero, N.,

Wood, E. H. 1969. Cardiovascular responses to hypertension and hypotension in dogs with denervated hearts. *J. Appl. Physiol.* 27:817–21

28. Bishop, V. S., Horwitz, L. D., Stone, H. L., Stegall, H. F., Engelken, E. J. 1969. Left ventricular internal diameter and cardiac function in conscious dogs. *J. Appl. Physiol.* 27:619–23

29. Hermansen, L., Ekblom, B., Saltin, B. 1970. Cardiac output during submaximal and maximal treadmill and bicycle exercise. *J. Appl. Physiol.* 29:82–86

29a. Donald, D. E., Shepherd, J. T. 1964. Initial cardiac adjustment to exercise in dogs with chronic denervation. *Am. J. Physiol.* 207:1325–29

30. Kline, H. J., et al 1970. Hemodynamic and metabolic effects of hyperbaric oxygenation in myocardial infarction. *J. Appl. Physiol.* 28:256–63

31. Wintroub, B. U., Schroeder, J. S., Schroll, M., Robison, S. L., Harrison, D. C. 1969. Hemodynamic response to dopamine in experimental myocardial infarction. *Am. J. Physiol.* 217:1716–20

32. Mueller, H., Ayres, S. M., Gregory, J. J., Giannelli, S., Jr., Grace, W. J. 1970. Hemodynamics, coronary blood flow, and myocardial metabolism in coronary shock; response to norepinephrine and isoproterenol. *J. Clin. Invest.* 49:1885–902

33. Kumar, R. et al 1970. Experimental myocardial infarction. VI. Efficacy and toxicity of digitalis in acute and healing phase in intact conscious dogs. *J. Clin. Invest.* 49:358–64

34. Hood, W. B., Jr., Bianco, J. A., Kumar, R., Whiting, R. B. 1970. Experimental myocardial infarction. IV. Reduction of left ventricular compliance in the healing phase. *J. Clin. Invest.* 49:1316–23

35. Prather, J. W., Taylor, A. E., Guyton, A. C. 1969. Effect of blood volume, mean circulatory pressure, and stress relaxation on cardiac output. *Am. J. Physiol.* 216:467–72

36. Coleman, T. G., Bower, J. D., Guyton, A. C. 1970. Chronic hemodialysis and circulatory function. *Simulation* 15:222–28

37. Warren, J. V., Nickerson, J. L., Elkin, D. C. 1951. The cardiac output in patients with arteriovenous fistulas. *J. Clin. Invest.* 30:210–14

38. Guyton, A. C., Coleman, T. G., Bower, J. D., Granger, H. J. 1970.

Circulatory control in hypertension. *Circ. Res.* 26, 27: *Suppl.* 2, 135–47

39. Bianchi, G., Tenconi, L. T., Lucca, R. 1969. Effect in the conscious dog of constriction of the renal artery to a sole remaining kidney on haemodynamics, sodium balance, body fluid volumes, plasma renin concentration and pressor responsiveness to angiotensin. *Clin. Sci.* 38:741–66

40. Ferrario, C. M., Page, I. H., McCubbin, J. W. 1970. Increased cardiac output as a contributory factor in experimental renal hypertension in dogs. *Circ. Res.* 27:799–810

41. Julius, S., Pascual, A. V., Sannerstedt, R., Mitchell, C. 1971. Relationship between cardiac output and peripheral resistance in borderline hypertension. *Circulation* 43:382–90

42. Hampers, C. L. et al 1969. Hemodynamic and body composition changes following bilateral nephrectomy in chronic renal failure. *Circulation* 40:367–76

43. Tarazi, R. C., Dustan, H. P., Frohlich, E. D. 1969. Relation of plasma to interstitial fluid volume in essential hypertension. *Circulation* 40:357–65

44. Crawford, M. P., Richardson, T. Q., Guyton, A. C. 1967. Renal servocontrol of arterial blood pressure. *J. Appl. Physiol.* 22:139–42

45. Funder, J. W., et al 1970. Circulatory and humoral changes in the reversal of renovascular hypertension in sheep by unclipping the renal artery. *Circ. Res.* 27:249–58

46. Tarazi, R. C., Dustan, H. P., Frohlich, E. D. 1970. Long-term thiazide therapy in essential hypertension. *Circulation* 41:709–17

47. Ueda, H., Iwai, J., Yasuda, H. 1969. Effects of diet on blood pressure in experimental renal hypertensive rat. *Jap. Heart J.* 10:149–60

48. Brown, W. J., Jr., Brown, F. K., Krishan, I. 1971. Exchangeable sodium and blood volume in normotensive and hypertensive humans on high and low sodium intake, *Circulation* 43:508–19

49. de la Riva, I. J., Blaquier, P., Basso, N. 1970. Water and electrolytes during experimental renal and DCA hypertension. *Am. J. Physiol.* 219:1559–63

50. Davidov, M., Gavrilovich, L., Mroczek, W., Finnerty, F. A., Jr. 1969. Relation of extracellular fluid volume to arterial pressure during

drug-induced saluresis. *Circulation* 40:349–55

51. Langston, J. B., Guyton, A. C., Douglas, B. H., Dorsett, P. E. 1963. Effect of changes in salt intake on arterial pressure and renal function in partially nephrectomized dogs. *Circ. Res.* 12:508–13

52. Herd, J. A. 1971. Behavior and cardiovascular function. *Physiologist* 14:83–89

53. Gill, J. R., Jr., Casper, A. G. T. 1969. Role of the sympathetic nervous system in the renal response to hemorrhage. *J. Clin. Invest.* 48:915–22

54. Conway, J. 1966. Hemodynamic consequences of induced changes in blood volume. *Circ. Res.* 18:190–98

55. Folkow, B., Hallback, M., Lundgren, Y., Weiss, L. 1970. Background of increased flow resistance and vascular reactivity in spontaneously hypertensive rats. *Acta Physiol. Scand.* 80:93–106

56. Macdonald, G. J., Louis, W. J., Renzini, V., Boyd, G. W., Peart, W. S. 1970. Renal-clip hypertension in rabbits immunized against angiotensin II. *Circ. Res.* 27:197–211

57. Flasher, J., Drury, D. R. 1950. Relationship of renin to early renal hypertension in the rabbit. *Am. J. Physiol.* 162:385–92

58. Jerums, G., Doyle, A. E. 1969. Renal sodium handling and responsiveness of plasma renin levels in hypertension. *Clin. Sci.* 37:79–90

59. Werning, C. et al 1969. Plasma renin activity in patients with coarctation of the aorta. A comment on the pathogenesis of prestenotic hypertension. *Circulation* 40:731–37

60. Koletsky, S., Pavlicko, K. M., Rivera-Velez, J. M. 1971. Renin-angiotensin activity in hypertensive rats with a single ischemic kidney. *Lab. Invest.* 24:41–44

61. Dustan, H. P., Tarazi, R. C., Frohlich, E. D. 1970. Functional correlates of plasma renin activity in hypertensive patients. *Circulation* 41:555–67

62. Fourcade, J., Navar, L. G., Guyton, A. C. 1971. Possibility that angiotensin resulting from unilateral kidney disease affects contralateral renal function. *Nephron* 8:1–16

63. Fukiyama, K., McCubbin, J. W., Page, I. H. 1971. Chronic hypertension elicited by infusion of angio-tensin into vertebral arteries of unanaesthetized dogs. *Clin. Sci.* 40:283–91

64. Andersson, B., Eriksson, L. 1971. Conjoint action of sodium and angiotensin on brain mechanisms controlling water and salt balances. *Acta Physiol. Scand.* 81:18–29

65. Scroop, G. C., Lowe, R. D. 1969. Efferent pathways of the cardiovascular response to vertebral artery infusions of angiotensin in the dog. *Clin. Sci.* 37:605–19

66. Ueda, H., Uchida, Y., Ueda, K., Gondaira, T., Katayama, S. 1969. Centrally mediated vasopressor effect of angiotensin II in man. *Jap. Heart J.* 10:243–47

67. Mouw, D., Bonjour, J. P., Malvin, R. L., Vander, A. 1971. Central action of angiotensin in stimulating ADH release. *Am. J. Physiol.* 220:239–42

68. Cowley, A. W., Jr., Miller, J. P., Guyton, A. C. 1971. Open-loop analysis of the renin-angiotensin system in the dog. *Circ. Res.* 28:568–81

69. Meyer, P., Worcel, M. 1970. Role of angiotensin in the salt-hypertension of rats. *Pfluegers Arch.* 317:327–35

70. Oparil, S., Vassaux, C., Sanders, C. A., Haber, E. 1970. Role of renin in acute postural homeostasis. *Circulation* 41:89–95

71. Dluhy, R. G., Underwood, R. H., Williams, G. H. 1970. Influence of dietary potassium on plasma renin activity in normal man. *J. Appl. Physiol.* 28:299–302

72. Sealey, J. E., Clark, I., Bull, M. B., Laragh, J. H. 1970. Potassium balance and the control of renin secretion. *J. Clin. Invest.* 49:2119–27

73. Vander, A. J. 1970. Direct effects of potassium on renin secretion and renal function. *Am. J. Physiol.* 219:455–459

74. Brunner, H. R., Baer, L., Sealey, J. E., Ledingham, J. G. G., Laragh, J. H. 1970. The influence of potassium administration and of potassium deprivation on plasma renin in normal and hypertensive subjects. *J. Clin. Invest.* 49:2128–38

75. Arbrecht, P. H., Vander, A. J. 1970. Effects of chronic potassium deficiency on plasma renin activity. *J. Clin. Invest.* 49:1510–16

76. Blaine, E. H., Davis, J. O., Witty, R. T. 1970. Renin release after hemorrhage and after suprarenal

aortic constriction in dogs without sodium delivery to the macula densa. *Circ. Res.* 27:1081–89

77. Cooke, C. R., Brown, T. C., Zacherle, B. J., Walker, W. G. 1970. The effect of altered sodium concentration in the distal nephron segments on renin release. *J. Clin. Invest.* 49:1630–38

78. Blair-West, J. R. et al. 1971. Inhibition of renin secretion by systemic and intrarenal angiotensin infusion. *Am. J. Physiol.* 220:1309–15

79. Fojas, J. E., Schmid, H. E. 1970. Renin release, renal autoregulation, and sodium excretion in the dog. *Am. J. Physiol.* 219:464–68

80. Blair-West, J. R. et al 1968. Effects of adrenal steroid withdrawal on chronic renovascular hypertension in adrenalectomized sheep. *Circ. Res.* 23:803–9

81. McCaa, C. S., Richardson, T. Q., McCaa, R. E., Sulya, L. L., Guyton, A. C. 1965. Aldosterone secretion by dog during the developmental phase of Goldblatt hypertension. *J. Endocrinol.* 33:97–102

82. Bull, M. B., Hillman, R. S., Cannon, P. J., Laragh, J. H. 1970. Renin and aldosterone secretion in man as influenced by changes in electrolyte balance and blood volume. *Circ. Res.* 27:953–60

83. Horton, R. 1969. Stimulation and suppression of aldosterone in plasma of normal man and in primary aldosteronism. *J. Clin. Invest.* 48:1230–36

84. Johnson, J. A., Zehr, J. E., Moore, W. W. 1970. Effects of separate and concurrent osmotic and volume stimuli on plasma ADH in sheep. *Am. J. Physiol.* 218:1273–80

85. Goetz, K. L., Bond, G. C., Hermreck, A. S., Trank, J. W. 1970. Plasma ADH levels following a decrease in mean atrial transmural pressure in dogs. *Am. J. Physiol.* 219:1424–28

86. Stricker, E. M. 1969. Osmoregulation and volume regulation in rats: inhibition of hypovolemic thirst by water. *Am. J. Physiol.* 217:98–105

87. Stricker, E. M., Jalowiec, J. E. 1970. Restoration of intravascular fluid volume following acute hypovolemia in rats. *Am. J. Physiol.* 218:191–96

88. Reyburn, J. A., Gilmore, J. P. 1971. Natriuretic response to preferential plasma volume expansion in normal unanaesthetized dogs. *Clin. Sci.* 40:73–79

89. Higgins, J. T., Jr. 1971. Role of extracellular volume in diuretic response to saline loading. *Am. J. Physiol.* 220:1367–72

90. Schrier, R. W., Fein, R. L., McNeil, J. S., Cirksena, W. J. 1969. Influence of interstitial fluid volume expansion and plasma sodium concentration on the natriuretic response to volume expansion in dogs. *Clin. Sci.* 36:371–85

91. Higgins, J. T., Jr. 1971. Role of plasma volume in control of proximal tubular sodium reabsorption. *Am. J. Physiol.* 220:1373–78

92. Stumpe, K. O., Lowitz, H. D., Ochwadt, B. 1970. Fluid reabsorption in Henle's loop and urinary excretion of sodium and water in normal rats and rats with chronic hypertension. *J. Clin. Invest.* 49:1200–12

93. Bank, N., Koch, K. M., Aynedjian, H. S., Aras, M. 1969. Effect of changes in renal perfusion pressure on the suppression of proximal tubular sodium reabsorption due to saline loading. *J. Clin. Invest.* 48:271–83

94. Schultze, R. G., Shapiro, H. S., Bricker, N. S. 1969. Studies on the control of sodium excretion in experimental uremia. *J. Clin. Invest.* 48:869–77

95. Bonjour, J. P., Peters, G. 1970. Nonoccurrence of a natriuretic factor in circulating blood of rats after expansion of the extracellular or the intravascular space. *Pfluegers Arch.* 318:21–34

96. Sealey, J. E., Kirshman, J. D., Laragh, J. H. 1969. Natriuretic activity in plasma and urine of salt-loaded man and sheep. *J. Clin. Invest.* 48:2210–24

97. Navar, L. G., Uther, J. B., Baer, P. G. 1971. Pressure diuresis in dogs with diabetes insipidus. *Nephron* 8:97–102

98. Schnermann, J., Wright, F. S., Davis, J. M., Stackelberg, W. V., Grill, G. 1970. Regulation of superficial nephron filtration rate by tubuloglomerular feedback. *Pfluegers Arch.* 318:147–75

99. Gagnon, J. A., Keller, H. I., Kokotis, W., Schrier, R. W. 1970. Analysis of role of renin-angiotensin system in autoregulation of glomerular filtration. *Am. J. Physiol.* 219:491–96

100. Thurau, K., Dahlheim, H., Granger, P. 1970. On the local formation of angiotensin at the site of the juxtaglomerular apparatus. *Proc. Int. Congr. Nephrol. 4th* 2:24–30

101. Spitzer, A., Windhager, E. E. 1970. Effect of peritubular oncotic pressure changes on proximal tubular fluid reabsorption. *Am. J. Physiol.* 218:1188–93

102. Guyton, A. C., Granger, H. J., Taylor, A. E. 1971. Interstitial fluid pressure. *Physiol. Rev.* 51:527–63

103. Taylor, A. E., Gibson, H., Gaar, K. A. 1970. Effects of tissue pressure on lymph flow. *Biophys. J.* 10:45A

104. Oberg, B., White, S. 1970. Circulatory effects of interruption and stimulation of cardiac vagal afferents. *Acta Physiol. Scand.* 80:383–94

105. Beiser, G. D., Zelis, R., Epstein, S. E., Mason, D. T., Braunwald, E. 1970. The role of skin and muscle resistance vessels in reflexes mediated by the baroreceptor system. *J. Clin. Invest.* 49:225–31

106. Epstein, S. E. et al 1969. Circulatory effects of electrical stimulation of the carotid sinus nerves in man. *Circulation* 40:269–76

107. Kontos, H. A., Vetrovec, G. W., Richardson, D. W. 1970. Role of carotid chemoreceptors in circulatory response to hypoxia in dogs. *J. Appl. Physiol.* 28:561–65

108. Allison, J. L., Sagawa, K., Kumada, M. 1969. An open-loop analysis of the aortic arch barostatic reflex. *Am. J. Physiol.* 217:1576–84

109. Hainsworth, R., Ledsome, J. R., Carswell, F. 1970. Reflex responses from aortic baroreceptors. *Am. J. Physiol.* 218:423–29

110. Kumada, M., Sagawa, K. 1970. Aortic nerve activity during blood volume changes. *Am. J. Physiol.* 218:961–65

111. Kumada, M., Schmidt, R. M., Sagawa, K., Tan, K. S. 1970. Carotid sinus reflex in response to hemorrhage. *Am. J. Physiol.* 219:1373–79

112. Krieger, E. M. 1970. Time course of baroreceptor resetting in acute hypertension. *Am. J. Physiol.* 218:486–90

113. Alexander, N., De Cuir, M. 1970. Heart rate resetting after partial or total sinoaortic denervation in conscious rabbits. *Am. J. Physiol.* 219:107–13

REGULATION OF CARDIAC CONTRACTION

JOHN ROSS, JR. AND BURTON E. SOBEL[1]

Department of Medicine, University of California, San Diego,
La Jolla, California

Primary emphasis in this review will be placed on recent significant advances in the following four areas:

Biochemical integration in the myocardial cell (page 47).

Structure-function relations in the contractile units of muscle and heart (page 156).

Methods for the assessment of ventricular function (page 161).

Factors which affect the performance of the mammalian heart (page 71).

Important topics largely omitted which have received comprehensive review elsewhere include Mommaerts' review of the energetics of muscular contraction (1), Young's analysis of the molecular basis of muscular contraction (2), the review by Katz on contractile proteins of the heart (3), Korner's review of integrated neural control mechanisms (4), Johnson & Lieberman's analysis of excitation-contraction coupling and the structure of the sarcotubular system (5), and Levy & Berne's review of cardiac neural control and the coronary circulation (6).

BIOCHEMICAL INTEGRATION IN THE MYOCARDIAL CELL

This section will focus on recent advances concerning the control of myocardial protein synthesis, aerobic and anaerobic metabolism, and the biochemical modulation of the inotropic state in heart muscle.[2]

MYOCARDIAL PROTEIN AND NUCLEIC ACID SYNTHESIS

The following general scheme has been established (excluding reverse transcription): firstly, DNA, containing genetic information, specifies complementary synthesis of mRNA (transcription); and secondly, amino acids, linked with adaptor tRNA molecules, are aligned in unique sequences specified by the base sequence in mRNA, and combined to form polypeptide chains (translation). Translation occurs in the cytoplasm on ribosomes, aggregated subunits of rRNA and protein. During active protein synthesis

[1] Supported by USPHS National Institutes of Health Program Project Grant HE–12373 and by Myocardial Infarction Research Unit Contract No. PH43-68-1332.

[2] Abbreviations: AIB (alpha-amino isobutyric acid); TCA (tricarboxylic acid); PFK (phosphofructokinase); HK (hexokinase); PGLUM (phosphoglucomutase); PK (pyruvate kinase); CPK (creatine phosphokinase); ICD (isocitric dehydrogenase); FDP (fructose 1,6-diphosphate); cyclic AMP (3',5'-cyclic adenylic acid); dbcAMP (dibutyryl cyclic AMP); FA (fatty acid); alpha KG (alpha-keto-glutarate); OA (oxaloacetate).

monomeric ribosomes combine with mRNA to form polysomes.

Regulation of these processes has been investigated in heart muscle undergoing hypertrophy. According to Meerson (7), myocardial compensatory hyperfunction is triphasic: (a) damage—increased nucleic acid and protein synthesis and concentration, and increasing myocardial mass; (b) stable hypertrophy—normal synthesis and concentration, and stable (though increased) myocardial mass; and (c) exhaustion—decreased synthesis, decreasing macromolecule concentration, and myocardial atrophy with fibrosis.

Replication and transcription in myocardial hypertrophy.—In confirmation of earlier reports, it was shown that the increase in DNA during cardiac hypertrophy comes from connective tissue rather than from myocardium (8, 9), and it was reported that myocardial hyperplasia does not occur in the adult (10). However, cardiac hypertrophy is characterized by an early burst of RNA synthesis, associated with enhanced activity of several participating enzymes including uridine kinase (11). Nuclear RNA polymerase activity (mediating transcription) increased promptly in the overloaded perfused guinea pig heart (12), but in vivo incorporation of precursor into myocardial RNA preceded the increase in myocardial content of this enzyme (10). Similar temporal relationships have been observed in skeletal muscle undergoing hypertrophy (13). Thus, increased RNA synthesis may occur in two phases, the first reflecting enhanced activity of RNA polymerase already present in vivo, and the second representing increased cellular content of the enzyme itself. Most evidence indicates that augmented synthesis affects all classes of RNA to much the same extent, although in 1968 Schreiber and associates had observed apparent preferential augmentation of mRNA synthesis in the overloaded perfused guinea pig heart.

Translation.—Increased synthesis of rRNA is characteristic in hypertrophied tissue but only after protein synthesis has increased (10). In the stressed rat heart-lung preparation, increased leucine incorporation into acid insoluble product persisted despite inhibition of RNA synthesis with actinomycin-D. However, it was blocked by cycloheximide or puromycin, inhibitors of translation (14). Translation may increase because of increased intracellular amino acid concentration or changes in the proportion of charged (aminoacyl) to uncharged tRNA. Both intracellular transport and myocardial concentration of amino acids increased in hypertrophied rat hearts, and restriction of dietary protein reduced the extent of hypertrophy (15). Passive stretch was shown to augment transport of a nonmetabolized amino acid (AIB) in the cat capillary muscle (16), and AIB transport increased following aortic constriction in the rat (17). The proportion of charged RNA decreased while amino acid turnover of the charged RNA pool increased in the stressed, perfused rat heart (18).

In comprehensive studies by Morgan and his co-workers (19), the perfused rat heart was exposed to known concentrations of ^{14}C-phenylalanine, chosen to avoid reutilization of label. Amino acid pool size and protein degradation rates were quantified, alterations in oxidative metabolism were excluded, and the synthesis of the specific protein myosin (rather than simply the total acid insoluble product) was measured. Increased amino acid concentration in the perfusate markedly augmented net synthesis of whole heart protein and myosin; intracellular amino acid concentrations reflected perfusate levels, and altered protein synthesis was not due to altered myocardial high energy phosphate stores. Polypeptide chain initiation and elongation rates were determined by analysis of the ribosomal subunit cycle (release of subunits from polysomes and recruitment of newly synthesized subunits into polysomes directly) and by assessment of net rates of protein synthesis. Facilitation of protein synthesis by amino acid conspicuously affected chain initiation. In hypoxic myocardium, protein synthesis was restricted despite increased amino acid transport, apparently because of diminutions in both chain initiation and elongation (20).

Characteristic shifts in isoenzyme profiles in hypertrophied heart muscle (21) underscore the differential regulation of synthesis of specific protein moieties, although the mechanisms responsible have not been elucidated. On the other hand, growing evidence suggests that overall changes in protein synthesis associated with hypertrophy are controlled at several levels, including intracellular amino acid transport and translation. Augmented RNA synthesis may be a secondary response important in sustaining augmented protein synthesis as myocardial mass increases.

REGULATION OF GLYCOGENOLYSIS AND GLYCOLYSIS

Although the heart's dependence on aerobic metabolism is well known, glycogenolytic and glycolytic metabolism may protect it against anoxic injury. Furthermore, since fatty acid oxidation requires TCA cycle intermediates generated when carbohydrate is oxidized, intracellular glucose is important even when oxygen is not rate limiting. Glycogenolysis and glycolysis are regulated largely by allosteric activation, by inhibition of multiple enzymes, or by both. In general, reactions with substrate and product concentrations deviating markedly from thermodynamic equilibrium are those over which major allosteric control is exerted.

Glycolysis and PFK.—Salient conclusions established earlier in several laboratories include: (a) myocardial glucose uptake is rate limiting at physiologic glucose concentrations in the absence of insulin; (b) phosphorylation becomes limiting at high glucose concentrations; (c) insulin increases glucose membrane transport markedly and probably affects phosphorylation modestly, and therefore phosphorylation is limiting at glucose concentrations exceeding 25 mg/100 ml when insulin is present; (d) phosphorylation is essentially irreversible in the heart since glucose-6-phosphatase activity is virtually absent; (e) glucose transport and phosphorylation increase with anoxia—the latter because G-6-P inhibition of HK is released as glycolytic flux increases and G-6-P concentration falls. Flux increases as PFK is released from inhibition by declining citrate and ATP and as PFK is activated by rising phosphate; and (f) catecholamine stimulation does not result in glycogen depletion in the well-oxygenated working heart. On the other hand, glycogen stores are rapidly depleted during anoxia since phosphorylase b itself is stimulated by phosphate and released from inhibition by G-6-P, and because of the transformation of phosphorylase b to a.

A detailed study of binding properties and allosteric kinetics of sheep heart PFK has confirmed and extended these earlier findings (22). These authors showed that FDP decreases enzyme affinity for ATP; that cyclic AMP, phosphate, and 5'-AMP inhibit citrate binding; and that these metabolites relieve ATP and citrate inhibition. Allosteric effects were prominent only at acid pH (22) when total PFK activity was reduced. Accordingly, the metabolic pattern in the ischemic myocardium differs from that in the anoxic, perfused myocardium since PFK activity is reduced by acidosis only in the former (see below).

Glycogenolysis and phosphorylase.—Augmentation of myocardial glycogen stores by reserpine pretreatment and increased glucose concentration protects the perfused rat heart during subsequent anoxia and permits maintenance of higher peak left ventricular pressure (LVP) and dP/dt (23). Neely and co-workers showed that elevation of LVP increased glycogen utilization while the combination of free FA and glucose decreased it (24). Glycogenolysis increased when developed LVP was augmented in the absence of FA; but when FA substrate was available, increased LVP did not accelerate glycogenolysis. Regulation of glycogenolytic rates in response to altered LVP has been explored by analysis of numerous myocardial metabolites as well as phosphorylase b and a activities. Accelerated glycogenolysis primarily reflected regulation of phosphorylase b activity, rather than phosphorylase b to a transformation. Release of inhibition due to decreased G-6-P and activation by phosphate accounted for increased phosphorylase b activity. Changes in ATP and AMP contributed only negligibly. G-6-P disposal was regulated primarily by PFK activity. Because of declining intracellular citrate (see below), PFK activity increased when LVP was increased in the absence of, but not in the presence of, FA. Addition of FA to the perfusate precluded a fall in citrate concentration, with FA oxidation to acetyl CoA favoring citrate accumulation (25).

Additional studies with perfused rat hearts stimulated mechanically emphasize important metabolic patterns dependent upon insulin (26). With insulin, radioactivity from glucose incorporated into glutamic acid, aspartic acid, TCA intermediates, and lactate significantly exceeded that seen at comparable work loads without insulin. Yet, glucose uptake and total $^{14}CO_2$ production were similar. Insulin appeared to facilitate aerobic, energy dependent reactions that participate in glycogen synthesis. The increased synthesis of glutamic and aspartic acid, involved in transamination reactions, may facilitate utilization of cytoplasmic reducing equivalents when oxygen exceeds supply (see *Shuttle reactions* below).

Ischemia vs hypoxia.—Kubler and associates (27) recently explored the conspicuous differences seen in carbohydrate metabolism in the ischemic as contrasted with the anoxic perfused myocardium. They examined ischemic and anoxic cardiac arrest with and without glucose in the perfusate under normothermic and hypothermic conditions, and determined concentration ratios of numerous metabolites sequentially as intracellular myocardial Po_2 fell below a critical level (2–5 mm Hg). Results indicated the following: (*a*) under all conditions studied, anaerobic metabolism was insufficient to maintain high energy phosphate stores; (*b*) consequently, creatine phosphate and, later, ATP stores diminished; (*c*) lactate production and glycolytic flux increased more than 20 fold; (*d*) most glycolytic reactions proceeded at less than 10% the maximum rate because of allosteric kinetic limitations in the intact cell. In ischemic tissue (*a*) phosphorylase and HK stimulation by rising phosphate and stimulation of PK led to initial activation of glycolysis; (*b*) subsequently, PFK became rate limiting in part due to acidosis and HK was inhibited by G-6-P; (c) later PGLUM, which utilizes ATP as a cofactor, became rate limiting as ATP concentration fell below 3.5 μmoles/g, and thus the G–1–P/G–6–P ratio deviated progressively from equilibrium; and (*d*) when ATP concentration fell below 2 μmoles/g, glycolytic flux ceased because insufficient ATP was available to phosphorylate F-6-P.

Responses in the anoxic perfused heart differed. (*a*) Glycolytic activation occurred at the PFK site; (*b*) accordingly, G-6-P decreased (while it increased in ischemic myocardium); (*c*) activation of HK resulted; and (*d*) thus, in anoxic perfused myocardium compared to ischemic tissue, more exogenous glucose and less glycogen were utilized, PFK did not become rate limiting, and total glycolytic flux was greater. Augmented glycolytic flux met only 70% of energy demands of ischemic tissue, but up to 90% of those in the anoxic perfused heart (27).

Interrelationships between fatty acid and glucose metabolism.—The normal heart depends primarily upon FA oxidation, which in turn requires TCA cycle intermediates ultimately derived from carbohydrate oxidation. FA oxidation exerts negative feedback on glucose catabolism by augmenting intracellular citrate and diminishing PFK activity. Other relationships between FA and carbohydrate metabolism have been elucidated recently by Neely, Bowman, & Morgan (24). When LVP was increased in perfused rat hearts exposed to physiological concentrations of FA, FA uptake increased but glucose transport and glycogenolysis remained unaltered. However, increased LVP augmented both glucose uptake and glycogenolysis in the absence of FA. Results with 3-0-methyglucose, a non-metabolized sugar, substantiated the conclusion that FA inhibits hexose transport. Palmitate inhibited hexose transport facilitated by insulin but not that induced by anoxia. In anoxia both phosphorylation and transport are increased when G-6-P depletion releases HK from inhibition (24). However, when the oxygenated heart is subjected to increased afterload and exposed to FA, citrate accumulates, PFK is inhibited, and G-6-P accumulates. The latter effect diminishes phosphorylation by inhibiting HK, and probably contributes to decreased glucose uptake. In addition, free intracellular glucose does not increase; this suggests that FA inhibits membrane transport directly, by mechanisms not yet fully characterized (24, 28).

Interactions between FA and carbohydrate metabolism may be particulary important in ischemic myocardium. In dogs with diminished coronary blood flow, the glucose A-V difference increased while FA extraction remained unchanged (29). This increased ratio of glucose to fatty acid utilization may reflect inadequate FA oxidation resulting from insufficient TCA cycle intermediates in the ischemic tissue. Since free FA may precipitate arrhythmia (30) or depress contractility (31), increased glucose utilization and decreased FA oxidation may set the stage for deleterious physiologic consequences in ischemic myocardium.

Assessment of myocardial metabolism both in the intact animal and in the human has been difficult since compartmentalization within the cell and variations in flux between fluid compartments may cloud interpretation of changes in extracellular fluid. Nevertheless, recent data confirm the fidelity of extracellular lactate/pyruvate ratios in reflecting altered intracellular myocardial redox state, as long as diabetes and nutritional factors are adequately considered (32). Although biochemical indices of irreversible myocardial injury have been elusive, myocardial CPK depletion was found to reflect quantitatively infarct size and blood flow reduction (33). Furthermore, regional CPK depletion in dogs 24 hours after coronary occlusion was linearly related to acute ST segment changes in epicardial electrocardiograms (34). Accurate quantification of infarct size in conscious dogs also was obtained by serial analyses of serum CPK interpreted with a model that relates myocardial degradation to the rate of release, distribution in body fluids, and rate of disappearance from serum of CPK (35).

Studies on the effects of ischemia and manipulations of the myocardial metabolic milieu carry broad implications. Asanguinous perfusion prolongs viability and maintains function of anoxic dog heart supported extracorporeally (36), perhaps because glycolytic flux is facilitated. Hyperosmolar perfusions may be protective (37). Preservation of mitochondria isolated from human and dog hearts perfused asanguinously has been achieved (38). Extensions of these and related approaches toward preservation of myocardial integrity can be anticipated.

AEROBIC METABOLISM

TCA cycle regulation.—Mitochondria are the loci for oxidative phosphorylation (energy conservation in ATP) and TCA cycle substrate utilization. This cycle is regulated in part by ADP stimulation of NAD-dependent mitochondrial ICD. Control of the TCA cycle has been characterized further in studies of rat heart mitochondria incubated with labeled substrates. Analysis of pool size and specific activity of TCA cycle intermediates indicated that the intramitochondrial NADH/NAD ratio exerts allosteric effects on pyruvate dehydrogenase, citrate synthase, and ICD, accounting for coordinated changes in cycle flux without accumulation of intermediates under steady state conditions (39). In perfused rat heart exposed to acetate, discrepancies became apparent between the slow rate of increased citrate and the rapid changes in acetyl-CoA concentration. This displacement of the citrate synthase reaction from equilibrium was largely due to limited OA generation from aspartate by transamination, a reaction that competes ineffectively with alanine transamination for incompletely understood reasons. With acetate availability, TCA flux was regulated in the aceytl-CoA to alpha KG segment (citrate synthase) by OA availability, and in the alpha KG to OA segment (alpha KG dehydrogenase) by CoA availability. Increased flux resulted initially from increased acetyl-CoA and decreased CoA, from augmentation of citrate synthesis, and from increased formation of alpha KG. Increased AMP from the acetyl-CoA synthetase reaction was probably converted to ADP by myokinase thus stimulating respiration. Subsequently, TCA flux was controlled by (a) OA availability which limited the citrate synthase segment; and (b) decreased CoA availability and competing alpha KG transamination which limited the alpha KG dehydrogenase segment (40).

Shuttle reactions.—Reducing equivalents formed in the cytosol must ultimately be oxidized in mitochondria. Since NADH does not penetrate intact mitochondria, "shuttles," principally the malate-aspartate shuttle, serve to facilitate intramitochondrial transport of reducing equivalents. In the cytosol, alpha KG+aspartate→glutamate+OA. OA, reduced by NADH, forms malate which penetrates the mitochondria. In the mitochondria, malate+NAD→NADH+OA, and OA+glutamate→alpha KG +aspartate. Effective shuttle activity requires efflux of alpha KG and aspartate from mitochondria to cytosol, requiring intramitochondrial OA for transamination. Recent results with rat heart mitochondria by LaNoue, Nicklas, & Williamson (39, 41) support the following conclusions: (a) Mitochondrial OA varies directly with the NAD/NADH ratio and with intramitochondrial malate concentration; (b) intramitochondrial OA activates citrate synthase, augmenting alpha KG formation; (c) alpha KG may enter the cytosol (shuttle activation) or undergo dehydrogenation by alpha KG dehydrogenase which predominates when intramitochondrial ATP/ADP falls and increased GDP becomes available for substrate phosphorylation; and (d) aspartate efflux to cytosol is favored by increased intramitochondrial aspartate and by highly energized mitochondrial membranes. Thus, with oxygen lack the shuttle slows because of diminished alpha KG and aspartate efflux, and glucose oxidation in the cytosol diminishes because of NADH accumulation (41).

Myocardial FA synthesis de novo and chain elongation occur primarily in mitochondria. The former is stimulated by increased intramitochondrial NADH/NAD and succinate which augments NADH by reversed electron transport. FA synthesis and oxidation may function as a shuttle by which cytosol reducing equivalents (NADH) are oxidized at the outer mitochondrial membrane coupled to FA chain elongation, and elongated FA is subsequently oxidized within the mitochondria. During hypoxia when mitochondrial NADH increases, increased de novo FA synthesis from acetate would permit continued substrate level phosphorylation by maintaining some NAD in the oxidized form (42).

Mitochondria may facilitate ATP production during anoxia by other mechanisms. Anerobic ATP production coupled to fumarate dependent oxidation of NADH and OA reduction coupled to alpha KG oxidation have been described previously. In a recent report, perfusion of rat hearts with supplemental TCA cycle intermediates improved cardiac performance, increased energy expenditure with respect to lactate production, and maintained myocardial glycogen and ATP stores (43).

Thus, OA availability and NADH/NAD ratios are critically important in regulating TCA flux, permitting oxidation of reducing equivalents from cytosol, and integrating glycolytic, TCA, and fatty acid pathways of substrate utilization.

Mitochondrial function in heart failure.—Previous data on both oxidative phosphorylation and mitochondrial mass in failing heart muscle have been conflicting. In early failure in cardiomyopathic hamsters, oxidative phosphorylation remained normal (44), but this process deteriorated in later stages (44, 45). Normal oxygen consumption and ATP stores have been generally found in failing heart muscle (46). The concentration of mitochondria may remain normal in rat heart undergoing hypertrophy (47); mitochondrial structure may remain intact in late stages of heart failure in the rabbit (48); and normal respiration may (49) or may not (50) prevail in mitochondria from failing human hearts, perhaps depending on the severity of the failure (50). Thus, deranged oxidative phosphorylation does not appear to be a primary pathogenetic mechanism in early stages of congestive heart failure.

Containing most of the calcium of the intact heart, mitochondria exchange calcium with the extracellular compartment rapidly and take up calcium in energy dependent reactions stimulated by phosphate. The possible functional importance of these processes is underscored by inhibition of cardiac muscle relaxation with oligomycin, an inhibitor of mitochondrial respiration (51). Disturbances in mitochondrial energy-linked calcium uptake associated with early congestive heart failure may be physiologically important early in the development of the process (52).

BIOCHEMICAL MODULATORS OF MYOCARDIAL CONTRACTILITY

Cyclic AMP is the established mediator of several metabolic actions of catecholamines in heart muscle. Recent solubilization of myocardial adenyl cyclase, the enzyme regulating cyclic AMP synthesis, and restoration of hormonal responsiveness with phosphatides may help clarify the nature of the adrenergic beta receptor (53). Whether it is the formation of cyclic AMP, or the nucleotide itself, which is responsible for the positive inotropic effect of catecholamines and other agents is not entirely clear. Stimulation of adenyl cyclase parallels or precedes catecholamine induced increased contractility and occurs well before phosphorylase b to a transformation. Inotropic potency of adrenergic agonists is proportional to their capacity to stimulate adenyl cyclase. Glucagon, prostaglandins, and histamine stimulate both the enzyme and contractility (54, 55). Diminished adenyl cyclase activity in myocardial extracts and decreased responsiveness of myocardium to hormonal stimulation have been observed in several kinds of experimental heart failure (56–59). However, the perfused failing heart accumulates cyclic AMP normally following catecholamine stimulation (60).

Despite the cogent evidence that adenyl cyclase activity and the formation of cyclic AMP are associated with the positive inotropic effects of several hormones, the role of cyclic AMP per se has not been established. The nucleotide does not augment contractility in the isolated perfused heart, allegedly because of inadequate intracellular penetration. In isolated cat papillary muscle (61) and in the isolated perfused heart (62), dbcAMP reportedly increases contractile force, but stimulation is slow and protracted. Results in the isolated perfused heart are difficult to interpret because onset of an inotropic effect was delayed for 4 to 6 minutes following bolus administration; because apparent stimulation occurred in only 2/3 of the hearts studied; because variation in ventricular volume due to changes in coronary blood flow were not excluded; and because the doses of dbcAMP employed may have released endogenous myocardial catecholamines (63). Furthermore, dbcAMP exerts metabolic effects different from those of cyclic AMP itself (64), is rapidly degraded in physiological buffers (65), and exhibits qualitatively different chronotropic effects depending on dose (66).

In the isolated perfused rat heart (67), glucagon increased myocardial cyclic AMP *after*-augmentation of contractility. Augmentation of intracellular cyclic AMP by myocardial exposure to low temperature (68) or to dimethylsulfoxide (69) did not augment contractility, although phosphorylase b to a transformation did occur and the hearts remained physiologically responsive to catecholamines. Dissociation between increased contractility and intracellular cyclic AMP levels has been reported in pharmacologic studies (70). Although an increase in sarcotubular calcium uptake induced by cyclic AMP has been observed (71), and might provide a mechanism for cyclic AMP modulation of contractility, this increase is not typically energy dependent. In other studies (72), calcium uptake did not increase in sacroplasmic reticulum (SR) exposed to epinephrine despite stimulation of adenyl cyclase in the preparation. Fluoride activation of adenyl cyclase in SR was associated with decreased (rather than increased) calcium uptake, and cyclic AMP was without affect.

Rasmussen suggested in 1968 that conversion of membrane-bound ATP to cyclic AMP may liberate calcium chelated to ATP, thus accounting for physiological effects associated with stimulation of adenyl cyclase in numerous tissues (73). Confirmation of this or a similar hypothesis would reconcile the disparate results between effects of cyclic AMP and those seen with adenyl cyclase activation (i.e. cyclic AMP formation) in the heart. Thus, contractility would increase with liberation of calcium from a membrane-ATP complex concomitantly with the process of cyclic AMP formation, but would not necessarily be influenced by cyclic AMP itself.

Among other biochemical modulators of contractility, calcium and digitalis glycosides have received considerable recent attention. Evidence suggests that the glycosides bind to Na^+, K^+-ATPase of the membrane and inhibit the enzyme allosterically, that binding may induce conformational changes which facilitate mobilization of a labile calcium store, and that binding corresponds temporally with induced physiological effects (74). On the other hand, apparent digitalis affects on SR, mitochondria, and other cellular components noted in some studies may reflect contamination with Na^+, K^+-ATPase (75).

The influence of sugar transport on physiological responses to digitalis has been recognized for some time. Insulin increased the rate of onset of the positive inotropic response to digitalis, but an increase in contractility of incubated rabbit atria was not seen with substrates other than glucose, nor was it seen when transport was inhibited with Phloretin [beta-p-hydroxyphenyl)-2,4,6-trihydroxypropriophenone]. Thus, both sugar metabolism and transport appear to be required (76).

Since increased free intracellular calcium appears to initiate and sustain cardiac contraction and decreased free calcium to initiate relaxation, recent reports of the influence of hydrogen ion on calcium binding by SR are of particular interest. Since decreased pH increased SR affinity for calcium, intracellular acidosis might impair contractility by reducing free calcium concentration (77). Calcium binding was diminished in both mitochondria and SR from failing heart muscle of humans and of several experimental animals (78–80), but the pathogenetic significance of this decrease in calcium binding is not yet entirely clear.

STRUCTURE OF THE CONTRACTILE UNITS AND HEART

Through a new approach for quantifying the subcellular components of the cardiac muscle cell, the following fractions of cell volume in the rat ventricle were found, exclusive of nuclear and perinuclear volumes and the intercalated disc: mitochondria 34%, myofibrils 48%, T system 1.2%, total sarcotubular system 0.35%, other components 13% (81).

The Fibrils

It seems likely that physical contact occurs between the globular portion of myosin and a site on the actin-containing filaments during muscle contraction. Initial steps toward a structural analysis of this actomyosin interaction in mammalian skeletal muscle have been taken by Moore, Huxley & DeRosier (82). They used a purified preparation of the globular head of myosin to obtain "decorated" actin filaments, and developed a three-dimensional model of the F-actin filaments. The myosin subfragment molecules attached to the G-actin substructure of the actin filament were tilted and "slewed" with respect to its long axis and this, together with the variation in the projected view of the myosin subfragments at crossover points on the actin helix, was held responsible for the electronmicroscopic "arrowhead appearance" of decorated actin. The amount of extra material identified between the two actin strands was considered to be roughly appropriate for the tropomyosin and troponin known to be contained in these filaments. In the proposed model, there was no steric difficulty in attaching one myosin subfragment molecule to every G-actin monomer (82).

The Intercalated Disc

Among the components of the intercalated disc of cardiac muscle, the nexus ("gap junction") probably is involved in electronic coupling between adjacent cardiac muscle cells (83). Revel & Karnovsky in 1967 showed that the nexus consisted of a seven layered structure containing a central 20–30 Å electron-lucent zone. Furthermore, this central zone was partially permeable to the extracellular tracer colloidal lanthanum hydroxide and exhibited a hexagonal array of subunits when viewed *en face*. Recently, McNutt & Weinstein (84) have confirmed this array in mammalian myocardium using lanthanum and a combination of thin section and freeze-cleave electron microscopic techniques. Freeze-cleaving probably causes internal splitting of membranes, so that the surface anatomy produced by freeze-cleaving consists of the inner surfaces of these split membranes. The surfaces of the two plasma membranes of the nexus membranes facing the cytoplasm are revealed only by etching, and the opposing surface between the two membranes has not been shown (presumably because they are in direct contact, with no etchable space between). The internal structures of the two nexus membranes from the adjacent cells were similar: protruding from the inner side of each split membrane was a closely packed array of particles 50–70 Å in diameter, each with a small central pit at its tip. The other face of each split membrane (the inner surface of the outer lamellae) exhibited a series of depressions, nearly complementary in size to the particles on the opposite face, which contained small centrally placed pits at their bases. It appears that the subunit array demonstrated with lanthanum represents spaces around the opposed particles and their caps, which come into direct contact. McNutt & Weinstein postulated that thin channels (approximately 20 Å in diameter), described above as pits and depressions in the particles, pass entirely through the nexus to join the cytoplasm of the two adjacent cells (84). Direct continuity through these proposed hydrophilic channels remains to be demonstrated, however.

SARCOMEROGENESIS

Relevant to studies discussed below are other fine details of the intercalated disc (85). The maculae adherentes (the "desmosomes," found primarily in the longitudinal component along with the nexus) are small and discoid and lie adjacent to a layer of condensed filamentous material in the cytoplasm. The fasciae adherentes (the transverse components of the disc) generally are much larger, contain a 250 to 300 Å interspace and a myofilament lattice into which the actin filaments insert, and also are adjacent to a dense "filamentous mat" in the cytoplasm. This filamentous mat has characteristics resembling those of the Z-band and can occasionally be seen to be continuous with the Z-band, particularly in developing cardiac muscle (85).

Electronmicroscopic studies by Legato (86) have suggested that the Z-band is more than a simple anchoring structure in the myocardial cell and may serve as a template for synthesis of new contractile units. In specimens from human hearts obtained at operation, she noted areas of anomalous Z-band configuration arising from accumulations of "Z substance" in three areas: just under the sarcolemmal membrane (often with extensions laterally in opposite directions to join Z-band substance of an adjacent sarcomere); at the maculae and fasciae adherentes where the accumulated Z substance showed clearly identifiable fragments of thick and thin filaments; and at localized swellings of the sarcomeric Z-bands deep within the cell, sometimes with symmetrical large expansions 1.5–2 μ in width. It was postulated that the latter accumulations represent proliferation of Z-band material beginning in the midline, the matched halves proliferating at the same rate. This view was supported by observations that the mode of insertion of the thin actin filaments into the peripheral edges of the Z substance appeared undisturbed, and that sometimes the M zone of a developing sarcomere lay under the Z-band of a normal sarcomere. Subsarcolemmal and intracellular accumulations of Z substance were also observed in cells of rat ventricular myocardium grown in tissue culture and harvested at 48 to 96 hours, and in mycoardial cells of the 24-hour old puppy. In view of Huxley's concept of the Z-band as a polarized structure containing tropomyosin (the latter extending beyond the thin filaments of adjacent sarcomeres into the Z disc as four anchoring strands), it was of additional interest that these intracellular Z-band accumulations exhibited a longitudinal periodicity of 200 Å compatible with that of tropomyosin (86). Moreover, it is known that another component of the Z-band, B-actinin, fosters the in vitro aggregation of actin into linear strands 1 μ in length.

Other observations pertinent to new synthesis of sarcomeres include those of Bishop & Cole (87), who found scattered accumulations of Z substance in the hypertrophied and failing right ventricles of dogs. Hatt and co-workers (88) investigated papillary muscles of rabbits subjected to chronic aortic insufficiency and noted deformed Z lines and intercalated discs; they postulated that "stretched-Z lines" represent either lesions of the contractile proteins or a process of myofilament growth. Also related may be the finding by light microscopy of widened intercalated discs in the right ventricles of dogs subjected to chronic pulmonary artery banding (89).

STRUCTURE-FUNCTION RELATIONS IN CARDIAC MUSCLE AND THE HEART

Sarcomere lengths.—Grimm and co-workers (90) examined the isolated left ventricular papillary muscle of the rat: above resting lengths of approximately 85% optimum length, sarcomere length, muscle length, and developed tension were directly related. Over this range, sarcomere lengths varied between 1.8 and 2.03 μ; however, formalin fixation and light microscopy were employed, and the authors considered these short lengths appropriate when corrected for shrinkage. Below 85% optimum length, sarcomere lengths remained constant at approximately 1.75 μ; this was thought to be consistent with the curling of myofibers and myofibrils. These studies tend to support previous observations in isolated cardiac muscle and the diastolic heart which show that between sarcomere lengths of 1.8 and 2.25 μ, changes in sarcomere length are appropriate to muscle length and volume changes.

Earlier work indicated that even at high left ventricular end diastolic pressures the sarcomeres at the midwall of the in situ ventricle cannot be forced acutely much beyond optimum sarcomere length (2.2 μ). This was confirmed in the balloon-filled isolated dog heart contracting isovolumetrically (91), and, when end diastolic pressures of up to 100 mm Hg were induced, average sarcomere lengths of only 2.3 μ were reported. While it appears that the sarcomeres of the left ventricular wall are remarkably resistant to acute overstretch, the structures responsible for this property of cardiac muscle are unknown. Interesting in this respect were studies of the properties of the sarcolemma of skeletal muscle fibers (92). It was proposed that with certain assumptions, collagen fibers arranged helically around the muscle fiber could account for properties attributed to the parallel elastic element in skeletal muscle, such as the steep rise in passive tension with muscle stretch beyond 140% of resting length.

Studies on sarcomere lengths have been extended to the chronically dilated dog left ventricle (93). After chronic volume overloading was induced by means of an arteriovenous fistula, hearts were rapidly fixed in diastole at the in vivo transmural left ventricular end diastolic pressure (average 27 mm Hg). Midwall sarcomere lengths averaged 2.19 μ and slippage between myofibrils, reflecting loss in normal alignment of the Z lines, was observed. The possible significance of slippage and increased myocardial cell length (94, 95) and of increased number of sarcomeres per cell in chronically overloaded right ventricles (95), are discussed later in this article in relation to chronic factors which affect cardiac performance. In left

ventricular papillary muscles of rabbits with chronic aortic regurgitation
(88), and in biopsies of right and left ventricles of patients undergoing open-
heart operations (96), sarcomeres longer than 2.2 μ have not been observed,
although shorter sarcomeres were present. However, measurements in the
papillary muscles may not reflect those in the ventricular wall, and in the
latter study specimens were not obtained at known levels of cardiac filling.

Myofiber orientation and heart wall forces.—The architecture of the muscle
bundles of the ventricles has been studied by Armour & Randall (96a), who
analyzed the angular change in muscle fiber direction between epicardium
and endocardium, and the radii of curvature in the right and left ventricles of
the dog. They observed an angular change in the fibers across most of the
myocardial wall of each ventricle, but the change was small (except near the
endocardium and epicardium). Therefore, the dominant fiber orientation at
any site was referred to as the "principal fiber direction". Using strain
gauges, they found that the principal fiber orientation was a primary factor
in determining right ventricular function: developed wall force was unaltered
when an incision was placed in the direction of the circumconal fibers, but
was greatly impaired when the fibers were cut across their axes. In the left
ventricle, the principal fiber direction was reported to be 80° at the base, 50°
to 55° in the mid free wall septum, and 40° to 80° at the apex.

Streeter et al (97) have recently extended earlier studies on the architecture of the canine left ventricle, which had demonstrated a continuum of
fiber helix angles, to an analysis of calculated wall stress distributions during
diastole and systole. The principal radii of curvature near the ventricular
minor equator were both measured directly and calculated by means of an
ellipsoidal model. At end diastole and end systole, measured circumferential
stresses predominated in the middle 80% of the wall, whereas longitudinal
stresses predominated in the outer 20%. Circumferential and longitudinal
stress distributions, which took fiber direction into account, were found to
peak at the midwall, whereas the pressure (or radial stress) decreased across
the wall from endocardium to epicardium. Stress distributions calculated
from direct measurements at the selected local site were similar to those obtained using the ellipsoidal model, and the average circumferential stresses
per unit length calculated at end diastole (12.7 gm/cm) and end systole
(103 mg/cm) agreed surprisingly well with direct measurements of mean
force using auxotonic force transducers (97, 98). Therefore, recent investigations point to the importance of precise knowledge concerning radii of
curvature and fiber angles in calculating local wall stress distributions but
also suggest that simplified geometric models can provide reasonable estimates of mean stress across the ventricular wall.

In comparing stress values in the heart to forces reported in isolated
muscle, it is worth noting that in the former instantaneous geometry and
wall thickness often are considered [Eulerian stress (111)], whereas in

isolated muscle the calculated muscle cross sectional area at zero stress [Lagrangian stress (111)] usually is employed.

METHODS FOR ASSESSMENT OF CARDIAC PERFORMANCE

The search for specific measures of cardiac inotropic state that are independent of changes in preload and afterload has been an important recent theme in physiologic, pharmocologic, and clinical studies. Before considering current methods employed in the analysis of cardiac performance, certain general issues pertaining to the physiology of isolated cardiac muscle deserve comment.

It is accepted that positive and negative inotropic influences can shift the active length-tension curve of isolated cardiac muscle; change the rate of tension development and time to peak tension in the single isometric twitch when resting length is constant; and alter the extent and speed of shortening in the isotonic contraction when resting length and afterload are constant. Moreover, changes in resting length or in afterload also affect the velocity and extent of shortening of the isotonic contraction. However, controversy has arisen concerning the validity of the force-velocity relation and V_{max} in cardiac muscle and their usefulness for defining inotropic state alterations. Brady (99) and others have emphasized the problems caused by inability to tetanize cardiac muscle, by an apparent delay in onset of active state, and by the fact that resting tension cannot be neglected in cardiac as in skeletal muscle. Although at present no analog or model for cardiac muscle is generally accepted, and no anatomic correlates are available, it is agreed that measured force, velocity, and shortening of the muscle need not reflect these events in the contractile elements (CE) since they can be influenced by at least two other components of such a model—the series elastic (SE) and parallel elastic (PE) elements. For example, with reference to the force-velocity relation, the problem is recognized that in a series of afterloaded isotonic contractions, as afterload is progressively increased the SE is further extended, and the velocity of muscle shortening is determined not only later in time but at progressively shorter CE lengths. Other issues recently emphasized have included the shape of the force-velocity relation in cardiac muscle and the question of whether the velocity of the unloaded muscle and the contractile elements (V_{max}) is independent of changes in preload (100, 101).

Proposed analogs for cardiac muscle have included the Voigt model, in which the SE is attached in series to both the CE and the PE, and the Maxwell model, in which the SE is attached only to the CE, the PE encompassing both the CE and SE. With the Voigt model Pollack (101) has suggested that during initial isotonic shortening, since dF/dt in the muscle is zero, the velocity of the SE must be zero and CE velocity can be considered equal to muscle velocity. However, force in the muscle must be corrected for transfer of preload from the PE to the CE during isometric contraction.

When the afterload is low, little CE shortening would occur and only a small correction must be added, whereas when the afterload is high CE shortening is large, and a value approaching the preload must be added to the active force in the muscle to determine the load on the CE. In addition, with the Voigt model, changes in resting length alter SE length and stiffness. Applying such corrections to force-velocity curves published by Sonnenblick in 1962, Pollack calculated force-velocity curves of the CE at different preloads and found that they did not extrapolate to the same V_{max} (101). However, with the Voigt model, the PE has been found experimentally to be very stiff, and by the time shortening velocity is actually measured in the isotonic contraction (maximum, not initial, shortening velocity is usually measured), the PE will have already shortened and the load on the CE is probably close to the total load on the muscle (102).

With the Maxwell model, the SE is usually presumed not to be altered by changes in resting muscle length, and PE length remains unchanged during isometric contraction. Therefore, no correction is made for transfer of load from the PE during isometric contraction. However, during isotonic shortening, since muscle force remains constant, as PE length decreases SE length must increase, and CE velocity (V_{CE}) therefore must exceed that of the SE. V_{CE} is higher than muscle velocity by a factor related to the ratio of the moduli of stiffness (S) of the PE and SE, the relationship being $V_{CE} = V_{muscle}[1+(S_{PE}/S_{SE})]$. Pollack also has applied this correction to published isotonic force-velocity curves of muscle and found that V_{max} of the CE again was not independent of resting muscle length (101). Sonnenblick has indicated, however (102), that Pollack's calculations are based on an atypical experiment (one in which initial velocity of shortening increased with increasing preloads) and that Pollack also failed to understand that in subsequent publications maximum rather than initial shortening velocities were employed. Therefore, such corrections should be applied after some muscle shortening has occurred. Additional objections that velocities are affected by delayed onset of active state have been countered by the argument that in both skeletal and cardiac muscle the ability to reach maximum velocity with light loads is developed considerably sooner than the capacity to develop maximum force (102).

Edman in 1968, using a quick release technique, found V_{max} to be dependent on instantaneous muscle length, particularly at shorter muscle lengths (103). He introduced the possibility that V_{max} might not represent the true shortening velocity of the completely unloaded muscle, but that internal frictional forces could effectively prevent measurement of true V_{max}. Noble et al (100) also found, with quick release techniques, that muscle V_{max} and calculated CE V_{max} were not independent of resting muscle length, although a problem with these findings is that quick release itself appears to alter the level of active state (99, 100). These authors did not systematically approach the question of whether muscle V_{max} obtained with standard isotonic force-velocity curves is independent of resting length; however, a number of isotonic force-velocity curves have shown that muscle V_{max}, obtained by extrapolation, is independent of preload (e.g. 119, 120). It is worth noting that these curves generally are obtained at ranges of preload that are low relative to active tension.

Since extrapolation is required to determine V_{max} from force-velocity curves, efforts have been made to examine shortening velocity in very lightly loaded or unloaded muscles. In single skeletal muscle fibers, Gordon et al showed in 1966 (104) that the degree of myocardial filament overlap at sarcomere lengths at and below 2.2 μ did not influence the velocity of unloaded shortening (V_{max}), although P_0 was affected. Brutsaert, Claes & Sonnenblick (105) have found that shortening velocity is also independent of initial muscle length in unloaded isolated cardiac muscles over a range of resting lengths from L_{max} to 12.5% less than L_{max}.

With reference to inotropic state changes, Edman & Nilsson (106), using quick releases to correct for SE changes and time, recently have shown that V_{max} and maximum isometric force are augmented proportionately during increased frequency of contraction in rabbit papillary muscle. Brutsaert, Parmley & Sonnenblick (107), applying corrections for SE extension during the isometric phase, have computed instantaneous CE lengths and velocity and found that V_{max} is increased following paired stimulation, or administration of calcium or isoproterenol. A number of studies, some of them recent (reviewed later in this article), indicate that inotropic state changes can be documented by means of the isotonic force-velocity relation of cardiac muscle when resting fiber length is constant.

A further complication, however, has been the finding by Noble et al (100) that the force-velocity relation of isolated cardiac muscle was not hyperbolic as in skeletal muscle (99). Hyperbolic curves were found only near L_{max} using afterloaded isotonic contractions, and were not found in force-velocity curves determined by quick release, even when corrected by means of Voigt and Maxwell models. Brutsaert & Sonnenblick, on the other hand, have recently reported that the contractile element force-velocity relation is hyperbolic when corrected for SE changes (108).

In summary, with respect to isolated cardiac muscle, most work indicates that muscle and contractile element V_{max} are altered by a variety of inotropic stimuli. A number of previous studies and some current work suggest that when resting tension is not greatly elevated relative to active tension, and when very short muscle lengths during contraction are avoided, muscle V_{max} is independent of resting muscle length. However, controversy continues to exist on this point as well as on the significance of V_{max} of the CE calculated by use of various models. Finally, there is still no concurrence on the exact shape of the force-velocity curves of cardiac muscle or of the CE, nor has the most appropriate model for the contractile and elastic elements been agreed upon.

An interesting solution to the latter problem has recently been proposed by Y. C. Fung (109) who points out that the so-called Voigt and Maxwell

models refer to spring-dashpot systems used to describe the elasticity of
fluids (J. C. Maxwell, 1831–1879) or the viscosity of crystals (W. Voigt,
1850–1919), and that the equations relative to muscle models bear no
resemblance to those concerned with viscoelasticity. He indicates moreover
that another 3-element model (Kelvin) more closely resembles the analogs
usually applied to muscle than do the Voigt and Maxwell models. The latter,
he therefore contends, are misnomers. Fung further shows that Brady's (110)
classification of papillary muscles into Voigt, Maxwell or non-nominate
model types can be avoided by omitting the simplifying assumption that
tension in the SE is a function only of SE extension; he then shows that the
Maxwell and Voigt models can then be made interconvertible. Earlier,
Fung presented evidence that tension in the series elastic must be a function
of muscle length (111), a solution that would imply that the CE be considered less than freely extensible at rest. He also developed in that work
a general mathematical description of force-velocity-length-time relations
based on experimental data from the literature in isolated cardiac muscle and
the whole heart. Fung recommends use of the term "3-element Hill model"
(Maxwell model), because with this model (in contrast to the Voigt model),
the parallel elastic element can be tested in the resting state, and such
potentially important factors as viscosity and plasticity can be analyzed.
Therefore, there appears to be theoretical support, as well as the empirical
support discussed below, for applying a 3-element Hill model to the intact
heart.

   Methods based on hemodynamic and cardiac dimension measurements.—
For practical purposes, changes in cardiac performance induced by alterations in the inotropic state of the heart generally are considered to be independent of those mediated by changing either resting fiber length (related
to the preload) or the resistance to ejection (afterload, a function of systolic
intraventricular pressure and ventricular geometry). It seems well accepted
that when ventricular end diastolic pressure and aortic pressure are held
constant, the stroke volume, stroke work, stroke power, maximum left
ventricular dP/dt, and ejection velocity increase and decrease respectively
with positive and negative inotropic stimuli. Likewise, as discussed later in
this article, it now seems clear that acute variations in preload or afterload
alone importantly affect these hemodynamic measures.

   Recently, such observations have been expanded to include analyses of
left ventricular volumes and dimensions by means of biplane left ventric-
ulography using cineradiography or videometry (112, 113), biplane cineradiography using implanted radiopaque beads (114), and measurement of left
ventricular diameter by means of implanted sonomicrometers (115, 116).
These approaches have confirmed a positive relationship between left
ventricular end diastolic volume (EDV) and stroke volume in intact animals
and showed that positive inotropic agents produce an increased stroke
volume and ejection fraction from any given EDV. Earlier work indicating

that ventricular function curves must be compared at a constant level of mean aortic pressure was confirmed, and the stroke work and the duration of systole were found to be unreliable indices of inotropic change (117).

Of interest were the demonstrations that when EDV was increased the ejection fraction also increased (114) and that a decrease in the ejection fraction accompanied an increased aortic pressure (113). Both of these findings support a number of previous investigations indicating that acutely induced changes in the ejection fraction are not specific for variations in inotropic state.

Furnival et al (117) emphasized the usefulness of maximum dP/dt of the left ventricle as a sensitive indicator of changes in inotropic state when mean aortic pressure is held constant. However, these authors reached the puzzling conclusion that an increase in ventricular end diastolic pressure is not associated with a significant increase in maximum dP/dt; indeed, one of their pressure tracings (Figure 7) fails to show an increase in maximum dP/dt on the second beat following an increase in aortic pressure, whereas ventricular end diastolic pressure is further augmented. These findings seem unusual, since the well known effect of aortic diastolic pressure level on maximum dP/dt should not have been a factor here; numerous previous observations by ourselves and others using similar preparations, recent studies by Morgenstern et al (118), and experiments in isolated cardiac muscle (119, 120) have all indicated that maximum isometric dP/dt increases when resting fiber length is increased. Nevertheless, recent reports (117, 118) emphasize that maximum dP/dt is more markedly affected by changes in inotropic state than by hemodynamic factors, and quantitative relations between the relative changes produced by variations in cardiac filling and inotropic state bear detailed reexamination, both in controlled preparations and in conscious animals.

Morgenstern et al (118) also reaffirmed older studies indicating that time to maximum dP/dt was little affected by variations in cardiac filling but was altered by changing inotropic state. Hisada (121) reassessed the ratio $(dP/dt)/IIT$ (IIT = integrated ventricular pressure from the apex of the R wave to maximum dP/dt), corroborating this by measurements of $(DT/dt)/IIT$ using a force gauge on the ventricular wall. His studies support earlier conclusions indicating that this ratio is relatively independent of changes in ventricular filling but responsive to inotropic state alterations.

Recent studies on the dynamic geometry of the left ventricle using cineradiographic and ultrasonic techniques have caused some reorientation of previous concepts by showing that the endocardial surface of the left ventricle shows little change during the pre-ejection period. Minimal or no changes in left ventricular wall thickness, length, and chamber diameter during isovolumic contraction were observed in dogs under general anesthesia (122). Others noted slight narrowing of the apical region and a small expansion of the region subjacent to the aortic valve (113). Bugge-Asperheim, Leraand & Kiil (116) used pairs of ultrasonic elements implanted in the

myocardium and were unable to detect significant dimensional changes
during the isovolumic phase of contraction, although with an external rubber
gauge they showed the systolic outward expansion described by Hinds and
co-workers (123). The systolic expansion was progressively increased by
increasing pre-stretch of the rubber gauge, which cast doubt on the quantitative usefulness of this device. Most recent evidence, therefore, indicates that
minimal changes in left ventricular geometry occur during isovolumic contraction in the normal heart. This finding lends support to the view that, for
practical purposes, the left ventricular pressure pulse reflects isometric contraction of the muscle fibers in the ventricular wall.

Methods based on derived force-velocity-length relations.—The mechanical
responses of the muscle of the intact heart to various loading conditions and
inotropic influences have been found to mimic in many ways that of isolated
cardiac muscle (124). We and others were perhaps too eager to apply the
terminology of isolated muscle mechanics to the intact heart, particularly in
view of the controversies currently surrounding the physiology of isolated
cardiac muscle. Nevertheless, the performance of the heart can now be
described reasonably well in mechanical terms. These descriptions account
for important differences in cardiac geometry and loading conditions that
are not considered in ordinary hemodynamic analyses, and from a practical
point of view semantic difficulties need not impair the empirical usefulness of
such derived variables.

Analyses of the ejecting phase of ventricular contraction.—As discussed
earlier, current approaches for calculating wall forces in the intact left
ventricle appear relatively accurate for determining mean wall stress. Probably the most accurate method for determining wall stress and the extent
and velocity of wall shortening in the intact left ventricle during the ejecting
phase of contraction is that which employs high-fidelity micromanometry,
and high-speed calibrated cineangiograms from which wall motion and
thickness are measured directly. These approaches have now been applied in
animals and in man (112, 113, 125); Bove, for example, has recently demonstrated directly that both velocity and extent of left ventricular wall
shortening are reduced when afterload is increased acutely (126). With these
methods, normal human subjects usually exhibit circumferential shortening
rates in the minor left ventricular equator greater than 1.3 circumferences (or
muscle lengths)/sec, whereas patients with diseased left ventricles show
substantially lower rates, sometimes as low as 0.2 to 0.3 circumferences/sec
measured at peak of calculated wall stress (125). This appears to be the case
despite chronically increased end diastolic volumes and, in some instances,
normal wall stress values.

Falsetti et al (127), using standard catheter-manometer systems and
uncorrected single plane angiography have recently noted low velocities even
in normal subjects. The potential error with these methods is sizeable, how-

ever (128), and these authors (127) normalized measurements for end-diastolic dimensions rather than for instantaneous dimensions as has been done in earlier studies (125). The finding, discussed below, that normal dogs subjected to chronic volume overload exhibit a constant mean rate of wall shortening despite progressive cardiac dilatation, makes it possible that the rate of fiber shortening during ejection can provide a measure of the level of inotropic state under basal conditions. A simplified measure, the mean rate of wall shortening alone, has also been proposed as a measure of left ventricular inotropic state in man (129).

A device has been described which continuously regulates the volume within the isolated left ventricle of the dog and allows determination of the maximum velocity of wall shortening in a series of afterload contractions that are regulated to be nearly isotonic (130). An inverse relation between wall stress and the velocity and extent of wall shortening was demonstrated, the shape of this force-velocity relation being curvilinear with a fall near maximum (isovolumic) wall stress. The curves resembled isotonic force-velocity curves obtained in isolated cardiac muscle by some investigators prior to correction for the SE component (108). However, the curves differed from the linear inverse relation that we described in 1966 in variably afterloaded auxotonic beats. Additional recent studies in the isotonically contracting ventricle indicate that the extrapolation of the force-velocity curves to zero wall stress is influenced by altered inotropic state but appears to be little affected by change in end diastolic volume (131).

In terms of muscle models, the objections discussed earlier to isotonic force-velocity curves in isolated cardiac muscle apply to the intact heart. Thus, velocities and forces of the ventricular wall cannot necessarily be equated with those of the contractile elements, since the measured variables are presumably taken at different CE and PE lengths, and at slightly different times during ejection. It should be pointed out that in the normal dog heart the level of preload is low relative to active stress [about 10% of peak stress (98)], which tends to minimize the difficulties due to transfer of forces to the PE element. However, in animals subjected to volume or pressure overload, or in the failing human heart, elevated diastolic ventricular pressures probably make consideration of this variable even more important than in isolated cardiac muscle.

Analyses of the isovolumic phase of ventricular contraction.—There has been great interest in deriving force-velocity relations from the isovolumic phase of contraction to the intact heart by assuming a 2 or 3 component model for muscle. As suggested earlier, it seems likely that such derivations have gone beyond our current knowledge of series and parallel elastic elements in the heart, particularly in relation to their application in chronically diseased hearts. Nevertheless, if these derived data are considered as empirical indices of inotropic state only, rather than as true measures of the behavior of the contractile elements, they may prove useful.

The time course of "velocity of the contractile elements" (V_{CE}) has previously been derived in experimental animals by a number of investigators assuming a two component muscle model during isovolumic contraction of the left ventricle. Thus, the rate of SE extension (and CE shortening) is considered directly related to the rate of force development and inversely related to the stiffness of the SE (the latter usually estimated from isolated muscle data). In completely isovolumic left ventricular beats, the V_{CE} so derived, when plotted against the corresponding wall stress at each point, describes an inverse relation after the first 30 to 50 msec of systole. V_{max} has been estimated by extrapolation to zero stress, and maximum isovolumic wall stress (P_0) at peak pressure also can be determined. Such curves in the intact dog ventricle (124, 132) respond to various interventions in a manner resembling force-velocity curves calculated from isometric twitches in isolated cardiac muscle on the basis of a similar model and an appropriate elastic modulus for the SE[3] (133). In the isolated muscle, V_{CE} at zero stress and the V_{CE} vs time curve wave were independent of initial muscle length (a range of 3–10% less than muscle length at L_{max}) but were altered by inotropic stimuli (133).

Recently, efforts have been made to apply this approach in patients, in whom corrected biplane cineangiograms and in some instances high fidelity pressures were recorded. The value of $(dP/dt)/KP$ (K = 28 cm^{-1}, a constant determined from isolated muscle data) was plotted vs stress during the brief isovolumic phase of left ventricular systole, and the extrapolation of this curve to zero stress by a least squares exponential fit was carried out to determine "V_{max}" (134). In normal patients V_{max} was usually above 3.0 (range: 1.5 to 6.5) circumferences/sec, a value which agrees well with that calculated from completely isovolumic beats in normal, lightly sedated dogs (132). On the other hand, with different methods (standard catheter-manometers and uncalibrated single plane cineangiograms), V_{max} obtained in normal human subjects by linear extrapolation from the isovolumic phase ranged from only 1.07 to 2.64 circumferences/sec (127). Using still different techniques (thermodilution for calculating end diastolic volume) and different K values, standard catheter-manometers and linear extrapolations, Levine et al (198) calculated values averaging 1.82 circumferences/sec in patients with aortic stenosis having no hemodynamic evidence of heart failure.

Simplified methods for determining V_{max} using pressure data alone during the isovolumic phase of ejecting beats have also been advocated, and similar values for this "index of V_{max}" have been reported in patients when V_{CE} is plotted against the corresponding total pressure rather than against wall stress (135). This "index of V_{max}" was found in experimental animals to be

---

[3] The relation is $dl/dt = (dP/dt)/(dP/dl)$, where dP/dt is the rate of tension development, dP/dl ($= KP+C$, K and C being constants) is the SE modulus, and dl/dt is the velocity of lengthening of the SE. The intercept C was neglected, since when dP/dl was plotted as a function of total rather than developed stress the value was small (133).

independent of preload at low ventricular end diastolic pressures, but to fall at end diastolic pressures over 10 mm Hg (136). Mason, Spann & Zelis (using a K value of 32 cm^{-1} for calculating V_{CE}) and total left ventricular pressure) held that V_{max} so derived was independent of preload and afterload, and reported average values of V_{max} of 1.19 circumferences/sec in postoperative subjects considered to be near-normal (137). In another study (using a K value of 40 cm^{-1}) the same investigators found V_{max} in normal subjects to average 1.53 circumferences/sec (138). Mirsky Ellison, & Hugenholtz, however, noted difficulties in extrapolating such curves, and their reported values for V_{max} in hemodynamically normal subjects ranged from 1.4 to 40.5 circumferences/sec (135).

More recently, preliminary data in experimental animals have appeared, which suggest that if developed left ventricular pressure (DP) is used [appropriate to a 3-element Hill (Maxwell) model], then V_{max}, estimated by exponential extrapolation of $(dP/dt)/KDP$ vs DP, is independent of ventricular end diastolic pressure (139), and the extrapolation of $(dP/dt)/DP$ to zero DP in completely isovolumic beats in dogs also appears to be independent of acute variations in ventricular filling (130).

The approaches employed clinically for estimating V_{max} from V_{CE} vs force or V_{CE} vs pressure curves are hampered by the serious difficulty in extrapolating (some by linear extrapolation, others by exponential fitting) very short segments of curves obtained during the isovolumic phase of ejecting contractions. The shape of this portion of the V_{CE} vs pressure or tension curve is not linear in studies of isolated muscle (132) nor in studies in isovolumic beats of the intact heart (124), and the large variations in the values described above may be explained in part by inaccuracies in the extrapolation process. In addition, when cardiac filling is altered experimentally in the ejecting heart, little change in peak left ventricular pressure may occur; some studies analyzing force-velocity and pressure-velocity relations have used completely isovolumic contractions, and the considerable changes in peak tension or pressure produced by changing preload under these conditions can influence the extrapolation of these nonlinear curves. This factor may play a role in determining whether V_{max} obtained from such curves or segments of curves based on P or TP is affected by altered preload. Whether or not SE stiffness in the normal human ventricle is different from that in the diseased ventricle, as recently reported in hypoxic isolated muscle (140), and whether it varies at high levels of end diastolic pressure (as much experimental work suggests) remains to be established. Other errors may be introduced by inadequate catheter-manometer systems, by inaccurate radiographic estimates of ventricular volume, and by the presence of mitral regurgitation. All of these problems will require careful evaluation.

In some studies, difficulties with extrapolation have been avoided by selecting certain points on the plots of V_{CE} or $(dP/dt)/P$ vs pressure, tension, or time. Unfortunately, a plethora of different terms ("$max\ V_{CE}$", "V_{pm}", etc.) and variations in approach have caused considerable confusion. However, basically two types of "indices" have been most widely analyzed:

(a) $max\,[(dP/dt)/P]$ and (b) $(max\,dP/dt)/P$. The pressures employed may be total (TP) or developed (DP), and a K value is sometimes added. Several investigators have shown theoretically that $(max\,dP/dt)/P$, the point of peak CE power, should be directly proportional to V_{CE} and independent of muscle length and ventricular dimensions (141, 132, 135). Nejad et al (136) have measured $max\,[(dP/dt)/TP]$ in animals and have proposed that this ratio (termed "V_{pm}") is independent of both afterload and preload and sensitive to inotropic state changes. This ratio also has been suggested to provide an index of inotropic state in patients (135, 143). On the other hand, Mehmel, Krayenbuehl & Rutishauser (142), using similar techniques in animals observed that V_{pm} decreased with increasing end diastolic pressure, and others have confirmed this finding (139). However, enthusiams for this approach has reached the point that an instrument, the Myoputer[4], is now available for continuous computation of myocardial contractility using this approach.

It has been suggested that using developed rather than total pressure might be more appropriate, particularly when end diastolic pressure (EDP) is elevated (139, 142, 144) as discussed earlier. In this regard, recent unpublished studies in our laboratory have indicated that $[(dP/dt)/DP]$ at a DP of 40 mm Hg is independent of acute variations in EDP, whereas these and other studies have suggested that $max\,[(dP/dt)/DP]$ is not (139). Using high fidelity pressure tracings in patients, the plotted relation between dP/dt and the corresponding DP throughout isovolumic systole was recently found to be insensitive to alterations in filling and responsive to inotropic state changes (144a).

Whether any of these indices will prove definitive for determining inotropic state in patients with chronic heart disease remains to be clearly established. It does seem evident that no standard for defining a given level of inotropic state, against which the validity of various indices can be assessed, is acceptable to all investigators. Differences arising from the use of different preparations and different instrumentation also require further investigation. Some of the confusion arising from variations in terminology could be alleviated if, in reference to the whole heart, the terms V_{max}, $V_{CE}max$, and V_{CE} at maximum dP/dt could be reserved for reference to points on the relation $(dP/dt)/KP$, V_{max} being obtained by extrapolation against developed wall stress or total wall stress. Extrapolations to zero pressure could be termed $V_{max}\,TP$, or $V_{max}\,DP$ (139). Other data derived from pressures alone could be specified by the terms used above.

In summary, it seems established that a number of valid hemodynamic measures can be employed to define acute alterations in inotropic state, provided left ventricular EDP or volume, and aortic pressure (afterload) are known or controlled. A three-dimensional construct encompassing ventricular pressure, ventricular volume, and the velocities of pressure de-

---

[4] Medical Instrumentation Laboratories, Winston-Salem, North Carolina.

velopment and ejection, as suggested some years ago by Fry (145), may add to the power of these techniques. Problems continue in comparing the level of inotropic state in one animal with that in another, and in defining inotropic state in the presence of chronically altered geometry and chronic myocardial disease. Force-velocity data derived from completely isovolumic and afterloaded isotonic beats of the whole heart provide useful descriptions of inotropic state changes, and three-dimensional constructs using force, velocity, and ventricular circumference have been developed (124, 126) which appear to provide a complete description of cardiac performance and the inotropic state of the ventricular muscle. It appears that certain simpler measures derived from developed pressure in the isovolumic phase of left ventricular contraction, or from shortening velocities during the ejecting phase of contraction, may also allow a separation of effects arising from acutely altered inotropic state and to altered filling; numerous studies are underway on their value for detecting the level of inotropic state in the presence of chronic heart disease, and the effects of chronic as opposed to acute changes in diastolic ventricular volume on these measures also must be clarified.

FACTORS WHICH AFFECT VENTRICULAR PERFORMANCE

For convenience, emphasis will be placed on three major factors which acutely affect ventricular performance: the afterload, the preload and the inotropic state (146). In addition, attention will be directed toward chronic factors which influence performance.

Afterload

When end diastolic volume is unchanged, rapid alterations in afterload markedly affect ventricular performance. Stroke volume, and the extent of fiber shortening and its velocity are inversely related to the level of afterload. These important effects of afterload alone, which resemble those observed in isolated muscle, have recently been confirmed in the isotonically contracting left ventricle of the dog (130).

The response to a sustained increase in aortic pressure when compensatory augmentation of left ventricular end diastolic pressure and volume are allowed to occur has been a more controversial topic. Recently, Jose & Taylor (147) confirmed previous studies in patients which indicated that the normal heart responds to the pressor effect of angiotensin by maintaining or increasing stroke volume and stroke work while augmenting left-ventricular EDP, whereas in the diseased heart the stroke volume and stroke work tend to fall. In these experiments, reflex effects were blocked by atropine and propranolol. On the other hand, Tsakiris and co-workers found in open-chest experiments on normal dogs with controlled heart rates that when left ventricular EDP was increased up to 20 mm Hg during angiotensin infusion, the stroke volume dropped slightly (148). Others have reported significant reductions in stroke volume in conscious dogs during a similar pressor stress,

when left ventricular EDP averaged 22 mm Hg (149). Bugge-Asperheim &
Kiil (150) studied open-chest, cardiac denervated dogs and conscious animals in which aortic pressure was raised by aortic constriction or by infusion of angiotensin, and found stroke volume to remain unchanged or to
decrease when aortic pressure was elevated in control experiments; however, stroke volume increased with the same pressor stress during isoproterenol infusion, and they concluded that the cardiac response to increased
aortic pressure depended on the level of inotropy.

Recent experiments cited below (151) indicate that in open-chest experiments on animals the left ventricle is able to maintain stroke volume during increased afterload up to a left ventricular EDP of approximately 40
mm Hg provided a volume expander is infused. In view of this, the possibility should be considered that some of the differences in these experiments may be partly explained by relative hypovolemia or drug induced
alterations in venous return to the heart, as well as by differences in the
levels of inotropic state. Thus, in the experiments discussed above, left
ventricular EDP rarely exceeded 20–25 mm Hg during the pressor stress, and
it seems possible that when reductions in stroke volume are observed following acute pressure loading in the relatively normal heart, inadequate venous
return has prevented complete compensation by the Frank-Starling mechanism.

Many previous investigators, most recently Linden et al (117), have
concluded that there is a small positive inotropic effect (homeometric
autoregulation) of raising systolic left ventricular pressure. Further studies
on the mechanism of this phenomenon have demonstrated an increased rate
of norepinephrine efflux from the coronary sinus when peak left ventricular
systolic pressure is elevated in the innervated canine heart (152). These
workers have postulated that improved contractility is in part due to this
local release of norepinephrine.

PRELOAD

Several investigations in isolated cardiac muscle and in the heart have
indicated that when changes in resting muscle length are induced, contracted muscle length at constant afterload is relatively independent of time;
i.e., regardless of starting length the muscle shortens to near the isometric
length-tension curve. Taylor (153) studied isolated cat papillary muscles
at 30°C and found some discrepancy between contracted lengths initiated
from different resting lengths—the length-tension curve at the end of shortening from the larger fiber length was displaced somewhat to the right.
This difference tended to decrease, particularly at low afterloads, following
acetylstrophanthidin. The discrepancy with earlier and more recent studies
by Brutsaert, Claes & Sonnenblick (105) carried out at 21°C could in part
be related to the effects of the preload itself during contraction, which were
minimized in the later study (105), as well as to the temperature difference.

Erickson et al (154) recorded left ventricular internal diameter, using a sonar technique, during severe exercise induced by swimming. They found increases in left ventricular EDP and small increases in ventricular diameter, indicating that the Frank-Starling mechanism may be brought into play during severe exercise in the conscious dog. Ventricular function curves were performed in dogs during treadmill exercise (155). At near maximum levels of exercise, the rapid infusion of Tyrode's solution produced a further increased in stroke volume, which suggests that venous return may limit the heart's maximum output.

Descending limb of Starling's curve.—The question of whether a descending limb of cardiac function exists in the whole left ventricle is debated. Monroe and co-workers (91) reported that in the isovolumetrically contracting isolated canine heart, no descending limb of developed wall stress or systolic pressure occurred until the EDP exceeded 60 mm Hg; developed pressure then declined by only 7.5% up to an end diastolic pressure of 100 mm Hg. As discussed earlier, at these high EDPs sarcomere lengths averaged only 2.27 to 2.30 μ. Based on this, and earlier work showing that sarcomere lengths did not exceed 2.27 μ at EDPs up to 40 mm Hg, we postulated that a descending limb of performance might not be caused by operation of the heart on a descending limb of the sarcomere length-tension relation (93). Recently, this hypothesis was further evaluated in open-chest experiments on dogs (151). A descending limb of the curves relating left ventricular EDP to stroke volume and stroke work was demonstrated when volume loading was continued to EDP levels exceeding 40 mm Hg with the mean aortic pressure elevated and held constant. The findings suggest that under these circumstances slight increases in afterload (mediated by increase in heart size alone, perhaps via interfibril slippage and the La Place effect) can effect a reduction in stroke volume. Thus, a marked reduction in stroke volume can be produced by increased afterload alone when EDV is held constant (see above), or when the ventricle is unable to compensate by further increases in sarcomere length at extremely elevated filling pressures. It appears that a descending limb is more readily demonstrable in the ejecting than in the isovolumic ventricle.

Diastolic properties of the heart.—In isolated muscle a restoring force is thought to exist following active shortening. A considerable body of work (1958—Brecher, 156) has supported the idea that restoring forces also exist during early diastole in the heart. Tyberg and co-workers (157), using an isolated canine heart preparation, appear to have provided further evidence for a restoring force by demonstrating substantial negative pressures in the relaxing ventricle when inflow was abruptly prevented. The magnitude of the negative pressure was increased by such factors as decreased impedance to injection and enhancement of inotropic state which induced smaller end systolic volumes.

Whether significant changes in the ventricular diastolic pressure-volume relation can be induced acutely by pharmacologic or other means continues to be explored. Previous work suggesting that vagal stimulation altered the left ventricular end diastolic pressure-volume relation was countered by Wildenthal, Mierzwiak & Mitchell (158) who found no such alterations using implanted radiopaque markers and biplane cinefluorography. They also demonstrated no change in the left ventricular end diastolic pressure-volume relation in open-chest experiments on anesthetized dogs following norepinephrine or propranolol administration (159). Others reported, however, that cardiac denervation altered this relation and that angiotensin infusion during cardiac pacing at 160–165 per minute also caused a shift of the pressure-volume relation (113). Examination of the pressure tracings suggests incomplete relaxation under these circumstances, however, as discussed by the authors (113).

Many earlier investigators, with some exceptions, have found little change in the ventricular diastolic pressure-volume relation during acute pharmacologic interventions, provided incomplete relaxation due to rapid heart rate was excluded. Recent careful studies by Noble and co-workers (160), who analyzed radiographically multiple tantalum screws implanted in the left ventricular myocardium, throw additional light on possible causes of discrepancies. Saline, isoproterenol, calcium gluconate, and methoxamine caused no apparent shift in the diastolic pressure-volume relationship during the slow phase of ventricular filling; however, inertial and viscous properties appeared to influence compliance significantly during the rapid phases of filling (160).

In the intact heart further studies will be necessary to define changes in compliance and pressure-volume relations during the various phases of cardiac filling, as well as in time dependent responses during various interventions. The time dependent nature of stress relaxation and creep are well recognized in resting isolated muscle; changes in compliance as well as a shift in the diastolic pressure-volume curve of the left ventricle can be demonstrated during chronic overloading (161, 125), as discussed below. Also of relevance is the recent observation by Romero & Friedman (162) that in fetal lambs the left ventricle is significantly less compliant than in either the newborn lamb or the adult sheep.

INOTROPIC STATE

Calcium and cardiac glycosides.—A detailed consideration of ion fluxes in cardiac muscle and excitation-contraction studied by voltage clamping techniques is beyond the scope of the present review and was recently analyzed by Johnson & Lieberman (5). However, a few important studies that are relevant to mechanisms by which cardiac inotropic state is altered deserve comment. The central role of calcium in muscle contraction has received increasing attention, and some of its effects at the cellular level are discussed elsewhere in this review. Recent studies in skinned skeletal muscle fibers by Podolsky & Teichholz (163) which show that the amount of free calcium apparently affects the number of active sites and not fiber velocity when relative force (P/P_0) is constant are of interest relative to observations in isolated cardiac muscle and the heart. Thus, in heart muscle, calcium and increased frequency of contraction, paired electrical stimulation and digitalis (all of which may act through altered intracellular calcium levels) increase maximum isometric dP/dt and apparent V_{max}. As pointed out by Katz (164) certain conceptual difficulties are raised by these observations, although the modulation of calcium levels by differences in excitation-contraction coupling between cardiac and skeletal muscle is undoubtedly of central importance. Likewise, the relationship of variations in performance induced in cardiac muscle by calcium to those produced by altering resting muscle length, which presumably also affects the number of available active sites (163), requires further clarification. Interrelationships between sodium, potassium, and calcium exchange and muscle performance have been studied extensively in perfused dog papillary muscle and in rabbit interventricular septum by Langer and his associates (164a).

Recently, Suko, Ueba & Chidsey (165) have also observed increased calcium influx associated with mechanical augmentation induced by paired electrical stimulation of the isolated rabbit heart. Langer's observations have supported the view that the Bowditch staircase is due to a lag, and cardiac glycoside action to an inhibition, of active sodium pumping (166). The associated increase of intracellular sodium appears to result in increased calcium influx upon excitation by an unknown mechanism, and the quantity of calcium held on intracellular releasing membranes, in turn, is thought to be diminished by competition for these sites with sodium (164a). A related hypothesis concerning cardiac glycoside action put forth by Besch & Schwartz (167) is based on demonstration of specific inhibition of Na^+, K^+-ATPase from cardiac tissue, as mentioned earlier (74, 75). They suggest (167) that the glycoside may interact with membrane ATPase and, perhaps by a conformational change, cause increased affinity for both calcium and sodium at the same or closely related binding sites on the internal surface of the sarcolemma. An increased labile pool of calcium would then be available for release to active sites on the myofibrils upon electrical depolarization.

Of additional interest in this regard is the recent evidence obtained by Beeler & Reuter (168) that a slow inward calcium current, previously demonstrated by these workers in Purkinje fibers, also exists in dog ventricular muscle cells. If, as these authors suggest, this calcium current carries the main charge in the inward direction during the action potential plateau, this might explain older observations indicating that the initial effect of cardiac glycosides is to increase action potention duration. Besch & Schwartz have further speculated (167) that subsequent shortening of the action potential following digitalis administration (169) could then be due to impedance of further calcium influx by an increase in the calcium bound to the internal surface membrane, but this possibility and the complex relations between calcium movements and the movements of other ions (168), remain unestablished.

In other studies on the cardiac glycosides, Koch-Weser (170) demonstrated in isolated cardiac muscle that the full positive inotropic effect developed when the drug was exposed to the muscle during complete quiescence and that contraction frequency had only a small influence on the time course of development of the positive inotropic effect. This investigator also showed in isolated kitten papillary muscles, that propranolol had no effect on the positive inotropic action of several cardiac glycosides, which suggests that release of myocardial norepinephrine stores plays no role in their action (171). Prindle et al (172) analyzed the relation between external potassium concentration and the inotropic effect of digoxin in isolated cat papillary muscles. The rate of development of the inotropic response was inversely related to external potassium concentration, but the peak inotropic response achieved was not modified.

The effects of digitalis in conscious chronically instrumented dogs were studied (173), and cardiac reserve, as estimated by ventricular output curves, was decreased by ouabain. Whereas the overall cardiac response was adversely influenced by the glycosides, presumably indirect reflex effects on atrial and ventricular function and changes in aortic impedance and heart rate precluded assessment of the direct myocardial effects of this agent. However, recent studies by Vatner and associates suggest that in the conscious dog digitalis has a relatively small positive inotropic effect (e.g. maximum dP/dt increased 20%) (174). Using a model for myocardial infarction and left ventricular failure in the conscious dog, Kumar and associates (175) demonstrated that acetylstrophanthidin had little effect one hour after myocardial infarction but improved left ventricular performance at one week.

Sympathetic and parasympathetic influences.—An improved technique for total cardiac denervation has appeared involving a two stage transsection and re-anastomosis of the atria, interatrial septum, and venae cavae, and transsection of nerves along the origin of the great vessels (176).

All four isovolumically beating cardiac chambers of the dog were studied by means of strain gauge arches, extending previous observations to indicate that not only the left ventricle but also the right ventricle and both atria can respond to sympathetic trunk stimulation with a negative inotropic response (177). It was also demonstrated that cervical vagosympathetic trunk stimulation simultaneously activates both inhibitory and augmentory fibers, with the net effect on contractility reflecting the relative number of the two fiber types distributed to each chamber. Martin, Levy & Zieske (178) analyzed the interplay between parasympathetic and sympathetic stimulation of the isovolumetric left ventricle and presented a computer analysis of the effects of combined stimulation. The response to simultaneous stimulation was nonlinear: the decrease in response due to vagal stimuli was greater at higher levels of sympathetically induced augmentation of contractility.

In the isolated rat atrium, Grodner et al (179) showed that concentrations of norepinephrine which greatly increased atrial frequency, and of acetylcholine which greatly decreased frequency, when combined, did not produce an effect equal to the algebraic sum of these doses; when low concentrations of both acetylcholine and norepinephrine were given, reduction of atrial frequency was the same as that induced by acetylcholine alone, whereas only the highest concentration of norepinephrine increased atrial frequency when the lowest concentration of acetylcholine was present. This effect of acetylcholine was blocked by atropine (179). Dempsey & Cooper (180), extending earlier studies which showed that acetylcholine can exert either positive or negative inotropic effects upon ventricular myocardium, demonstrated an antagonism between acetylcholine and norepinephrine. A decreased inotropic response to norepinephrine occurred after an equipotent dose of acetylcholine. Two muscarinic actions of acetylcholine were postulated, one a direct negative inotropic effect, the other an antagonistic effect on norepinephrine. It was proposed that the positive inotropic effect of high doses of acetylcholine represents the net effect of these two muscarinic effects and the known nicotinic effect (norepinephrine release).

Integrated reflex responses in the intact animal have been reviewed elsewhere (4), but a relevant study on heart rate responses in unanesthetized dogs by Scher & Young (181) has appeared. Using sinusoidal aortic pressure changes, these investigators showed that reflex bradycardia was vagally mediated, and that R-R interval was linearly related to increasing arterial pressure with essentially no time lag. With decreasing aortic pressure, changes in R-R interval lagged behind pressure changes, with the slower alterations sympathetically mediated. Vagal and sympathetic effects were considered to be combined when aortic pressure was lowered, and the relation between pressure and R-R interval was nonlinear.

The effects of exogenously administered catecholamines on the dog left ventricle was studied by Furnival, Linden, & Snow (182). Vagectomy was performed, the stellate ganglia crushed, mean aortic pressure held constant, and maximum dP/dt of the left ventricle used as the index of inotropic state change (possible limitations of this measure alone when alterations in cardiac filling occur were noted earlier). Relative abilities to produce a positive inotropic effect for the same increase in heart rate were, from greatest to least: norepinephrine, epinephrine, isoproterenol. Cocaine hydrochloride potentiated the inotropic and chronotropic responses to norepinephrine but not those to isoproterenol, and abolished the greater inotropic effect of norepinephrine as compared with that of isoproterenol for the same chronotropic effect. These interesting findings were postulated to result from greater uptake of norepinephrine by nerve endings in the sino-atrial node than by the muscle of the left ventricle in the absence of cocaine.

Other factors.—Edmands, Greenspan & Fisch (183), using a left ventricular strain gauge arch, studied inotropic mechanisms in the ventricle during atrial fibrillation. Ventricular performance, assessed by the pulse pressure, was more closely related to the inotropic state of the ventricle as reflected in the percent change of peak dT/dt than to the degree of ventricular filling as measured by the diastolic filling period and the left ventricular EDP. Studies employing a right ventricular strain gauge arch in the dog also demonstrated a poor correlation between active tension and preceding cycle length during atrial fibrillation (184). However, in beats with equal preceding R-R intervals, the myocardial tension was increased as the "prepreceding interval" was reduced. Both of these studies indicate that postextrasystolic potentiation plays a major role in the cardiac response to atrial fibrillation.

Investigations in isolated cardiac muscle indicated that changes in extracellular pH did not cause alterations in inotropic state, since when both Pco_2 and $NaHCO_3$ were increased with pH constant, a reduction in contractility was observed (185). It was suggested that changes in Pco_2 or intracellular pH mediate the inotropic response to acid-base alterations.

The direct myocardial effects of angiotensin II were analyzed in isolated hearts of normal cats and in cats subjected to extrinsic cardiac denervation (186). A positive inotropic effect of angiotensin, consisting of an increased ventricular dP/dt—but with no change in time to peak tension, was demonstrated in both the normal and the denervated cats. In addition, "exaggeration" of the plateau phase of the transmembrane action potential was observed. These studies appeared to exclude any effect of angiotensin via local catcholamines.

During pulsus alternans in anesthetized dogs, the left ventricular inotropic state, as assessed by calculated force-velocity relations in isovolumic beats, varied on a beat-to-beat basis (187). Guntheroth and co-workers (188) failed to show consistent correlations between stroke volume and left ventricular EDP and diameter during pulsus alternans induced by rapid pacing, but a significant negative correlation was found with the aortic pressure just prior to ejection of the weak beat. This higher pressure could tend to inhibit ventricular ejection and to exaggerate further the alternans, but it was calculated that neither the Frank-Starling mechanism nor an effect of afterload alone could explain sustained pulsus alternans. The authors postulated that the weak beat is generated when a failure of electromechanical coupling in some cells causes fewer cells to contract normally, whereas the strong beat is generated by all cells, of which some are potentiated. The observation of a "double staircase" phenomenon (a progressive decrease in stroke volume coupled with a progressive increase in stroke volume in alternating beats) during the initiation and disappearance of pulsus alternans was considered to support this view.

CHRONIC FACTORS AFFECTING PERFORMANCE

In the cardiomyopathic Syrian hamster, elevated right and left ventricular filling pressures and reduced maximum dP/dt were noted (189), and depression of the isometric length-tension curve of the left ventricle was found by Lochner and associates (45). Therefore, a model may be provided for chronic myocardial failure.

Endocrine factors.—Depressed myocardial performance was demonstrated in chronic adrenal insufficiency in the cat, evidenced by reduced maximum dP/dt and peak left ventricular pressure during transient aortic occlusion when compared to control animals (190). Previous studies showing a positive inotropic effect of hyperthyroidism in isolated cat papillary muscles were confirmed (191). In addition, the decrease in force which followed the initial positive inotropic response to increased frequency in hyperthyroid muscles was greater than that which occurred in normal muscles, an effect attributed to relative hypoxia. Studies showing inotropic effects of altered thyroid state on the ventricle in intact animals (191a) were confirmed (192). A reduced positive inotropic response to catecholamines in the hyperthyroid guinea pig was demonstrated, and it was suggested that the hyperthyroid state induces a near maximal increase in contractility. In studies on atrial and ventricular strips from hyperthyroid rabbits, Anton & Gravenstein (193) found no evidence that the inotropic effects of thyroid hormone are related to catecholamine action.

Hypertrophy.—The importance of increased wall thickness and changes in cardiac shape in producing a reduction of wall stress in the chronically dilated and hypertrophied heart has been emphasized (93, 194). However, the question of whether hypertrophy is associated with depressed myocardial inotropic state has been controversial. Bing and co-workers (195) studied the aortic constricted rat heart and confirmed earlier work by showing that V_{max} was depressed in isolated left ventricular trabeculae carneae 1 to 4 weeks after constriction. However, in contrast to previous findings by Spann et al (196), when changes in muscle thickness were taken into account, isometric tension was unchanged and time to peak tension was prolonged, results supporting earlier studies by Grimm, Kubota & Whitehorn (197). Resting tension was also found to be increased, again in contrast to Spann's results. Bing et al postulated that an increased stiffness of the parallel elastic elements might have caused the apparent decrease in muscle V_{max}. [For example, as discussed above, if a 3-element Hill (Maxwell) model is used, V_{max} of the CE would be more than muscle V_{max} if PE stiffness were increased.] Kaufman, Homburger & Wirth (94), on the other hand, reported depression of the force-velocity relation of isolated cat papillary muscles obtained several weeks after pulmonary artery constriction. In addition, using light microscopy, they observed increases in average fiber length and diameter, and noted that the relation between cell surface and cell volume changed from 2 μ^2 per μ^3 in the control to 5 μ^2 per μ^3 in the hypertrophied muscles. In addition, elevation of calcium concentration (11 mM) together with reduction of sodium concentration (75% of normal) resulted in nearly complete restoration of the force-velocity relation. It was suggested that if the amount of calcium entering the cell per unit membrane area is not changed in hypertrophy, a decrease in the amount of calcium distributed per unit cell volume might explain the apparent depression in inotropic state (94).

Conflicting reports on inotropic state in patients with left ventricular hypertrophy have appeared. Using indices of CE velocity obtained from the isovolumic and early ejection phases of contraction (with a conventional catheter-manometer system), Levine et al (198) found that of 12 patients with aortic stenosis, 8 without other evidence of left ventricular failure had normal contractility. Simon and co-workers (199), also estimating inotropic state from several derived variables in the isovolumic phase of contraction, concluded that inotropic state was not depressed in patients with aortic stenosis who had pressure gradients less than 50 mm Hg, but was depressed in patients with pressure gradients exceeding 50 mm Hg; however, the indices were depressed in patients over 40 years of age, regardless of the pressure gradient. Spann, Mason & Zelis (138) found marked depression of V_{max} (estimated by extrapolation of $(\mathrm{d}P/\mathrm{d}t)/KP$, as discussed earlier)in patients with left ventricular hypertrophy but without evidence of cardiac failure. Until the validity and limitations of these various clinical measures of inotropic state can be established, the question remains unclear whether hypertrophy alone produces depression of the inotropic state in the whole heart.

Regression of hypertrophy in adult rats after correction of several abnormalities has been demonstrated (200). Cardiac hypertrophy of 60% produced by unilateral nephrectomy reverted to near normal by the end of 2 to 3 weeks, a 45% increase produced by aortic constriction fell to an average of 11% of the expected weight by 2 weeks, and a 100% enlargement produced by chronic anemia was reduced to 8% above expected normal weight by 12 weeks.

Chronic volume overloading.—Left ventricular end diastolic volume (EDV) was found to be increased in dogs subjected to acute and chronic heart block by Turina, Bussmann & Krayenbühl (201), but when such dogs were compared at matched heart rates and EDVs, no differences were observed in maximum left ventricular $\mathrm{d}P/\mathrm{d}t$ or other indices of inotropic state determined during the isovolumic phase of contraction. These findings support previous studies in dogs with chronic arteriovenous fistula, in many of which no depression of inotropic state could be detected by force-velocity analyses or by length-tension relations in completely isovolumic contractions (202).

Studies in dogs with chronic arteriovenous fistula, discussed in part earlier (93), have shown a substantial increase in left ventricular EDV without elevation of left ventricular EDP beyond that observed under acute conditions, indicating a rightward displacement of the diastolic pressure-volume relationship. Other recent studies have shown that this shift of the diastolic pressure-volume relation occurs over several weeks and is largely reversible after closure of the fistula (161). In addition, it has been found that despite the chronic augmentation of ventricular EDV and stroke volume, the percent shortening of the minor equator, the left ventricular equator, and the mean rate of fiber shortening corrected for heart size remain unchanged as progressive dilatation occurs.[5]

Related clinical studies carried out before and after surgical correction of severe volume overloading due to aortic regurgitation (125) demonstrated that the left ventricular diastolic pressure-circumference relation was shifted to the right preoperatively. It returned to normal, however, within one year following surgical treatment in patients having normal inotropic state preoperatively (estimated from the velocity of left ventricular wall shortening during ejection, as discussed earlier), whereas in patients with depressed inotropic state there was a fixed abnormality in the diastolic pressure-circumference relation. Recent studies by Jarmakani et al (203) in children following surgical correction of chronic volume overloading produced by ventricular septal defect tend to corroborate some of these findings. EDVs fell from an average of 134 ml/m² preoperatively to 90 ml/m² postoperatively (normal 71 ml/m²), and left ventricular mass was reduced from 138 g/m² to 109 g/m² postoperatively (normal 82 g/m²), whereas the left ventricular EDPs were not significantly changed. These findings indicate that regression of hypertrophy and a shift of the pressure-volume relation toward normal occurred, although the authors noted that the changes appeared to be only partially reversed after an average of two years postoperatively.

The above findings, coupled with the experimental observations on sarcomere lengths alluded to earlier, allow the development of an hypothesis concerning the functional response of the left ventricle to chronic volume overloading. Since diastolic sarcomere lengths are maximal (2.2μ) and essentially the same following the dilatation produced by chronic volume overloading as they are during acute volume overloading, it is proposed that the chronic adaptation of the myocardium to this form of stress does not involve the Frank-Starling mechanism at the sarcomere level. Rather, following the use of increased sarcomere length to mediate an increased stroke volume during the acute stage of volume overloading, progressive cardiac dilatation subsequently appears to occur while end diastolic sarcomere lengths remain constant. This dilatation presumably is accomplished by an increase in the size of myocardial cells (94), by an increased number of sarcomeres developing in series during the hypertrophy process (86, 95), and also perhaps by slippage between fibrils (93). This adaptive mechanism could allow the delivery of an increased stroke volume with no more shortening of each sarcomere than occurs normally during acute volume overloading, a view supported by the experimental finding that the rate and extent of wall shortening per unit of circumference are the same in the acutely and chronically

[5] McCullagh, H. J., and Ross, J. Jr. Unpublished observations.

volume overloaded heart. It also supports the use of dP/dt and derivatives of it, as well as the use of wall shortening velocity, for defining inotropic state levels despite chronic cardiac dilataion. Clinical and experimental studies further suggest that this chronic adaptive mechanism is reversible, provided cardiac failure, perhaps associated with myocardial fibrosis, has not ensued.

LITERATURE CITED

1. Mommaerts, W. F. H. M. 1969. Energetics of muscular contraction. *Physiol. Rev.* 49:427–508
2. Young, M. 1969. The molecular basis of muscle contraction. *Ann. Rev. Biochem.* 38:913–50
3. Katz, A. M. 1970. Contractile proteins of the heart. *Physiol. Rev.* 50:63–158
4. Korner, P. I. 1971. Integrative neural cardiovascular control. *Physiol. Rev.* 51:312–67
5. Johnson, E. A., Lieberman, M. 1971. Heart: Excitation and contraction. *Ann. Rev. Physiol.* 33:479–532
6. Levy, M. N., Berne, R. M. 1970. Heart. *Ann. Rev. Physiol.* 32:373–414
7. Meerson, F. Z. 1969. The myocardium in hyperfunction hypertrophy and heart failure. *Circ. Res.* 25:Suppl. 2, 1–163
8. Grove, D., Zak, R., Nair, K. G., Aschenbrenner, V. 1969. Biochemical correlates of cardiac hypertrophy: IV. Observations on the cellular organization of growth during myocardial hypertrophy in the rat. *Circ. Res.* 25:473–85
9. Grimm, A. F., De La Torre, L., La Porta, M., Jr. 1970. Ventricular nuclei-DNA relationships with myocardial growth and hypertrophy in the rat. *Circ. Res.* 26:45–52
10. Fanburg, B. L. 1970. Experimental cardiac hypertrophy. *N. Engl. J. Med.* 282:723–32
11. Matsushita, S., Fanburg, B. L. 1970. Pyrimidine nucleotide synthesis in the normal and hypertrophying rat heart: Relative importance of the de novo and "salvage" pathways. *Circ. Res.* 27:415–28
12. Schreiber, S. S., Oratz, M., Rothschild, M. A. 1969. Nuclear RNA polymerase activity in acute hemodynamic overload in the perfused heart. *Am. J. Physiol.* 217:1305–9
13. Sobel, B. E., Kaufman, S. 1970. Enhanced RNA polymerase activity in skeletal muscle undergoing hypertrophy. *Arch. Biochem. Biophys.* 137:469–76
14. Kako, K., Minelli, R. 1969. Regulation of leucine incorporation into cardiac protein by work loads. *Experientia* 25:34–36
15. Wannemacher, R. W., Jr., McCoy, J. R. 1969. Regulation of protein synthesis in the ventricular myocardium of hypertrophic hearts. *Am. J. Physiol.* 216:781–87
16. Lesch, M., Gorlin, R., Sonnenblick, E. H. 1970. Myocardial amino acid transport in the isolated rabbit right ventricular papillary muscle: General characteristics and effects of passive stretch. *Circ. Res.* 27:445–60
17. Koide, T., Ozeki, K. 1971. Increased amino acid transport in experimentally hypertrophied rat heart. *Jap. Heart J.* 12:177–84
18. Stringfellow, C., Brachfeld, N. 1970. A study of transfer RNA, total RNA and protein interrelationships in control and stressed isolated perfused rat hearts. *J. Molec. Cell Cardiol.* 1:221–33
19. Morgan, H. E. et al 1971. Regulation of protein synthesis in heart muscle. I. Effect of amino acid levels on protein synthesis. *J. Biol. Chem.* 246:2152–62
20. Morgan, H. E., Jefferson, L. S., Wolpert, E. B., Rannels, D. E. 1971. Regulation of protein synthesis in heart muscle. II. Effect of amino acid levels and insulin on ribosomal aggregation. *J. Biol. Chem.* 246:2163–70
21. Sobel, B. E., Henry, P. D., Ehrlich, B. J., Bloor, C. M. 1970. Altered myocardial lactic dehydrogenase isoenzymes in experimental cardiac hypertrophy. *Lab. Invest.* 22:23–27
22. Lorenson, M. Y., Mansour, T. E. 1969. Studies on heart phosphofructokinase. *J. Biol. Chem.* 244:6420–31
23. Scheuer, J., Stezoski, S. W. 1970. Pro-

tective role of increased myocardial glycogen stores in cardiac anoxia in the rat. *Circ. Res.* 27:835–49

24. Neely, J. R., Bowman, R. H., Morgan, H. E. 1969. Effects of ventricular pressure development and palmitate on glucose transport. *Am. J. Physiol.* 216:804–11

25. Neely, J. R., Whitfield, C. F., Morgan, H. E. 1970. Regulation of glycogenolysis in hearts: effects of pressure development, glucose, and FFA. *Am. J. Physiol.* 219:1083–88

26. Chain, E. B., Mansford, K. R. L., Opie, L. H. 1969. Effects of insulin on the pattern of glucose metabolism in the perfused working and Langendorff heart of normal and insulin-deficient rats. *Biochem. J.* 115:537–46

27. Kubler, W., Spieckermann, P. G. 1970. Regulation of glycolysis in the ischemic and the anoxic myocardium. *J. Molec. Cell. Cardiol.* 1:351–77

28. Grass, M. F., III, McCaskill, E. S., Shipp, J. C. 1970. Glucose-free fatty acid interactions in the working heart. *J. Appl. Physiol.* 29:87–91

29. Owen, P., Thomas, M., Opie, L. 1969. Relative changes in free-fatty-acid and glucose utilisation by ischaemic myocardium after coronary-artery occlusion. *Lancet* 1:1187–90

30. Kurien, V. A., Oliver, M. F. 1970. A metabolic cause for arrhythmias during acute myocardial hypoxia. *Lancet* 1:813–15

31. Henderson, A. H., Craig, R. J., Gorlin, R., Sonnenblick, E. H. 1970. Free fatty acids and myocardial function in perfused rat hearts. *Cardiovasc. Res.* 4:466–72

32. Opie, L. H., Mansford, K. R. L. 1971. The value of lactate and pyruvate measurements in the assessment of the redox state of free nicotinamide-adenine dinucleotide in the cytoplasm of perfused rat heart. *Eur. J. Clin. Invest.* In press

33. Kjekshus, J. K., Sobel, B. E. 1970. Depressed myocardial creatine phosphokinase activity following experimental myocardial infarction in rabbit. *J. Clin. Invest.* In press

34. Maroko, P. R. et al 1971. Factors influencing infarct size following experimental coronary artery occlusions. *Circ. Res.* 43:67–82

35. Shell, W. E., Kjekshus, J. K., Sobel, B. E. 1971. Biochemical measurement of the extent of myocardial

infarction in the intact animal. *Clin. Res. Abstr.* 19:339

36. Mundth, E. D., Sokol, D. M., Levine, F. H., Austen, W. G. 1970. Evaluation of methods for myocardial protection during extended periods of aortic cross-clamping and hypoxic cardiac arrest. *Bull. Soc. Int. Chir.* 29:227–35

37. Ferrans, V. J., Buja, L. M., Levitsky, S., Roberts, W. C. 1971. Effects of hyperosmotic perfusate on ultrastructure and function of the isolated canine heart. *Lab. Invest.* 24:265–72

38. Sordahl, L. A. et al 1970. Respiratory activity of mitochondria from isolated human and dog hearts maintained in a portable preservation chamber. *J. Molec. Cell. Cardiol.* 1:379–88

39. LaNoue, K., Nicklas, W. J., Williamson, J. R. 1970. Control of citric acid cycle activity in rat heart mitochondria. *J. Biol. Chem.* 245:102–11

40. Randle, P. J., England, P. J., Denton, R. M. 1970. Control of the tricarboxylate cycle and its interactions with glycolysis during acetate utilization in rat heart. *Biochem. J.* 117:677–95

41. LaNoue, K. F., Williamson, J. R. 1971. Interrelationships between malate-aspartate shuttle and citric acid cycle in rat heart mitochondria. *Metabolism* 20:119–40

42. Whereat, A. F., Orishimo, M. W., Nelson, J. 1969. The location of different synthetic systems for fatty acids in inner and outer mitochondrial membranes from rabbit heart. *J. Biol. Chem.* 244:6498–506

43. Penney, D. G., Cascarano, J. 1970. Anaerobic rat heart. Effects of glucose and tricarboxylic acid-cycle metabolites on metabolism and physiological performance. *Biochem. J.* 118:221–27

44. Lindenmayer, G. E., Harigaya, S., Bajusz, E., Schwartz, A. 1970. Oxidative phosphorylation and calcium transport of mitochondria isolated from cardiomyopathic hamster hearts. *J. Molec. Cell. Cardiol.* 1:249–59

45. Lochner, A., Brink, A. J., Van Der Walt, J. J. 1970. The significance of biochemical and structural changes in the development of the myocardiopathy of the Syrian hamster. *J. Molec. Cell. Cardiol.* 1:47–64

46. Pool, P. E. 1969. Congestive heart failure: Biochemical and physiologic observations. *Am. J. Med. Sci.* 258:328–39

47. Dart, C. H., Jr., Holloszy, J. O. 1969. Hypertrophied non-failing rat heart. *Circ. Res.* 25:245–53

48. Hatt, P. Y., Berjal, G., Moravec, J., Swynghedauw, B. 1970. Heart failure: An electron microscopic study of the left ventricular papillary muscle in aortic insufficiency in the rabbit. *J. Molec. Cell. Cardiol.* 1:235–47

49. Willebrands, A. F., Ter Welle, H. F., Tasseron, S. J. A. 1971. Functional state of mitochondria isolated from failing and from hypertrophic non-failing human hearts. *Clin. Chim. Acta* 32:251–60

50. Lindenmayer, G. E. et al 1971. Some biochemical studies on subcellular systems isolated from fresh recipient human cardiac tissue obtained during transplantation. *Am. J. Cardiol.* 27:277–83

51. Haugaard, N., Haugaard, E. S., Lee, N. H., Horn, R. S. 1969. Possible role of mitochondria in regulation of cardiac contractility. *Fed. Proc.* 28:1657–62

52. Harigaya, S., Schwartz, A. 1969. Rate of calcium binding and uptake in normal animal and failing cardiac muscle: Membrane vesicles (relaxing system) and mitochondria. *Circ. Res.* 25:781–94

53. Levey, G. S. 1971. Restoration of glucagon responsiveness of solubilized myocardial adenyl cyclase by phosphatidylserine. *Biochem. Biophys. Res. Commun.* 43:108–13

54. Klein, I., Levey, G. S. 1971. Activation of myocardial adenyl cyclase by histamine in guinea pig, cat, and human heart. *J. Clin. Invest.* 50:1012–15

55. Klein, I., Levey, G. S. 1971. Effect of prostaglandins on guinea pig myocardial adenyl cyclase. *Metabolism.* In press

56. Sobel, B. E., Henry, P. D., Robison, A., Bloor, C., Ross, J., Jr. 1969. Depressed adenyl cyclase activity in the failing guinea pig heart. *Circ. Res.* 24:507–12

57. Dhalla, N. S., Sulakhe, P. V., Khandelwal, R. L., Olson, R. E., 1971. Adenyl cyclase activity in the perfused rat heart made to fail by substrate-lack. *Cardiovasc. Res.* In press

58. Gold, H. K., Prindle, K. H., Levey,

G. S., Epstein, S. E. 1970. Effects of experimental heart failure on the capacity of glucagon to augment myocardial contractility and activate adenyl cyclase. *J. Clin. Invest.* 49:999–1006

59. Laraia, P. J., Gertz, E. W., Sonnenblick, E. H. 1971. Adenyl cyclase in hamster cardiomyopathy. *Circ. Res.* In press

60. Henry, P. D., Sobel, B. E., Kjekshus, J. K., Robison, A., Stull, J. T., Jr. 1971. Cyclic AMP in the perfused failing guinea pig heart. *Proc. Soc. Exp. Biol. Med.* In press

61. Skelton, C. L., Levey, G. S., Epstein, S. E. 1970. Positive inotropic effects of dibutyryl cyclic adenosine 3',5'-monophosphate. *Circ. Res.* 26:35–43

62. Kukovetz, W. R., Poch, G. 1970. Cardiostimulatory effects of cyclic 3',5'-adenosine monophosphate and its acylated derivatives. *Arch. Pharmakol. Exp. Pathol.* 266:236–54

63. Buckley, N. M. 1970. Role of endogenous norepinephrine in cardiac inotropic effects of nucleosides. *Arch. Int. Pharmacodyn.* 188:92–104

64. Hilz, H., Tarnowski, W. 1970. Opposite effect of cyclic AMP and its dibutyryl derivative on glycogen levels in hela cells. *Biochem. Biophys. Res. Commun.* 40:973–81

65. Swislocki, N. I., 1970. Decomposition of dibutyryl cyclic AMP in aqueous buffers. *Anal. Biochem.* 38:260–69

66. Berti, F., Mandelli, V., Paoletti, R. 1970. The effect of cyclic AMP on the heart rate of the isolated rat atria. *Int. Z. Klin. Pharmakol. Ther. und Toxikol.* 4:123–24

67. Mayer, S. E., Namm, D. H., Rice, L. 1970. Effect of glucagon on cyclic 3',5'-AMP, phosphorylase activity and contractility of heart muscle of the rat. *Circ. Res.* 26:225–33

68. Langslet, A., Oye, I. 1970. The role of cyclic 3',5'-AMP in the cardiac response to adrenaline. *Eur. J. Pharmacol.* 12:137–44

69. Kjekshus, J. K., Henry, P. D., Sobel, B. E. 1971. Activation of phosphorylase produced by cyclic AMP in the perfused guinea pig heart without augmentation of contractility. *Circ. Res.* In press

70. Shanfeld, J., Frazer, A., Hess, M. E. 1969. Dissociation of the increased formation of cardiac adenosine 3',5'-monophosphate from the positive inotropic effect of norepineph-

rine. *J. Pharmacol. Exp. Ther.* 169: 315–20

71. Entman, M. L., Levey, G. S., Epstein, S. E. 1969. Mechanism of action of epinephrine and glucagon on the canine heart. *Circ. Res.* 25:429–38

72. Sulakhe, P. V., Dhalla, N. S. 1970. Excitation-contraction coupling in heart. III. Evidence against the involvement of adenosine cyclic 3′,5′-monophosphate in calcium transport by sarcotubular vesicles of canine myocardium. *Molec. Pharmacol.* 6:659–66

73. Rasmussen, H. 1970. Cell communication, calcium ion, and cyclic adenosine monophosphate. *Science* 170: 404–12

74. Schwartz, A., Allen, J. C., Harigaya, S. 1969. Possible involvement of cardiac Na$^+$, K$^+$-adenosine triphosphatase in the mechanism of action of cardiac glycosides. *J. Pharmacol. Exp. Ther.* 168:31–41

75. Allen, J. C., Besch, H. R., Jr., Glick, G., Schwartz, A. 1970. The binding of tritiated ouabain to sodium- and potassium-activated adenosine triphosphatase and cardiac relaxing system of perfused dog heart. *Molec. Pharmacol.* 6:441–43

76. Bailey, L. E., Dresel, P. E. 1971. Role of the sugar transport system in the positive inotropic response to digitalis. *J. Pharmacol. Exp. Ther.* 176:538–44

77. Nakamaru, Y., Schwartz, A. 1970. Possible control of intracellular calcium metabolism by [H$^+$]: Sarcoplasmic reticulum skeletal and cardiac muscle. *Biochem. Biophys. Res. Commun.* 41:830–36

78. Harigaya, S., Schwartz, A. 1969. Rate of calcium binding and uptake in normal and failing human cardiac muscle. *Circ. Res.* 25:781–94

79. Suko, J., Vogel, J. H. K., Chidsey, C. A. 1970. Intracellular calcium and myocardial contractility. III. Reduced calcium uptake and ATPase of the sarcoplasmic reticular fraction prepared from chronically failing calf hearts. *Circ. Res.* 27:235–47

80. Muir, J. R., Dhalla, N. S., Orteza, J. M., Olson, R. E. 1970. Energy-linked calcium transport in subcellular fractions of the failing rat heart. *Circ. Res.* 26:429–38

81. Page, E., Fozzard, H. A. 1971. Capacitive, Resistive and Syncytial Properties of Heart Muscle: Ultra-

structural and Physiological Considerations. *The Structure and Function of Muscle*, 2nd ed. New York: Academic. In press

82. Moore, P. B., Huxley, H. E., DeRosier, D. J. 1970. Three-dimensional reconstruction of F-actin, thin filaments and decorated thin filaments. *J. Mol. Biol.* 50:279–95

83. Dewey, M. M. 1969. The structure and function of the intercalated disc in vertebrate cardiac muscle. *Experientia Suppl.* 15:10–28

84. McNutt, N. S., Weinstein, R. S. 1970. The ultrastructure of the nexus. A correlated thin-section and freeze-cleave study. *J. of Cell. Biol.* 47: 666–88

85. McNutt, N. S. 1970. Ultrastructure of intercellular junctions in adult and developing cardiac muscle. *Am. J. Cardiol.* 25:169–83

86. Legato, M. J. 1970. Sarcomerogenesis in human myocardium. *J. Molec. Cell. Cardiol.* 1:425–37

87. Bishop, S. P., Cole, C. R. 1969. Ultrastructural changes in the canine myocardium with right ventricular hypertrophy and congestive heart failure. *Lab. Invest.* 20:219–29

88. Hatt, P. Y. et al 1970. Heart Failure: An electron microscopic study of the left ventricular papillary muscle in aortic insufficiency in the rabbit. *J. Molec. Cell. Cardiol.* 1:235–47

89. Laks, M. M., Morady, F., Adomian, G. E., Swan, H. J. C. 1970. Presence of widened and multiple intercalated discs in the hypertrophied canine heart. *Circ. Res.* 27:391–402

90. Grimm, A. F., Katele, K. V., Kubota, R., Whitehorn, W. V. 1970. Relation of sarcomere length and muscle length in resting myocardium. *Am. J. Physiol.* 218:1412–16

91. Monroe, R. G., Gamble, W. J., La-Farge, C. G., Kumar, A. E., Manasek, F. J. 1970. Left ventricular performance at high end-diastolic pressures in isolated, perfused dog hearts. *Circ. Res.* 26:85–99

92. Fields, R. W., Faber, J. J. 1970. Biophysical analysis of the mechanical properties of the sarcolemma. *Can. J. Physiol. Pharmacol.* 48:394–404

93. Ross, J., Jr., Sonnenblick, E. H., Taylor, R. R., Spotnitz, H. M., Covell, J. W. 1971. Diastolic geometry and sarcomere lengths in the chronically dilated canine left ventricle. *Circ. Res.* 28:49–61

94. Kaufmann, R. L., Homburger, H.,

Wirth, H. 1971. Disorder in excitation-contraction coupling of cardiac muscle from cats with experimentally produced right ventricular hypertrophy. *Circ. Res.* 28:346–57

95. Laks, M. M., Morady, F., Swan, H. J. C. 1969. Canine right and left ventricular cell and sarcomere lengths after banding the pulmonary artery. *Circ. Res.* 24:705–10

96. Rackley, C. E., Dalldorf, F. G., Hood, W. P., Jr., Wilcox, B. R. 1970. Sarcomere length and left ventricular function in chronic heart disease. *Am. J. Med. Sci.* 259:90–96

96a. Armour, J. A., Randall, W. C. 1970. Structural basis for cardiac function. *Am. J. Physiol.* 218:1517–23

97. Streeter, D. D., Jr. et al 1970. Stress distribution in the canine left ventricle during diastole and systole. *Biophys. J.* 10:345–63

98. Burns, J. W., Covell, J. W., Myers, R., Ross, J., Jr. 1971. Comparison of directly measured left ventricular wall stress and stress calculated from geometric reference figures. *Circ. Res.* 28:611–21

99. Brady, A. J. 1968. Active state in cardiac muscle. *Physiol. Rev.* 48:570–600

100. Noble, M. I. M., Bowen, T. E., Hefner, L. L. 1969. Force-velocity relationship of cat cardiac muscle, studied by isotonic and quick-release techniques. *Circ. Res.* 24:821–33

101. Pollack, G. H. 1970. Maximum velocity as an index of contractility in cardiac muscle. *Circ. Res.* 26:111–27

102. Sonnenblick, E. H. 1970. Contractility of cardiac muscle. (Letters to Editor.) *Circ. Res.* 27:479–81

103. Edman, K. A. P., Nilsson, E. 1968. Mechanical parameters of myocardial contraction studied at a constant length of the contractile element. *Acta Physiol. Scand.* 72:205–10

104. Gordon, A. M., Huxley, A. J., Julian, F. J. 1966. The variation in isometric tension with sarcomere length in vertebrate muscle fibers. *J. Physiol. London* 184:170–92

105. Brutsaert, D. L., Claes, V. A., Sonnenblick, E. H. 1971. Velocity of shortening of unloaded heart muscle relative to the length-tension relation. *Circ. Res.* 29:63–75

106. Edman, K. A. P., Nilsson, E. 1969. The dynamics of the inotropic change produced by altered pacing of rabbit papillary muscle. *Acta Physiol. Scand.* 76:236–47

107. Brutsaert, D. L., Parmley, W. W., Sonnenblick, E. H. 1970. Effects of various inotropic interventions on the dynamic properties of the contractile elements in heart muscle of the cat. *Circ. Res.* 27:513–22

108. Brutsaert, D. L., Sonnenblick, E. H. 1969. Force-velocity-length-time relations of the contractile elements in heart muscle of the cat. *Circ. Res.* 24:137–49

109. Fung, Y. C. 1971. Comparison of different models of the heart muscle. *J. Biomechanics.* In press.

110. Brady, A. J. 1967. The three element model of muscle mechanics: Its applicability to cardiac muscle. *Physiologist* 10:75–86

111. Fung, Y. C. 1970. Mathematical representation of the mechanical properties of the heart muscle. *J. Biomechanics* 3:381–404

112. Bove, A. A., Lynch, P. R. 1970. Measurement of canine left ventricular performance by cineradiography of the heart. *J. Appl. Physiol.* 29:877–83

113. Tsakiris, A. G., Donald, D. E., Sturm, R. E., Wood, E. H. 1969. Volume, ejection fraction, and internal dimensions of left ventricle determined by biplane videometry. *Fed. Proc.* 28:1358–67

114. Mitchell, J. H., Wildenthal, K., Mullins, C. B. 1969. Geometrical studies of the left ventricle utilizing biplane cinefluorography. *Fed. Proc.* 28:1334–43

115. Bishop, V. S., Horwitz, L. D., Stone, H. L., Stegall, H. F., Engelken, E. J. 1969. Left ventricular internal diameter and cardiac function in conscious dogs. *J. Appl. Physiol.* 27:619–23

116. Bugge-Asperheim, B., Leraand, S., Kiil, F. 1969. Local dimensional changes of the myocardium measured by ultrasonic techniques. *Scand. J. Clin. Lab. Invest.* 24:361–71

117. Furnival, C. M., Linden, R. J., Snow, H. M. 1970. Inotropic changes in the left ventricle: The effect of changes in heart rate, aortic pressure and end-diastolic pressure. *J. Physiol. (Lond.)* 211:359–87

118. Morgenstern, C., Arnold, G., Höljes, U., Lochner, W. 1970. Die Druck-

anstiegsgeschwindigkeit im linken Ventrikel als Mass für die Kontraktilität unter verschiendenen hämodynamischen Bedingungen. *Pfluegers Arch.* 315:173–86

119. Abbott, B. C., Mommaerts, W. F. H. M. 1959. A study of inotropic mechanisms in the papillary muscle preparation. *J. Gen. Physiol.* 42:533–51

120. Sonnenblick, E. H. 1962. Force-velocity relations in mammalian heart muscle. *Am. J. Physiol.* 202: 931–39

121. Hisada, S. 1969. Myocardial contactility and pumping function of the ventricle. *Jap. Circ. J.* 33:1557–63

122. Lynch, P. R., Bove, A. A. 1969. Geometry of the left ventricle as studied by a high-speed cineradiographic technique. *Fed. Proc.* 28: 1330–33

123. Hinds, J. E., Hawthorne, E. W., Mullins, C. B., Mitchell, J. H. 1969. Instantaneous changes in the left ventricular lengths occurring in dogs during the cardiac cycle. *Fed. Proc.* 28:1351–57

124. Ross, J., Jr., Sonnenblick, E. H. 1970. The mechanics of contraction of the intact heart. *Pathophysiology of Congenital Heart Disease*, ed. F. Adam, H. J. C. Swan, V. E. Hall, 149–161. Berkeley: Univ. Calif.

125. Gault, J. H., Covell, J. W., Braunwald, E., Ross, J., Jr. 1970. Left ventricular performance following correction of free aortic regurgitation. *Circulation* 42:773–80

126. Bove, A. A., Lynch, P. R. 1970. Radiographic determination of force-velocity-length relationship in the intact dog heart. *J. Appl. Physiol.* 29:884–88

127. Falsetti, H. J., Mates, R. E., Greene, D. G., Bunnell, I. L., 1971. V_{max} as an index of contractile state in man. *Circulation* 43:467–79

128. Sandler, H. 1970. Dimensional analysis of the heart—A review. *Am. J. Med. Sci.* 260:56–70

129. Karliner, J. S., Gault, J. H., Eckberg, D., Mullins, C. B., Ross, J., Jr. 1971. Mean velocity of fiber shortening: A simplified measure of left ventricular myocardial contractility. *Circulation* 44: 323–33

130. Covell, J. W., Fuhrer, J. S., Boerth, R. C., Ross, J., Jr. 1969. Production of isotonic contractions in the intact canine left ventricle. *J. Appl. Physiol.* 27: 577–81

131. Burns, J. W., Covell, J. W., Ross, J., Jr. 1971. Force-velocity relations in isotonic contraction of the whole heart. *Abstr. Fed. Proc.* 30:611

132. Taylor, R. R., Ross, J., Jr., Covell, J. W., Sonnenblick, E. H. 1967. A quantitative analysis of left ventricular myocardial function in the intact sedated dog. *Circ. Res.* 21:99–115

133. Yeatman, L. A., Jr., Parmley, W. W., Urschel, C. W., Sonnenblick, E. H. 1971. Dynamics of contractile elements in isometric contractions of cardiac muscle. *Am. J. Physiol.* 220:534–42

134. Hugenholtz, P. G., Ellison, R. C., Urschel, C. W., Mirsky, I., Sonnenblick, E. H. 1970. Myocardial force-velocity relationships in clinical heart disease. *Circulation* 41:191–202

135. Mirsky, I., Ellison, R. C., Hugenholtz, P. G. 1971. Assessment of myocardial contractility in children and young adults from ventricular pressure recordings. *Am. J. Cardiol.* 27:359–67

136. Nejad, N. S., Klein, M. D., Mirsky, I., Lown, B. 1971. Assessment of myocardial contractility from ventricular pressure recordings. *Cardiovasc. Res.* 5:15–23

137. Mason, D. T., Spann, J. F., Jr., Zelis, R. 1970. Quantification of the contractile state of the intact human heart. *Am. J. Cardiol.* 26:243–57

138. Spann, J. F., Jr., Mason, D. T., Zelis, R. F. 1969. The altered performance of the hypertrophied and failing heart. *Am. J. Med. Sci.* 258: 291–303

139. Urschel, C. W. et al 1970. A comparison of indices of contractility derived from the isovolumic force-velocity relation. *Abstr. Circ. 51, 52*, Oct., Suppl. III, p. 115

140. Henderson, A. H., Parmley, W. W., Sonnenblick, E. H. 1971. The series elasticity of heart muscle during hypoxia. *Cardiovasc. Res.* 5:10–14

141. Taylor, R. R. 1970. Theoretical analysis of the isovolumic phase of left ventricular contraction in terms of cardiac muscle mechanics. *Cardiovasc. Res.* 4:429–35

142. Mehmel, H., Krayenbuehl, H. P., Rutishauser, W. 1970. Peak measured velocity of shortening in the canine left ventricle. *J. Appl. Physiol.* 29:637–45

143. Grossman, W., Brooks, H., Meister, S., Sherman, H., Dexter, L. 1971. New technique for determining instantaneous myocardial force-velocity relations in the intact heart. *Circ. Res.* 28:290–97

144. Peirce, E. C., II, Kent, B. B., Patterson, R. E., Temples, J. 1970. A curious approximate construction for V_{CEmax}. *J. Appl. Physiol.* 28:507–9

144a. Mason, D. T., Braunwald, E., Covell, J. W., Sonnenblick, E. H., Ross, J., Jr. 1971. Assessment of cardiac contractility: The relation between the rate of pressure rise and ventricular pressure during isovolumic systole. *Circ. Res.* 44:47–58

145. Fry, D. L. 1962. Discussion. *Fed. Proc.* 21:991–93

146. Ross, J., Jr. 1969. The assessment of myocardial performance in man by hemodynamic and cineangiographic techniques. *Am. J. Cardiol.* 23:511–15

147. Jose, A. D., Taylor, R. R. 1969. Autonomic blockade by propranolol and atropine to study intrinsic myocardial function in man. *J. Clin. Invest.* 48:2019–31

148. Tsakiris, A. G., Donald, D. E., Rutishauser, W. J., Banchero, N., Wood, E. H. 1969. Cardiovascular responses to hypertension and hypotension in dogs with denervated hearts. *J. Appl. Physiol.* 27:817–21

149. O'Rourke, R., Pegram, B., Bishop, V. 1970. Variable effect of increasing afterload on ventricular function. *Abstr. Circ.* 42:Suppl. III, p. 185

150. Bugge-Asperheim, B., Kiil, F. 1969. Cardiac response to increased aortic pressure: Changes in output and left ventricular pressure pattern at various levels of inotropy. *Scand. J. Clin. Lab. Invest.* 24:345–360

151. MacGregor, D. C., Covell, J. W., McCullagh, W. H., Ross, J., Jr. 1971. The descending limb of left ventricular performance. *Abstr. Clin. Res.* 19:326

152. LaFarge, C. G., Monroe, R. G., Gamble, W. J., Rosenthal, A., Hammond, R. P. 1970. Left ventricular pressure and norepinephrine efflux from the innervated heart. *Am. J. Physiol.* 219:519–24

153. Taylor, R. R. 1970. Active length-tension relations compared in isometric, afterloaded and isotonic contractions of cat papillary muscle. *Circ. Res.* 26:279–88

154. Erickson, H. H., Bishop, V. S., Kardon, M. B., Horwitz, L. D. 1971. Left ventricular internal diameter and cardiac function during exercise. *J. Appl. Physiol.* 30:473–78

155. Keroes, J., Ecker, R. R., Rapaport, E. 1969. Ventricular function curves in the exercising dog. *Circ. Res.* 25:557–67

156. Brecher, G. A. 1958. Critical review of recent work on ventricular diastolic suction. *Circ. Res.* 6:554–66

157. Tyberg, J. V., Keon, W. J., Sonnenblick, E. H., Urschel, C. W. 1970. Mechanics of ventricular diastole. *Cardiovasc. Res.* 4:423–28

158. Wildenthal, K., Mierzwiak, D. S., Mitchell, J. H. 1969. Influence of vagal stimulation on left ventricular end-diastolic distensibility. *Am. J. Physiol.* 217:1446–50

159. Wildenthal, K., Mullins, C. B., Harris, M. D., Mitchell, J. H. 1969. Left ventricular end-diastolic distensibility after norepinephrine and propranolol. *Am. J. Physiol.* 217:812–18

160. Noble, M. I. M. et al 1969. Left ventricular filling and diastolic pressure-volume relations in the conscious dog. *Circ. Res.* 24:269–83

161. McCullagh, W. H., MacGregor, D. C., Covell, J. W., Ross, J., Jr. 1971. Left ventricular dilatation and diastolic compliance changes during chronic volume overloading. *Abstr. Clin. Res.* 19:328

162. Romero, T., Friedman, W. F., Covell, J. W. 1970. The pressure volume relations of the fetal, newborn, and adult heart. *Circulation* 41:Suppl. III, p. 152

163. Podolsky, R. J., Teichholz, L. E. 1970. The relation between calcium and contraction kinetics in skinned muscle fibres. *J. Physiol. (Lond.)* 211:19–35

164. Katz, A. M. 1970. Quantification of myocardial contractility. (Editorial.) *Am. J. Cardiol.* 26:331–32

164a. Langer, G. A. 1970. The role of sodium ion in the regulation of myocardial contractility. (Editorial.) *J. Molec. Cell. Cardiol.* 1:203–7

165. Suko, J., Ueba, Y., Chidsey, C. A. 1970. Intracellular calcium and myocardial contractility. *Circ. Res.* 27:227–33

166. Langer, G. A., Serena, S. D. 1970. Effects of strophanthidin upon contraction and ionic exchange in rabbit ventricular myocardium:

Relation to control of active state. *J. Molec. Cell. Cardiol.* 1:65–90

167. Besch, H. R., Jr., Schwartz, A. 1970. On a mechanism of action of digitalis. (Letter to the Editors.) *J. Molec. Cell. Cardiol.* 1:195–99

168. Beeler, G. W. J., Reuter, H. 1970. Membrane calcium current in ventricular myocardial fibres. *J. Physiol.* 207:191–209

169. Edmands, R. E., Greenspan, K., Fisch, E. 1967. An electrophysiological correlate of ouabain inotropy in canine cardiac muscle. *Circ. Res.* 21:515–24

170. Koch-Weser, J. 1971. Myocardial contraction frequency and onset of cardiac glycoside action. *Circ. Res.* 28:34–48

171. Koch-Weser, J. 1971. Beta-receptor blockade and myocardial effects of cardiac glycosides. *Circ. Res.* 28: 109–18

172. Prindle, K. H., Jr., Skelton, C. L., Epstein, S. E., Marcus, F. I. 1971. Influence of extracellular potassium concentration on myocardial uptake and inotropic effect of tritiated digoxin. *Circ. Res.* 28:337–45

173. Horwitz, L. D., Bishop, V. S. 1970. Effects of ouabain on left ventricular performance in conscious dogs. *Cardiovasc. Res.* 4:31–35

174. Vatner, S. F., Higgins, C. B., Patrick, T., Franklin, D., Braunwald, E. 1971. Inotropic effects of digitalis on the nonfailing heart of the conscious dog. *Abstr. Fed. Proc.* 30:612

175. Kumar, R. et al 1970. Experimental myocardial Infarction VI. Efficacy and toxicity of digitalis in acute and healing phase in intact conscious dogs. *J. Clin. Invest.* 49:358–64

176. Geis, W. P., Tatooles, C. J., Kaye, M. P., Randall, W. C. 1971. Complete cardiac denervation without transplantation: A simple and reliable technique. *J. Appl. Physiol.* 30:289–93

177. Priola, D. V., Fulton, R. L. 1969. Positive and negative inotropic responses of the atria and ventricles to vagosympathetic stimulation in the isovolumic canine heart. *Circ. Res.* 25:265–75

178. Martin, P. J., Levy, M. N., Zieske, H. 1969. Analysis and simulation of the left ventricular response to autonomic nervous activity. *Cardiovasc. Res.* 3:396–410

179. Grodner, A. S., Lahrtz, H.-G., Pool, P. E., Braunwald, E. 1970. Neuro-transmitter control of sinoatrial pacemaker frequency in isolated rat atria and in intact rabbits. *Circ. Res.* 27:867–73

180. Dempsey, P. J., Cooper, T. 1969. Ventricular cholinergic receptor systems: Interaction with adrenergic systems. *J. Pharmacol. Exp. Ther.* 167:282–90

181. Scher, A. M., Young, A. C. 1970. Reflex control of heart rate in the unanesthetized dog. *Am. J. Physiol.* 218:780–89

182. Furnival, C. M., Linden, R. J., Snow, H. M. 1971. The inotropic and chronotropic effects of catecholamines on the dog heart. *J. Physiol.* 214:15–28

183. Edmands, R. E., Greenspan, K., Fisch, C. 1970. The role of inotropic variation in ventricular function during atrial fibrillation. *J. Clin. Invest.* 49:738–46

184. Rogel, S., Mahler, Y. 1969. Myocardial tension in atrial fibrillation. *J. Appl. Physiol.* 27:822–25

185. Cingolani, H. E., Mattiazzi, A. R., Blesa, E. S., Gonzalez, N. C. 1970. Contractility in isolated mammalian heart muscle after acid-base changes. *Circ. Res.* 26:269–78

186. Dempsey, P. J., McCallum, Z. T., Kent, K. M., Cooper, T. 1971. Direct myocardial effects of angiotensin II. *Am. J. Physiol.* 22:477–81

187. Noble, R. J., Nutter, D. O., Crumly, H. J., Jr. 1970. The demonstration of alternating contractile state in pulsus alternans. *J. Clin. Invest.* 49: 1166–77

188. Guntheroth, W. G., Morgan, B. C., McGough, G. A., Scher, A. M. 1969. Alternate deletion and potentiation as the cause of pulsus alternans. *Am. Heart J.* 78:669–81

189. Jeffrey, F. E., Wagner, R., Abelmann, W. H. 1970. Left and right ventricular pressures in the normal and the cardiomyopathic Syrian hamster. *Proc. Soc. Exp. Biol. Med.* 135:940–43

190. Verrier, R. L., Rovetto, M. J., Lefer, A. M. 1969. Blood volume and myocardial function in adrenal insufficiency. *Am. J. Physiol.* 217: 1559–64

191. Taylor, R. R. 1970. Contractile properties of cardiac muscle in hyperthyroidism. *Circ. Res.* 27:539–49

191a. Taylor, R. R., Covell, J. W., Ross, J., Jr. 1969. Influence of thyroid state on left ventricular tension-velocity relations in the intact, sedated dog. *J. Clin. Invest.* 48:775–84

192. Goodkind, M. J. 1969. Myocardial contractile response to norepinephrine, isoproterenol, and calcium chloride in hyperthyroid guinea pigs. *Circ. Res.* 25:237–44

193. Anton, A. H., Gravenstein, J. S. 1970. Studies of thyroid-catecholamine interactions in the isolated rabbit heart. *Eur. J. Pharmacol.* 10:311–18

194. Sandler, H., Ghista, D. N. 1969. Mechanical and dynamic implications of dimensional measurements of the left ventricle. *Fed. Proc.* 28:1344–50

195. Bing, O. H. L., Matsushita, S., Fanburg, B. L., Levine, H. J. 1971. Mechanical properties of rat cardiac muscle during experimental hypertrophy. *Circ. Res.* 28:234–45

196. Spann, J. F. J., Buccino, R. A., Sonnenblick, E. H., Braunwald, E. 1967. Contractile state of cardiac muscle obtained from cats with experimentally produced ventricular hypertrophy and heart failure. *Circ. Res.* 21:341–54

197. Grimm, A. F., Kubota, R., Whitehorn, W. V. 1963. Properties of myocardium in cardiomegaly. *Circ. Res.* 12:118–24

198. Levine, J. H., McIntyre, K. M., Lipana, J. G., Bing, O. H. L. 1970. Force-velocity relations in failing and nonfailing hearts of subjects with aortic stenosis. *Am. J. Med. Sci.* 259:79–89

199. Simon, H., Krayenbuehl, H. P., Rutishauser, W., Preter, B. O. 1970. The contractile state of the hypertrophied left ventricular myocardium in aortic stenosis. *Am. Heart J.* 79:587–602

200. Beznak, M., Korecky, B., Thomas, G. 1969. Regression of cardiac hypertrophies of various origin. *Can. J. Physiol. Pharmacol.* 47:579–86

201. Turina, M., Bussmann, W. D., Krayenbühl, H. P. 1969. Contractility of the hypertrophied canine heart in chronic volume overload. *Cardiovasc. Res.* 3:486–95

202. Taylor, R. R., Covell, J. W., Ross, J., Jr. 1968. Left ventricular function in experimental aorto-caval fistula with circulatory congestion and fluid retention. *J. Clin. Invest.* 47:1333–42

203. Jarmakani, J. M. M., Graham, T. P., Jr., Canent, R. V., Jr., Capp, M. P. 1971. The effect of corrective surgery on left heart volume and mass in children with ventricular septal defect. *Am. J. Cardiol.* 27:254–58

RESPIRATION

JOHN B. WEST

*Department of Medicine, University of California, San Diego,
La Jolla, California*

This review makes no attempt to cover all the papers on respiratory physiology published during the period May 1970 to May 1971 but rather concentrates on those that seem to the reviewer to be of particular interest. For convenience, the articles have been grouped under four headings: morphology, mechanics, blood flow, and gas exchange. Inevitably many important papers within these areas and indeed whole areas of pulmonary physiology, such as ventilatory control, have been completely omitted.

During the last year, the avalanche of publications in this area has continued unabated, evoking in many people the response to read less rather than more. It is of passing interest that the number of papers cited by these yearly reviews on respiration has steadily declined over the last five years with the result that the line of best fit ($R = 0.96$) predicts that zero papers will be cited this year! This trend has not been followed.

MORPHOLOGY

SCANNING ELECTRON MICROGRAPHS

For physiologists who like to relate function to structure, a high point of the year was the publication by Nowell & Tyler (87), and by Wang & Thurlbeck (109) of scanning electron micrographs of the surface morphology of hamster and horse lung. This technique depends on the scattering of eletrons from surfaces (15, 60) and is therefore particularly suitable for examining the lung with its enormous air-tissue interface. The advantages are not only the great range of possible magnifications but also the prodigious depth of focus which gives a dramatic three-dimensional effect.

The preparation of the specimens is critical if serious artifacts are to be avoided. Nowell, Pangborn & Tyler used two methods (86). Some of the lungs were fixed by perfusing them via the airways with buffered glutaraldehyde; others were rapidly frozen with liquid propane (25, 106). Pieces were subsequently freeze-substituted and dried by the critical point method, or freeze dried. They were then coated with gold.

A striking feature of the low power appearance of the lung's cut surface is the large number of pores of Kohn; those of us who occasionally picture the alveolus as a small balloon have had this notion punctured. The appearances certainly reinforce recent interest in collateral ventilation (77, 117). Equally

91

dramatic are the micrographs of bronchiolar cilia which look like the fringe of a rug (12). In the respiratory bronchioles, some cilia extend down to the mouths of the alveoli. Between tufts of cilia are nonciliated bronchial epithelial cells, some of which have patulous openings through which mucigen droplets are presumably discharged. On the alveolar walls, dumpy type II alveolar cells can often be seen adjacent to alveolar pores. These cells have microvilli and show openings or depressions through which the osmiophilic inclusions presumably move to the alveolar surface to become the surfactant. Alveolar macrophages are also clearly shown, again often adjacent to pores.

Wang & Thurlbeck (109) prepared human, mouse, baboon and pig lungs in various ways but illustrations from only the first two species were shown. Again the pores of Kohn stood out in the alveoli. The tufts of cilia in the bronchioles had in these pictures the appearance of bushes in a field. Between the tufts were protrusions which are apparently the flame-shaped cytoplasmic processes of Clara cells. Microvilli could also be seen in this area. It is hoped that these elegant and informative studies will persuade more physiologists to look at lungs.

MORPHOLOGY OF PARENCHYMA

Weibel and his colleagues (22, 43, 114) have set out to determine the pulmonary diffusing capacity under various conditions using morphometric methods. First, a number of formidable practical and theoretical problems were discussed (114). For example, one of these is the difficulty of adequate sampling when using the small sections necessary for transmission electron microscopy. Next, the effects of oxygen concentration on the growing lung of rats were measured (22). The rats were exposed to partial pressures of oxygen of 100, 150, and 290 mm Hg from the 34th to the 44th day of life, a period of intense lung growth. With hypoxic exposure, the alveolar, capillary, and tissue volumes, the alveolar and capillary surface areas, and the calculated diffusing capacity were higher than in the controls, though the differences were not statistically significant. Since the hypoxic rats weighed less than the controls the differences were significant if the specific volumes, i.e. per 100 g body weight, were calculated. However this may simply reflect the inhibiting effect of hypoxia on general body growth, as concluded by Bartlett in a similar study (14). Hyperoxia resulted in a significant fall in the specific values.

Lastly, in an ingenious study, the effects of increased oxygen consumption were observed in Japanese waltzing mice (43). These animals have a genetic defect in their central nervous system which results in periodic bouts of rapid body rotation. As a consequence, their average oxygen consumption is 80% more than that of normal laboratory mice. Morphometric measurements showed that the alveoli were smaller and more numerous than in the controls and that the alveolar and capillary surface areas were larger. Calculated diffusing capacity was increased in approximate proportion to the oxygen consumption.

Forrest (41) reported a study of the effect of changes in lung volume on the size and shape of alveoli in guinea pigs. The anesthetized animals had their chests widely opened and were ventilated with positive pressure. They were supported by a trapdoor over a bath of isopentane kept cold with liquid nitrogen. At the appropriate moment, the trapdoor was released and the lungs rapidly frozen. Dimensions were measured by morphometric techniques. The total volume of the alveoli increased linearly with lung volume, although the volume of the alveolar ducts changed little until the lungs were inflated to 40% of their maximal volume, above which it increased steeply. This finding conflicts with previous reports in the cat (107) and dog (45) which show that the volumes of the alveoli and their ducts increased proportionally. However, Dunnill (38) found that during lung inflation the alveolar volume (as a fraction of the total volume) increased linearly and that the alveolar duct fraction decreased linearly. Forrest (41) also showed that as the lung was inflated the total surface area increased with lung volume and that the thickness of the blood gas barrier decreased. He noticed no "submicronic" surface corrugation of the alveolar wall at low lung volumes, using electron microscopy. However, according to Klingele and Staub (61), folding of the alveolar walls is a feature of cat lungs at low volumes. These authors also reported that cat alveoli became narrower as minimal volume was approached, whereas Forrest (41) found no change in alveolar shape.

Morphology of Airways

Another morphological study, by Hughes and his colleagues (56), sought the site of airway closure in excised dog lungs when pleural pressure was raised 6 cm H_2O above airway pressure. Two techniques were used. First the bronchi were outlined with radiocontrast liquid or lead dust and radiographs taken using a 0.3 mm focal spot tube. After magnification, airways of diameters from 17 to 1 mm were scrutinized and their increase in diameter with increasing transpulmonary pressure was plotted. No sites of airway closure were seen. Secondly, lungs were rapidly frozen with liquid Freon and blocks of tissue were transferred to a freezing microtome. In this way, the frozen surface could be examined with a stereoscopic microscope as 20 μ slices were shaved away. Closure was seen in airways that had diameters of about 180 μ near the closed portion. On the basis of diameter-pressure curves, these airways had diameters of 0.4 to 0.6 mm in the inflated state, i.e. terminal bronchioles. This study has been criticized because the smooth muscle tone of the airways in excised lungs is unphysiologically high (77), but actual measurements seem preferable to calculations based on opening pressures and an assumed surface tension and geometry.

Changes in terminal bronchiole diameter changes in volume in excised cat lung were reported by Klingele & Staub (62). They found that as the lobes were deflated from 100% maximal volume (25 cm H_2O transpulmonary pressure) to 8%, the average diameters of the terminal bronchioles fell from 432 μ to 100 μ. This difference is considerably greater than that found by Hughes et al (56) in 0.8 to 1 mm diameter bronchioles in the dog. The average terminal bronchiole in the cat changed proportionally to the cube root of lung volume and the authors pointed out that this is what would be predicted assuming an isotropic lobe. This observation is consistent with the theory that terminal bronchioles are very compliant structures whose behavior is determined by the expansion of the surrounding parenchyma. No closed airways were detected in this study.

MECHANICS

AIRWAYS RESISTANCE AND COLLATERAL VENTILATION

A timely review of the recent literature on airway obstruction and collateral ventilation has been published by Macklem (77). This review and the publication in 1970 of the proceedings of 1968 symposium on "Airway Dynamics" (17) cover a lot of ground. Although it seems pointless to review a review at any length, Macklem's article is so useful because of the recent rapid changes in the field that it is worth indicating the areas covered. Moreover, it contains an appreciable amount of new material from the author's laboratory.

After a brief look at recent work on the morphology of the bronchial tree, Macklem then discussed information on the chief sites of resistance to airflow. There is now good evidence that in dogs and in several other species including man, the resistance of airways smaller than 2 mm diameter is only a small proportion of the total; this agrees well with anatomical predictions. The lower airway resistance decreases rapidly as lung volume increases from minimal volume to functional residual capacity (FRC), though there is evidence that at high volume the resistance begins to increase. Macklem drew an analogy with the increase in pulmonary vascular resistance during overinflation of the lung, but it seems likely that the latter increase is caused by flattening of the capillary bed as the linear tension in the alveolar walls rises (46).

Macklem also reviewed the evidence for airway closure at low lung volumes. This is found in the most dependent regions of the lung of normal man and apparently occurs when pleural pressure exceeds airway pressure (work on regional differences in pleural pressure is discussed below). The volume at which human airways close is very dependent on age. In persons less than 20 years old, the average volume is about 8% of vital capacity (9). In seated persons about 65 years old, the closing volume begins to exceed FRC (68). However there is considerable variability and it is possible that some airways transiently close at FRC even in young healthy man (21, 37).

In this review, Macklem also noted recent findings on the mechanical properties of airways and considered at some length the possible role of surface tension on the opening of small bronchioles. He then discussed, in the light of current knowledge concerning the uneven regional expansion of the lung parenchyma caused by gravity, the relationship between the distribution of ventilation and respiratory frequency. Although it was thought at one time that the time constants of all regions of the lung were the same (81), measurements of the distribution of radioactive xenon when sulphur hexa-fluoride was breathed at increased ambient pressure (with consequent increased resistance to gas flow) have shown that at least in some subjects, airways resistance at the base exceeded that at the apex (120). Indeed the remarkable extent to which the lung behaves as if time constants were the same in the face of airways of different path lengths and regional differences in expansion may have a lot to do with "interdependence" (82) (see below).

Finally, Macklem's article includes a review of the information on the pathways for collateral ventilation, a section which should be read in association with Loosli's review (75) in 1937 of the pores of Kohn. In addition, mechanisms of airways obstruction were also considered at some length. The reader is encouraged to consult this valuable review.

Returning to original papers, mechanical factors determining collateral ventilation in dog, pig, and human lungs were studied by Woolcock & Macklem (121). These workers measured the time constant of collateral channels by wedging a catheter of 3.5 mm outside diameter in small bronchi. First, they followed the time course of change in pressure in the wedged lung after a rapid inflation. This was split into three exponential components, though the significance of these is not clear. Using a second method, the whole lung was exposed to a sinusoidally oscillating pressure of a frequency between 0.3 and 1.5 cycles/sec via the tracheal cannula, and this was compared with the pressure caused by in the wedged catheter. From the phase difference they derived the time constant. They found that the time constant of collateral channels was remarkably small—comparable in magnitude to the whole lung for the dog and human. However, this does not necessarily mean that the resistance to collateral flow is similar to the airway resistance in an equivalent volume of lung, because there is evidence that the compliance of a wedge of lung is considerably reduced if it is not ventilating in phase with the surrounding parenchyma [see discussion of "interdependence" (82) below]. Indeed the present study suggested that the resistance to collateral flow was considerably greater than the airway resistance of a comparable volume of lung.

In the pig, collateral ventilation could not be demonstrated, possibly because the pig lung is highly lobulated and the channels (wherever they are) do not cross interlobular septa. The time constants in both dog and man decreased markedly with increasing lung volume because of a decrease in resistance to collateral flow; whether this was caused by recruitment or by dilatation of channels could not be determined.

Factors affecting trapped gas volume in excised dog lungs were studied by Hughes & Rosenzweig (55). They noticed that excised perfused lungs failed to deflate as expected at low distending pressures after periods of perfusion of only an hour or two. This was surprising because in many other aspects the preparations remained remarkably stable. The volume of trapped gas was measured by slowly deflating the lungs from a submaximal volume—at a transpulmonary pressure of 21—to a transpulmonary pressure of −6 cm H_2O; expulsion of gas ceased at about −2.5 cm H_2O. Initially the volume of trapped gas averaged 20% of submaximal volume, but after 4 hours of perfusion it had doubled. Measurements with radioactive xenon showed that the gas was predominantly trapped in the more dependent parts of the lung where histological edema was most prominent. Infusion of the bronchoconstrictor histamine into the pulmonary artery also increased the volume of trapped gas.

The authors concluded that although edema fluid in the airways was probably responsible for large increases in trapped volume in some lungs—especially those which had been perfused for long periods—this could not have explained the results of those studies in which weight gain was minimal and no alveolar edema was visible histologically. Although changes in surfactant may have been a factor, it seemed likely that in these lungs interstitial edema allowed small airways to close at abnormally high lung volumes. An analysis of the presumed pressure-volume behavior of small airways in the presence of peribronchial edema was presented on a Campbell diagram (24). This showed that depending on the initial peribronchial pressures and on the compliances of the airway and its peribronchial sheath, relatively small accumulations of peribronchial fluid could easily result in airway closure. Recent evidence suggests that the same phenomenon may be responsible for the airway closure above FRC which is seen in some patients with hepatic cirrhosis (101). The notion is attractive because it puts the small airways on the same footing as the extra-alveolar blood vessels which show an increase in pulmonary vascular resistance when surrounded by a cuff of interstitial edema (115).

An interesting facet of airways resistance was considered by Clarke, Jones & Oliver (27) when they studied the consequences of energy losses in fluid lining the bronchi. These authors measured the pressure drop caused by air flow through glass tubes lined with several non-Newtonian liquids and specimens of fresh sputum. They found dramatic increases in airflow resistance at relatively high flow rates (above 1.5 liters per second) when the thickness of the liquid lining layer was more than 300 μ. The effect was most marked with liquids of low viscosity. In many instances, an abrupt increase in resistance was accompanied by the formation of visible waves on the liquid surface.

The thickness of the mucus layer in the airways of the normal lung is only about 5 μ (59), and in addition the normal flow rates are much lower so that these interactions are unlikely there. However, the authors claimed that in diseases in which bronchial secretions probably form liquid lining layers more than 300 μ thick, large increases in air flow resistance can be expected during rapid breathing (as on exercise) or coughing. A minor point is that although efforts are often made to liquefy bronchial secretions, i.e., to reduce their viscosity, this exaggerates the increase in airways resistance caused by these liquid-gas interactions.

Pedley, Schroter & Sudlow (91, 92) examined the energy losses and pressure drop for air flow in systems of branched tubes, and then went on to predict the variations of resistance within the human bronchial tree. They used the results of earlier observations (104) that even at low Reynold's numbers (in the range 180–700), flow in a branching tube is not strictly laminar but that just downstream from the bifurcation disturbances occur, caused by inertial forces acting at the junction. As a consequence, energy dissipation exceeds that calculated on the basis of Poiseuille flow, for which the rate of dissipation of energy by viscosity is a minimum. The authors calculated the rate of dissipation of energy per unit length of tube for the observed velocity profiles and showed that this can be up to five times greater than that for fully developed laminar flow. From this they derived the pressure drop along the tube—which may be more than threefold what would be expected for purely laminar conditions.

Using these observations in conjunction with anatomical data on dimensions of the human bronchial tree (51, 113), they calculated the pressure drop at each airway generation. Previous calculations in an elegant short paper by Green (47) showed that on the basis of assumed laminar flow, viscous flow resistance had a striking maximum value in the sixth generation. However, when the complicating effects of airway branching were included, the calculated flow resistance gradually increased up to the fourth generation and then fell rapidly. The resistance of the smaller airways (beyond, say, the tenth generation) was less than 10%. This latter result agrees with all modern calculations but is at variance with the classical analysis by Rohrer (97), whose dimensions for the small bronchioles were erroneously small because they were measured in the collapsed lung. Pedley et al have suggested that in studies of lower airways (from the trachea down), Rohrer's original equation $\Delta P = K_1 \dot{V} + K_2 \dot{V}^2$ should be replaced by $\Delta P = K_3 \cdot (\mu\rho)^{1/2} \dot{V}^{3/2}$ where μ and ρ are the viscosity and density of the gas respectively and K is a constant which depends on lung anatomy and volume. Comparing published experimental data with this equation, using gases of various viscosities and densities, gives reasonable agreement, except that for sulfur hexafluoride the observed resistance is much higher than that predicted.

Efforts, such as the recent analysis by Pedley and his colleagues, to apply modern fluid mechanics to a complicated system like the bronchial tree are very worthwhile—though the necessary simplifications should not be forgotten. For example in the present analysis, the anatomical model is in many respects idealized with its assumptions of symmetrical dichotomy and constant branching angle. Again the dominant effect of lung volume on airways resistance is impossible to treat realistically until more is known about the effect of inflation on bronchial caliber.

Experimental data on the caliber of airways in the intact animal can be obtained by bronchography, the use of tantalum powder with a small focal spot X-ray tube and magnification allows measurements to be made on very small bronchioles (85). Clarke, Graf & Nadel (28) reported the appearance of airways down to a 1 mm in diameter following pulmonary microembolism with barium sulfate in cats and dogs. They found that the reduction in airway diameter was greatest for airways with initial diameters of less than 1 mm and became progressively less marked for airways of initial diameters up to 3 mm. Above this, the airways either showed no change or a slight increase in diameter. In general, the changes in airway caliber were larger in cats than in dogs. Following embolism, the swings in transpulmonary pressure with positive pressure ventilation became larger, and these correlated well with the changes in diameter of the small airways but not of the large. Intravenous injections of isoproterenol reversed the airway constriction. The findings were consistent with earlier work on the pulmonary effects of barium sulfate embolism (84) but their relationship to less exotic types of emboli such as blood thrombi was not discussed.

Some of the factors influencing pulmonary resistance were studied by Vincent and her colleagues (108). They applied forced oscillatory flow at the mouth by means of a loudspeaker cone, which allowed the continuous measurement of resistance at all lung volumes. In addition, a catheter was passed through the tracheal wall to permit separation of the contributions of upper and lower pulmonary resistance. They confirmed the approximately hyperbolic relationship between total resistance and lung volume (23), and they found that the volume history of the lung affected resistance: both total and lower pulmonary resistance were greater at a given lung volume when this was approached from residual volume (RV) rather than from total lung capacity (TLC). Administration of atropine eliminated the difference. "Upstream resistance"—the resistance of airways upstream from equal pressure points, as measured from recoil pressure and maximum expiratory flow at 50% vital capacity (VC)—showed similar hysteresis. These findings are consistent with previous demonstrations of hysteresis of the airways (80), anatomic dead space (42), and pulmonary resistance (16).

Leblanc, Macklem & Ross (67) reported an entertaining study of the distribution of breath sounds over the chest. They placed microphones over the apex of the left lung (third intercostal space anteriorly) and left base (3 to 4 cm below the left scapula) and recorded the output. During inspiration, the intensity of the breath sounds invariably increased with increasing flow in any body position, at any microphone location, and at any lung volume. When the seated subject inhaled at a steady flow rate from RV to TLC, the intensity of the sound at the lung apex progressively decreased while that at the base progressively increased. Similar differences between the upper and lower regions of the lungs were shown in the left and right lateral positions. Thus the breath sounds reflect nicely the regional distribution of ventilation as described by Milic-Emili and his colleagues (83). The authors claim that by using a "stereostethoscope" (8)—one diaphragm on the end of each rubber tube—and placing one diaphragm over the apex and the other over the base of the lung, the experienced listener can hear the differential filling during a single vital capacity respiration. Surprisingly, the tracings did not detect the crackles during inspiration from RV which Forgacs, in his delightful study (40), attributed to the opening of small airways.

Surface Tension

There has been a flurry of interest in the apparent effect of steroids on the acceleration of surfactant formation in the fetal lung. Liggins (70) found that lambs, born prematurely at 117–123 days of gestation (the normal term is 147 days) after receiving infusions of the glucocorticoid dexamethasone in utero, showed partial aeration of their lungs. This was unexpected because the lungs usually remain airless with this degree of immaturity (52). Infusions into the ewe had no effect. Kotas & Avery (63) measured pressure-volume curves, dry weight of the lung, and surface tension of lung extracts from fetal rabbits killed between the 24th day of gestation and term (31 days). Some of the fetuses were injected with a single dose of g-fluoroprednisolone (a potent glucocorticoid) intramuscularly and into the amniotic fluid at 24 days, and others were given saline as a control. The lungs of the steroid-injected animals were more distensible at an airway pressure of 35 cm H_2O, retained a larger percentage of maximum volume on deflation, and showed a lower minimal surface tension on a Wilhelmy balance.

The lungs of some of the animals were examined by microscopy and the results reported in a companion paper by Wang and co-workers (110). Although some of the details of the morphometric techniques are not clearly described, lungs of fetal lambs injected with the steroid at a gestational age of 26 days apparently showed an increased percentage of cuboidal cells containing osmiophilic bodies. In addition, the number of osmiophilic bodies per alveolar lining cell was increased in the injected animals. These histological results are consistent with the physiological evidence of accelerated maturation.

An additional short note (34) reported the preliminary results of hydrocortisone injections on the lungs of fetal lambs. Twins served as controls. Again the lungs of the injected animals were apparently more distensible and the surface tension of lung extracts was lower. However none of the treated fetuses survived more than 12 hours after birth, and the possibility was raised that the steroid was detrimental to other developing organs.

Some investigators have become increasingly dissatisfied with measurements of surface activity of lung extracts on surface balances because conditions are very artificial in vitro compared with the situation in vivo. For this reason, there has been a return of interest to the methods, originally proposed by Pattle (89), that use bubbles of alveolar dimensions. Slama, Schoedel & Hansen (105) described a method for studying the dynamic and static properties of small bubbles in liquids. A minute air bubble is sucked part way into a liquid-filled cuvette through a 1/2 mm diameter circular hole in the bottom. Surface active material is injected on to the surface of the bubble by means of a micropipette. While the volume of the bubble is changed by displacing liquid from the cuvette, the radius and transmural pressure of the bubble are simultaneously measured. Since the radius of the bubble is between 0.25 and 0.4 mm, the authors claim that its surface tension behavior more closely resembles that of the lung than observations made on a film of large area.

The same group of workers (103) used this method to study the time-dependent behavior of alveolar washings. They found that when the surface area of a bubble was rapidly decreased by 75%, the surface tension at first became very low but then rose within a few minutes. When the surface area was rapidly increased, the surface tension at first became high but then fell. This behavior was temperature-dependent, at 37°C, the peak surface tension measured after expansion was lower than at 24°C. Surface films of dipalmitoyl-lecithin showed similar behavior except that after expansion, the tension reached higher values which decreased less rapidly.

Young, Tierney & Clements (122) investigated the mechanism of compliance change in excised rat lungs held at low transpulmonary pressures. They found that in lungs which were maintained at a transpulmonary pressure of 3 cm H_2O for 20 min, compliance decreased by 42%. They reviewed the various possible mechanisms. Airway obstruction and atelectasis were ruled out because they were not seen in sections of lung which were frozen rapidly. Changes in air-space configuration were sought by measuring the mean chord length of test lines in histological sections to give the surface-to-volume ratio of the air spaces; in addition, the ratio of alveolar and alveolar duct volumes was determined by point counting. No differences over the 20 min period were detected. Alterations in tissue compliance were rejected because saline-filled lungs held at a transpulmonary pressure of 3 cm H_2O showed no compliance change. The authors concluded by default that the most likely mechanism was a decrease in alveolar surface tension for the same surface area.

STRESS DISTRIBUTION

In an influential paper Mead, Takishima & Leith (82) have analyzed the forces that develop across an imaginary surface within the lung parenchyma during inflation. By considering the balance of forces acting inwards and outwards, they showed that the effective pressure expanding a spherically shaped region is $\Sigma F_o/A$ where F_o denotes the outward acting forces provided by the tissue elements crossing the surface, and A the area of the surface. This is balanced by the pressure equivalent of the inward acting stresses $\Sigma F_i/A$ combined with the transmural pressure developed by the curvature of the wall.

This notion has important implications if there is a region of local distortion in the lung. For example, suppose the volume of a local region changes relative to that of surrounding regions. As a result its surface area will alter and with it the effective distending pressure $\Sigma F_o/A$. This pressure will always change in a direction that opposes the change in distension. Thus when the region decreases in volume, the outward acting forces will, if anything, increase, while at the same time the area over which these forces are distributed will decrease. As a result the effective expanding pressure increases, thus tending to restore the volume of the region. Opposite changes occur if a local region becomes overinflated. This resistance to independent elastic behavior of local regions is termed "interdependence."

There are a number of situations in the actual lung where this behavior may be important. One is when the lung is being expanded from the completely gas-free state. Presumably the surface forces opposing expansion will first be overcome in those regions with lowest opening pressures. Once an unexpanded region has been completely surrounded by expanded air spaces, the distending pressure applied to it can be shown to exceed transpulmonary pressure in the ratio $(V/V_0)^{2/3}$ where V is the volume that the region would have if there were no distortion and V_0 is its gas-free volume. Taking reasonable volumes, this means that at a transpulmonary pressure of 30 cm H_2O, the effective distending pressure on the atelectatic region would be about 140 cm H_2O.

Similar considerations suggest that transudation from pulmonary capillaries would occur as atelectasis developed in inflated lungs following airway obstruction. That this does not occur means that either interdependence is not so effective or that a major role of surfactant is to prevent transudation (90). The traditional role of surfactant in promoting alveolar stability (29) could apparently be assumed to a large extent by interdependence.

Peribronchial and perivascular pressures will be lower than pleural pressure by the same reasoning. Measurements that have been made are consistent with this. The low pressure helps to explain why edema fluid is so frequently seen in these regions in the early stages of interstitial pulmonary edema.

The examples given show that the idea of mechanical interdependence within the lung has already been very fruitful in several areas of pulmonary physiology. Perhaps it is remarkable that it should have been necessary to emphasize the dependence of neighboring regions in a closely knit structure like the lung; a cynic might say that only a respiratory physiologist with his obsession for simple diagrams could picture an alveolus as a balloon on a tube exposed to pleural pressure. It is certainly more difficult to justify the use of such a model now in discussions of lung mechanics.

REGIONAL DIFFERENCES IN INTRAPLEURAL PRESSURE

The way in which the lung is distorted by gravity remains an intriguing problem. There is now overwhelming evidence for regional differences in lung expansion (45, 83) and exaggeration of these by acceleration (20). However, the relationships between the pattern of deformation, the elastic properties of the lung, and gravity are obscure.

Agostoni and his colleagues have carried out an extensive investigation of the vertical differences in intrapleural pressure and reported their results in seven papers in little over a year (3–7, 31, 32). These authors introduced an ingenious new technique for measuring local intrapleural pressure in experimental animals (31). The chest wall is incised and a small nick made in the parietal pleura. With care, no pneumothorax occurs because of surface tension at the air-liquid interface. A small bristle is positioned to throw a shadow on the exposed visceral pleura; this shows any distortion of the pleural surface. A transparent chamber is then placed over the incision and the pressure within it is reduced until the pleural surface is returned to its distortion-free state. This pressure is taken as the local pleural pressure.

Pleural pressure was found to be atmospheric in the lowermost part of the lungs of rabbits and dogs in the lateral, supine and prone postures (31). It was subatmospheric over the rest of the lung in these postures and at all levels in the head-up posture. In the head-down position, the pressure was positive in the dependent apex. For any given species, the pressure was related to the percentage of lung maximal height, regardless of posture. The investigators found that the abdomen had an important effect on the vertical differences in pleural pressure (5). For example, in horizontal rabbits, the vertical gradient decreased two to three times after the removal of the abdominal contents, whereas lung density changed less. In prone rabbits suspended from the spine, the vertical gradient of pressure decreased after evisceration while lung density increased. In addition, head-up rabbits and dogs had a vertical gradient of about twice that expected on the basis of lung density. The authors concluded that the chief factor responsible for the regional differences in pleural pressure was not the weight of the lung but the weight of the abdominal viscera.

While there can be no question about the value of the large amount of data collected by this group, its interpretation can be disputed. Suppose that the differences in pleural pressure are caused by the weight of the lung; there is no reason why the magnitude of the gradient should be predictable on the basis of lung density, or that evisceration should not decrease it. Although following their first demonstration of the vertical gradient of pleural pressure (65), Krueger and his colleagues drew an analogy between lung tissue and a fluid of similar density, it is clear that the support of a structure like the lung must actually be more complicated. Analysis of the behavior of a lung-shaped elastic structure, supported at its periphery and loaded by its own weight, showed that the vertical difference of pleural pressure depended on lung volume (118). When this was high, and the lung became very stiff, the change in surface pressure with distance was nearly linear and relatively small. By contrast, at low volumes the pressure gradient became nonlinear and its magnitude larger. In addition, the pleural pressure gradient was found to be related to the shape of the lung and chest wall. For example, in the inverted posture, the model showed a smaller pressure gradient for the same lung volume and weight. Thus the changes in pleural pressure following evisceration may well be caused by the change in volume and shape of the chest cavity and are not inconsistent with the notion that the chief factor is the weight of the lung.

Agostoni and his co-workers measured the effects of positive pressure inflation on the topography of pleural surface pressure in paralyzed rabbits and dogs (3). They found that the vertical gradient progressively decreased as alveolar pressure was raised until eventually the differences could no longer be detected. This required a much higher pressure (22 cm H_2O) in the head-up than in the supine lateral positions or when the animals were eviscerated. The authors tentatively interpreted the results in terms of regional differences in the compliance of the lung and chest wall, reduction of weight of the lung by displacement of blood, increase in area of the supporting pleural surface, increase of "tensile rigidity" of the lung, and "pneumatic rigidity."

This reviewer finds the description of the last two factors difficult to understand. One would expect the vertical differences in pleural pressure to decrease at high lung volumes as the increasingly rigid lung is better able to resist the gravity-induced distortion, because the latter exaggerates the differences in surface pressures (118). But for the gradient to disappear is surprising, unless perhaps the ability of the pleural surfaces to slide over each other is abolished when the lung is expanded hard against the chest wall. This factor may well be what is meant by "pneumatic rigidity" and will presumably not operate when the lung is expanded by negative pressure and the pressure in the intrapleural space falls. Evidence to support this came from experiments carried out on animals breathing spontaneously. The technique in which the visceral pleura is exposed can be used only in the paralyzed animal and only when the lung volume is above FRC. However if a thin sheet of parietal pleura is exposed but not incised, measurements can be made during spontaneous respiration and below FRC (4). Using this modification, no change in the gradient of pleural pressure was detected during spontaneous breathing up to transpulmonary pressures of 10–12 cm H_2O.

A comparative study of pleural pressures in rats, rabbits, small and large dogs, and rams (6) showed that the vertical gradient at FRC in the lateral position decreased from 0.88 to 0.24 cm H_2O/cm from rats to rams as the height of the lung increased. The authors noted that as a result, the transpulmonary pressure at the top of the lung varied over a relatively narrow range (about 2.5 to 5.7 cm H_2O in the species studied) and argued that this might be necessary to prevent overexpansion and thus inadequate ventilation in that region. They concluded that the marked differences in the vertical gradient among species is further evidence that the weight of the lung is not the culprit. An alternative explanation is that the increase in FRC/TLC which is found with increase in animal size (1) confers more rigidity on the lung, thus preventing undue distortion by gravity. This increase in FRC would reduce the topographical differences in pleural pressure (118) and protect the lung from undue distortion by gravity.

In a further investigation, D'Angelo and his colleagues (32) studied the relative contributions of the weight of the lung and abdominal contents to the regional differences of intrapleural pressure. They found that the reduction of lung weight by about 1/3 by exsanguination caused no detectable

change in the vertical gradient of pressure if the extrapulmonary intrathoracic blood was replaced. Increasing lung weight by placing tungsten
beads in the airways increased the vertical pressure gradient, but the change
was less than that found after removing the diaphragm in eviscerated animals. The authors could not explain why removal of the light diaphragm
alone should cause such large gravity-induced changes but they concluded
that lung weight alone was responsible for only some 15–25% of the regional
differences in intrapleural pressure.

In a final study (7) the abdominal pressure of rabbits was reduced by
placing the caudal part of the abdomen and the hind limbs in a plethysmo-
graph. When the abdominal pressure was decreased until lung volume
equaled that in the head-up posture at FRC, a cranio-caudal gradient of intrapleural pressure similar to that in the head-up posture was produced. In
head-down rabbits, the expected vertical gradient (apex pressure more positive than basal) could be reversed by decreasing the abdominal pressure.
The conclusion was that the distribution of intrapleural pressure depends
essentially on the shape of the chest wall.

It is difficult at this stage to digest the large amount of valuable data produced by these workers. The conclusion seems inescapable that for the animals they studied the shape of the chest wall played a major role in determining the regional differences in intrapleural pressure. It is perhaps a pity that
they concentrated so heavily on small animals such as the rabbit in which
the vertical height and weight of the lung and consequent gravitational effects are small. In such animals, deformation of the chest wall will presumably be more important than in the dog or man. Certainly Hoppin and his
colleagues (49) were able to change chest shape in the dog substantially
without affecting the vertical gradient of pressure. The subject remains as
intriguing as ever.

Brandi (18) has made a theoretical study of the manner in which the
lung is distorted by gravity. He pointed out that the fluidlike model of
Krueger and his colleagues (65) is in error if a constant density down the
lung is assumed, and much of the analysis is concerned with the relationship
between density and vertical height in a compressible fluid-like material
which has a nonlinear pressure-volume curve like that of the lung. Brandi,
like Hoppin and his colleagues (49), was aware of the dilemma that, although
the lung has some fluid-like properties at low states of inflation in that it is
flabby and almost shapeless, it takes on the properties of a structure with a
recognizable shape as its volume is increased. Because it seems impossible to
cope with the consequences of this progressively increasing stiffness by intuitive methods, Brandi elected to treat the lung as a fluid.

An alternative approach, based on the engineering technique of finite-
element analysis (10), is to regard the lung as a structure composed of material with nonlinear stress–strain properties (118). In this way, the transi-
tion from a "fluidlike" to a "solid" consistency during inflation can be ac-
commodated. Although this is a formidable procedure, it does allow a very

general analysis of the distribution of stresses, strains, and surface pressures in the lung caused by its weight. An unexpected prediction is that as the lung is inflated, the apical alveoli may become smaller because the increasing stiffness of the lung allows it to resist distortion by its weight. Evidence to support this is that in dog lungs fixed in situ by freezing, the apical alveoli become smaller as the lung is inflated by positive pressure (45).

Avasthey, Coulam & Wood (11) measured regional differences in pericardial pressures in dogs using fluid-filled catheters. They found that the pressure increased at the rate of 1 cm H_2O/cm distance and the pericardium therefore behaved as a hydrostatic system. Regional differences in transmural pressure over the vertical height of each cardiac chamber are therefore avoided.

PULMONARY BLOOD FLOW
Vascular Resistance

It is remarkable that there should still be so much uncertainty about the chief sites of vascular resistance in the pulmonary circulation. For example indirect measurements of the percentage of the total resistance residing in the pulmonary veins range from about 20% (19, 76) to 60% (2). The way in which pressure falls along the capillary bed is unknown. Maloney & Castle (79) have used the micromanometer of Wiederhielm (78) to record pressures in the pulmonary vessels of the frog down to 80 μ in diameter. The diameter of the tip of the glass probe was only 0.5 μ. Left atrial pressure was controlled by means of a reservoir. When alveolar pressure exceeded venous pressure (zone II) and the mean pulmonary arterial pressure was 11.7 cm H_2O, the veins contributed about 68% of the total pressure drop, while the arteries and capillaries (vessels with diameters less than 80 μ) contributed about 16% each. At higher pulmonary arterial pressures, the venous contribution fell to about 50%. In zone III conditions (venous pressure higher than alveolar pressure), the proportions were about 44% for veins and 28% for arteries and capillaries. Almost no pressure drop could be detected in the arterial system in vessels from 600 to 80 μ in diameter. Attenuation of the amplitude of the pressure pulse was also measured and found to be most marked in arteries with diameters over 600 μ and in the capillary bed, especially in zone II conditions.

In assessing these results, the marked differences between the primitive frog lung and the much more highly organized mammalian organ should be borne in mind. For example, the diameter of the pulmonary capillaries in the frog is about 20 μ (78). However the relatively large venous pressure drop is notable and it emphasizes the striking difference between the distribution of resistance in the pulmonary and systemic circulations.

Interesting evidence about the transmural pressures of the small vessels running in the corners of alveoli was obtained by Rosenzweig, Hughes & Glazier (100). They studied excised dog lungs held at transpulmonary pressures of about 15 cm H_2O and noticed that even when alveolar pressure exceeded vascular pressures by 10 cm H_2O, small amounts of blood moved between the arteries and veins. By injecting India ink they were able to show that the probable routes of communication were the alveolar corner vessels. This observation is consistent with observations of open corner vessels in lungs rapidly frozen when alveolar pressure exceeded arterial pressure by up to 24 cm H_2O (46).

Distribution of Blood Flow

Glaister (44) measured the effect of forward acceleration ("eyeballs in") of up to 5 G on the distribution of blood flow and ventilation in human volunteers. The studies were carried out on a centrifuge; the investigators used radioactive xenon and scanned the chest with counters from back to front. As the G level increased, the slope of blood flow per unit lung volume against antero-posterior distance consistently increased. At 5 G, the anterior lung margin was apparently unperfused in some subjects, although scattering of the radiation by the chest wall made this uncertain. The finding of a marked change in the distribution of perfusion was at variance with a previous study by Hoppin and his co-workers (48) who noted no change at 8 G acceleration, an observation which remains unexplained.

When the distribution of blood flow was expressed as per alveolus (by scanning the lung at TLC), a region of reduced blood flow was seen posteriorly and this was exaggerated by acceleration. The decrease in blood flow could be explained by the reduced expansion of the lung parenchyma and the consequent increase in vascular resistance of the extra-alveolar vessels (54). The reduced expansion and resulting airway closure in the posterior lung also explained the reduction of ventilation which occurred in this region with acceleration.

Kazemi and his colleagues (58) studied the distribution of blood flow in 15 patients with recent myocardial infarctions as diagnosed on the basis of medical history, physical findings, and serial electrocardiographic and serum enzyme changes. Measurements were made at three levels in the lung using [133]Xenon and fixed counters. They found that six days after infarction the proportion of the blood flow going to the lowest zone was reduced, while that to the upper was increased, compared with the distribution in healthy volunteers. Changes of smaller magnitude but in the same direction were seen in five patients who had severe angina and electrocardiographic changes that suggested ischemia but not definite infarction. The distribution of ventilation was normal in both groups as measured with a normal tidal inspiration of xenon. Studies in six patients up to 25 weeks after infarction showed a partial return to the normal distribution of perfusion. No measurements of pulmonary vascular pressures were made. However the authors argued that the most likely mechanism of the change in blood flow distribution was a rise in pulmonary venous pressure causing perivascular interstitial edema and thus increased vascular resistance in the lung bases (53, 115). The same mechanism has been postulated for the inversion of the normal distribution of blood flow which occurs in patients with mitral stenosis (35). In both groups, the initial perivascular edema probably progresses to adventitial thickening (88) and perhaps to other pathological changes in the vessels (36) which explains the persistence of an abnormal pattern so long after infarction.

Iliff (57) demonstrated the formation of interstitial perivascular edema from extra-alveolar vessels in isolated dog lungs. She showed that lungs in which the capillaries were closed because alveolar pressure exceeded both arterial and venous pressures nevertheless developed perivascular cuffs of edema over a period of an hour or so. By separately raising arterial and venous pressures and measuring the rate of weight gain of the lung, she deduced that the rate of fluid leakage through the small veins exceeded that through the arteries. The degree of inflation of the lung did not affect the rate of formation of edema, a surprising finding in view of the evidence that the pressure around the extra-alveolar vessels falls even with positive pressure inflation (93). It is possible that some of the edema came from the alveolar corner vessels which remain open in the face of an alveolar pressure which is high enough to close capillaries. However, good evidence that larger vessels were leaking was that Evans Blue dye which had been added to the blood could be seen in the walls of veins up to $750\,\mu$ diameter and of arteries to $200\,\mu$ diameter. Although there have been many previous suggestions that edema fluid can pass through extra-alveolar vessels, this study seems to settle the issue.

CONTROL OF PULMONARY CIRCULATION

The mechanism involved in hypoxic pulmonary vasoconstriction continues to be elusive. Lloyd has continued his work on isolated strips of pulmonary arterial wall by comparing their responses to hypoxia when immersed in the fluorocarbons FX80 and FC34 (which have different solubilities for oxygen) and in humidified gas (73). In previous studies, he found that hypoxia caused no spontaneous changes in baseline tensions of strips bathed in physiological salt solutions while the responses of the hypoxic strips to various stimuli were reduced (71). However strips with some parenchyma attached did constrict in response to hypoxia (72). In the present experiments he showed that strips immersed in FX80 (a good solvent for many water soluble materials) behaved in the same way, but strips in FC34 (a relatively poor solvent) and in humidified gas showed an increase in tension when the oxygen partial pressure was reduced. A possible explanation is that hypoxic constriction cannot occur if water-soluble substances are allowed to escape in the surrounding medium. Lloyd also found that strips of aorta behaved like pulmonary artery in both aqueous and humid gas environments. He concluded that the responses of the smooth muscle of the pulmonary artery and aorta may depend in large part on the nature of the perivascular tissue.

Barer, Howard & Shaw (13) obtained stimulus-response curves to hypoxia and hypocapnia for the pulmonary vascular bed of open-chest cats and dogs.

The animals were anesthetized with chloralose or a barbiturate, the left lower lobe bronchus was cannulated so that it could be ventilated with various gas mixtures, and flow from the left lower lobe was measured with an electromagnetic probe. Main pulmonary artery pressure was not controlled but varied little. In cats, the stimulus-response curve for hypoxia showed a small but definite fall of blood flow as the P_{O_2} in pulmonary venous blood was reduced from 500 to 100 mm Hg; below this flow fell sharply, and at very low P_{O_2} values, was often near zero. The results in dogs were similar though the maximum reductions in flow were less. Hypercapnia (carbon dioxide–oxygen mixtures) caused a sharp decrease in flow up to a P_{CO_2} of about 55 mm Hg; thereafter flow flattened out or occasionally rose.

Barer and her colleagues (13) noted the similarity between the shapes of the stimulus-response curves for the pulmonary vessels and those reported for the carotid body (50). Both have high thresholds and a steep increase in response in the physiological range. This suggests either an unusual biochemical mechanism (30) or a long diffusion path. There are also some similarities for carbon dioxide: in both organs, the action of carbon dioxide is less than hypoxia, and in both the two gases interact.

GAS EXCHANGE
DIFFUSION

It is not often that new lines appear on the O_2–CO_2 diagram; perhaps the last was the R (respiratory exchange ratio) line for aquatic respiration some eight years ago (94, 95). Now Wangensteen & Rahn (112) have pointed out that when O_2 and CO_2 move to and from the gas exchange surface by diffusion (as in the hen egg), O_2 moves with more facility than CO_2 because of its higher diffusion coefficient. Thus the conductance for O_2 is higher. Since the pressure difference between the environment and the gas exchanging surface is given by the conductance divided by the flux (determined by the metabolic rate), the pressure difference for CO_2 exceeds that for O_2. Thus the R lines for diffusion gas exchange have a steeper slope than those for convective exchange when both gases move with equal facility. The same principles have been applied to gas exchange in a watery environment (96).

The notion is elegant and it is a little disappointing to see that in practice, the resultant differences in gas exchange are small. For example, with an alveolar P_{CO_2} of 40 mm Hg and R value of 1, the alveolar P_{O_2} for convective and diffusion respiration are about 100 and 110 mm Hg respectively. Moreover in most situations a mixture of convection and diffusion transport occurs. This almost certainly seems so in the human lung as clearly pointed out 50 years ago by Krogh & Lindhard (64). In an aqueous environment, a larger difference for P_{O_2} between convective and diffusive respiration would be expected (96) but there is doubt whether pure diffusional respiration in water breathing animals ever occurs.

Wangensteen, Wilson & Rahn (111) reported on the diffusion rates of gases across the shell of the hen's egg which, astonishingly, were not previously known. They measured the oxygen flux through a section of shell across which there was initially a difference in oxygen partial pressure but not in total gas pressure. From the permeability of oxygen they calculated the values for carbon dioxide and water vapor. The permeability characteristics of the shell were found to be constant during the period of incubation. The average diameter of the pores through which diffusion occurs was calculated from the diffusion measurements to be about 17 μ; these measurements agree well with morphological studies. Evidence was obtained that most of the resistance to diffusion resides in the shell itself and not in the membranes inside it.

In a companion paper (112), changes in the gas composition of the air cell of the hen's egg during incubation were reported. The oxygen partial pressure fell from about 140 to 100 mm Hg while the carbon dioxide tension rose from 10 to 40 mm Hg. These data agreed fairly well with predictions based on the constant diffusion properties of the shell and on the volumes of oxygen and carbon dioxide exchanged (98). The authors point out a dilemma concerning the developing chick. If the shell permeability remains constant during incubation, its magnitude must be great enough to maintain a sufficiently high P_{O_2} and low P_{CO_2} inside the egg in the face of increasing metabolic requirements. However, the permeability cannot be too large because this would lead to an excessive loss of water vapor. It is of interest that an increase in the bicarbonate concentration of chick blood accompanies the increase in P_{CO_2}, thus maintaining a constant blood pH (33, 39).

Conflicting results on the permeability of the avian egg were found by Kutchai & Steen (66). They measured O_2 and CO_2 permeabilities by an almost identical method and concluded that these increased strikingly during incubation in fertilized but not in unfertilized eggs. The discrepancy may perhaps be explained by the fact that these authors included both the inner and outer shell membranes whereas Wangensteen and his colleagues (111) removed the inner membrane. Kutchai & Steen believe that about half of the resistance to oxygen diffusion is located in the membranes. Romijn (99) also claimed that permeability increased with incubation, though it appears that his measurements were made with a difference of total gas pressure across the shell and thus reflected bulk flow filtration rather than true diffusion. Kutchai & Steen also found that drying the shell membranes greatly increased their permeability and suggested that this was the mechanism for increase in permeability during the incubation period.

Diffusion of inert gases across the dog placenta was studied by Longo and his colleagues (74). They perfused blood containing hydrogen and sulfur hexafluoride into the umbilical artery of fetal dogs in utero. Blood was collected from the umbilical and uterine veins. They argued that if placental membranes limited diffusion significantly, hydrogen would have crossed preferentially into the mother since its diffusion rate is 18 times that of sulfur hexafluoride. In their study, they found hydrogen/sulfur hexafluoride ratios of nearly 1:1 in both uterine and umbilical veins. They concluded that inert gases equilibrate between maternal and fetal placental exchange vessels within the time of a single capillary transit.

The role of diffusion within the terminal air spaces in moving inspired gas to the alveolar walls continues to be of great interest. However, since the topic was dealt with at length in last year's Annual Review, it will only be touched on here. Saltzman and his colleagues (102) reasoned that at high ambient pressures of several atmospheres, the diffusion rate of oxygen within the terminal units might be sufficiently impaired to increase the alveolar-arterial oxygen difference. This could conceivably have been the mechanism for the uncoordination and paralysis that Chouteau (26) observed in goats at ambient pressures of about 50 atm and an inspired Po_2 of 154 mm Hg. These animals behaved normally when the inspired Po_2 was raised by about 40 mm Hg.

Saltzman and his co-workers exposed three normal subjects, breathing various nitrogen, neon and helium mixtures, to pressures of up to 7 atm absolute. Inspired Po_2 was held constant at 150 mm Hg. No increase in the alveolar-arterial oxygen difference with pressure was observed; indeed there was a tendency for it to fall. There was no correlation between arterial Pco_2 and gas density but an unexpected and unexplained correlation between an increase in arterial Pco_2 and pressure.

Liese, Muysers & Pichotka (69) measured alveolar-arterial oxygen differences in normal subjects breathing 20.9% oxygen in nitrogen, helium and argon. The blood measurements were made on "arterialized" blood from an ear lobe, a technique which is liable to errors when the Po_2 is high on the oxygen dissociation curve. The mean alveolar-arterial difference for the air breathing was significantly higher than for the helium-oxygen and argon-oxygen mixtures: the mean values were 8.7, 15.3, and 16.3 mm Hg respectively. The authors point out that there is no clear correlation between these differences and such physical properties of the gases as viscosity and density which might be expected to play a role in intrapulmonary mixing. These intriguing findings remain unexplained.

VENTILATION-PERFUSION INEQUALITY

Traditionally the effects of uneven ventilation and blood flow on gas exchange have been analyzed by treating the lung as a group of units ventilated in parallel, all receiving some fresh inspired air. However there is increasing interest in the gas exchange that occurs when one lung region inspires alveolar gas from another region (117). An example of such a situation is the collateral ventilation, discussed above that presumably occurs in both healthy and diseased lungs. Another possible example exists in diseases such as centrilobular emphysema where dilatations develop in the region of the respiratory bronchioles with the result that peripheral alveoli may receive no fresh inspired air.

A lung region which inspires gas from another can be described as "parasitic." Theoretical studies show that such a region has a high alveolar Pco_2, usually higher than mixed venous blood because of the Haldane effect. Its carbon dioxide output is grossly impaired. By contrast, its oxygen uptake is much less affected and its respiratory exchange ratio is therefore very low. Lung models containing parasitic compartments in general have great difficulty eliminating carbon dioxide, and this may be a factor in the carbon dioxide retention of chronic obstructive lung disease. It is of interest that while the effects of ventilation-perfusion inequality on oxygen transfer have long been recognized, the equally important interference with carbon dioxide transfer has only recently been emphasized (116).

The gas exchange behavior of these lung models with series inequality of ventilation differs in several respects from models with parallel inequality. For example, the former show small alveolar-arterial oxygen differences when the inspired Po_2 is raised, and they also show a fast rise in arterial Po_2 with increasing overall ventilation. These features are generally not so marked with parallel inequality and may eventually allow the patterns to be distinguished in practice.

The knotty problem of the cause of hypoxemia in pulmonary embolism was tackled by Wilson and his colleagues (119). They studied 21 patients who were otherwise normal and in whom the diagnosis was confirmed by angiography. Alveolar-arterial differences for oxygen were measured when the patients were breathing air and again while breathing 100% oxygen. Virtually all the hypoxemia found in patients breathing air could be accounted for on the basis of shunt-like effect. However the magnitude of the shunt was poorly correlated with the amount of the vascular bed occluded and with the rise in pulmonary artery pressure. The hypoxemia gradually disappeared during the month following embolism. The authors concluded that atelectasis in the embolized region was the most likely cause of the hypoxemia.

LITERATURE CITED

1. Agostoni, E., Thimm, F. F., Fenn, W. O. 1959. Comparative features of the mechanics of breathing. *J. Appl. Physiol.* 14:679–83

2. Agostoni, E., Piiper, J. 1962. Capillary pressure and distribution of vascular resistance in isolated lung. *Am. J. Physiol.* 202:1033–36

3. Agostoni, E., D'Angelo, E., Bonanni, M. V. 1970. Topography of pleural surface pressure above resting volume in relaxed animals. *J. Appl. Physiol.* 29:297–306

4. Agostoni, E., Miserocchi, G. 1970. Vertical gradient of transpulmonary pressure with active and artificial lung expansion. *J. Appl. Physiol.* 29:705–12

5. Agostoni, E., D'Angelo, E., Bonanni, M. V. 1970. The effect of the abdomen on the vertical gradient of pleural surface pressure. *Resp. Physiol.* 8:332–46

6. Agostoni, E., D'Angelo, E. 1970. Comparative features of the transpulmonary pressure. *Resp. Physiol.* 11:76–83

7. Agostoni, E., D'Angelo, E. 1971. Topography of pleural surface pressure during simulation of gravity effect on abdomen. *Resp. Physiol.* 12:102–9

8. Alison, S. S. 1858. On the differential stethophone, and some new phenomena observed by it. *Proc. Roy. Soc. Med.* 9:196

9. Anthonisen, N. R., Danson, J., Robertson, P. C., Ross, W. R. D. 1969. Airway closure as a function of age. *Resp. Physiol.* 8:58–65

10. Argyris, J. H. 1965. Matrix analysis of the three dimensional elastic media small and large displacements. *AIAA J.* 3:45–51

11. Avasthey, P., Coulam, C. M., Wood, E. H. 1970. Position-dependent regional differences in pericardial pressures. *J. Appl. Physiol.* 28:622–29

12. Barber, V. C., Boyde, A. 1968. Scanning electron microscopic studies of cilia. *Z. Zellforsch.* 84:269–84

13. Barer, G. R., Howard, P., Shaw, J. W. 1970. Stimulus-response curves for the pulmonary vascular bed to hypoxia and hypercapnia. *J. Physiol. London* 211:139–55

14. Bartlett, D., Jr. 1970. Postnatal growth of the mammalian lung: influence of low and high oxygen

tensions. *Resp. Physiol.* 9:58–64

15. Black, J. T. 1970. SEM: Scanning electron microscope. *Photographic Applications in Science, Technology, and Medicine.* 23:29–35

16. Bouhuys, A., Jonson, B. 1967. Alveolar pressure, airflow rate, and lung inflation in man. *J. Appl. Physiol.* 22:1086–1100

17. Bouhuys, A., Ed. 1970. *Airway Dynamics, Physiology and Pharmacology.* Springfield, Ill.: Thomas. 345 pp.

18. Brandi, G. 1970. Theoretical considerations on the response of lung tissue to the acceleration of gravity. *Resp. Physiol.* 9:356–70

19. Brody, J. S., Stemmler, E. J., DuBois, A. B. 1968. Longitudinal distribution of vascular resistance in the pulmonary arteries, capillaries and veins. *J. Clin. Invest.* 47:783–99

20. Bryan, A. C., Milic-Emili, J., Pengelly, D. 1966. Effect of gravity on the distribution of pulmonary ventilation. *J. Appl. Physiol.* 21:778–84

21. Burger, E. J., Mead, J. 1969. Static properties of the lung after O_2 exposure. *J. Appl. Physiol.* 27:191–97

22. Burri, P. H., Weibel, E. R. 1971. Morphometric estimation of pulmonary diffusion capacity. II. Effect of P_{O_2} on the growing lung. *Resp. Physiol.* 11:247–64

23. Butler, J., Caro, C. G., Alcala, R., DuBois, A. B. 1960. Physiological factors affecting airway resistance in normal subjects and in patients with obstructive respiratory disease. *J. Clin. Invest.* 39:584–91

24. Campbell, E. J. M. 1958. *The Respiratory Muscles and the Mechanics of Breathing.* London: Lloyd-Luke 131 pp.

25. Chase, W. H. 1959. The surface membrane of pulmonary alveolar walls. *Exp. Cell Res.* 18:15–28

26. Chouteau, J. 1969. Saturation diving: the Conshelf experiments. In *The Physiology and Medicine of Diving and Compressed Air Work,* ed. P. B. Bennett, D. H. Elliott, 491–504 London: Bailliere, Tindall & Cassell.

27. Clarke, S. W., Jones, J. G., Oliver, D. R. 1970. Resistance to two-phase gas-liquid flow in airways. *J. Appl. Physiol.* 29:464–71

28. Clarke, S. W., Graf, P. D., Nadel, J. A. 1970. In vivo visualization of

small-airway constriction after pulmonary microembolism in cats and dogs. *J. Appl. Physiol.* 29:646–50

29. Clements, J. A., Tierney, D. F. 1965. Alveolar instability associated with altered surface tension. In *Handbook of Physiology: Respiration*, Sec. 3, 2: 1565–83. Washington, DC: Am. Physiol. Soc.

30. Coxon, R. V. 1968. Regulation of biochemical reactions by oxygen and carbon dioxide. In *Proceedings of Wates Foundation Symposium on Arterial Chemoreceptors*, ed. R. W. Torrance, 91–102. Oxford: Blackwell.

31. D'Angelo, E., Bonanni, M. V., Michelini, S., Agostoni, E. 1970. Topography of the pleural surface pressure in rabbits and dogs. *Resp. Physiol.* 8:204–29

32. D'Angelo, E., Michelini, S., Agostoni, E. 1971. Partition of factors contributing to the vertical gradient of transpulmonary pressure. *Resp. Physiol.* 12:90–101

33. Dawes, C., Simkiss, K. 1969. The acid-base status of the blood of the developing chick embryo. *J. Exp. Biol.* 50:79–86

34. deLemos, R. A., Shermeta, D. W., Knelson, J. H., Kotas, R., Avery, M. E. 1970. Acceleration of appearance of pulmonary surfactant in the fetal lamb by administration of corticosteroids. *Am. Rev. Resp. Dis.* 102:459–61

35. Dollery, C. T., West, J. B. 1960. Regional uptake of radioactive oxygen, carbon monoxide and carbon dioxide in the lungs of patients with mitral stenosis. *Circ. Res.* 8:765–71

36. Doyle, A. E., Goodwin, J. F., Harrison, C. V., Steiner, R. E. 1957. Pulmonary vascular patterns in pulmonary hypertension. *Brit. Heart J.* 19:353–65

37. DuBois, A. B., Turaids, T., Mammen, R. E., Norbrega, F. T. 1966. Pulmonary atelectasis in subjects breathing oxygen at sea level or at simulated altitude. *J. Appl. Physiol.* 21:828–36

38. Dunnill, M. S. 1967. Effect of lung inflation on alveolar surface area in the dog. *Nature, London* 214:1013–14

39. Erasmus, B. W., Howell, B. J., Rahn, H. 1970. Ontogeny of acid-base balance in the bullfrog and chicken. *Resp. Physiol.* 11:46–53

40. Forgacs, P. 1967. Crackles and wheezes. *Lancet* 2:203

41. Forrest, J. B. 1970. The effect of changes in lung volume on the size and shape of alveoli. *J. Physiol., London* 210–533–47

42. Froeb, H. F., Mead, J. 1968. Relative hysteresis of the dead space and lung in vivo. *J. Appl. Physiol.* 25:244–48

43. Geelhaar, A., Weibel, E. R. 1971. Morphometric estimation of pulmonary diffusion capacity. III. The effect of increased oxygen consumption in Japanese waltzing mice. *Resp. Physiol.* 11:354–66

44. Glaister, D. H. 1970. Distribution of pulmonary blood flow and ventilation during forward (+Gx) acceleration. *J. Appl. Physiol.* 29:432–39

45. Glazier, J. B., Hughes, J. M. B., Maloney, J. E., West, J. B. 1967. Vertical gradient of alveolar size in lungs of dogs frozen intact. *J. Appl. Physiol.* 23:694–705

46. Glazier, J. B., Hughes, J. M. B., Maloney, J. E., West, J. B. 1969. Measurements of capillary dimensions and blood volume in rapidly frozen lungs. *J. Appl. Physiol.* 26:65–76

47. Green, M. 1965. How big are the bronchioles? *St. Thomas's Hosp. Gaz.* 63:136–39

48. Hoppin, F. G., Jr., York, E., Kuhl, D. E., Hyde, R. W. 1967. Distribution of pulmonary blood flow as affected by transverse (+Gx) acceleration. *J. Appl. Physiol.* 22:469–74

49. Hoppin, F. G., Jr., Green, I. D., Mead, J. 1969. Distribution of pleural surface pressure in dogs. *J. Appl. Physiol.* 27:863–73

50. Hornbein, T. F. 1968. The relation between stimulus to chemoreceptors and their response. In *Proceedings of the Wates Foundation Symposium on Arterial Chemoreceptors*, ed. R. W. Torrance, 65–76. Oxford: Blackwell.

51. Horsfield, K., Cumming, G. 1968. Functional consequences of airway morphology. *J. Appl. Physiol.* 24:384–90

52. Howatt, W. F. et al 1965. Factors affecting pulmonary surface properties in the foetal lamb. *Clin. Sci.* 29:239–48

53. Hughes, J. M. B., Glazier, J. B., Maloney, J. E., West, J. B. 1968. Effect of extra-alveolar vessels on dis-

tribution of blood flow in the dog lung. *J. Appl. Physiol.* 25:701–12

54. Hughes, J. M. B., Glazier, J. B., Maloney, J. E., West, J. B. 1968. Effect of lung volume on the distribution of pulmonary blood flow in man. *Resp. Physiol.* 4:58–72

55. Hughes, J. M. B., Rosenzweig, D. Y. 1970. Factors affecting trapped gas volume in perfused dog lungs. *J. Appl. Physiol.* 29:332–39

56. Hughes, J. M. B., Rosenzweig, D. Y., Kivitz, P. B. 1970. Site of airway closure in excised dog lungs: histologic demonstration. *J. Appl. Physiol.* 29:340–49

57. Iliff, L. D. 1971. Extra-alveolar vessels and edema development in excised dog lungs. *Circ. Res.* 28: 524–32

58. Kazemi, H., Parsons, E. F., Valenca, L. M., Strieder, D. J. 1970. Distribution of pulmonary blood flow after myocardial ischemia and infarction. *Circulation* 61:1025–30

59. Kilburn, K. H. 1968. A hypothesis for pulmonary clearance and its implications. *Am. Rev. Resp. Dis.* 98: 449–63

60. Kimoto, S., Russ, J. C. 1969. The characteristics and applications of the scanning electron microscope. *Am. Sci.* 57:112–33

61. Klingele, T. G., Staub, N. C. 1970. Alveolar shape changes with volume in isolated, air-filled lobes of cat lung. *J. Appl. Physiol.* 28:411–14

62. Klingele, T. G., Staub, N. C. 1971. Terminal bronchiole diameter changes with volume in isolated, air-filled lobes of cat lung. *J. Appl. Physiol.* 30:224–27

63. Kotas, R. V., Avery, M. E. 1971. Accelerated appearance of pulmonary surfactant in the fetal rabbit. *J. Appl. Physiol.* 30:358–61

64. Krogh, A., Lindhard, J. 1917. The volume of the dead space in breathing and the mixing of gases in the lungs of man. *J. Physiol. London.* 51: 59–90

65. Krueger, J. J., Bain, T., Patterson, J. L., Jr. 1961. Elevation gradient of intrathoracic pressure. *J. Appl. Physiol.* 16:465–68

66. Kutchai, H., Steen, J. B. 1971. Permeability of the shell and shell membranes of hen's eggs during development. *Resp. Physiol.* 11: 265–78

67. Leblanc, P., Macklem, P. T., Ross, W. R. D. 1970. Breath sounds and distribution of pulmonary ventilation. *Am. Rev. Resp. Dis.* 102:10–16

68. Leblanc, P., Ruff, F., Milic-Emili, J. 1970. Effects of age and body position on "airway closure" in man. *J. Appl. Physiol.* 28:448–51

69. Liese, W., Muysers, K., Pichotka, J. P. 1970. Influence of inert gases upon the alveolar-arterial O_2 pressure, *Pfluegers Arch.* 321:316–31

70. Liggins, G. C. 1969. Premature delivery of foetal lambs infused with glucocorticoids. *J. Endocrinol.* 45: 515–23

71. Lloyd, T. C., Jr. 1967. Influences of P_{O_2} and pH on resting and active tensions of pulmonary arterial strips. *J. Appl. Physiol.* 22:1101–9

72. Lloyd, T. C., Jr. 1968. Hypoxic pulmonary vasoconstriction: role of perivascular tissue. *J. Appl. Physiol.* 25:560–65

73. Lloyd, T. C., Jr. 1970. Responses to hypoxia of pulmonary arterial strips in nonaqueous baths. *J. Appl. Physiol.* 28:566–69

74. Longo, L. D., Delivoria-Papadopoulos, M., Power, G. G., Hill, E. P., Forster, R. E., II. 1970. Diffusion equilibration of inert gases between maternal and fetal placental capillaries. *Am. J. Physiol.* 219:561–69

75. Loosli, C. G. 1937. Interalveolar communications in normal and pathologic mammalian lungs; review of literature. *Arch. Pathol.* 24:743–76

76. Luchsinger, P. C., Seipp, H. W., Jr., Patel, D. J. 1962. Relationship of pulmonary artery-wedge pressure to left atrial pressure in man. *Circ. Res.* 11:315–18

77. Macklem, P. T. 1971. Airway obstruction and collateral ventilation. *Physiol. Rev.* 51:368–436

78. Maloney, J. E., Castle, B. L. 1969. Pressure-diameter relations of capillaries and small blood vessels in frog lung. *Respir. Physiol.* 7:150–62

79. Maloney, J. E., Castle, B. L. 1970. Dynamic intravascular pressures in the microvessels of the frog lung. *Resp. Physiol.* 10:51–63

80. Martin, H. B., Proctor, D. F. 1958. Pressure-volume measurements on dog bronchi. *J. Appl. Physiol.* 13: 337–43

81. Mead, J. 1961. The mechanical properties of lungs. *Physiol. Rev.* 41:281–330

82. Mead, J., Takishima, T., Leith, D. 1970. Stress distribution in lungs: a model of pulmonary elasticity. *J. Appl. Physiol.* 28:596–608

83. Milic-Emili, J., Henderson, J. A. M., Dolovich, M. B., Trop, D., Kaneko, K. 1966. Regional distribution of inspired gas in the lung. *J. Appl. Physiol.* 21:749–59

84. Nadel, J. A., Colebatch, H. J. H., Olsen, C. R. 1964. Location and mechanism of airway constriction after barium sulfate microembolism. *J. Appl. Physiol.* 19:387–94

85. Nadel, J. A., Wolfe, W. G., Graf, P. D. 1968. Powdered tantalum as a medium for bronchography in canine and human lungs. *Invest. Radiol.* 3:229–38

86. Nowell, J. A., Pangborn, J., Tyler, W. S. 1970. Scanning electron microscopy of the avian lung. *Proc. Ann. Scanning Electron Microsc. Symp., 3rd, Chicago.* p. 249. Chicago: Illinois Institute of Technology

87. Nowell, J. A., Tyler, W. S. 1971. Scanning electron microscopy of the surface morphology of mammalian lungs. *Am. Rev. Respir. Dis.* 103: 313–28

88. Olsen, E. G. J. 1966. Perivascular fibrosis in lungs in mitral valve disease. *Brit. J. Dis. Chest* 60:129–36

89. Pattle, R. E. 1955. Properties, function and origin of the alveolar lining layer. *Nature, London.* 175: 1125–26

90. Pattle, R. E. 1958. Properties, function, and origin of the alveolar lining layer. *Proc. Roy. Soc. London Ser. B* 148:217–40

91. Pedley, T. J., Schroter, R. C., Sudlow, M. F. 1970. Energy losses and pressure drop in models of human airways. *Resp. Physiol.* 9:371–86

92. Pedley, T. J., Schroter, R. C., Sudlow, M. F. 1970. The prediction of pressure drop and variation of resistance within the human bronchial airways. *Resp. Physiol.* 9:387–405

93. Permutt, S. 1965. Effect of interstitial pressure of the lung on pulmonary circulation. *Med. Thoracalis* 22: 118–31

94. Rahn, H., West, J. B. 1963. Aquatic gas exchange: prediction of arterial gas tensions and "ventilation" of gills. *The Physiologist* 6:259

95. Rahn, H. 1966. Aquatic gas exchange: theory. *Resp. Physiol.* 1:1–12

96. Rahn, H., Wangensteen, O. D., Farhi, L. E. 1971. Convection and diffusion gas exchange in air or water. *Resp. Physiol.* 12:1–6

97. Rohrer, F. 1915. Der Strömungswiderstand in den menschlichen Atemwegen und der Einfluss der unregelmässigen Verzweigung des Bronchialsystems auf den Atmungsverlauf in verschiedenen Lungenbezirken. *Pfluegers Arch. Gesamte Physiol. Menschen Tiere* 162:225–99

98. Romanoff, A. L. 1967. *Biochemistry of the Avian Embryo.* New York: Wiley.

99. Romijn, C. 1950. Foetal respiration in the hen. Gas diffusion through the egg shell. *Poultry Sci.* 29:42–51

100. Rosenzweig, D. Y., Hughes, J. M. B., Glazier, J. B. 1970. Effects of transpulmonary and vascular pressures on pulmonary blood volume in isolated lung. *J. Appl. Physiol.* 28: 553–60

101. Ruff, F., Hughes, J. M. B., Iliff, L. D., McCarthy, D., Milic-Emili, J. 1971. Distribution of pulmonary blood flow and ventilation in patients with liver cirrhosis. *Thorax* 26:229

102. Saltzman, H. A., Salzano, J. V., Blenkam, G. D., Kylstra, J. A. 1971. Effects of pressure on ventilation and gas exchange in man. *J. Appl. Physiol.* 30:443–49

103. Schoedel, W., Slama, H., Hansen, E. 1971. Zeitabhängiges Verhalten von Filmen von oberflächenaktivem Material aus Lungenalveolen. *Pfluegers Arch.* 322:336–46

104. Schroter, R. C., Sudlow, M. F. 1969. Flow patterns in models of the human bronchial airways. *Resp. Physiol.* 7:341–55

105. Slama, H., Schoedel, W., Hansen, E. 1971. Bestimmung der Oberflächeneigenschaften von Stoffen aus den Lungenalveolen mit einer Blasenmethode. *Pfluegers Arch.* 322:355–63

106. Staub, N. C., Storey, W. F. 1962. Relation between morphological and physiological events in lung studied by rapid freezing. *J. Appl. Physiol.* 17:381–90

107. Storey, W. F., Staub, N. C. 1962. Ventilation of terminal air units. *J. Appl. Physiol.* 17:391–97

108. Vincent, N. J., Knudson, R., Leith, D. E., Macklem, P. T., Mead, J.

1970. Factors influencing pulmonary resistance. *J. Appl. Physiol.* 29:236–43

109. Wang, N. S., Thurlbeck, W. M. 1970. Scanning electron microscopy of the lung. *Hum. Pathol.* 1:227–31

110. Wang, N. S., Kotas, R. V., Avery, M. E., Thurlbeck, W. M. 1971. Accelerated appearance of osmiophilic bodies in fetal lungs following steroid injection. *J. Appl. Physiol.* 30:362–65

111. Wangensteen, O. D., Wilson, D., Rahn, H. 1970. Diffusion of gases across the shell of the hen's egg. *Resp. Physiol.* 11:16–30

112. Wangensteen, O. D., Rahn, H. 1970. Respiratory gas exchange by the avian embryo. *Resp. Physiol.* 11:31–45

113. Weibel, E. R. 1963. *Morphometry of the Human Lung.* Berlin: Springer

114. Weibel, E. R. 1970. Morphometric estimation of pulmonary diffusion capacity. I. Model and method. *Resp. Physiol.* 11:54–75

115. West, J. B. Dollery, C. T., Heard, B. E. 1965. Increased pulmonary vascular resistance in the dependent zone of the isolated dog lung caused by perivascular edema. *Circ. Res.* 17:191–206

116. West, J. B. 1969. Ventilation-perfusion inequality and overall gas exchange in computer models of the lung. *Resp. Physiol.* 7:88–110

117. West, J. B. 1971. Gas exchange when one lung region inspires from another. *J. Appl. Physiol.* 30:479–87

118. West, J. B., Matthews, F. L. 1971. Stresses, strains and surface pressures in the lung caused by gravity. *Fed. Proc.* 30:620

119. Wilson, J. E., III et al 1971. Hypoxemia in pulmonary embolism, a clinical study. *J. Clin. Invest.* 50:481–91

120. Wood, L. D. H., Ruff, F., Bryan, A. C., Milic-Emili, J. 1969. Influence of air density on the distribution of ventilation. *The Physiologist* 12:398

121. Woolcock, A. J., Macklem, P. T. 1971. Mechanical factors influencing collateral ventilation in human, dog, and pig lungs. *J. Appl. Physiol.* 30:99–115

122. Young, S. L., Tierney, D. F., Clements, J. A. 1970. Mechanism of compliance change in excised rat lungs at low transpulmonary pressure. *J. Appl. Physiol.* 29:780–85

BIOLOGICAL MEMBRANES: THE DYNAMICS OF
THEIR ORGANIZATION

PHILIP SIEKEVITZ

The Rockefeller University, New York, N. Y.

INTRODUCTION

This review will be confined to a single topic—namely, the growing literature pointing to the apparent paradox between the specificity and stability of membrane structure on the one hand and its lability and dynamism on the other. I hope the exact meaning of this statement will become apparent in the course of this review. The examination of membranes is a favorite topic these days: witness the many recent reviews dealing with membrane organization (25, 33, 96, 125, 126, 130, 202). However, these reviews have dealt mainly with the organization of membranes in space; what I propose to do (the reason for yet another review on membranes!) is to concentrate on the temporal and dynamic characteristics of their organization. Not that membrane organization is well understood; quite the contrary, the fact that there is a spate of review articles illustrates the dictum that many ideas, good and bad, can be formulated in the relative absence of concrete data. Many of the experimental observations are good and to the point, but the modes of membrane organization are proving hard nuts to crack. There is a lack of really definitive data, compared to that in other fields: in a 44-page review on the assembly of biological structures (128), the topic of membranes occupies only 3 pages. Many models of membrane structure have been proposed (cf reviews above) including the oft cited model of Green and co-workers (93) and ending with Deamer's more recent formulation (43). In light of the data presented in this article, models will have to be modified to take into account changes in membrane organization within the dimension of time.

As a prologue, I need cite no specific references to point out the well known fact that morphologically—and cytologically—particular membrane types in cells are specific not only with regard to their localization in the cell but also with regard to their protein composition. Thus, at a single point in time, a membrane can be characterized by its content of enzyme proteins (cf reviews above) and also by that of other proteins, as seen by comparing the gel electropherograms of proteins extracted from various membranes (65, 123, 186, 234). That the different cellular membranes have lipid signatures as well (28, 67, 80) is not so well acknowledged. The specificity for lipid is of a different nature than that for proteins, in that while all animal cell membranes have the same major lipids, they have them in differing proportions; these tables of proportions among the phospholipids and neutral lipids are the signatures of the various membranes. Recent data on the lipid composition of relatively minor membrane components of cells, such as the Golgi apparatus (121) and the pancreas' zymogen granules (140, 226), only add to the confirmation of this statement.

MEMBRANE DIFFERENTIATION

In addition to the three spatial dimensions of membrane architecture, there is a fourth, the temporal one, which describes and proscribes changes in the properties and composition of membranes. A good way to determine whether changes do occur in membrane architecture is to examine the case of the normal developmental differentiation of a distinctive membrane. Perhaps the best example in the literature is the appearance of a fully differentiated endoplasmic reticulum (ER) system soon after birth in rat liver (39, 40, 132) as well as in chick liver (167, 203). In the rat, differentiation is complete after one week (40). Thus, if one examines a distinctive membrane, in this case the rough ER, one finds that while its morphology (as examined under the electron microscope) remains unchanged, its protein components, as examined by their enzymatic functioning, are constantly changing (39, 40), even among enzymes of the same electron transport pathway. These changes in enzyme activities are due to changes in enzyme amounts (40). However, the phospholipid components of the rat liver ER membrane remain unchanged during this period of time (39, 40), although some changes occur in the case of rabbit liver ER (141). In both examples (13, 39, 40) the fatty acid components do alter, but this is probably due to variations in diet during the period of the experiment (39, 40). In other words, enzymatic proteins are continuously either adding to existent membrane structures—since the new enzyme activities are the result, not of activation, but of new protein synthesis (39, 40)—or replacing nonenzymatic proteins possibly already there as part of the structure. In the case of one of these proteins, glucose 6-phosphatase, histochemical experiments indicate that it seems to be inserted at random throughout the entire ER system (132). Thus one can say that, with time, the proportions of membrane proteins to each other is not the same; the specificity of protein-membrane interaction is inviolate, but the proportions of different membrane proteins can be drastically altered during normal development and as will be noted below, during abnormal situations. A similar study with chick liver (203) uncovered patterns of membrane enzyme development different from that in rat liver; but again, there was no simultaneous appearance of enzymes, even among proteins of the same electron transport pathway.

Another example of this developmental plasticity of membrane composition is the one concerning enzymes in chloroplast membranes, obtained either by using a mutant (46, 83, 84, 153, 154, 190) or by using a synchronous wild-type culture (189) of the algae *Chlamydomonas reinhardi*. The results again showed that the proportions among proteins (cytochromes) (46, 189, 190) and among lipids (phospholipids, galactolipids, carotenoids) (46, 83, 84), changed either during the formation of entirely new membrane structures, as in the case of the mutant, or during the increase in membrane mass which took place in the light in the synchronous culture. In addition, in higher plants the lipids of the chloroplast membranes change in proportional amounts during the development of the lamellar system (5).

The same situation has been found in mitochondrial membranes during embryonic development of liver (107a, 134) and during liver regeneration (78). In both outer membrane (78) and inner membrane (134), the increase in membrane mass was accompanied by differential increases in membrane enzyme activities, and probably in enzyme amounts. Perhaps the best example of mitochondrial membrane differentiation involves the development of the organelle from its "promitochondrial" or undifferentiated state in anaerobic yeast to a fully functional one when the yeast cells are incubated aerobically (166, 219, 221). Alterations occur in the lipid (107, 111) and protein (enzyme activities and cytochrome amounts) (94, 109, 131) composition of the mitochondria during their differentiation. However, we must add a note of caution since inactive forms of enzymes, particularly the apoproteins of the cytochromes, have been found in the mitochondria of the "petite" yeast mutants (164, 213). Changes in lipid and protein patterns also occur during the release from glucose repression in this yeast (117, 135); again there were no qualitative changes in the kinds of proteins (either enzymatically or electrophoretically determined), but the proportions of components relative to each other showed marked alterations. Variations in growth conditions also altered the proportions of cytochromes in yeast mitochondria (122). Of particular interest is the finding (131, 135) that the completion of a fully functioning yeast mitochondrial membrane proceeds asynchronously with regard to its protein components, in a step-like manner, very much reminiscent of what happens during differentiation of the ER membranes (39, 40).

There is conflicting evidence in the case of the plasma membrane as to whether, in cell cultures, the macromolecules of the membrane are synthesized and inserted together or separately into the growing membrane mass. In one cell line it appeared that membrane proteins, phospholipids, and glycoproteins were all synthesized and incorporated into the surface membrane at the same time (79), whereas during synchronous culture of another cell line (24) there was a marked difference between membrane protein and membrane phospholipid and glycolipid as to the times of their synthesis; however in this latter case the surface membranes were not isolated. Also, the glycoprotein and glycolipid content of surface membranes of cultured cells can vary with the growth conditions of the culture (82).

Finally, work with bacteria also adds to evidence of a step-like assembly of membrane structure. In *Hemophilus parainfluenzae*, five different flavoprotein dehydrogenases are differentially produced and assembled into a developing electron transport membrane (224). There are differences in the appearances of different cytochromes and differences in the proportions of membrane lipid during the formation of an electron transport chain in *Staphylococcus aureus* (71). In *Escherichia coli*, membranes isolated from cells grown under various growth conditions were found to have differences in membrane-bound enzyme activities, but no differences in the patterns of the major protein bands on gel electrophoresis, which suggests a rather fixed membrane structure onto which different amounts of various enzymes may be complexed (187). This idea was also put forth to explain the synthesis and insertion of inducible permeases, again in *E. coli* (124). This intercalation of permeases, postulated to occur at all regions of the bacterial membrane (124), is reminiscent of the insertion during differentiation of new glucose 6-phosphatase molecules in an existing ER membrane system (132).

ABNORMALLY INDUCED ALTERATIONS IN MEMBRANES

Membranes can alter their composition under the influence of abnormal stimuli. Perhaps the best documented case is the one of the induced increase in smooth ER membranes (SER) of the hepatocyte after phenobarbital injection into the rat. The documentation is rather complete that phenobarbital causes a proliferation of smooth membranes (57, 159, 160, 172, 199) and an increase (up to ten times per liver cell) of some enzymes associated with these membranes (32, 57, 160, 171, 172). However, not all enzyme activities normally associated with the SER membranes increase and even those which do increase do so not all at once, but in a step-like manner (57, 159, 160, 171, 172). Furthermore, circumstantial evidence indicates that the "new" molecules resulting from phenobarbital induction are not associated with only the "new" membrane (158), for attempts to separate these "new" membranes containing the "additional" enzyme from existing membranes have proven fruitless (38, 81). In other words, it appears that the entire ER membrane system of the cell has been modified: while the same proteins, determined enzymatically or immunologically (136), are present as in normal liver cells, some enzymes, such as glucose 6-phosphatase, are in a much lower concentration in the ER membranes (158), while other proteins, like the TPNH-flavin reductase and cytochrome P_{450}, are in higher concentrations in the membranes (38, 81). Indeed the increase in smooth membrane mass can occur without the increase in all of the phenobarbital-induced proteins (168), and during the regressive phase, after phenobarbital administration has been halted, the increased amount of smooth ER membranes persists even though the elevated enzyme levels have returned to normal (159). That the ER system of membranes is a very labile one, capable of changing the proportions of its specific proteins, is indicated also by the changes in properties of the isolated membranes of rats after various treatments; among them, (*a*) in vivo injections of: ethanol (8, 9), ethionine plus phenobarbital (9), carbon disulfide (23), or thyroid hormone (119); (*b*) diets: deficient in iron (37), varied in fatty acid composition (52), refeeding on different diets after starvation (118); and (c) hepatomas with various growth rates (204).

The enzymatic properties of other mammalian cellular membranes can be altered experimentally, e.g. the liver mitochondria of regenerating liver, and the mitochondria from rats injected with chloramphenicol (86). Well documented cases have been made for changes in the surface membranes of cells, probably of the glycoproteins located there, with viral infection (26, 27, 95), and after steroid attack on cells in tissue culture (14, 15). Differences have been observed in the plasma membrane proteins of adult and embryonic and neoplastic cells (146), and between normal hepatocyte and hepatoma plasma membranes (53).

Contrary to the above, where we noted that fairly normal membrane structures have been found with abnormal proportions of constituents, work done on chloroplast membranes has almost invariably indicated that membrane structure is affected by changes in membrane composition. Mutants affecting plant chloroplasts, resulting either in deficient chlorophyll formation (6) or in abnormal carotenoid synthesis (63), have markedly deranged chloroplast membrane structures. Upon examining nine photosynthetic mutants of *Chlamydomonas reinhardi*, deranged structures were found in all but two cases (88). Changed ratios of chlorophylls *a* to *b* (89) and changes in the amounts or proportions of the cytochromes of the photosynthetic electron transport chain (77, 97, 133) are reflected in altered patterns of chloroplast membrane structure (89, 90)—particularly the stacking of the membranes to form grana. Similar alterations in membrane stacking have been noted (100), accompanied by reduction in photosynthetic electron transport efficiency (100) and changes in the proportions among membrane proteins (62, 99) and lipid synthesis (17), when *Chlamydomonas reinhardi* cells (62, 99, 100) or *Euglena* cells (17) were treated with chloramphenicol. However, it cannot be concluded that the chloroplast lamellar structure is more susceptible even to small changes in membrane composition than are other membranes—even the mitochondrial membranes mentioned earlier—since derangements of stacking are easy to detect in chloroplasts.

Bacterial membranes can also be modified. In the case of photosynthetic bacteria, the phospholipid composition of the membrane of *Rhodopseudomonas* is changed under various growth conditions (201), while *Anabaena* cells under the influence of diphenylamine make membranes markedly different from normal cells with regard to their carotenoid and cytochrome components, yet are still capable of photosynthetic electron transport (152). Other interesting cases are (a) the loss of membrane proteins in deletion (156) and temperature sensitive (104) mutants of *E. coli*, (b) the changes in protein to lipid ratios in *Bacillus subtilus* membranes which occur in a mutant unable to synthesize lipids (143), and (c) the integration into the membranes of a mutant of *S. aureus* unable to synthesize lipids of a permease in such a manner that it was not efficient in transport activity (144). In wild-type cultures of *Staphylococcus*, changes in membrane lipid components occur during temperature growth shifts (113) and during shifts from anaerobic to aerobic growth (225). However, in one case, that of the induction of galactoside and glucoside transport systems in E. coli, the new proteins and lipids seem to be coordinated in their synthesis and association into the membrane (229).

Thus, the evidence gleaned from work dealing with normal development, or with abnormally-induced permutation, leans heavily towards the characterization of membrane structure as one not definitely fixed in time. The specificity of a membrane does not change with time, in the sense that proteins specific to one membrane occur in morphologically different membranes during the life of a cell; but the presence or absence of a specific protein in a distinctive membrane varies with the degree of differentiation of that membrane; and the specific amount of this protein can in a given membrane structure vary considerably with time. The findings with abnormal membranes only emphasize the pleiomorphic character of this structure.

TURNOVER OF MEMBRANE CONSTITUENTS

The main constituents of membranes, their proteins and phospholipids, are also involved in the dynamic turnover of molecules in the cell. Even in the tissues of the adult animal, where there is very little increase in mass and very little cell division, there is still in this steady state a relatively rapid turnover of the macromolecules of the cell. Thus, in cells such as liver, heart, kidney, and brain, whose lifetimes have been estimated to be between six months and several years, there exists a continuous synthesis and degradation of the proteins and lipids of the mitochondria (11, 12, 34, 44, 48, 69, 123, 205, 207) of microsomes (7, 21, 48, 110, 123, 127, 155, 185, 194) and of other sub-cellular fractions (34, 123, 133, 185, 195, 196) including the plasma membranes (133, 195, 196, 220). Many of those examined are undoubtedly membrane proteins (7, 11, 21, 44, 48, 69, 110, 123, 127, 155, 185, 194, 220), as are all the lipids. The problem for membrane architecture is not only that these membrane proteins are turning over at a relatively rapid rate [from two to four days for most of the proteins of the ER membrane (7, 110, 127, 155, 185, 194)], but that the turnover rates of individual proteins isolated from the same membranes differ greatly. Thus, three proteins, extracted from the same ER membranes—by either proteolytic or lipolytic treatment of the membranes—and then purified, gave apparent half-lives ranging from 3–4 days for the NADPH-cytochrome c reductase (7, 110, 127, 155, 194), to 5 days for cytochrome b_5 (127, 155) [though a shorter half-life has been obtained (48)], to 18 days for NAD glycohydrolase (21), all under the same experimental conditions. The extraction of these particular proteins leaves the membrane comparatively unchanged (155), and it could be argued that only the loosely attached proteins have a rapid turnover. However, through the use of gel electrophoresis on all the proteins extracted from the membranes, it was found (7, 123, 185) that they all participate in a rapid turnover, and that furthermore, there are great differences among them in their rates of turnover. Also, recently published data shows that the haem and apoprotein portions of protein (22, 76) are turning over separately; this has been specifically indicated for microsomal cytochrome b_5 (22), although this latter finding has been disputed (48). However, the presence of apo-cytochrome b_5 in ER membranes (150) would have to indicate a real dichotomy in the turnover of the haem and protein portions of this molecule. This dichotomy is also seen in the different turnovers of the sugar and protein moieties of liver ER membrane glycoproteins (120), although in the L cell plasma membrane, the sugar and protein moieties seem to turn over together (220).

Moreover, when one looks at data on various lipids of the same membrane, one finds that they are turning over at different rates relative to each other (12, 34, 98, 163, 195, 196, 207). The raw data indicate that in some cases, for mitochondria (69) and for plasma membrane of L cells (220), the total proteins and total lipids are turning over as a unit (69); other data, for mitochondria (165), for microsomes (155) and for plasma membrane of *Mycoplasma* (116), indicate otherwise. However, the data concerning the magnitude and relative rates of phospholipid turnover are all suspect, since different labels can give different apparent half-lives (155, 207) and are suspect particularly with regard to the presence of transacylating enzymes in various membranes, and of the phospholipid exchange reactions which will be mentioned below. Nevertheless it would appear that all membrane components—particularly the proteins, and possibly the lipids—are turning over at rates not in concert with one another. Interestingly enough, recent data indicates that the various membranes could possibly have their own proteinases (92, 145, 161) and lipases (151, 174, 184)—enzymes possibly involved in the constant degradation of their membrane substrates.

The membrane can be looked upon as a very elastic, deformable brick wall, made up of bricks of many colors; each colored brick is being constantly replaced by a brick of similar color, but these replacements are not in harmony with one another. The wall, or membrane, persists, but its component molecules are continuously being replaced. Once again, we are faced with trying to visualize the architecture of a specific structure which keeps its singularity in the face of this dynamism, an architecture whose structure is yet open enough to allow for this constant exchange of its constituent building blocks.

Recent Data on Membrane Lipids

Recent experiments (114, 139, 228) have confirmed past indications (42) that, at least in animal cells, only the endoplasmic reticulum (ER) has all the enzymes involved in the complete synthesis of phospholipids: that the mitochondria, for example, are incapable of synthesizing their own phospholipids, except perhaps for cardiolipin (41). The mitochondria are capable of synthesizing some of the intermediates in phospholipid synthesis, such as phosphatidic acid (139, 193) and CDP-diglyceride (216), and of course possess one of the pathways concerned with the synthesis of fatty acids, that starting with acetyl-CoA (cf 47). Also, many of the cell membranes seem to have their own transacylating enzymes: such enzymes have been noted in plasma membranes (200), in ER membranes (35, 45, 51, 181, 214, 218), and, even though an earlier report (51) could not find them there, in the mitochondrial membranes, specifically in the outer membrane (35, 181, 218). However, the reason that it has only recently been realized (cf 42) that mitochondria in particular are incapable of complete phospholipid synthesis, is the existence of the by now well documented exchange reaction of entire phospholipid molecules between different membranes in the cell.

Exchange of entire lipid molecules had already been noted: between high and low density lipoproteins (50, 70), between α- and β-lipoproteins (178), and between chylomicrons and phospholipid micelles (142), although earlier reports (108, 178) of lipid exchange between red blood cells and plasma have now been questioned (Zilversmit, van Deenen, personal communication). This type of in vitro experiment has now been extended to show an exchange between lipids of liver microsomes (fragments of the ER) and lipids of the blood plasma (237). However, the interesting experiments from our viewpoint are the unequivocal demonstrations that different membranes in the cell exchange some of their phospholipids. Thus, mitochondria and microsomal membranes of animal cells (2, 139, 230) and of plant cells (1) participate in the exchange; the experiments have been accomplished by following the in vitro decrease of in vivo produced radioactivity in lipids from one organelle and its in vitro increase in the other, with all the appropriate controls. Phosphatidylcholine and phosphotidylethanolamine appear to be the major exchangers; interestingly enough, cardiolipin, found in the inner mitochondrial membrane but not in microsomal membranes, does not participate in this exchange (139, 230). This exchange has been further localized to one between the ER membrane and both the outer and inner mitochondrial membranes (18, 182), although it is not yet certain whether the lipids of the inner mitochondrial membrane exchange directly with those of the ER membranes or only indirectly through the intermediacy of the lipids of the outer membrane. The occurrence of this type of exchange between intracellular membranes has been also postulated to explain some observations on isolated liver cells (114, 115). There is also a histochemical indication (165) that phospholipids of the plasma membranes of cells in tissue culture exchange with those of other cells whenever the cells are in contact, but the in vitro experiments with plasma membranes and ER membranes of these cells have not yet been performed.

Another type of direct exchange has been postulated: that of the base, choline, with lecithin (211) (alternative to the CDP-choline pathway), and that of serine as well as choline (228). The exchange of lipids between mitochondrial and microsomal membranes requires a supernatant fraction (1, 2, 139, 230), a protein (231) which has been partially purified and which seems to be specific for the lipid transferred (232). It is not known whether the protein acts as a modifier of membranes, making them more receptive to lipid exchange, or acts as a carrier of lipid, taking it from the ER synthetic site to sites in other cell membranes, although it is interesting that a sterol carrier protein has been partially purified, implicated in cholesterol biosynthesis, and postulated as a cholesterol carrier from the ER membrane to other membrane sites (183). In vitro exchange reactions have not yet been performed between ER membrane and either plasma membrane, nuclear membrane, or Golgi apparatus membrane, but since none of these have ever been implicated in total phospholipid synthesis, it could be predicted that they too would be found to participate in reactions similar to the ones found to occur between ER membranes and mitochondrial membranes.

However, as in most advances, the above findings give rise to as many—though different—problems as those which they have solved. For example, there is no evidence (230) that there are differences in exchange rates among the phosphatidylcholine molecules within a particular membrane—i.e., no evidence for the existence of "structural" phospholipids as opposed to easily exchangeable ones. However, if exchange takes place quickly and at random, we are faced with the problem that in the face of this ubiquitous exchange, the phospholipid components of intracellular membranes remain distinctive; thus despite an apparently free exchange of phosphatidylcholine between ER membranes and mitochondrial membranes of liver, the percentage of phospholipids which are phosphatidylcholine are kept fairly constant in ER membranes and in outer- and inner-mitochondrial membranes at about 60%, 45%, and 52% respectively. It would seem that the extent and nature of the exchange is regulated by the proteins of the membranes, representing binding sites for the various lipid molecules. Furthermore, the distinctiveness of different membranes seems to be set by the specificity of their proteins per se, and secondarily by their lipids.

Unquestionably, our ideas concerning membrane organization will have to be modified to take into consideration the above exchange reactions. The membrane must be a more open structure than we have heretofore visualized, permitting most of, if not all, the phospholipid molecules to move in and out with such relative ease. Because the membrane is also a selectively permeable structure—a specific regulator of transport between the inside and outside of the cell, and between various intracellular compartments, we must at the same time visualize the membrane as a rather rigid discretionary barrier. It is this apparent paradox, between the membrane's structural stability, accounting not only for its permeability characteristics but also for the enzymatic properties of its proteins, and the membrane's dynamic lability, accounting for the exchange of its phospholipid molecules and for the turnover of its protein molecules, that must be resolved before an adequate model of membrane structure is formulated.

Mosaicism in Membranes

Are all of the components, proteins and lipids, distributed at random throughout the three-dimensional area of a morphologically and cytologically distinct membrane, or are there patches, mosaics of components, in one area which are not found in other areas? The answer to this depends on the resolving power of the viewer. For example, in one case, because of the nature of the necessary protein-protein interaction, we can say that there must certainly be patches of distinctive components of enzymes and, perhaps, of lipids: these are the cases of electron transport proteins, whether oxidative and localized in the inner mitochondrial membrane, or photosynthetic and situated in the chloroplast lamellae, or others, for example, those chains found in the ER membranes. The question is whether these assemblies are found at random throughout the inner membrane of the mitochondria, the chloroplast lamellae, or the ER membranes. The relevant types of experiments involved have been histochemistry, fractionation, solubilization and reformation, and isolation after specified conditions; the result has been that in some cases, a form of mosaicism has been uncovered, and in others no evidence for it has been found.

Perhaps the best characterized example yet found of what may be called large-scale mosaicism is that of the plasma membrane, particularly of the hepatic cell, where there are morphologically well defined secretive and adsorptive surfaces—the former identified with microvilli adjacent to bile caniculi, and the latter with junctional complexes connecting adjacent cells. Histochemical techniques (59) and experiments in which the hepatocyte plasma membranes were further subfractionated (21, 60, 61, 101, 197) indicated strongly that different enzymes probably reside at these two locations on the plasma membrane. Thus, a Mg^{++}-ATPase and a Mg^{++}-Na^{+}-K^{+}-ATPase seen to be at two different sites on the membrane, a finding also described when erythrocyte ghosts were sheared and subfractionated (188). In one case, added insulin was found bound to only a subfraction of the liver cell plasma membrane (101). Indeed, another liver plasma membrane enzyme, 5'-nucleotidase, which has been so differentially localized (59, 60, 61, 101, 197), has a specific lipid, sphingomyelin, associated with it (227). A plasma membrane preparation from kidney medulla has been isolated with an inferred high density of Na^{+}-K^{+}-ATPase molecules per unit area (112), while in the intestinal mucosal cell, where the plasma membrane is geometrically asymmetric, an asymmetry was also found in the ouabain-sensitive ATPase activity (74). A novel treatment of visualizing the surface H-2 antigens with electron microscopy has indicated that the antigen occurs in isolated small regions of the thymocyte membrane and in similar but larger regions of the lymphocyte membranes (198). Another approach for dealing with plasma membranes has been first to solubilize them and then to reaggregate them by removing the solubilizing agent; this method has produced differing results. In some cases, using *Mycoplasma laidlawii* as source, no differential aggregation occurred (55, 56, 173); while in other instances, using differing methods of reconstitution, the reassembled membranes showed differences from the original material—even with the same *Mycoplasma* source (170, 175, 210) and with erythrocytes (236), as if large self-assembling mosaics might have been originally in the membranes. An interesting result was the finding of cross-hybridization between membrane components, both proteins (169) and lipids (30), of different species of *Mycoplasma*.

In ER membranes, there is evidence that although one enzyme, glucose 6-phosphatase, was found histochemically to be distributed throughout the ER system (85, 132, 158, 209) even during differentiation (132), there seem to be some membrane areas which have proportionally more enzyme molecules than do the other areas—not only glucose 6-phosphatase, but other ER membrane enzymes as well (36, 38, 81, 102, 208). These biochemical experiments were performed by subfractionation on sucrose density gradients of untreated or sonicated microsomes, but even after more powerful detergent treatment, indirect evidence of heterogeneity has been obtained (54, 58). Also, there is an indication (148) that the increased cytochrome P_{450} molecules occur in different parts of the ER membrane, separated by density gradient centrifugations of microsomes from phenobarbital- and methyl-cholanthrene-treated rats.

In the case of chloroplasts, there are the well known experiments which indicate strongly that, by osmotic or detergent methods, it has been possible to separate photosystem I from photosystem II areas in the chloroplast lamellae (3, 4, 10, 19, 20, 87, 106, 147, 179, 206, 215, 223, 233). Whether the fractionation takes place lengthwise along the membrane, or whether there occurs a separation of grana from stroma lamella (87, 179), it is clear that large areas of the chloroplast membrane differ distinctly from other large areas. Indeed, early cytological observations also led to such a conclusion (222).

Finally, there are indications that in bacteria also, the cell membrane might be differentiated. A good example is the isolation of a DNA-RNA membrane complex (73, 176, 212), which suggests that there is a specific membrane site where DNA is bound and where DNA replication and RNA transcription may occur. Another example is the possibly localized site on a point of the cell membrane where penicillin is secreted (180); another, the concentration of certain "surface" enzymes in buds forming from the cell membrane as found in a "minicell" strain of *E. coli* (49). The isolation (149) of a membrane fraction with distinctive lipids and proteins (enzymes) also lends weight to the concept of mosaic pattern of membrane architecture.

However, in certain cases, in the fusion of different cells—mouse and human—instigated by virus adhesion, surface antigen of one cell membrane may diffuse rapidly throughout the entire membrane of the fused heterokaryon (72). On the other hand, in another heterokaryon, between different types of mouse cells, antigens showed up as patches in the fused heterokaryon membrane (91). Also, there is ample evidence (29, 97a) that, at least with certain viruses, the newly formed virus envelope proteins are incorporated into discrete regions of the cell membrane, preparatory to virus extrusion from the infected cell. All in all, there is by now enough evidence to state that in some instances certain membranes are composed of rather large mosaic patterns of their protein components, so that these areas are distinctly differ-

ent from adjacent ones; in other cases, looking at other proteins and other
membranes, the evidence is against this concept. It could well be that even
within the entire three-dimensional structure of a specific membrane, there
are strictly defined areas in which the various proteins are rigidly immo-
bilized, as has been shown recently with excitable membranes (217); but in
other areas, an openness can exist in the structure to allow for the relatively
rapid noncoordinated turnover mentioned above, and to permit a rather
large variation in the proportion of different molecules to each other, as
during differentiation.

Finally, it should be mentioned that controlled, staged treatment of
different membranes with lipolytic (64, 138, 191) or proteolytic (31, 103,
105, 129, 137, 138, 155, 157, 177, 192) enzymes show evidence of marked
differential susceptibility of the membrane to those reagents. In some cases
(31, 103, 137, 155, 177) a microscopically visible membrane structure remains, after some proteins are removed. The same occurs after acetone extraction of lipids (66) or acid extraction (68, 235) of so-called "structural"
mitochondrial proteins. Differential release of enzymes was also found to
occur during detergent treatment (58, 162). However, it is not certain
whether these experiments show an existent mosaicism in the membranes, or
a random ordering of the susceptible molecules in the membrane followed by
a reordering of the remaining membrane components after the extraction.

CONCLUSION

A study of the recent literature reviewed here makes it clear that no
single model of membrane organization can be broad enough to encompass all
the permutations which must be invoked to explain the data. The reviews
cited in the introduction mention the probable differences in membrane
architecture among different types of membranes; this review has presented
literature relevant to the thesis that any one type of membrane can change
its architecture during its lifetime. This thesis is based on the idea that
changes in membrane composition—some of them drastic—are reflected in
alterations in membrane organization. We have the instruments to determine
the composition, but as yet we lack the wit to devise a methodology em-
inently suitable for determining the organization. Thus, for the moment, we
will have to let the thesis stand as presented; nevertheless, following the
principle of Occam's Razor, the simplest interpretation of our data is that the
dynamism of membrane constituents, their different turnovers, their changing proportionalities, indeed the very fact of their presence or absence, their
exchangeability, their localizations within the membrane, and the mosaicism
apparent in some instances, are all reflections of the plasticity of the underlying architecture. Perhaps all that is required for a membrane to exist is
that the major constituents, proteins and lipids, obey the laws of ionic and
hydrophobic interactions, and once this criterion is satisfied, they can be
arranged, and are arranged, in various manners among themselves. I realize

that this formulation is vague, but it does have one superior attribute: the implied plasticity of the membrane is akin to that plasticity which all higher biological organizations possess. This concept, of plasticity of architecture combined with specificity of attachment, may be a first step toward the eventual explanation of further mysteries: of how membrane proteins synthesized at one site in the cell end up at other specific sites; of how specific molecules can be loosely or tightly crowded onto membranes; of whether, even, attachment proteins are present for other membrane proteins (cf. 16, 75); and, in general, of how specificity is preserved in the face of change.

Thus, not only does the cell differentiate and have a life cycle, but the membranes composing it also go through a regulated developmental pattern. The cell does not lose its identity during the differentiation process; neither do its membranes. They do not lose their identities because the various membranes are positioned as a whole within the architecture of the cell, and also perhaps because certain proteins within the membrane are there at all times as marks of its very existence. We can add finally, as cell arises from cell, so membrane arises from membrane: existent membranes have a role, not as templates, but as organizational fields within which occurs the coordinated development of further and more complete membrane structures. The future is open.

LITERATURE CITED

1. Abdelkader, A. B., Mazliak, P. 1970. Echanges de lipides entre mitochondries, microsomes et survageant cytoplasmique de cellules de pomme de terre ou de chou-fleur. *Eur. J. Biochem.* 15:250–62

2. Akiyama, M., Sakagami, T. 1969. Exchange of mitochondrial lecithin and cephalin with those in rat liver microsomes. *Biochim. Biophys. Acta* 187:105–12

3. Anderson, J. M., Boardman, N. K. 1966. Fractionation of the photochemical systems of photosynthesis. I. Chlorophyll contents and photochemical activities of particles isolated from spinach chloroplast. *Biochim. Biophys. Acta* 112:403–21

4. Anderson, J. M., Fork, D. C., Amesz, J. 1966. P₇₀₀ and cytochrome *f* in particles obtained by digitonin fragmentation of spinach chloroplasts. *Biochem. Biophys. Res. Commun.* 23:874–79

5. Appelqvist, L. A., Boynton, J. E., Stumpf, P. K., von Wettstein, D. 1969. Lipid biosynthesis in relation to chloroplast development in barley. *J. Lipid Res.* 9:425–36

6. Appelqvist, L. A., Boynton, J. E., Henningsen, K. W., Stumpf, P. K., von Wettstein, D. 1968. Lipid biosynthesis in chloroplast mutants of barley. *J. Lipid Res.* 9: 513–24

7. Arias, I. M., Doyle, D., Schimke, R. T. 1969. Studies on the synthesis and degradation of protein of the endoplasmic reticulum of rat liver. *J. Biol. Chem.* 244:3303–15

8. Ariyoshi, T., Takabatake, E. 1970. Drug metabolism in ethanol induced fatty liver. *Life Sci.* 9:361–69

9. Ariyoshi, T., Takabatake, E. 1970. Drug metabolism in methionine induced fatty liver. *Life Sci.* 9:371–77

10. Arntzen, C. J., Dilley, R. A., Crane, F. L. 1969. A comparison of chloroplast membrane surfaces visualized by freeze-etch and negative-staining techniques; and ultrastructural characterization of membrane fractions obtained from digitonin-treated spinach chloroplasts. *J. Cell Biol.* 43:16–31

11. Aschenbrenner, V., Druyan, R., Albin, R., Rabinowitz, M. 1970. Haem *a*, cytochrome *c* and total protein turnover in mitochondria from rat heart and liver. *Biochem. J.* 119: 157–60

12. Bailey, E., Taylor, C. B., Bartley, W. 1967. Turnover of mitochondrial components of normal and essential fatty acid-deficient rats. *Biochem. J.* 104:1026–32

13. Baldwin, J., Cornatzer, W. E. 1968. Liver lipids during development. *Lipids* 3:361–67

14. Ballard, P. L., Tomkins, G. M. 1970. Glucocortical-induced alteration of the surface membrane of cultured hepatoma cells. *J. Cell Biol.* 47:222–34

15. Ballard, P. L., Tomkins, G. M. 1969. Hormone induced modification of the cell surface. *Nature (London)* 224:344–45

16. Baron, C., Abrams, A. 1971. Isolation of a bacterial membrane protein, nectin, essential for the attachment of adenosine triphosphatase. *J. Biol. Chem.* 246:1542–44

17. Bishop, D. G., Smillie, R. M. 1970. The effect of chloramphenicol and cycloheximide on lipid synthesis during chloroplast development in *Euglena gracilis*. *Arch. Biochem. Biophys.* 137:179–89

18. Blok, M. C., Wirtz, K. W. A., Scherphof, G. L. 1971. Exchange of phospholipids between microsomes and inner and outer mitochondrial membranes of rat liver. *Biochim. Biophys. Acta* 233:61–75

19. Boardman, N. K., Anderson, J. M. 1967. Fractionation of the photochemical systems of photosystem II. Cytochrome and carotenoid contents of particles isolated from spinach chloroplasts. *Biochem. Biophys. Acta* 143:187–203

20. Boardman, N. K., Thorne, S. W., Anderson, J. M. 1966. Fluorescence properties of particles obtained by digitonin fragmentation of spinach chloroplasts. *Proc. Nat. Acad. Sci.* 56:586–93

21. Bock, K. W., Siekevitz, P., Palade, G. E. 1971. Localization and turnover studies of membrane nicotinamide adenine dinucleotide glycohydrolase in rat liver. *J. Biol. Chem.* 246:188–95

22. Bock, K. W., Siekevitz, P. 1970. Turnover of heme and protein moieties of rat liver microsomal cytochrome b₅. *Biochem. Biophys. Res. Commun.* 41:374–80

23. Bond, E. J., De Matteis, F. 1969. Biochemical changes in rat liver after administration of carbon disulphide, with particular reference to microsomal changes. *Biochem. Pharmacol.* 18:2531

24. Bosmann, H. B., Winston, R. A. 1970. Synthesis of glycoprotein, glycolipid, protein, and lipid in synchronized L5178Y cells. *J. Cell Biol.* 45:23–33

25. Branton, D. 1969. Membrane structure. *Ann. Rev. Plant Physiol.* 20: 209–38

26. Buck, C. A., Glick, M. C., Warren, L. 1971. Glycopeptides from the surface of control and virus-transformed cells. *Science* 172:169–71

27. Burger, M. M. 1969. A difference in the architecture of the surface membrane of normal and virally transformed cells. *Proc. Nat. Acad. Sci.* 62:994–1001

28. Chesteron, C. J. 1968. Distribution of cholesterol precursors and other lipids among rat liver intracellular structures. *J. Biol. Chem.* 243: 1147–51

29. Choppin, P. W., Klenk, H. D., Compans, R. W., Caliguiri, L. A. 1971. The parainfluenza virus SV5 and its relationship to the cell membrane. *Perspectives in Virology*, ed. M. Pollard, 7:127–58. New York: Academic

30. Cole, R. M., Popkin, T. J., Prescott, B., Chanock, R. M., Razin, S. 1971. Electron microscopy of solubilized *Acholeplasma laidlawii* membrane proteins reaggregated with *Mycoplasma pneumoniae* glycolipids. *Biochim. Biophys. Acta* 233:76–83

31. Coleman, R., Finean, J. B., Thompson, J. E. 1969. Structural and functional modification induced in muscle microsomes by trypsin. *Biochim. Biophys. Acta* 173:51–61

32. Conney, A. H. 1967. Pharmacological implications of microsomal enzyme induction. *Pharmacol. Rev.* 19:317–66

33. Criddle, R. S. 1969. Structural protein of chloroplasts and mitochondria. *Ann. Rev. Plant Physiol.* 20:239–52

34. Cuzner, M. L., Davison, A. N., Gregson, N. A. 1966. Turnover of brain mitochondrial membrane lipids. *Biochem. J.* 101:618–26

35. Daae, L. N. W., Bremer, J. 1970. The acylation of glycerophosphate in rat liver. A new assay procedure for glycerophosphate acylation, stud-

ies on its subcellular and submitochondrial localization and determination of the reaction products. *Biochim. Biophys. Acta* 210:92–104

36. Dallman, P. R., Dallner, G., Bergstrand, A., Ernster, L. 1969. Heterogeneous distribution of enzymes in submicrosomal membrane fragments. *J. Cell Biol.* 41:357–77

37. Dallman, P. R., Goodman, J. R. 1971. The effects of iron deficiency on the hepatocyte: a biochemical and ultrastructural study. *J. Cell Biol.* 48:79–90

38. Dallner, G., Bergstrand, A., Nilsson, R. 1968. Heterogeneity of rough-surfaced liver microsomal membranes of adult, phenobarbital-treated, and newborn rats. *J. Cell Biol.* 38:257–76

39. Dallner, G., Siekevitz, P., Palade, G. E. 1966. Biogenesis of endoplasmic reticulum membranes. I. structural and chemical differentiation in developing rat hepatocyte. *J. Cell Biol.* 30:73–96

40. Dallner, G., Siekevitz, P., Palade, G. E. 1966. Biogenesis of endoplasmic reticulum membranes. II. Synthesis of constitutive microsomal enzymes in developing rat hepatocyte. *J. Cell Biol.* 30:97–117

41. Davidson, J. B., Stanacev, N. Z. 1971. Biosynthesis of cardiolipin in mitochondria isolated from guinea pig liver. *Biochem. Biophys. Res. Commun.* 42:1191–99

42. Dawson, R. M. C. 1966. The metabolism of animal phospholipids and their turnover in cell membranes. *Essays in Biochemistry*, ed. P. M. Campbell, G. D. Greville, 2:69–115. New York: Academic

43. Deamer, D. W. 1970. An alternative model for membrane organization in biological membranes. *Bioenergetics* 1:237–46

44. De Bernard, B., Getz, G. S., Rabinowitz, M. 1969. The turnover of the protein of the inner and outer mitochondrial membrane of rat liver. *Biochim. Biophys. Acta* 193: 58–63

45. De Kruyff, B., van Golde, L. M. G., van Deenen, L. L. M. 1970. Utilization of diacylglycerol species by cholinephosphotransferase, ethanolaminephosphotransferase and diacylglycerol acyltransferase in rat liver microsomes. *Biochim. Biophys. Acta* 210:425–35

46. De Petrocellis, B., Siekevitz, P.,

Palade, G. E. 1970. Changes in chemical composition of thylakoid membranes during greening of the $y-1$ mutant of *Chlamydomonas reinhardi*. *J. Cell Biol.* 44:618–34

47. Donaldson, W. E., Wit-Peeters, E. M., Scholte, H. R. 1970. Fatty acid synthesis in liver: relative contributions of the mitochondrial, microsomal and non-particulate systems. *Biochim. Biophys. Acta* 202:35–42

48. Druyan, R., De Bernard, B., Rabinowitz, M. 1969. Turnover of cytochromes labeled with δ-aminolevulinic acid-^{3}H in rat liver. *J. Biol. Chem.* 244:5874–78

49. Dvorak, H. F., Wetzel, B. V., Heppel, L. A. 1970. Biochemical and cytochemical evidence for the polar concentration of periplasmic enzymes in a "minicell" strain L of *E. Coli. J. Bacteriol.* 104:543–48

50. Eder, H. A. 1957. The lipoprotein of human serum. *Am. J. Med.* 23:269–82

51. Eibl, H., Hill, E. E., Lands, W. E. M. 1969. The subcellular distribution of acyltransferases which catalyze the synthesis of phosphoglycerides. *Eur. J. Biochem.* 9:250–58

52. Ellingson, J. S., Hill, E. E., Lands, W. E. M. 1970. The control of fatty acid composition in glycerolipids of the endoplasmic reticulum. *Biochim. Biophys. Acta* 196:176–92

53. Emmelot, P., Feltkamp, C. A., Vaz Dias, H. 1970. Studies on plasma membranes. XII. Fractionation of the ATPase of deoxycholate-solubilized rat liver and hepatoma plasma membranes and the morphological appearance of the preparations. *Biochim. Biophys. Acta* 211:43–55

54. Emmelot, P., Vaz Dias, H. 1970. Separation of membrane components produced by anionic detergents and maintained after the latter's removal. *Biochim. Biophys. Acta* 203:172–75

55. Engelman, D. M., Morowitz, H. J. 1968. Characterization of the plasma membrane of *Mycoplasma laidlawii*. III. The formation and aggregation of small lipoprotein structures derived from sodium dodecyl sulfate-solubilized membrane components. *Biochim. Biophys. Acta* 150:376–84

56. Engelman, D. M., Morowitz, H. J. 1968. Characterization of the plasma membranes of *Mycoplasma*

laidlawii. IV. Structure and composition of membrane and aggregated components. *Biochim. Biophys. Acta* 150:385–96

57. Ernster, L., Orrenius, S. 1965. Substrate-induced synthesis of the hydroxylating enzyme system of liver microsomes. *Fed. Proc.* 24:1190–99

58. Ernster, L., Siekevitz, P., Palade, G. E. 1962. Enzyme-structure relationships in the endoplasmic reticulum of rat liver. A morphological and biochemical study. *J. Cell Biol.* 15:541–42

59. Essner, E., Novikoff, A. B., Masek, B. 1958. Adenosinetriphosphatase and 5'-nucleotidase activities in the plasma membrane of liver cells as revealed by electron microscopy. *J. Biophys. Biochem. Cytol.* 4:711–16

60. Evans, W. H. 1969. Subfractionation of rat liver plasma membranes. *Fed. Eur. Biochem. Soc. Lett.* 3:237–41

61. Evans, W. H. 1970. Fractionation of liver plasma membranes by zonal centrifugation. *Biochem. J.* 166:833–42

62. Eytan, F., Ohad, I. 1970. Biogenesis of chloroplast membranes. VI. Cooperation between cytoplasmic and chloroplast ribosomes in the synthesis of photosynthetic lamellar proteins during the greening process in a mutant of *Chlamydomonas reinhardi*, $y-1$. *J. Biol. Chem.* 245:4297–307

63. Faludi-Daniel, A., Fridvalszky, L., Gyurjan, I. 1968. Pigment composition and plant structure in leaves of carotenoid mutants of maize. *Planta* 78:184–95

64. Finean, J. B., Martonosi, A. 1965. The action of phospholipase C on muscle microsomes: a correlation of electron microscope and biochemical data. *Biochim. Biophys. Acta* 98:547–53

65. Fleischer, B., Fleischer, S. 1970. Preparation and characterization of Golgi membranes from rat liver. *Biochim. Biophys. Acta* 219:301–19

66. Fleischer, S., Fleischer, B., Stoeckenius, W. 1967. Fine structure of lipid-depleted mitochondria. *J. Cell Biol.* 32:193–208

67. Fleischer, S., Rouser, G. 1965. Lipids of subcellular particles. *J. Am. Oil Chem. Soc.* 42:588–607

68. Fleischer, S., Zahler, W. L., Ozawa,

H. 1968. The extraction of structural protein from submitochondrial vesicles. *Biochem. Biophys. Res. Commun.* 32:1001–38

69. Fletcher, M. J., Sanadi, D. R. 1961. Turnover of rat liver mitochondria. *Biochim. Biophys. Acta* 51:356–60

70. Florsheim, W. H., Morton, M. E. 1957. Stability of phospholipid binding in human serum lipoproteins. *J. Appl. Physiol.* 10:301–4

71. Frerman, F. E., White, D. C. 1967. Membrane lipid changes during formation of a functional electron transport system in *Staphylococcus aureus*. *J. Bact.* 94:1868–74

72. Frye, L. D., Edidin, M. 1970. The rapid intermixing of cell surface antigens after formation of mouse-human heterokaryons. *J. Cell Sci.* 7:319–35

73. Fuchs, E., Hanawalt, P. 1970. Isolation and characterization of the DNA replication complex from *Escherichia coli*. *J. Mol. Biol.* 52:301–22

74. Fujita, M., Matsui, A., Nagano, K., Nakao, M. 1971. Asymmetric distribution of ouabain-sensitive ATPase activity in rat intestine mucosa. *Biochim. Biophys. Acta* 233:404–8

75. Ganschow, R., Paigen, K. 1967. Separate genes determining the structure and intracellular location of hepatic glucuronidase. *Proc. Nat. Acad. Sci.* 58:938–45

76. Garner, R. C., McLean, A. E. M. 1969. Separation of haem incorporation from protein synthesis in liver microsomes. *Biochem. Biophys. Res. Commun.* 37:883–87

77. Garnier, J., Maroc, J. 1970. Recherche de plusieurs transporteurs d'electrons, notamment des cytochromes b-559, et c-553, chez trois mutants non photosynthetiques de *Chlamydomonas reinhardi*. *Biochim. Biophys. Acta* 205:205–19

78. Gear, A. R. L. 1970. Inner- and outer-membrane enzymes of mitochondria during liver regeneration. *Biochem. J.* 120:577–87

79. Gerner, E. W., Glick, M. C., Warren, L. 1970. Membranes of animal cells. V. Biosynthesis of the surface membrane during cell cycle. *J. Cell Physiol.* 75:275–80

80. Getz, G. S., Bartley, W., Lurie, D., Notton, B. M. 1968. Phospholipids of various sheep organs, rat liver and their subcellular fractions.

Biochim. Biophys. Acta 152:325–39

81. Glaumann, H., Dallner, G. 1970. Subfractionation of smooth microsomes from rat liver. *J. Cell Biol.* 47:34–48

82. Glick, M. C., Comstock, C., Warren, L. 1970. Membranes of animal cells. VII. Carbohydrates of surface membranes and whole cells. *Biochim. Biophys. Acta* 219:290–300

83. Goldberg, I., Ohad, I. 1970. Biogenesis of chloroplast membranes. IV. Lipid and pigment changes during synthesis of chloroplast membranes in a mutant of *Chlamydomonas reinhardi y−1*. *J. Cell Biol.* 44:563–71

84. Goldberg, I., Ohad, I. 1970. Biogenesis of chloroplast membranes. V. A radioautographic study of membrane growth in a mutant of *Chlamydomonas reinhardi y−1*. *J. Cell. Biol* 44:572–91

85. Goldfischer, S., Essner, E., Novikoff, A. B. 1964. The localization of phosphatase activities at the level of ultrastructure. *J. Histochem. Cytochem.* 12:72–95

86. González-Cadavid, N. F., Bello, E. M. A., Ramírez, J. L. 1970. Differential long-term effects of D-chloramphenicol on the biogenesis of mitochondria in normal and regenerating rat liver. *Biochem. J.* 118:577–86

87. Goodchild, D. J., Park, R. B. 1971. Further evidence for stroma lamellae as a source of photosystem I fractions from spinach chloroplasts. *Biochim. Biophys. Acta* 226:393–99

88. Goodenough, U. W., Levine, R. P. 1969. Chloroplast ultrastructure in mutant strains of *Chlamydomonas reinhardi* lacking components of the photosynthetic apparatus. *Plant Physiol.* 44:990–1000

89. Goodenough, U. W., Armstrong, J. J., Levine, R. P. 1969. Photosynthetic properties of ac-31, a mutant strain of *Chlamydomonas reinhardi* devoid of chloroplast membrane stacking. *Plant Physiol.* 44:1001–12

90. Goodenough, U. W., Levine, R. P. 1970. Chloroplast structure and function in ac-20, a mutant strain of *Chlamydomonas reinhardi*. III. Chloroplast ribosomes and membrane organization. *J. Cell Biol.* 44:547–62

91. Gordon, S., Cohn, Z. A. 1970. Macrophage-melanocyte heterokaryons. I. Preparation and properties. *J. Exp. Med.* 131:981–1003

92. Gray, R. W., Arsenis, C., Jeffay, H. 1970. Neutral protease activity associated with the rat liver peroxisomal fraction. *Biochim. Biophys. Acta* 222:627–36

93. Green, D. E. et al 1967. Formation of membranes by repeating units. *Arch. Biochem. Biophys.* 119:312–35.

94. Groot, G. S. P., Kovac, L., Schatz, G. 1971. Promitochondria of anaerobically grown yeast. V. Energy transfer in the absence of an electron transfer chain. *Proc. Nat. Acad. Sci.* 68:308–11

95. Hakomori, S. 1970. Cell density-dependent changes of glycolipid concentrations in fibroblasts, and loss of this response in virus-transformed cells. *Proc. Nat. Acad. Sci.* 67:1741–47

96. Hendler, R. W. 1971. Biological membrane ultrastructure. *Physiol. Rev.* 51:66–97

97. Hiyama, T., Nishimura, M., Chance, B. 1969. Energy and electron transfer systems of *Chlamydomonas reinhardi*. I. Photosynthetic and respiratory cytochrome systems of the pale green mutant. *Plant Physiol.* 44:527–34

97a. Holland, J. J., Kiehn, E. D. 1970. Influenza virus effects on cell membrane proteins. *Science* 167:202–5

98. Holtzman, J. C., Gram, T. E., Gillette, J. R. 1970. The kinetics of ^{32}P incorporation into the phospholipids of hepatic rough and smooth microsomal membranes of male and female rats. *Arch. Biochem.* 138:199–207

99. Hoober, J. K. 1970. Sites of synthesis of chloroplast membrane polypeptides in *Chlamydomonas reinhardi* y–1. *J. Biol. Chem.* 245:4327–34

100. Hoober, J. K., Siekevitz, P., Palade, G. E. 1969. Formation of chloroplast membranes in *Chlamydomonas reinhardi* y–1. Effects of inhibitors of protein synthesis. *J. Biol. Chem.* 244:2621–31

101. House, P. D. R., Weidermann, M. J. 1970. Characterization of an [^{125}I]-insulin binding plasma membrane fraction from rat liver. *Biochem. Biophys. Res. Commun.* 41:541–48

102. Imai, Y., Ito, A., Sato, R. 1966. Evidence for biochemically different types of vesicles in the hepatic microsomal fraction. *J. Biochem. Tokyo* 60:417–28

103. Inesi, G., Asai, H. 1968. Trypsin digestion of fragmented sarcoplasmic reticulum. *Arch. Biochem. Biophys.* 126:469–77

104. Inouye, M., Guthrie, J. P. 1967. A mutation which changes a membrane protein of *E. coli. Proc. Nat. Acad. Sci.* 64:957–61

105. Ito, A., Sato, R. 1969. Proteolytic microdissection of smooth-surfaced vesicles of liver microsomes. *J. Cell Biol.* 40:179–89

106. Jacobi, G., Lehmann, H. 1969. Photochemical activities of chloroplast fragments. *Prog. Photosyn. Res.* 1:159–73

107. Jakovic, S., Getz, G. S., Rabinowitz, M., Jakob, H., Swift, H. 1971. Cardiolipin content of wild type and mutant yeasts in relation to mitochondrial function and development. *J. Cell Biol.* 48:490–502

107a. Jakovic, S., Haddock, J., Getz, G. S., Rabinowitz, M., Swift, H. 1971. Mitochondrial development in liver of foetal and newborn rats. *Biochem. J.* 121:341–47

108. James, A. T., Lovelock, J. E., Webb, J. P. W. 1959. The lipids of whole blood. I. Lipid biosynthesis in human blood *in vitro. Biochem. J.* 73:106–15

109. Jayaraman, J., Cotman, C., Mahler, H. R., Sharp, C. W. 1966. Biochemical correlates of respiratory deficiency. VII. Glucose repression. *Arch. Biochem. Biophys.* 116:224–51

110. Jick, H., Shuster, L. 1966. The turnover of reduced nicotinamide adenine dinucleotide phosphate-cytochrome c reductase in the livers of mice treated with phenobarbital. *J. Biol. Chem.* 241:5366–69

111. Jollow, D., Kellerman, G. M., Linnane, A. W. 1968. The biogenesis of mitochondria. III. The lipid composition of aerobically and anaerobically grown *Saccharomyces cereviciae* as related to the membrane system of the cells. *J. Cell Biol.* 37:221–30

112. Jorgensen, P. L., Skou, J. C., Solomonson, L. P. 1971. Purification and characterization of $(Na^+ + K^+)$-ATPase. II. Preparation by zonal centrifugation of highly active $(Na^+ + K^+)$-ATPase from the outer medulla of rabbit kidney. *Biochem. Biophys. Acta* 233:381–94

113. Joyce, G. H., Hammond, R. K., White, D. C. 1970. Changes in membrane lipid composition in exponentially growing *Staphylococcus aureus*

during the shift from 37 to 25 C. *J. Bacteriol.* 104:323–30

114. Jungawala, F. B., Dawson, R. M. C. 1970. The origin of mitochondrial phosphatidyl-choline within the liver cell. *Eur. J. Biochem.* 12:399–402

115. Jungawala, F. B., Dawson, R. M. C. 1970. Phospholipid synthesis and exchange in isolated liver cells. *Biochem. J.* 117:481–90

116. Kahane, I., Razin, S. 1969. Synthesis and turnover of membrane protein and lipid in *Mycoplasma laidlawii*. *Biochim. Biophys. Acta* 183:79–89

117. Kaplan, D., Criddle, R. S. 1970. A comparison of insoluble mitochondrial membrane proteins from glucose repressed and derepressed *Saccaromyces carlsbergensis*. *Biochim. Biophys. Acta* 203:249–55

118. Kato, R. 1967. Effects of starvation and refeeding on the oxidation of drugs by liver microsomes. *Biochem. Pharmacol.* 16:871–81

119. Kato, R., Takahashi, A. 1968. Thyroid hormone and activities of drug-metabolizing enzymes and electron transport systems of rat liver microsomes. *Mol. Pharmacol.* 4:109–20

120. Kawasaki, T., Yamashina, I. 1970. The metabolism of glycoprotein of rat liver microsomes. *J. Biochem. Tokyo* 68:689–99

121. Keenan, T. W., Morré, D. J. 1970. Phospholipid class and fatty acid composition of Golgi apparatus isolated from rat liver and comparison with other cell fractions. *Biochemistry (Wash.)* 9:19–25

122. Kellerman, G. M., Biggs, D. R., Linnane, A. W. 1969. Biogenesis of mitochondria. XI. A comparison of the effects of growth-limiting oxygen tension, intercalating agents, and antibiotics on the obligate aerobe *Candida parapsilosis*. *J. Cell Biol.* 42:378–91

123. Kiehn, E. D., Holland, J. J. 1970. Membrane and non-membrane proteins of mammalian cells. Synthesis, turnover and size distribution. *Biochemistry (Wash.)* 9:1716–28

124. Koch, A. L., Boniface, J. 1971. Intercalation of permeases during membrane growth. *Biochim. Biophys. Acta* 225:239–47

125. Korn, E. D. 1969. Cell membranes: structure and synthesis. *Ann. Rev. Biochem.* 38:263–88

126. Korn, E. D. 1969. Biological membranes. *Theor. Exp. Biophys.* 2:1–65

127. Kuriyama, Y., Omura, T., Siekevitz, P., Palade, G. E. 1969. Effects of phenobarbital on the synthesis and degradation of protein components of rat liver microsomal membranes. *J. Biol. Chem.* 244:2017–26

128. Kushner, D. J. 1969. Self-assembly of biological structures. *Bacteriol. Rev.* 33:302–45

129. Kuylensterna, B., Nicholls, D. G., Hovmöller, S., Ernster, L. 1970. Effect of trypsin on mitochondrial and microsomal enzymes. *Eur. J. Biochem.* 12:419–26

130. Lehninger, A. L. 1969. The neuronal membrane. *Proc. Nat. Acad. Sci.* 60:1069–80

131. Lenaz, G., Littarru, G. P., Castelli, A. 1969. Asynchronous development of different functions in mitochondria of *Saccharomyces cerevisiae*. *Fed. Eur. Biochem. Soc. Lett.* 2:198–200

132. Leskes, A., Siekevitz, P., Palade, G. E. 1971. Differentiation of endoplasmic reticulum in hepatocytes. I. Glucose-6-phosphatase distribution *in situ*. II. Glucose-6-phosphatase in rough microsomes. *J. Cell Biol.* 49:264–302

133. Levine, R. P., Paszewski, A. 1970. Chloroplast structure and function in ac-20, a mutant strain of *Chlamydomonas reinhardi*. II. Photosynthetic electron transport. *J. Cell Biol.* 44:540–46

134. Levy, M., Toury, R. 1970. Etude de l'evolution des activities des enzymes mitochondriaux de l'hepatocyte au cours du developpement au rat. *Biochim. Biophys. Acta* 216:318–27

135. Lukins, H. B., Jollow, D., Wallace, P. G., Linnane, A. W. 1968. The biogenesis of mitochondria. 7. The effects of glucose repression on the lipid and enzyme composition of mitochondria from yeast. *Aust. J. Exp. Biol. Med. Sci.* 46:651–65

136. Lundkvist, V., Perlmann, P. 1967. Immunochemical characterization of submicrosomal membranes from normal and phenobarbital-treated rats. *Peptides of Biological Fluids*, 15:347–52. Amsterdam:Elsevier

137. Lust, J., Drochmans, P. 1963. Effect of trypsin on liver microsomes. *J. Cell Biol.* 16:18–92

138. Martonosi, A. 1968. Sacroplasmic reticulum. V. The structure of sarcoplasmic reticulum membranes. *Bio-*

chim. Biophys. Acta 150:694–704

139. McMurray, W. C., Dawson, R. M. C. 1969. Phospholipid exchange reactions within the liver cell. Biochem. J. 112:91–108

140. Meldolesi, J., Jamieson, J. D., Palade, G. E. 1971. Composition of cellular membranes in the pancreas of the guinea pig. II. Lipids. J. Cell Biol. 49:130–49

141. Miller, J. E., Cornatzer, W. E. 1966. Phospholipid metabolism in mitochondria and microsomes of rabbit liver during development. Biochim. Biophys. Acta 125:534–41

142. Mínari, O., Zilversmit, D. B. 1963. Behavior of dog lymph chylomicron lipid constituents during incubation with serum. J. Lipid Res. 4:424–36

143. Mindich, L. 1970. Membrane synthesis in Bacillus subtilis. I. Isolation and properties of strains bearing mutations in glycerol metabolism. II. Integration of membrane proteins in the absence of lipid synthesis. J. Mol. Biol. 49:415–439

144. Mindich, L. 1971. Induction of Staphylococcus aureus lactose permease in the absence of glycerolipid synthesis. Proc. Nat. Acad. Sci. 68:420–24

145. Moore, G. L., Kocholaty, W. F., Cooper, D. A., Gray, J. L., Robinson, S. L. 1970. A proteinase from human erythrocyte membranes. Biochim. Biophys. Acta 212:126–33

146. Moscona, A. A. 1971. Embryonic and neoplastic cell surfaces: availability of receptors for concanavalin A and wheat germ agglutinin. Science 171:905–7

147. Murata, N., Brown, J. 1970. Photochemical activities of spinach chloroplast particles fractionated after French press treatment. Plant Physiol. 45:360–61

148. Murphy, P. J., Van Frank, R. M., Williams, T. L. 1969. Subfractionation of rat liver microsomes: effects of phenobarbital and 3-methylcholanthrene. Biochim. Biophys. Res. Commun. 37:697–704

149. Nachbar, M. S., Salton, M. R. J. 1970. Characteristics of a lipid-rich NADH dehydrogenase-containing particulate fraction obtained from Micrococcus lysodeikticus membranes. Biochim. Biophys. Acta 223:309–20

150. Negishi, M., Omura, T. 1970. Presence of apo-cytochrome b_5 in microsomes from rat liver. J. Biochem. Tokyo 67:745–47

151. Newkirk, J. D., Waite, M. 1971. Identification of a phospholipase A_1 in plasma membranes of rat liver. Biochim. Biophys. Acta 225:224–33

152. Ogawa, T., Vernon, L. P. 1971. Increased content of cytochromes 554 and 562 in Anabaena variabilis cells grown in the presence of diphenylamine. Biochim. Biophys. Acta 226:88–97

153. Ohad, I., Siekevitz, P., Palade, G. E. 1967. Biogenesis of chloroplast membranes. I. Plastid dedifferentiation in a dark-grown algal mutant (Chlamydomonas reinhardi). J. Cell Biol. 35:521–52

154. Ohad, I., Siekevitz, P., Palade, G. E. 1967. Biogenesis of chloroplast membranes. II. Plastid differentiation during greening of a dark-grown algal mutant (Chlamydomonas reinhardi). J. Cell Biol. 35:553–84

155. Omura, T., Siekevitz, P., Palade, G. E. 1967. Turnover of constituents of the endoplasmic reticulum membranes of rat hepatocytes. J. Biol. Chem. 242:2389–96

156. Onodera, K., Rolfe, B., Bernstein, A. 1970. Demonstration of missing membrane proteins in deletion mutants of E. coli K12. Biochim. Biophys. Res. Commun. 39:969–75

157. Orrenius, S., Berg, A., Ernster, L. 1969. Effects of trypsin on the electron transport system of liver microsomes. Eur. J. Biochem. 11:193–200

158. Orrenius, S., Ericsson, J. L. E. 1966. On the relationship of liver glucose-6-phosphatase to the proliferation of endoplasmic reticulum in phenobarbital induction. J. Cell. Biol. 31:243–56

159. Orrenius, S., Ericsson, J. L. E. 1966. Enzyme-membrane relationships in phenobarbital induction of synthesis of drug-metabolizing enzyme system and proliferation of endoplasmic membranes. J. Cell Biol. 28:181–98

160. Orrenius, S., Ericsson, J. L. E., Ernster, L. 1965. Phenobarbital-induced synthesis of the microsomal drug-metabolizing enzyme system and its relationship to the proliferation of endoplasmic membranes. J. Cell. Biol. 25:627–39

161. Paik, W. K., Lee, H. W. 1970. Enzymatic hydrolysis of histones in rat

kidney microsomes. *Biochem. Biophys. Res. Commun.* 38:333–40

162. Pascaud, H., Auliac, P. B., Ehrhart, J.-C., Pascaud, M. 1970. Proteines constitutives des membranes microsomiques de la cellule hepatique du rat. *Biochim. Biophys. Acta* 219: 339–48

163. Pasternak, C. A., Bergeron, J. J. M. 1970. Turnover of mammalian phospholipids. Stable and unstable components in neoplastic mast cells. *Biochem. J.* 119:473–80

164. Perlman, P. S., Mahler, H. R. 1971. Formation of yeast mitochondria. III. Biochemical properties of mitochondria isolated from a cytoplasmic petite mutant. *Bioenergetics* 1:113–38

165. Peterson, J. A., Rubin, H. 1970. The exchange of phospholipids between cultured chick embryo fibroblasts as observed by autoradiography. *Exp. Cell Res.* 60:383–92

166. Plattner, H., Salpeter, M. M., Salzgaber, J. M., Schatz, G. 1970. Promitochondria of anaerobically-grown yeast. IV. Conversion into respiring mitochondria. *Proc. Nat. Acad. Sci.* 66:1252–59

167. Pollack, J. K., Ward, D. B. 1967. Changes in the chemical composition and enzymatic activities of hepatic microsomes of the chick embryo during development. *Biochem. J.* 103:730–38

168. Raisfeld, I. H., Bacchin, P., Hutterer, F., Schaffner, F. 1970. The effect of 3-amino-1,2-triazole on the phenobarbital-induced formation of hepatic microsomal membranes. *Mol. Pharmacol.* 6:231–39

169. Razin, S., Kahane, I. 1969. Hybridization of solubilized membrane components from different *Mycoplasma* species by reaggregation. *Nature London* 223:863–64

170. Razin, S., Ne'eman, Z., Ohad, I. 1969. Selective reaggregation of solubilized *Mycoplasma*-membrane proteins and the kinetics of membrane formation. *Biochim. Biophys. Acta* 193:277–93

171. Remmer, H. 1962. Drug tolerance. *Ciba Found. Symp. Enzymes Drug Action*, ed. J. L. Mongar, A. V. S. de Rueck, 276–300. London: Churchill

172. Remmer, H., Merker, H.-J. 1963. Enzyminduktion und Vermehrung von endoplasmatischen Reticulum in der Leberzelle während der Behandlung mit Phenobarbital. *Klin. Wochen Schr.* 41:276–83

173. Rodwell, A. W., Razin, S., Rottem, S., Argaman, M. 1967. Association of protein and lipid in *Mycoplasma laidlawii* membrances disaggregated by detergents. *Arch. Biochem. Biophys.* 122:621–28

174. Rossi, C. R., Sartorelli, L., Tato, L., Baretta, L., Siliprandi, N. 1965. Phospholipase A activity of rat-liver mitochondria. *Biochim. Biophys. Acta* 98:207–9

175. Rottem, S., Stein, O., Razin, S. 1968. Reassembly of *Mycoplasma* membranes disaggregated by detergents. *Arch. Biochem. Biophys.* 125: 46–56

176. Rouviére, J., Lederberg, S., Granboulan, P., Gros, F. 1969. Structural sites of RNA synthesis in *Escherichia coli. J. Mol. Biol.* 46:413–30

177. Sabatini, D. D., Blobel, G. 1970. Controlled proteolysis of nascent polypeptides in rat liver fractions. II. Location of the polypeptides in rough microsomes. *J. Cell Biol.* 45: 146–57

178. Sakagami, T., Minari, O., Orii, T. 1965. Behavior of plasma lipoproteins during exchange of phospholipids between plasma and erythrocytes. *Biochim. Biophys. Acta* 98:111–16

179. Sane, P. V., Goodchild, D. J., Park, R. B. 1970. Characterization of chloroplast photosystems 1 and 2 separated by a non-detergent method. *Biochim. Biophys. Acta* 216: 162–78

180. Sargent, M. G., Lampen, J. O. 1970. A mechanism for penicillinase secretion in *Bacillus licheniformis. Proc. Nat. Acad. Sci.* 65:962–69

181. Sarzala, M. G., van Golde, L. M. G., De Kruyff, B., van Deenen, L. L. M. 1970. The intramitochondrial distribution of some enzymes involved in the biosynthesis of rat-liver phospholipids. *Biochim. Biophys. Acta* 202:106–19

182. Sauner, M.-T., Levy, M. 1971. Study of the transfer of phospholipids from the endoplasmic reticulum to the outer and inner mitochondrial membranes. *J. Lipid. Res.* 12:71–75

183. Scallen, T. J., Schuster, M. W., Dhar, A. K. 1971. Evidence for a non-catalytic carrier protein in cholesterol biosynthesis. *J. Biol. Chem.* 246:224–30

184. Scherphof, G. L., van Deenen, L. L.

138 SIEKEVITZ

M. 1965. Phospholipase A activity of rat liver mitochondria. *Biochim. Biophys. Acta* 98:204–6

185. Schimke, R. T., Granschow, R., Doyle, D., Arias, I. M. 1968. Regulation of protein turnover in mammalian tissue. *Fed. Proc.* 27:1223–30

186. Schnaitman, C. A. 1969. Comparison of rat liver mitochondrial and microsomal membrane proteins. *Proc. Nat. Acad. Sci.* 63:412–19

187. Schnaitman, C. A. 1970. Examination of the protein composition of the cell envelope of *Escherichia coli* by polyacrylamide gel electrophoresis. *J. Bacteriol.* 104:882–89

188. Schrier, S. L., Giberman, E., Danon, D., Katchalski, E. 1970. Studies on ATPase in sheared micro vesicles of human erythrocyte membranes. *Biochim. Biophys. Acta* 196:263–73

189. Schor, S., Siekevitz, P., Palade, G. E. 1970. Cyclic changes in thylakoid membranes of synchronized *Chlamydomonas reinhardi*. *Proc. Nat. Acad. Sci.* 66:174–80

190. Schuldiner, S., Ohad, I. 1969. Biogenesis of chloroplast membranes. III. Light-dependent induction of proton pump activity in whole cells and its correlation to cytochrome *f* photooxidation during greening of a *Chlamydomonas reinhardi* mutant (*y*−1). *Biochim. Biophys. Acta* 180:165–77

191. Seiji, M., Yoshida, T. 1968. Enzymatic digestion of smooth surfaced membrane of mouse melanoma I. *J. Biochem. Tokyo* 63:670–74

192. Sellinger, O. Z., Borens, R. N., Nordrum, L. M. 1969. The action of trypsin and neuraminidase on the synaptic membranes of brain cortex. *Biochim. Biophys. Acta* 173:185–91

193. Shephard, E. H., Hubscher, G. 1969. Phosphatidate biosynthesis in mitochondrial subfractions of rat liver. *Biochem. J.* 113:429–40

194. Shuster, L., Jick, H. 1966. The turnover of microsomal protein in the livers of phenobarbital-treated mice *J. Biol. Chem.* 241:5361–65

195. Smith, M. E., Eng, L. F. 1965. The turnover of the lipid components of myelin. *J. Am. Oil Chem. Soc.* 42:1013–18

196. Smith, M. E. 1968. The turnover of myelin in the adult rat. *Biochim. Biophys. Acta* 164:285–93

197. Song, C. S., Rubin, W., Rifkind, A. B., Kappas, A. 1969. Plasma membranes of rat liver. Isolation and enzymic characterization of a fraction rich in bile canaliculi. *J. Cell Biol.* 41:124–32

198. Stackpole, C. W., Aoki, T., Boyse, E. A., Old, L. J., Lumley-Frank, J. de Harven, E. 1971. Cell surface antigens: serial sectioning of single cells as an approach to topographical analysis. *Science* 172:472–74

199. Stäubli, W., Hess, R., Weibel, E. R. 1969. Correlated morphometric and biochemical studies on the liver cell. II. Effects of phenobarbital on rat hepatocytes. *J. Cell Biol.* 42:92–112

200. Stein, Y., Widnell, C., Stein, O. 1968. Acylation of lysophosphatides by plasma membrane fractions of rat liver. *J. Cell Biol.* 39:185–92

201. Steiner, S., Sojka, G. A., Conti, S. F., Gest, H., Lester, R. L. 1970. Modification of membrane composition in growing photosynthetic bacteria *Biochim. Biophys. Acta* 203:571–74

202. Stoeckenius, W., Engelman, D. M. 1969. Current models for the structure of biological membranes. *J. Cell Biol.* 42:613–46

203. Strittmatter, C. F., Umberger, F. T. 1969. Oxidative enzyme components of avian liver microsomes. Changes during embryonic development and the effects of phenobarbital administration. *Biochim. Biophys. Acta* 180:18–27

204. Sugimura, T., Ikeda, K., Hirota, K., Hozumi, M., Morris, H. P. 1966. Chemical, enzymatic, and cytochrome assays of microsomal fraction of hepatomas with different growth rates. *Cancer Res* 26:1711–16

205. Swick, R. W., Rexroth, A. K., Stange, J. L. 1968. The metabolism of mitochondrial protein. II. The dynamic state of rat liver mitochondria. *Biochem. J.* 243:3581–87

206. Tachiki, K. H., Parlette, P. R., Pon, N. G. 1969. Water soluble spinach chloroplast chlorophyll-protein complexes prepared without added detergents or organic solvents. *Biochem. Biophys. Res. Commun.* 34:162–69

207. Taylor, C. B., Bailey, E., Bartley, W. 1967. Studies on the biosynthesis of protein and lipid components of rat liver mitochondria. *Biochem. J.* 105:605–9

208. Thines-Sempoux, D., Amar-Costesec, A., Beaufay, H., Berthet, J. 1969. The association of cholesterol,

5'-nucleotidase and alkaline phosphodiesterase I with a distinct group of microsomal particles. *J. Cell Biol.* 43:189–92

209. Tice, L. W., Barrnett, R. J. 1962. The fine structural localization of glucose-6-phosphatase in rat liver. *J. Histochem. Cytochem.* 10:754–62

210. Tillack, T. W., Carter, R., Razin, S. 1970. Native and reformed *Mycoplasma laidlawii* membranes compared by freeze-etching. *Biochim. Biophys. Acta* 219:123–30

211. Treble, D. H., Frumkin, S., Balint, J. A., Beeler, D. A. 1970. The entry of choline into lecithin, *in vivo*, by base exchange. *Biochim. Biophys. Acta* 202:163–71

212. Tremblay, G. Y., Daniels, M. J., Schaechter, M. 1969. Isolation of a cell membrane DNA-nascent RNA complex from bacteria. *J. Mol. Biol.* 40:65–76

213. Tuppy, H., Birkmayer, G. D. 1969. Cytochrome oxidase apoprotein in "petite" mutant yeast mitochondria. Reconstruction of cytochrome oxidase by combining apoprotein with cytohemin. *Eur. J. Biochem.* 8:237–43

214. Van den Bosch, H., van Golde, L. M. G., Eibl, H., van Deenen, L. L. M. 1967. The acylation of 1-acylglycero-3-phosphorylcholine by rat liver microsomes. *Biochim. Biophys. Acta* 144:613–23

215. Vernon, L. P., Shaw, E. R., Ke, B. 1966. A photochemically active particle derived from chloroplasts by the action of the detergent Triton X-100. *J. Biol. Chem.* 241:4101–9

216. Vorbeck, M. L., Martin, A. P. 1970. Glycerophosphatide biogenesis. I. Subcellular localization of cytidine triphosphate: phosphatidic acid cytidyl transferase. *Biochem. Biophys. Res. Commun.* 40:901–8

217. Wahl, P., Kasai, M., Changeux, J.-P. 1971. A study on the motion of proteins in excitable membrane fragments by nanosecond fluorescence polarization spectroscopy. *Eur. J. Biochem.* 18:332–41

218. Waite, M., Sisson, P., Blackwell, E. 1970. Comparison of mitochondrial with microsomal acylation of monoacyl phosphoglycerides. *Biochemistry (Wash.)* 9:746–53

219. Wallace, P. G., Huang, M., Linnane, A. W. 1968. The biogenesis of mitochondria. II. The influence of

220. Warren, L., Glick, M. C. 1969. Membranes of animal cells. II. The metabolism and turnover of the surface membrane. *J. Cell Biol.* 37:729–46

221. Watson, K., Haslam, J. M., Linnane, A. W. 1970. Biogenesis of mitochondria. XIII. The isolation of mitochondrial structure from anaerobically grown *Saccharomyces cerevisiae. J. Cell Biol.* 46:88–96

222. Weier, T. E., Stocking, C. R., Shumway, L. K. 1966. The photosynthetic apparatus in chloroplasts of higher plants. *Brookhaven Symp. Biol.* 19:353–74

223. Wessels, J. S. C. 1966. Isolation of a chloroplast fragment fraction with NADP⁺-photoreducing activity dependent on plastocyanin and independent of cytochrome *f. Biochim. Biophys. Acta* 126:581–83

224. White, D. C. 1964. Differential synthesis of five primary electron transport dehydrogenases in *Hemophilus parainfluenzae. J. Biol. Chem.* 239:2055–60

225. White, D. C., Frerman, F. E. 1968. Fatty acid composition of the complex lipids of *Staphylococcus aureus* during the formation of the membrane-bound electron transport system. *J. Bacteriol.* 95:2198–209

226. White, D. A., Hawthorne, J. N. 1970. Zymogen secretion and phospholipid metabolism in the pancreas. Phospholipids of the zymogen granule. *Biochem. J.* 120:533–38

227. Widnell, C. C., Unkeless, J. C. 1968. Partial purification of a lipoprotein with 5'-nucleotidase activity from membranes of rat liver cell. *Proc. Nat. Acad. Sci.* 61:1050–57

228. Williams, M. L., Bygrave, F. L. 1970. Incorporation of inorganic phosphate into phospholipids by the homogenate and by subcellular fractions of rat liver. *Eur. J. Biochem.* 17:32–38

229. Wilson, G., Fox, C. F. 1971. Biogenesis of microbial transport systems: evidence for coupled incorporation of newly synthesized lipids and proteins into membrane. *J. Mol. Biol.* 55:49–60

230. Wirtz, K. W. A., Zilversmit, D. B. 1968. Exchange of phospholipids between liver mitochondria and

microsomes *in vitro. J. Biol. Chem.* 243:3596–602

231. Wirtz, K. W. A., Zilversmit, D. B. 1969. Participation of soluble liver proteins in the exchange of membrane phospholipids. *Biochim. Biophys. Acta* 193:105–16

232. Wirtz, K. W. A., Zilversmit, D. B. 1970. Partial purification of a phospholipid exchange protein from beef heart. *Fed. Eur. Biochem. Soc. Lett.* 7:44–46

233. Yamamoto, H. Y., Vernon, L. P. 1969. Characterization of a partially purified photosynthetic reaction center from spinach chloroplasts. *Biochemistry (Wash.)* 8:4131–37

234. Zahler, W. L., Fleischer, B., Fleischer, S. 1970. Gel electrophoresis patterns of the proteins of organelles isolated from bovine liver. *Biochim. Biophys. Acta* 203:283–90

235. Zahler, W. L., Saito, A., Fleischer, S. 1968. Removal of structural protein from mitochondria. *Biochim. Biophys. Res. Commun.* 32:512–18

236. Zahler, P., Weibel, E. R. 1970. Reconstitution of membranes by recombining proteins and lipids derived from erythrocyte stroma. *Biochim. Biophys. Acta* 219:320–38

237. Zilversmit, D. 1971. Exchange of phospholipid classes between liver microsomes and plasma: comparison of rat, rabbit and guinea pig. *J. Lipid Res.* 12:36–42

TRANSPORT MECHANISMS IN THE TELEOSTEAN GILL AND AMPHIBIAN SKIN   1076

RENÉ MOTAIS AND FEDERICO GARCIA-ROMEU

Laboratoire de Physiologie Cellulaire et Groupe de Biologie Marine du C.E.A.
Faculté des Sciences-06-Nice France

INTRODUCTION

Writing a review on transepithelial transport mechanisms within the limits imposed here is possible only if a choice of certain precise topics is made. We have decided to restrict ourselves to mechanisms in the teleostean gill and amphibian skin because so much has been published relating to these that numerous aspects of interest can be considered. Even among these, a choice must be made, a necessarily arbitrary one based on the personal experiences of the authors, their views of the problems involved, and their desire to express them clearly. For these reasons we have resisted the temptation to include many references, citing only those works that are pertinent to the discussion of the problems analyzed rather than those of perhaps greatest intrinsic importance. We have limited ourselves to a study of sodium and chloride since they are the principal ions transported across the epithelia in the groups considered.

Studies on the amphibian skin have greatly advanced our knowledge of transport mechanisms. The frog skin has acquired such a key position for two reasons: firstly, it can be studied with relative ease in vitro, and secondly, it was with this material that Ussing and his colleagues laid the rational foundations of the subject. Although skin and gill have many functional resemblances the gill has proved to be a much more difficult organ to study in vitro; research into the transport mechanisms in fish has therefore been conducted mainly in vivo. In view of this fundamental difference in approach, we have considered it wise to avoid over-simplified generalizations based on results obtained from the two vertebrate groups.

We sincerely hope that readers will regard our proposed interpretations with constructive scepticism, for it is in this spirit that we have allowed ourselves the liberty to express such hypotheses.

Excellent reviews on the role of hormones in the regulation of hydromineral metabolism in the lower vertebrates have recently been published, and the interested reader can refer to them for comprehensive information (7, 106, 123). In other publications concerning transport mechanisms he will find either a different approach or data complementary to ours (25, 82, 155, 178, 188).

141

THE TELEOSTEAN GILL

The ionic concentration of fish blood is relatively independent of that of the external medium in both stenohaline and euryhaline teleosts. Since seawater and freshwater environments are, respectively, hypertonic and hypotonic to the blood of fishes, and since some parts of the external boundaries are permeable to water, ionic and water regulations are required for the survival of fishes. The principles governing these regulations have been formulated by Smith (168) and Krogh (93).

In freshwater, water enters through the gills and the excess is eliminated by the kidneys. Passive losses of Na^+ and Cl^- in the urine and as a result of diffusion along the electrochemical gradient are compensated by active salt absorption through the gills. These Na^+ and Cl^- exchanges between the fish and the external medium bring about a renewal of the internal electrolytes. The rate of this renewal, which can be measured by means of radioactive isotopes, is very low: about 0.2% of the internal sodium per hour (124).

In seawater, to replace body water lost along the osmotic gradient, the teleost swallows the external medium, and water together with salt is absorbed by the gut. The mechanism of this solute-linked water absorption is now well known (138, 166, 167, 182). To abolish the salt load incurred by drinking seawater, the fish eliminates the monovalent ions by the gills, as the kidney is unable to secrete hypertonic urine. The kidney function is characterized by reduction of the free water clearance and excretion of divalent ions (63, 94, 139). By using radioactive tracers, it can be seen that sodium and chloride turnovers involve amounts of salt more than ten times greater than can be accounted for by gut absorption and gill excretion (124, 125, 134, 149). This phenomenon is of importance and can be explained as follows: The intestinal absorption of salt represents only a small fraction (about one tenth) of the total NaCl influx. The bulk of the sodium enters through the gill (132), which is also responsible for the total excretion of NaCl absorbed, whether through the gills or through the intestine, since the renal salt excretion is negligible (94, 125). The marine teleostean gill is thus extremely permeable to electrolytes. It would seem a priori that only a small fraction of these transfers, the net flux compensating for the intestinal absorption, would have a physiological significance. Measurements of the ionic permeabilities of the gills of other groups of salt water animals which possess the characteristic low salt concentration in the body fluids, show that the unidirectional ionic fluxes of hypo-osmotic regulators such as the crustaceans *Artemia* (20, 169, 175) and *Sphaeroma* (Thuet, personal communication) are also very high while those of isosmotic species such as the elasmobranchii (113, 142) are very low. It would appear, therefore, that it is not the presence of an important ionic concentration gradient between external and internal media which is responsible for these high unidirectional fluxes, but rather, it is the presence of an osmotic gradient. These ionic movements, apparently without significance, would thus seem to be involved in the maintenance of the water balance. This hypothesis will be discussed later.

The teleostean gill is thus the most important osmoregulatory organ in both fresh- and seawater. We shall first show that different types of euryhaline and stenohaline fish can be defined simply by analyzing the evolution of their branchial ionic fluxes in an altered environment. Next, we will consider how the gill brings about this electrolyte "handling," and then thirdly we will examine the gill's regulatory function with respect to water movements. Finally, we will propose two possible models of the mode of functioning of the marine fish gill, incorporating experimental results which until now have proved difficult to interpret.

The Different Forms of Euryhalinity

In seawater the gill is very permeable to Na and Cl. What takes place when a marine fish is suddenly transferred to freshwater? In the absence of sodium in the external medium, the sodium influx stops immediately. The outflux, a function of the internal sodium concentration, should remain unchanged and, because of the huge sodium outflux in seawater, this should result in a rapid diminution of the internal sodium. As the same would happen with the chloride, transference from seawater to freshwater would therefore normally result in rapid demineralization and death of the fish. But certain fish, known as euryhaline, survive such sudden changes of salinity, and must therefore possess regulatory mechanisms which more or less rapidly stop this electrolyte outflux. The description and the analysis of this regulation have been given by Motais (125) and by Motais, Garcia-Romeu & Maetz (128).

Considering first a euryhaline fish, the flounder (*Platichthys flesus*), transference from seawater to freshwater can be shown to cause practically no change in this fish's internal sodium and chloride concentrations. Regulation in this species must be very rapid and efficient. It has been studied by analyzing the sodium outflux after rapid changes of external salinity. Transference from sea to freshwater results in an instantaneous and very important (90%) reduction of the sodium outflux, which is reversible if the stay in freshwater does not exceed half an hour, for on placing the fish in seawater the outflux readjustment is instantaneous (Figure 1a). These outflux changes have been called "instantaneous regulation" (128). A longer period in freshwater (Figure 1b) results in a second outflux reduction which is more progressive and suggestive of a "deferred regulation." This deferred regulation causes the impermeabilization of the gill to Na, since upon replacing the fish in seawater after such a period, the outflux readjustment is progressive. The chloride outflux changes are similar.

The stability of the internal medium of the flounder after a rapid salinity change is thus the result of the swift and particularly efficient intervention of these two types of regulation. However, the two differ in nature: the instantaneous regulation does not change the potential permeability of the gill, since the gill recovers its previous characteristics immediately upon returning to seawater after such regulation, whereas the deferred regulation

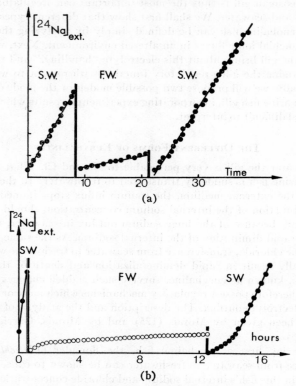

FIGURE 1a. Evolution of the Na outflux of seawater-adapted flounder transferred from seawater to freshwater and then replaced in seawater. The fish is kept in freshwater for 15 minutes. Ordinate, external concentration of ^{24}Na in arbitrary units, abscissa, time in minutes.

FIGURE 1b. Evolution of the outflux of seawater-adapted flounder from seawater to freshwater and then replaced in seawater. The fish is kept in freshwater for several hours. Ordinate, external concentration of ^{24}Na in arbitrary units, abscissa, time in hours.

lowers the membrane permeability, which suggests that a structural modification has taken place.

Taking now a stenohaline fish, the seaperch (*Serranus* sp.) (Figure 2), the outflux is only very slightly reduced upon transference from seawater to freshwater. In fact, if the freshwater is made isotonic to seawater by addition of mannitol (to eliminate the solvent drag effect) there is no reduction at all. The absence of any regulation leads naturally to the demineralization and rapid death of the fish.

The flounder and the seaperch represent two extreme types of fish. Intermediate types exist: for example, the euryhaline *Fundulus* and the stenohaline *Scorpaena* (Figure 3).

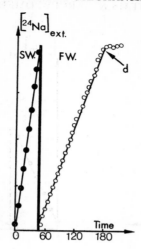

Figure 2. Evolution of the Na outflux of *Serranus* transferred from seawater to freshwater. Time is in minutes. *d* indicates death of animal.

In *Fundulus* the instantaneous regulation is hardly apparent since the fish undergoes demineralization during the first half hour after transfer, before the deferred regulation reduces and then stops further demineralization. Thus *Fundulus* survives a changed medium, but the ionic composition of its internal medium becomes changed in the process (128) and it appears probable that it is at the level of the various internal organs that ionic regulation occurs. Such a euryhaline can be defined as an *osmoconformer*,[1] in contrast to the flounder which is an *osmoregulator* (125).

In the stenohaline *Scorpaena*, there is, rather surprisingly, a very well marked instantaneous regulation (the outflux diminution is not a drag effect), but this is never followed by deferred regulation. Demineralization is slow, thanks to the instantaneous regulation, so the fish can survive several days in freshwater (29). *Scorpaena* can be defined as a stenohaline osmoregulator as opposed to *Serranus* which is a stenohaline osmoconformer.

From a consideration of the above types of fish certain generalities can be made:

By definition, a euryhaline fish is one which can resist a transference from seawater to freshwater and then adapt to the new medium. For this adaptation the fish must possess or acquire in freshwater the branchial mechanism of active ion absorption. During the period of ionic unbalance, euryhalinity is revealed by the existence of deferred regulation and not by that of instan-

[1] Prosser (153) defined physiological adaptations as any functional property of an individual which favors continued successful living in an altered environment and argued that there are two extreme ways of adapting: (*a*) alteration of the internal state with the environment (physiological *conformity*), (*b*) maintenance of relative constancy of the internal state (physiological *regulation*).

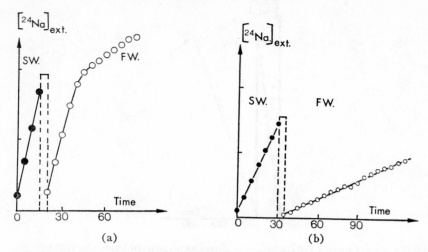

FIGURE 3. Evolution of the Na outflux of *Fundulus* (a) and *Scorpaena* (b) transferred from seawater to freshwater. Times in minutes. In *Scorpaena*, there exists an instantaneous regulation but no evidence of a deferred regulation. In *Fundulus*, there is no evidence of an instantaneous regulation but there is deferred regulation.

taneous regulation. The extent to which the latter is present only determines the type of euryhalinity: that of an osmoregulator or of an osmoconformer (125). The above definition has a dynamic significance: it is concerned with the evolution of the internal medium in the period following transfer but is not necessarily restricted by the levels of the ionic concentrations after adaptation. Thus, the level of plasmatic sodium is significantly higher in the eel in seawater than in freshwater, while in *Fundulus*, an osmoconformer, it is similar in the two media.

The length of survival of a stenohaline fish in a dilute medium is a function of two parameters: the degree of instantaneous regulation and the rate of electrolyte renewal. It is evident that the higher the renewal rate, the higher the outflux, and the shorter the survival time.

It should be stressed that from an ionic point of view the most important modification occurring during freshwater adaptation is the reduction of branchial permeability. Even if the fish is only kept in freshwater for a short period (a few hours for example), the gill retains a low ionic permeability for several hours after return to seawater (124, 125, 150). The longer the period in freshwater, the longer does this impermeabilization persist (124, 125). This clearly indicates that the high Na and Cl renewal rates of a seawater adapted gill cannot be interpreted as an inward leakiness through a freshwater type of gill, but must really be due to an increased branchial permeability in salt water which should thus be considered as a necessary condition for life in seawater. Although the advantages of a low ionic permeability in freshwater are obvious, those of a high permeability in seawater are not so evident. We have already suggested above that these ion movements are probably related to the water balance.

MECHANISMS UNDERLYING BRANCHIAL NaCl FLUXES

The ionic uptake mechanisms in freshwater.—It is certain that freshwater teleosts absorb both Na^+ and Cl^- actively (55, 86, 109).[2] It should be noted however that in contrast to that of amphibians, the transepithelial electric potential is always negative with respect to the blood (42, 69, 111). That of the trout is the only known exception (81). The system of active Na transport obeys saturation kinetics (81, 109) and the rate of absorption is controlled by the internal Na^+ level (109). Chloride absorption is practically zero in the eel (56), but is roughly equal to that of Na^+ in the gold fish (55, 92). Chloride balance seems to be achieved by more complicated feedback mechanisms than those prevailing for Na^+ (84, 109).

As in the amphibians, Na^+ and Cl^- absorptions are brought about by two independent mechanisms (55, 81, 93), whereby the external cation and anion are exchanged against endogenous ions of the same charge. The only endogenous ions suitable to play this role are NH_4^+, H^+ and HCO_3^-. The ammonium ion, the principle breakdown product of ammonotelic aquatic animals, is excreted mainly by the gill, which is also the site of Na absorption (110) and would therefore seem well suited to be the sodium counterion (93). The fact that the Na^+ influx can be modified by adding ammonium salts to the external medium or by injecting them into the fish supports this hypothesis (56, 81, 112, 125), but it has been shown that, at least under certain conditions, the amount of sodium absorbed is not equivalent to that of ammonium excreted (81, 186). For these cases a Na^+/H^+ exchange has been suggested (81). At the present, two possibilities must be retained: according to the first hypothesis (110), a Na^+/NH_4^+ exchange normally occurs, but when Na^+ absorption is higher than NH_4 excretion, the excess influx corresponds to a Na^+/H^+ exchange. When Na^+ absorption is lower than NH_4^+ excretion, the ammonium is excreted in two forms: the ionized in exchange with Na^+ and the rest in molecular form. According to the second hypothesis (81), only the Na^+/H^+ exchange occurs, with the ammonium being excreted by simple diffusion.

The H^+ ion which directly, or indirectly in combination with NH_3, is exchanged with Na^+ would appear to be formed by the hydration of CO_2 (112). Carbonic anhydrase inhibition by Diamox does, in fact, inhibit Na^+ absorption (81, 105). The fact that the gill excretes CO_2 in excess of that necessary to satisfy a Cl^-/HCO_3^- exchange, the presence of carbonic anhydrase in the gill epithelium, and the inhibition of Cl^- absorption by acetazolamide (112), all point to the existence of a Cl^-/HCO_3^- exchange as

[2] Recently, it has been shown that fresh water teleosts absorb I^- actively through the gills. This uptake mechanism, which is different from the Cl^- one, is controlled by circulating thyroid hormones (99).

originally proposed by Krogh (93). That the Cl⁻ influx can be modified by varying the external or internal HCO_3 concentrations (112) provides further evidence. Direct proof of the existence of an obligatory Cl^-/HCO_3^- exchange has been furnished by Dejours (23) who showed that CO_2 excretion was strictly dependent on the presence of Cl⁻ in the external medium. Na-K ATPase has been found in the gill epithelium of freshwater fish (36, 79, 80, 127). Its role is relevant here. According to the simplest hypothesis, Na absorption involves transfers across two successive membranes—the external and the internal. As no Na^+/K^+ exchange occurs between the gill and the external medium, the internal membrane is the more likely site of the Na-K ATPase. To account for the discrepancy between the relatively high Michaelis constant Km of the enzyme in both the trout (81) and the eel (126) and the low Km of the Na absorption in these fish (81, 109), the only possible model is that of an obligatory coupled exchange Na^+/H^+ or Na^+/NH_4^+ at the outer membrane, with the completion of the Na^+ transport across the inner membrane brought about by the Na-K ATPase (81).

The ionic transfer mechanisms in seawater.—The most important advances in our understanding of the mechanisms of ionic exchanges across the gill in seawater have been due to experiments such as we described earlier in which fish were subjected to rapid changes of salinity.

The first, instantaneous, regulation which occurs in certain fish such as the flounder (Figure 1) is apparent as soon as the salinity is changed. The modification of the outflux is a response to the changed electrolyte concentration and not to the osmotic pressure variation (125, 128). Furthermore, the outfluxes of Na and of Cl may be modified independently: thus a lack of Na in the external medium results in a very considerable reduction of the Na outflux (Na free effect) but leaves the Cl outflux unchanged, and conversely, the removal of external Cl causes a reduction of Cl outflux (Cl free effect) without affecting the Na outflux. In several species of fishes, transfer from seawater to freshwater is accompanied by such Na and Cl free effects (40, 96, 97, 149, 152). From these results the following can be concluded:

1. In fish, the Na and Cl transfers are on the whole independent.

2. Since the Na and Cl fluxes may act in diametrical opposition, the instantaneous regulation cannot be explained in terms of modifications of the branchial hemodynamics permitting the alternative irrigation of permeable and impermeable zones.

3. The phenomenon of greatest significance is the influence exerted by the lack of a certain ion in the external medium on the outflux of this same ion. The simplest hypothesis so far advanced to explain these "trans" effects is that of exchange diffusion (176). According to Ussing's model, the membrane contains a mobile carrier which can only cross the membrane in the compound form of "carrier+ion." Thus, if the carrier picks up an ion at the external face of the membrane, then crosses it and liberates the ion at the internal face, it can only recross the membrane if it picks up a similar ion

from the internal compartment. The carrier is thus responsible for a strict linkage of the influx and outflux of any given ion. Such an exchange can be revealed only by using isotopes: its energy requirements are minimal and it does not result in any net transport of ions. Motais et al and Motais (125, 128) have interpreted the Na and Cl free effects seen in certain fish as evidence of the existence of such exchange mechanisms, specific for Na^+/Na^+ and Cl^-/Cl^- exchanges. As these cannot be responsible for net fluxes of ions, the excretion of NaCl to offset the intestinal absorption, as in the osmoregulatory system of Smith, must be accomplished by some other mechanism. The experiments of Kamiya (78) on in vitro eel gills suggest that the Na excretion is dependent on a Na^+/K^+ exchange. Such an exchange has been demonstrated in vivo by Maetz (107) in flounders. More recently, we have shown for the eel (Motais & Isaia, unpublished data) that when ouabain, a specific inhibitor of Na/K exchanges, is added to the external medium there is an instantaneous 10–20% inhibition of the Na outflux and, after 24 hours, a significant increase of the internal sodium concentration. This must indicate that the Na^+/K^+ pump is localized on the external cell face and that it is responsible for only a small part of the Na transfers. The Na^+-K^+ ATPase activity recorded in the gills of various marine fish (36, 76, 79, 85, 126, 127) must have a bearing on this ouabain-sensitive Na^+/K^+ pump. The role of the ATPase in the mechanism of Na excretion is borne out by the recorded parallel variations of enzymatic activity and branchial ion exchanges after hypophysectomy (36), cortisol treatment (35) or actinomycin treatment (127). Nevertheless, no ouabain effect has been observed in the flounder or seaperch (Motais & Isaia, unpublished data).

With regard to a pump for Cl excretion, no experimental evidence is available, but, to account for the transepithelial potential measured, it has been suggested that the pump is electrogenic (109).

In marine teleosts, such as the flounder, which are capable of an instantaneous regulation, therefore, the branchial ionic mechanisms would appear to consist of two processes, more or less directly linked: an exchange diffusion system for the Na^+ and Cl^-, and an excretory system consisting of a Na^+/K^+ exchange pump for the excretion of Na^+ and a Cl^- extrusion pump of an as yet hypothetical nature.

In marine teleosts, such as the seaperch, in which no instantaneous regulation occurs, the branchial ionic mechanisms remain to be determined. One might infer, by analogy, that in addition to pumps for the excretion of Na and Cl (possibly identical to those of the above group) there would exist Na/Na transfers, either diffusional and therefore independent, or although carrier-mediated, not rigidly linked if the shuttle were capable of crossing the membrane in its uncoupled form.

Recently, the interpretation of the Na free effect in terms of exchange diffusion has been criticized. The objections raised are of two kinds. Firstly, Maetz (107) clearly demonstrated a competition between Na_{ext} and K_{ext} and concluded that as in the human erythrocyte, Na^+/Na^+ and Na^+/K^+ exchanges are mediated by the same transporter. This suggestion is of interest because a more or less direct relationship between these two exchanges does seem to exist (114, 126). If this is the case however, any specific inhibitor of the Na^+/K^+ exchange, such as ouabain, should also inhibit the Na^+/Na^+ exchange (59). But this does not agree with recent results on the eel (see above). The results of Maetz can be interpreted as indicating that the Na^+/Na^+ exchange is catalyzed by a specific transporter which is insensitive to ouabain and that it is for this transporter that competition between Na_{ext} and K_{ext} occurs.

Secondly, even the occurrence of exchange diffusion of Na in marine teleosts has been questioned. The crustacean *Artemia salina* shows well marked Na free and Cl free effects (20, 169, 175). A study of the flux-force relationships in this species lead Smith (169) to postulate an active extrusion together with an exchange diffusion component for the Cl, but only diffusional movements for the Na. As the transepithelial potentials are similar in marine fish to those he found in the brine shrimp, it was suggested that in the marine teleostean gill in addition to the excretory pumps, there is an exchange diffusion for chloride but that the nonactive Na outflux component is purely diffusional. This hypothesis is supported by the fact that increasing the Na_{int} results in a partial uncoupling of the influx and outflux (121). However, the outflux increase resulting from salt loading may simply be a result of stimulation of the excretory pump. The results shown in Figure 2 in the publication of Maetz (107) are difficult to interpret in terms of this hypothesis of diffusional Na movements, for, as previously discussed (109), replacing 5 mM KCl by 5 mM NaCl cannot change the potential sufficiently to explain the huge change in Na outflux observed experimentally. On the other hand, this result can be explained if K is competing for the exchange diffusion carrier.

With our current knowledge, the possibility that purely diffusional sodium movements occur cannot be dismissed. Confirmation of these depends on analyses of flux-force relationships. But in such an analysis the point of reference regarding both the potential and the ionic concentration should be the transport cell, not the blood (see scheme proposed at the end of this article). The same would apply to the brine shrimp.

Instantaneous regulation has no effect on the potential permeabilities of the gill to Na or Cl: suppression of Cl_{ext} for example, blocks the Cl transfer mechanism but this functions again immediately the Cl_{ext} returns. Deferred regulation on the other hand, impermeabilizes the branchial epithelium, which suggests a structural modification (see above). The results of Motais et al (128) and Motais (125) expressed in terms of the exchange diffusion concept, suggest an interesting interpretation of this deferred regulation.

The extent of the "Na free effect" is a function of the difference of Na concentrations of the adaptation medium and that of the medium to which the fish is transferred. If the branchial influx and the exchange diffusion component of the outflux are plotted against different values of Na_{ext} the result is a curve which fits the well known Michaelis Menten equation. Such saturation kinetics are to be expected of a carrier-mediated process such as exchange diffusion. As Figure 4 shows, the observed flux variations of three groups of fish adapted to three different salinities (SW, 1/2 SW, 1/4 SW) are in good accordance with saturation kinetics but the maximum flux, representing the "capacity" of the transport system, differs in the three groups. The Michaelis constant, Km, which is an expression of the "affinity" of the carrier for Na, is on the contrary identical in the three groups. This suggests that adaptation to reduced salinities does not induce a modification in structure, but induces only a reduction in the quantity of exchange diffusion transporter present in the gill. The effect of a salinity change may be followed on Figure 4. A' represents the exchange diffusion component of the outflux Δf_{out} at the sodium concentration of seawater in a seawater adapted fish. If the external concentration falls to 1/4 SW the outflux diminishes along the curve to B'. This diminution corresponds to the instantaneous regulation. If the fish is now adapted to 1/4 SW the outflux progressively decreases to B'' as adaptation proceeds. This outflux drop corresponds to the deferred regulation. It is thus the result of a reduction in the quantity of available carrier (by partial destruction or noncompetitive inhibition). Conversely, transferring a fish adapted to 1/4 SW to SW results in two successive increases of outflux: from B'' to A'' (instantaneous regulation) then from A'' to A' (deferred regulation involving synthesis or unmasking of the transporter). Antibiotics inhibiting protein synthesis have been used to investigate the molecular processes involved in this deferred regulation (115). The results suggest that two processes, unmasking and synthesis, are involved simultaneously.

The progressive functional variations accompanying adaptation may, however, be the result not only of molecular renewal within the transport cells (17), but also of renewal of the cells themselves, especially in the case of freshwater to seawater transfer when undifferentiated basal cells become chloride cells (16, 165).

Evolution of the Na-K ATPase of the gill during seawater adaptation.—The role of Na-K ATPase in Na absorption in the freshwater teleost has previously been discussed. The enzyme is generally considered to be involved in the branchial sodium excretion in marine stenohaline fish and in euryhaline fish adapted to seawater. Evidence for this is not only the existence of Na^+/K^+ exchanges discussed above, but also the fact that the enzymatic activity of the gills of stenohaline marine species is greater than that of stenohaline freshwater species (80), and similarly, that of seawater adapted euryhaline fish is higher than that of freshwater adapted ones (36, 79, 127). The question arises as to what the relationship is between the "freshwater ATPase" and the "seawater ATPase" in euryhaline species. The progressive increase of enzymatic activity brought about by the change from freshwater to seawater can be explained in several ways: either the freshwater enzyme

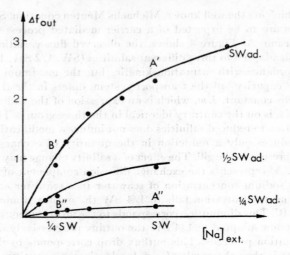

FIGURE 4. Exchange diffusion component of the outflux as a function of external Na concentration for three groups of fishes. *ad* signifies adapted. The curves have been calculated from the Michaelis-Menten equation $F = F_{max}C/Km + C$ to fit empirically the experimental data. The values are for

$$SWad: F_{max} = 4.20 \qquad Km = 400$$
$$1/2\,SWad: F_{max} = 1.55 \qquad Km = 400$$
$$1/4\,SWad: F_{max} = 0.35 \qquad Km = 400$$

Observed that the equations corresponding to the different adaptation media differ in their F_{max} values but not in the Km values. For discussion of A', A'', B', B'' see text.

disappears and is replaced by a seawater enzyme with improved efficiency or in higher concentration, or the two enzymes exist side by side. If the latter is the case, the freshwater enzyme either conserves its primitive functional characteristics (Na absorption) during seawater adaptation, or, like the seawater enzyme, turns to excreting Na, which implies a change of polarity of the enzyme in response to the increased salinity. Experimental data relative to these possibilities are scarce: the specific characteristics, especially the Km, of the seawater and freshwater enzymes of the eel are known to be different (126). Furthermore, injection of actinomycin D is without effect on the activity of the Na-K ATPase of the freshwater gill, whereas it significantly decreases the activity in the seawater gill (127). These results can be correlated with the lack of effect of the antibiotic on the sodium pump in freshwater whereas it causes a considerable impairment of the excretory pump in seawater (115). These results suggest that not only are these two Na-K ATPase pools in the seawater gill but also that the enzyme involved in the excretory pump has a shorter half-life than the freshwater enzyme. Finally, injection of ammonium chloride in the seawater adapted eel results in an increase Na_{int} which suggests that the Na uptake mechanism is still functional in seawater (126). The hypothesis of the juxtaposition in the seawater gill of two functionally different ATPases would therefore seem likely.

The role of the branchial Na-K ATPase during seawater adaptation remains obscure.[3] Thus, in the Japanese eel transferred from freshwater to seawater the enzymatic activity increases gradually during the first five days then more rapidly during the next two, and at the end of a month's adaptation has an even higher value (79). This progressive augmentation of enzyme (which parallels the increase of numbers of chloride cells (165, 183) contrasts with the rapid increase of Na exchanges, which in the European eel result in the complete readjustment of outflux within 48 hours (115, 126). If the discrepancy between these two phenomena is not due to specific differences in the two eels studied, it must mean that the permeabilization of the gill, that is the development of the excretory pump, during seawater adaptation is not closely dependent on the increase of Na-K ATPase. In any case, assuming that the proposed model of chloride cell function discussed later in this article is correct, the major part of the Na-K ATPase present in the gill plays no role in Na excretion, but simply intervenes in the functioning of the system of recycling ions.

The inducers of the increase of ionic permeability during seawater adaptation.—In a freshwater to seawater transfer, there are theoretically two ways in which the salt may act: directly on the outside of the transporting cells, or indirectly by increasing the Na_{int} and Cl_{int} as a result of dehydration or ingestion of seawater. An indirect internal action would seem most probable, and ingestion by the intestinal tract the factor of importance (84). The stimulus "variation of the internal NaCl concentration" probably acts indirectly, by some integrated mechanism such as endocrine secretion. The action of cortisol, which increases the ATPasic activity of the freshwater eel gill and thus facilitates the adaptation of the eel to seawater by augmenting its sodium excretory capacity (35), is an example of such an endocrine control. The importance of endocrine control in the gill and alimentary canal during osmoregulation has frequently been emphasised (48, 64, 65, 66, 67, 106, 108, 114, 116, 120, 131, 148, 181, 184).

BRANCHIAL WATER PERMEABILITY AND ITS REGULATION

According to the salinity of the external medium, teleosts have to resist either dehydration or excess internal water, and their organs compensating such effects must be capable of modulating their functional activities. This modulation is seen in the kidney as glomerular and tubular adjustments

[3] In euryhaline teleosts transferred from freshwater to seawater, the enzymatic activity also increases in the alimentary canal and decreases in the kidney (37, 76). There is no problem in interpreting such changes as they parallel changes in salt movement in these organs.

(63, 94) and in the alimentary canal[4] as changes in the efficiency of water reabsorption (102, 103, 138, 166, 167, 182) related to changes of Na-K ATPase activity (76, 138).

Initial unbalance after a change of external medium is a result of the permeability to water of the outer surfaces of the fish. Krogh (93), in view of what was known at that time, concluded that the gill surface, rather than the skin, was the principal "pathway" by which water moved "in and out of the fish." Recent work has confirmed this conclusion (84, 130). A certain number of workers have studied the diffusional and osmotic permeabilities of the gill (40, 41, 42, 43, 95, 97, 130, 131, 151). Although they are presumably strictly passive, water movements across the gill are also modulated with respect to the osmotic gradient: adaptation to an increased gradient results in a reduction of osmotic permeability (130). This permeability is considerably lower in seawater ($\Delta_{osm} = -800$ $mOsm/1$) than in freshwater ($\Delta_{osm} = +300$ $mOsm/1$). This impermeabilization of the gill to water, of obvious significance, is paradoxically accompanied by a considerable increase in "leakiness" to ions (see above). The mechanism responsible for these adaptive modifications of branchial water permeability are not clear. Comparing the osmotic permeability coefficient Pos and the diffusion coefficient Pd of several stenohaline and euryhaline fish at 20°C, Motais et al (130) have shown that freshwater fish always have a Pos higher than the Pd, the ratio varying from 2.5 to 6.0, whereas in marine fish the ratio is around 1.0. From thermodynamic considerations these results could indicate that water crosses the gills of marine fish by simple diffusion, whereas it passes by laminar flow through water-filled pores in the gills of freshwater fish. If this interpretation were correct, the adaptive mechanism underlying the reduction of osmotic permeability during adaptation to a higher salinity could correspond to the disappearance of the water-filled channels and their replacement by molecular pores (130). But the comparison of Pos and Pd, which forms the basis of this interpretation, involves assuming that the solute-solvent interaction is nil. It is not at all certain that this assumption is justified, especially in marine fish. To investigate a possible interaction, the permeabilities to sodium and water of the seawater eel have been studied at different temperatures (129). The results, although indicating a relative independence of the sodium and water movements, do not negate all possibility of an interaction. But they do supply interesting data on the evolution of the net flux with respect to temperature: at a low temperature, the in vivo net flux (i.e. the drinking rate minus the urine flow) is always lower than the theoretically "expected" net flux, calculated from the diffusion flux measured with tritiated water and the water concentrations of the external medium and of the blood, in other words $Pos/Pd \ll 1$. This is especially so at 5°C, at which temperature the osmotic net flux is very low: the drinking rate is 23.8 ± 6.4 μl

---

[4] Kirsch (84) has recently used an elegant technique to show that the drinking reflex is not set off by dehydration but represents a shock reaction, the shock being an osmotic one.

h^{-1} (100g)$^{-1}$ for 13 animals whereas the expected flux is 151 μl. Kirsch (84) records that even at 15°C, the seawater eel, kept for 2 months without any stress, has a practically negligible drinking rate.

These results show that in the seawater eel, the actual water loss is much lower than that which is to be expected from the permeability of the gill to tritiated water and the osmotic pressure differences between seawater and blood. Therefore, one must assume that either the apparent osmotic pressure difference is not the real osmotic gradient across the membrane or that there is a region of the gill specialized for the reabsorption of water against its activity gradient, a reabsorption linked with solute movements. These possibilities will be considered below.

An Attempt to Correlate Problematic Observations

The significance of some of the phenomena described above remains unclear: the increased ionic permeability of the gill when salinity increases the high ionic permeability of all marine teleosts and the loss of water by osmosis inferior to that expected at a given osmotic gradient. Our understanding of the processes concerned in osmoregulation must of necessity depend on a satisfactory interpretation of these phenomena. The aim of the following paragraphs is to propose an interpretation of the data which will stimulate further research.

The role of the chloride cells.—The mitochondria-rich cells were considered by Keys and Willmer (83) to be the site of ionic transport in the gills. The presence of a net chloride transport and the resemblance of these cells to the acid secreting cells of the stomach were the basis of this hypothesis and of the name "chloride-transporting cells" or CCs. Much evidence in favor of this suggestion has since been forthcoming (18, 122, 146, 147, 165) although no actual direct proof of the osmoregulatory role of the C.C. has yet been advanced. Keys' hypothesis has in fact been contested (28, 140, 141), but direct evidence against their supposed function is also lacking. No other specific function for this type of cell has been proposed. We suggest that these cells could well play a role similar to that of the tubular cells in the kidney and bring about the extrarenal excretion of various organic and inorganic substances—one of which is NaCl in marine fish. This suggestion is based on the following observations: heavy metal complexes and large molecules injected into the organism find their way to the microtubules (146); intracardiac injection of an organic base such as methylene blue is eliminated exclusively by the CCs (Masoni, Garcia-Romeu & Motais, unpublished data); the extrarenal excretion of urea and inulin is known to take place (98); and autohistoradiographic examination shows a preferential localization of these substances in the CC (Masoni, Garcia-Romeu & Motais, unpublished data). The presence of numerous chloride cells (28, 119) with well developed tubular systems in the gill of selachians is difficult to explain considering these animals' very low ionic permeability (113), if the only function of these cells is osmoregulatory. If, however, they serve to eliminate more complex molecules, their presence is understandable, as urinary excretion is of little importance in this group. In teleosts, the increase in number of CCs after transference from freshwater to seawater could be interpreted as an augmentation of extrarenal excretion necessitated by the reduced renal activity.

Without conclusive evidence of the specific function of this cell type, the two possible roles of the CC must be kept in mind.

Possible microcircuits for water and ions in the seawater gill.—According to which role the CC cells are considered to play, two different interpretations of the problematic observations discussed above are possible.

If the chloride cells function in osmoregulation and in the elimination of organic waste products: The respiratory epithelium, of which most of the branchial surface consists, is necessarily permeable to gases and thus to water. It must be across this epithelium that the greater part of the net water fluxes occur. In the marine teleost the measured water loss is lower than that "expected" (see above). This discrepancy can be explained by assuming that the osmotic loss through the respiratory epithelium is balanced by a water absorption in a different region of the gill. This water transport, although against its activity gradient, could occur coupled with solute movements. This hypothesis is supported by the facts that the permeability of the gill to ions increases considerably during seawater adaptation, and that gills of marine teleosts have a high ionic permeability. Assuming that the chloride cells are the site of most electrolyte transfers, water absorption could also be attributed to them. The specialized structure of the cells—in particular, the well-developed tubular system—can be easily interpreted in terms of a mechanism assuring this absorption. The suggested model (Figure 5a) is based on a "local osmosis" model proposed by Diamond (24). As there is no question about a net absorption of salt, the movement of water must be driven by a system of recycling ions within the cell, as has been postulated for cells in the rectal pad of insects (145). If the CC cells function according to this model, their NaCl concentration must be very high.

If the chloride cells function only in organic waste elimination: Extrarenal excretion, even when the fluid produced is hypertonic, nevertheless results in a loss of water from the organism in addition to the osmotic loss across the respiratory epithelium. As the measured water loss is already lower than the theoretical osmotic one, one is forced to assume that the loss through the respiratory epithelium is limited or nonexistent. This could be the case if the epithelial cells possess a mechanism similar to the double membrane model of Curran (21). This model (see Figure 5b) involves a system of recycling ions across the cell's basal membrane which is nonselective to the passage of water and salt (low reflection coefficient $\sigma = 0$). According to this model, the external membrane has a very high reflection coefficient for ions ($\sigma \neq 1$); in other words, it is practically impermeable to ions but permeable to water. In teleosts however, Na and Cl are known to cross the branchial epithelium

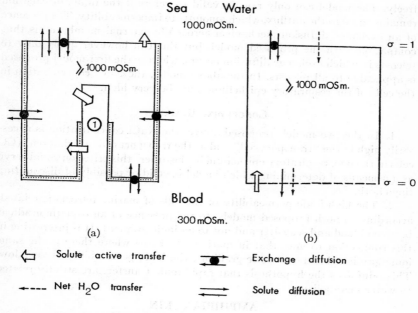

(a) (b)

FIGURE 5a. A hypothetical diagram showing how active transport and recycling of solute might cause a hypoosmotic absorbate to move across the *chloride cell* against an osmotic gradient. Movements of water are not shown on this diagram. The basal and lateral cell membranes and the basal part of the microtubule are considered to be impermeable to water. The large arrows indicate possible sites and direction of active transport of solutes. The localization of the greater part of the active transport at the tubular membranes agrees with the fact that the ATPase activity is principally located along the surface of the tubules (165), and that ouabin acts strongly on the Na net flux of isolated gills when it is administered by the internal circulation (78). The solute cycle between the two different parts of the tubule causes hypotonic fluid to flow down the channel which is in direct continuity with the internal medium. The external membrane is very permeable to both water and solutes, the latter moving across the membrane by diffusion (free or "facilitated") or by exchange diffusion according to the species of fish (see text). Active excretion at this membrane compensates for intestinal absorption of NaCl.

FIGURE 5b. A hypothetical mechanism whereby active transport and recycling of solute might cause a hypoosmotic absorbate to move across *cells of the respiratory epithelium* against an osmotic gradient.

This mechanism involves two barriers in series, one of which has restricted permeability to solutes relative to water ($\sigma = 1$), while the second is nonselective to passage of water and solute ($\sigma = 0$). Active transport of solute into the cell across the second membrane will create an osmotic gradient which in turn will cause water to flow into the cell from the external medium. Since the osmotic gradient across the nonselective membrane is ineffective there is no entry of water from the blood.

freely. The model can only remain valid therefore if the influx of each ion remains equal to the outflux, which amounts to impermeability. The presence of an exchange diffusion mechanism across the external membrane is thus compatible with the proposed model, but this can however apply only to teleosts in which exchange diffusion occurs, whereas the first model proposed is applicable to all teleosts. In the above model, the NaCl concentration in the cells of the respiratory epithelium must be very high.

CONCLUDING REMARKS

1. In the two models proposed above, the NaCl concentration is necessarily high in the "transport cell" and as the transport cells are different (CC cells in the one, respiratory epithelium in the other) this criterion could serve as a a means of determining which model is valid or possibly of discounting them both.

2. The high ionic permeability of the gills of marine teleosts is related, according to both proposed models, to the presence of an osmotic gradient between blood and seawater and not to an ionic gradient. It is interesting in this connection to note that in marine selachians where there is the same ionic gradient but no osmotic gradient, the ionic permeability is very low. This reinforces the hypothesis that rapid ionic transfers are strictly related to water metabolism.

AMPHIBIAN SKIN

IONIC TRANSPORT IN THE ISOLATED SKIN: MODELS

It is now 40 years since it was shown that isolated frog skin separating two Ringer solutions is capable of transporting NaCl towards the solution bathing the interior face (70, 71). Shortly afterwards, Krogh (91, 92) showed that salt-depleted frogs can absorb chloride and sodium actively from very dilute solutions (10^{-5}), and pointed out that the active uptake of salt must be of biological significance to the frogs in winter, when about 7 months are spent under water without food. Numerous studies have also been made to establish the relationship between the transepithelial potential difference and the ionic permeability of the skin (see 171).

Ussing and his co-workers, particularly Zerahn and Koefoed-Johnsen, were the first to propose a comprehensive interpretation of the data relating to ionic transport as known around 1950–1960. Ussing & Zerahn (180) evolved the short-circuit technique for the isolated skin as a means of eliminating the transepithelial electric potential gradient. When this is done, passive transport of a given ion can be recognized by the fact that if there is no concentration gradient of the ion in question across the skin, the unidirectional fluxes of the ion are identical. This elegantly simple technique has become the almost exclusive tool in the study of transepithelial ionic transport mechanisms. The experimental results on which Koefoed-Johnsen & Ussing's model of the ionic transport mechanism in the amphibian skin is based (89) may be summarized as follows:

1. The in vitro non-short-circuited skin transports sodium against its concentration gradient and against the electric potential gradient. Chloride on the other hand is transported along the electric gradient (177). The short-circuited skin, separating two Ringer solutions, shows an active transport of sodium, with a net flux equal to the short-circuit current, whereas chloride is transported passively (88, 180).

2. The spontaneous potential across the isolated frog skin develops as a result of the active transport of sodium and of the shunting effect of the anions; high chloride permeability is associated with low electric potential difference and vice versa (88, 90, 101, 180).

3. The transepithelial electric potential difference increases when the sodium concentration of the external solution increases, or when the potassium concentration of the internal solution diminishes. Variations of internal sodium or external potassium concentrations have no effect on the potential. When there is no anionic transport, transepithelial potential variations brought about by external sodium or internal potassium concentration changes are such as would be expected if barriers are present which are selectively permeable to sodium at the external face and to potassium at the internal face (89). The epithelial cells have high potassium and low sodium concentrations (75), and both the potential across the skin and the inward transport of sodium chloride are abolished if there is no potassium in the inside bathing solution (73, 75).

From these phenomena, Koefoed-Johnsen & Ussing (89) concluded that sodium diffuses passively into the cell across the outside, sodium-selective border and gives rise to a diffusion potential which makes the cell positive in relation to the outside. The cellular sodium concentration is assumed to be kept at a practically constant low level by active sodium transport across the internal border, which is permeable to potassium but almost completely impermeable to free sodium ions (as distinguished from sodium passing through the sodium pump). They considered the active transport mechanism to be a carrier-linked and possibly obligatory exchange of cellular sodium with potassium from the inside solution; this implies that the pump itself is not electrogenic. The free potassium ions will diffuse back from the cell into the inside bathing solution and give rise to another diffusion potential, making the inside solution positive in relation to the cell. Thus, potassium moves in the steady state in a closed circuit and causes no net gain or loss, and the active sodium/potassium exchange appears as a specific sodium transport. In the presence of an impermeant ion, therefore, the electric potential difference developed across the skin is equal to the addition of two diffusion potentials:

$$E = E_{Na} + E_K = \frac{RT}{F} \ln \left(\frac{Na_o}{Na_c} \cdot \frac{K_c}{K_i} \right)$$

where E is the total potential difference; E_{Na} and E_K the potential differences across the external and internal barriers respectively; R, T, and F the usual constants; Na and K the sodium and potassium concentrations; and o, c, and i represent the external, intracellular, and internal solutions respectively.

The osmotic behavior of the skin is that which can be deduced from the model when the sodium and potassium concentrations in the internal and external solutions are modified (104). Equally predictable from the model are two intraepithelial electric potential wells which certain authors have observed (34, 49, 189). It was subsequently apparent that the intraepithelial potential profile often has more than two (10, 154, 179).

Briefly, the essential characteristics of the model of Koefoed-Johnsen & Ussing are:

1. The presence of external and internal barriers selectively permeable to sodium and potassium respectively.

2. The passage of sodium through the external barrier by free diffusion.

3. At the internal barrier a neutral pump bringing about an obligatory sodium/potassium exchange.

4. The mechanism maintaining the steady-state concentration of sodium and potassium in the epithelial cells also being responsible for the trans-epithelial transport of sodium.

This initial model has had to be modified in the light of results obtained since 1958. Many new models have been proposed, varying to a greater or a lesser degree from the original model taken as a basis of reference. The following facts are inconsistent with Koefoed-Johnsen & Ussing's propositions:

1. Frequently the electric potential variation at the external barrier, even in the presence of an impermeant anion, does not lie on the theoretical slope of 58 mV to be expected from a ten-fold modification of the sodium concentration in the external solution (10, 179). This has been interpreted as evidence for a transport path for sodium and a shunt path for passive movements of sodium as well as of other ions; the shunt path would be partly between the cells (179). Although the external barrier should be selectively permeable to sodium, it can only act as a sodium electrode if the sodium crosses it by simple diffusion. This is not the case in the urinary bladder (52) or in the skin (8, 156) where the sodium crosses the external barrier by means of a saturable process (see below) which may partly account for the nonideal behavior of the external barrier. Furthermore, if sodium enters, even partly, in exchange for hydrogen (see below), one could assume that the hydrogen follows the transport path, and the external barrier cannot, therefore, function as an ideal sodium electrode but rather as a sodium electrode with a hydrogen error.

The transepithelial electric potential difference in relation to changes of the potassium concentration in the internal solution is in approximate accordance with that of a potassium electrode. Cereijido & Curran, however, have shown that only about 40 to 50 percent of the change in total potential difference can be ascribed to a change at a barrier between the tip of the microelectrode and the inside solution, while the remainder occurs between the electrode and the outside solution. Thus, the inner barrier does not appear to function as a potassium electrode, and the observed theoretical slope for the total potential may be fortuitous (10).

One must conclude therefore that the external and internal barriers do not behave as ideally permeable to sodium and potassium respectively.

2. In the urinary bladder sodium enters at the mucosal boundary in accordance with saturation kinetics (52), and other alkali metal ions, guanidine and aminoguanidine interfere competitively with its entry at this surface (50). Recently, various techniques have been evolved permitting direct measurement of the unidirectional uptake of sodium from the outside solution into the frog's skin (8, 15, 156). It has been shown that this uptake, while not inhibited by ouabain, is inhibited by potassium (156) or lithium (8) in the external solution. The sodium uptake of the epithelium is not a linear function of the sodium concentration, but appears to be composed of two components: a saturating one, and one that varies linearly with concentration (8). The effect of lithium would seem to be primarily on the saturating component and has the characteristics of competitive inhibition (8).

From the above, it seems probable that sodium enters the epithelium by a carrier-mediated process and not by simple diffusion (8, 15, 156).

3. In the model of Koefoed-Johnsen & Ussing, the current in the short-circuited skin is presumed to cross the internal boundary in the form of potassium ions diffusing down a concentration gradient. That being so, removing or inverting the potassium concentration gradient should abolish the short-circuit current. This, and active sodium transport, however, are maintained in short-circuited isolated frog skins exposed at their internal surfaces to potassium concentrations exceeding the estimated intracellular values (9, 87). These observations are consistent with the hypothesis that the sodium pump operates electrogenically (9, 87). Sodium transport is also electrogenic in the urinary bladder (51).

The existence of a Na^+/K^+ exchange with a 1:1 ratio can be discounted in view of the fact that there is no correlation between potassium influx from the internal solution into the epithelium and the transepithelial sodium net flux either in the bladder (39) or in the skin (22).

These experimental data would indicate that the sodium pump is electrogenic and that there is no obligatory sodium/potassium exchange.

4. One of the most attractive hypotheses in the Koefoed-Johnsen & Ussing model was that the mechanism assuring the cellular ionic equilibrium was identical to that concerned with the transepithelial sodium transport. Consequently, inhibition of the one function would also stop the other. This, however, is not the case, for it is possible to inhibit transepithelial sodium transport without affecting the ionic composition of the epithelium (22, 72, 100). It was therefore proposed that active sodium transport across the skin may be independent of the processes concerned with the maintenance of the cellular ionic composition (72), a proposition supported by

the observation that although potassium uptake at the inside of the skin is strongly dependent on the presence of internal sodium, no correlation exists between this potassium uptake and the transepithelial sodium net flux (22). Further observations are also in agreement with this hypothesis; for example, it has been shown that inhibition of the transepithelial sodium transport by ouabain does not affect the sodium transport pool (1, 38, 136), that is, that part of the intraepithelial sodium which equilibrates with external radiosodium; ouabain, on the other hand, causes a significant increase in the sodium (1, 38, 136) and reduction in the potassium (136) of a compartment communicating with the interior. A similar type of effect has been demonstrated in the toad bladder (62). Amiloride, an inhibitor of the transepithelial sodium transport acting on the influx of sodium into the epithelium (6, 19, 30), reduces the transport pool of the transport compartment without affecting the intracellular sodium which is exchangeable from the corium side (27, 135). The above interpretations of the effects of inhibitors on the sodium pool should be considered with a certain reserve since there is no proof that the external sodium equilibrates exclusively with the sodium transport pool (see below).

In short, the mechanism maintaining the steady-state concentrations of sodium and potassium in epithelial cells seems to be different from that responsible for the transepithelial sodium transport.

The problem of the compartmentalization of the epithelial sodium is pertinent to this discussion. At least two compartments are clearly concerned (1, 12, 13, 27, 135, 136), sodium transport involving one alone which, according to Cereijido & Rotunno (13) occurs throughout the epithelium. Many measurements of the sodium transport pool have been made (1, 5, 12, 68, 192). In spite of a certain variability in the data, all the results show that the sodium transport pool of the skin represents only a small fraction of the epithelial sodium; in the toad bladder, however, Finn (46) and Finn & Rockoff (47) found a sodium transport pool with a sodium content equal to about 30% of the total tissue sodium. A complex compartmentalization of sodium in toad bladder has been described (185). That the sodium transport pool represents the fraction of epithelial sodium equilibrating with the external radiosodium is a supposition common to all the published results, but this has not in fact been demonstrated, and the possibility of a sodium pool equilibrating with the exterior but not concerned with transport, should not for the moment be set aside.

The model of Koefoed-Johnsen & Ussing brought together a variety of phenomena concerned with the diffusion or active transport of ions. This synthesis was possible because the intraepithelial sodium was thought to be contained in a single compartment and because the cellular ionic equilibrium and the transepithelial transport were considered to be assured by the same mechanism. As we have seen above, these hypotheses no longer hold. It is relevant therefore to reconsider what conclusions can be drawn from the epithelial localization of ATPase (45), and the conductivities, ionic selectivities and potential differences across barriers now that their exclusive relationship with the transport compartment becomes less and less certain.

In view of the complexity of the problem, it would appear essential to approach it first by analyzing some of the more straightforward aspects, for instance, by trying to localize morphologically the transport compartment.

According to Voûte & Ussing (187) a marked reversible swelling of the outermost layer of the stratum granulosum ("first reacting cell layer") is observed during short-circuiting of the skin, contrasting with the homogeneous appearance of the epithelium under open circuit conditions. The authors proposed two hypotheses: (a) only the first reacting cell layer is concerned with the active sodium transport, and (b) the first reacting cell layer swells because all the sodium penetrating the epithelium enters it whereas only a part of this sodium attains the deeper regions which are also active in sodium transport. This latter hypothesis has been proposed several times (44, 45, 179). The problem has been restudied recently by Martinez-Palomo and co-workers (see 38), who showed that on the external border of the skin there are two barriers with different properties. Ruthenium red, a marker which does not traverse the tight junctions, passes from the interior through to the basal interspace of the stratum granulosum cells without entering these cells or traversing its tight junctions; from the external solution, it does not penetrate at all. Thus, the stratum corneum and stratum granulosum constitute a zone inaccessible to ruthenium red. Lanthane, on the other hand, when added to the external medium, penetrates into the stratum corneum cells and their interspaces but does not pass through the exterior tight junctions of the stratum granulosum cells. Erlij (38) tentatively suggests that the exterior barrier of the transport compartment is localized in the outside border of the stratum granulosum and even that the cells of this layer constitute the compartment concerned with transepithelial sodium transport.

An alternative to the interpretations involving a transcellular passage of sodium has been suggested by Cereijido & Rotunno (14). These authors propose a model whose essential feature is the location of the sodium-pumping route in the plasma membrane of the epithelial cells rather than through their cytoplasm. The main characteristics of the model may be summarized as follows: Sodium from the external solution reaches the outward-facing membrane and migrates over the outer leaflet of the plasma membrane from one sodium selective fixed negative charge to another. It passes through the zonula occludens and reaches the sodium-selective polar groups on the inner membrane. Pumps located all over the inward-facing membrane translocate the sodium from the sodium-selective polar groups to the intercellular spaces across the sodium impermeable barrier, which, according to the model, is located between the intercellular space and the polar groups where the sodium migrates. The overall effect of this system is to move the empty site towards the outward-facing membrane where more sodium can be absorbed.

The authors and their co-workers have reinterpreted various data in terms of the functioning of this model (11, 12, 15, 156). More recently,

Cereijido & Fraidenraich (11) add that the transporting compartment envisaged in the model need not be confined to the periphery of the cell but may be situated on membranes forming infoldings of the outer membrane. This model is commendable for many reasons, one of which is that it emphasizes the importance of fixed charges in transport; it also represents a conceptual framework on which future studies can be founded. A further merit of the model is to show that completely new interpretations are not only possible but desirable, as each interpretation has its own dynamism leading to the exploration of new problems. The fact that this model possesses such qualities does not necessarily mean that it gives an entirely correct explanation of ion transport; although attractive, we feel that no conclusive experimental support has yet been published confirming Cereijido & Rotunno's hypotheses.

COMPARISON OF SODIUM AND CHLORIDE TRANSPORT IN VIVO WITH TRANSPORT IN VITRO

In several species of anurans, the in vivo skin has been shown to absorb sodium and chloride independently from dilute external solutions. That the mechanism for sodium absorption is different from that of chloride is borne out by the following:

1. Either of these ions is absorbed without an accompanying ion when the latter is impermeant (2, 3, 4, 26, 58, 91, 92, 158).

2. Sodium and chloride can be absorbed in different amounts from a sodium chloride solution (58, 133, 157, 158).

3. A selective inhibition of the absorption of one of these ions can be produced experimentally, while the next flux of the other remains unchanged (58). In all these situations, the absorbed ion has to be exchanged against an endogenous ion of the same charge. Krogh (91, 92) suggested that chloride was exchanged against bicarbonate and sodium against ammonium but he did not produce any experimental evidence for the Na^+/NH_4^+ exchange. In fact, no direct evidence for the participation of ammonium in cationic exchange has yet been advanced, though the similarity between average ammonium excretion rate and sodium absorption rate in salamanders has been interpreted as supporting an Na^+/NH_4^+ exchange (2, 26). But, that these two rates should be similar does not prove that such an exchange occurs. This can only be done by measuring the two fluxes simultaneously on the same animals, and determining the degree of correlation. In both *Leptodactylus ocellatus* and *Calyptocephalella gayi*, two South American frogs, simultaneous measurements of the transepithelial net fluxes of sodium and ammonium show a much lower ammonium excretion than sodium absorption (57, 58). Nevertheless, in *Leptodactylus* a highly significant correlation does exist between the two fluxes (57), which has been provisionally interpreted as related to an acidification of the external medium brought about by the sodium transport mechanism (54). If the ammonium ion is not exchanged against sodium one may assume, for reasons of metabolic economy, that

hydrogen is the ion concerned; Ussing (177) and Huf et al (74) had proposed a sodium/hydrogen exchange to account for the difference between the sodium and chloride uptakes in the in vitro, non-short-circuited skin. If, when sodium is exchanged against hydrogen, chloride is at the same time exchanged against bicarbonate, the original stoichiometric relationship would become masked, and the reaction between bicarbonate and hydrogen would result in a temporary increase of CO_2 pressure in the external medium. Only if the chloride and sodium are not absorbed simultaneously, as for example when using solutions of choline chloride or sodium sulphate, is it possible to demonstrate the relation between absorbed and excreted ions (58). With this procedure a relationship between hydrogen excreted and sodium absorbed has been shown in *Calyptocephalella gayi* in vivo; a 1:1 ratio for these ions and a very high correlation coefficient ($r = 0.98$) show the linking of hydrogen and sodium in the exchange system. When *C. gayi* pumps chloride from choline chloride solutions there is a related base increase in the external bath with a very high and significant correlation coefficient between chloride uptake and base excretion ($r = 0.96$); nevertheless in all cases the base excreted exceeds the chloride absorbed. Both the buffering capacity of the excreted base and its pK indicate that is is bicarbonate (58). These results have recently been criticized (170), but in the light of experiments carried out under such different conditions that valid comparison with the above studies is not possible; in any case the criticisms are based on an ambiguous interpretation of the work in question.

The above results clearly show that independent mechanisms for sodium and chloride absorptions do exist, but the possibility of a mechanism linking the entrance of the two ions cannot be dismissed. Erlij (38) has suggested that a linked entrance of sodium and chloride coexists with the two independent mechanisms for the Na^+/H^+ and Cl^-/HCO_3^- exchanges, and considers that the relative importance of the coupled fluxes and independent fluxes could vary according to the circumstances (personal communication).

It has been shown that the in vitro frog skin can establish a H^+ gradient between the solutions bathing its two surfaces, acidifying the external solution and alkalizing the internal one. This phenomenon has recently been studied in the isolated skin of *Rana ridibunda* (33). A progressive acidification of the mucous side and alkalization of the serous surface were shown to occur, resulting in a difference of three or even more pH units between the two skin surfaces; the acidification, which is not due to metabolic CO_2, stops at an external pH of approximately five but may start again if the solutions are renewed. Emilio et al (33) did not find any relationship between the short-circuit current, measured periodically, and the hydrogen excretion. In *R. ridibunda* the short-circuit current measures the sodium net flux as in other *Rana* species (60) and one is forced to conclude that during short-circuiting the skin no longer transports hydrogen (54), for such a well-marked hydrogen flux would influence the short-circuit current. Thus, the sodium transport mechanism must be the motive force of the cationic exchange system and the hydrogen excretion must serve to equilibrate the charges—in other words, to act as a physiological short-circuit for the sodium transport. If the charges are equilibrated by an external circuit, as in the technique of Ussing & Zerahn, the linking of the two ionic fluxes disappears and only sodium continues to be transported (54).

Experiments using acetazolamide support these conclusions. On the in vitro short-circuited skin acetazolamide has no effect on sodium transport (33, 38) but inhibits hydrogen excretion. On the other hand, when it is administered in vivo at a does of 10^{-4} M it inhibits both sodium absorption and hydrogen excretion (Garcia-Romeu, Ehrenfeld & Motais, unpublished results). These results indicate that even if sodium absorption and hydrogen excretion are independent processes in vitro, they are not so in vivo. From what is known of hydrogen excretion, it would appear that this process is passive. More work under comparable experimental conditions is necessary to arrive at a better understanding of the differences between in vitro and in vivo skins with regard to sodium transport.

Our understanding of the chloride transport mechanism is severely limited by the fact that, except in certain rare cases (38, 118, 190, 191), this ion is passively transported in vitro (90). Since its transport in vivo is known to be active (26, 77, 91, 92) it would seem that the mechanism is damaged by the in vitro technique when both skin surfaces are bathed with Ringer solutions. At present not enough is known to furnish an explanation as to why the short-circuited skin does maintain an active chloride transport if its outer surface is bathed in a solution containing even as little as 2 mM chloride (38, 118). Under these conditions Erlij (38) has shown that acetazolamide inhibits chloride transport, but as we have seen above, not sodium transport. If the drug is administered in vivo, however, it inhibits both chloride and sodium transports, though not simultaneously (Garcia-Romeu, Ehrenfeld & Motais, unpublished results). The inhibition of chloride transport, both in vitro and in vivo, would suggest that the chloride/bicarbonate exchange is a more strictly linked process than the sodium/hydrogen exchange. Similar conclusions can be drawn from a different type of approach. Dietz, Kirschner & Porter (26) have shown that the transepithelial electric potential difference in *Ambystoma* larvae in vivo is determined by the external sodium concentration alone, the chloride concentration being without effect. The sodium and chloride mechanisms are nevertheless independent, and the authors suggest that the sodium pump is electrogenic, electroneutrality being maintained by a cation exchange system, while the chloride transport mechanism is not electrogenic and can function by means of a bicarbonate exchange.

There are no data concerning the effect of acetazolamide on the bicarbonate excretion of the skin, but the effect of the inhibitor on sodium and chloride absorption and on hydrogen excretion would be difficult to explain if, as has been stated (117), the skin contains no carbonic anhydrase. This enzyme has recently been shown to occur in the urinary bladder of the freshwater turtle *Pseudemys* (160) although previously it was thought to be absent in this tissue.

The relative independence of the sodium and chloride transport mechanisms would suggest that at least part of the anion and cation passages into the membrane occur at different sites. It is possible that fixed charges play an important role. The presence of membrane fixed charges (see 61, 174) could explain the following characteristics of ionic transport across the skin (54):

1. Na^+/H^+ and Cl^-/HCO_3^- exchanges: If pores with a negative charge (cationic exchanger) and others with a positive charge (anionic exchanger) occur in the skin, cation and anion fluxes could be independent of each other. In the ionic exchanger membranes the transport of ions of opposite charge to those fixed on the membrane would be facilitated, while that of co-ions would be retarded.

2. Effects of pH on Na^+ and Cl^- transport: Ussing (177) has shown that in the isolated non-short-circuited skin of *R. temporaria* raising the external pH increases the sodium influx and diminishes the chloride influx; conversely, acidification produces the opposite effect (see also 53, 159). These results can be explained by the differential effect of pH on the ionization of the positive and negative fixed charges of the membrane.

3. Development of "streaming currents": In a membrane performing ionic exchanges, pressure on one of the faces establishes an electric potential (streaming potential) by shifting the liquid pore, whose charge is determined by the counter ion. The streaming potential may be short-circuited, whereupon the current (streaming current) becomes a measure of the excess counterion transfer. Noutbourne (137) showed that small hydrostatic pressures on the isolated skin of *R. temporaria* increased the short-circuit current when the pressure was higher on the outside of the skin. These results suggest the presence of negative fixed charges in *R. temporaria* skin.

4. Effects of pH on cationic selectivity: In a cationic exchanger the selectivity sequence for the cations is largely determined by the strength of the negative charge field. A change in pH, altering this field, modifies the selectivity sequence. Acidification, which can cause a complete inversion of the selectivity sequence, changes the preference of the ionic exchanger towards ions of the smallest apparent hydrated diameter (25, 31, 32). Pesente (143, 144) states that at pH 5.0 the permeability order for the alkaline cations of the isolated skin of *R. esculenta* shifts to one in which the ion with the smallest hydrated diameter is prefered.

All these results indicate that membrane charges play an important role in sodium and chloride transport mechanisms.

Throughout this review, the importance of the independence of the sodium and chloride transport mechanisms has been stressed. Such mechanisms are widespread not only in the vertebrates but also in invertebrates (161, 162, 163, 164, 172, 173). We have emphasized this feature of transepithelial transport because, although important, it tends to be overlooked, and because future research relating to this phenomenon should prove fertile.

Nevertheless, we have no evidence for refuting the existence of a linked penetration of sodium and chloride into the skin. Under normal physiological conditions sodium and chloride uptakes are never completely isolated from one another. It is as important to study the mechanisms linking them as those which make their independence possible. An essential field of future research is the relative importance of the two types of process under different circumstances.

We have shown above how the technique of short-circuiting the isolated skin has resulted in great advances in our knowledge of transepithelial ionic transport. But, in spite of its advantages, this method has serious limitations. It was originally evolved to determine whether the transport of a given ion was active or passive, and its simplicity was one of its main attractions. The physiologist, who works by imposing simplicity on the natural complexity of physiological functions, however, may be inviting some troublesome consequences. This can be illustrated by our imperfect knowledge of the chloride transport mechanism for chloride is usually transported passively in vitro. All too frequently, processes which initially appeared simple have turned out to be full of unexpected complications, the significance of which still remains obscure. We feel that the moment has arrived to take a new look at old problems. The functioning of the in vivo skin should be considered as the point of reference from which to compare results obtained on the isolated skin; in this way the limitations incumbent to each method may be minimized. Such a comparative approach should enrich our understanding of the subject.

LITERATURE CITED

1. Aceves, J., Erlij, D. 1971. Sodium transport across the isolated epithelium of the frog skin. *J. Physiol. London* 212:195–210

2. Alvarado, R. H., Dietz, T. H. 1970. Effect of salt depletion on hydromineral balance in larval *Ambystoma gracile*. II. Kinetics of ion exchange. *Comp. Biochem. Physiol.* 33:93–110

3. Alvarado, R. H., Moody, A. 1970. Sodium and chloride transport in tadpoles of the bullfrog *Rana catesbeiana. Am. J. Physiol.* 218: 1510–16

4. Alvarado, R. H., Stiffler, D. F. 1970. The transepithelial potential difference in intact larval and adult Salamanders. *Comp. Biochem. Physiol.* 33:209–12

5. Andersen, B., Zerahn, K. 1963. Method for non-destructive determination of the sodium transport pool in frog skin with radiosodium. *Acta Physiol. Scand.* 59:319–29

6. Bentley, P. J. 1968. Amiloride: a potent inhibitor of sodium transport across the toad bladder. *J. Physiol. London.* 195:317–30

7. Bentley, P. J. 1971. *Endocrines and Osmoregulation.* Berlin:Springer

8. Biber, T. U. L., Curran, P. F. 1970. Direct measurement of uptake of sodium at the outer surface of the frog skin. *J. Gen. Physiol.* 56:83–99

9. Bricker, N. S., Biber, T., Ussing, H. H. 1963. Exposure of the isolated frog skin to high potassium concentrations at the internal surface. I. Bioelectric phenomena and sodium transport. *J. Clin. Invest.* 42:88–99

10. Cereijido, M., Curran, P. F. 1965. Intracellular electrical potentials in frog skin. *J. Gen. Physiol.* 48:543–57

11. Cereijido, M., Fraidenraich, N. 1970. Surface *vs.* transcellular route in the transport of sodium across epithelial membranes. *Horizons in Surface Science: Biological Applications,* ed. L. Prince, D. F. Sears. New York: Appleton

12. Cereijido, M., Reisin, I., Rotunno, C. A. 1968. The effect of sodium concentration on the content and distribution of sodium in the frog skin. *J. Physiol. London* 196:237–53

13. Cereijido, M., Rotunno, C. A. 1967. Transport and distribution of sodium across frog skin. *J. Physiol. London* 190:481–97

14. Cereijido, M., Rotunno, C. A. 1968. Fluxes and distribution of sodium in frog skin. A new model. *J. Gen. Physiol.* 51:280s–89s

15. Cereijido, M., Rotunno, C. A. 1971. The effect of antidiuretic hormone on Na movement across frog skin. *J. Physiol. London* 213:119–33

16. Conte, F. P., Lin, D. H. 1967. Kinetics of cellular morphogenesis in gill epithelium during sea water adaptation of *Onchorhynchus. Comp. Biochem. Physiol.* 23:945–57

17. Conte, F. P., Morita, T. N. 1968. Immunochemical study of cell differentiation in gill epithelium of euryhaline *Oncorhynchus. Comp. Biochem. Physiol.* 24:445–54

18. Copeland, D. E. 1948. The cytological basis of chloride transfer in the gills of *Fundulus heteroclitus. J. Morphol.* 82:201–27

19. Crabbé, J., Ehrlich, E. N. 1968. Amiloride and the mode of action of aldosterone on sodium transport across toad bladder and skin. *Pfluegers Arch.* 304:284–96

20. Croghan, P. C. 1958. Ionic fluxes in *Artemia salina. J. Exp. Biol.* 35: 425–36

21. Curran, P. F. 1960. Na, Cl and water transport by rat ileum in vitro. *J. Gen. Physiol.* 43:1137–48

22. Curran, P. F., Cereijido, M. 1965. K fluxes in frog skin. *J. Gen. Physiol.* 48:1011–33

23. Dejours, P. 1969. Variations of CO_2 output of a fresh water teleost upon change of the ionic composition of the water. *J. Physiol. London* 202: 113–14

24. Diamond, J. M. 1965. The mechanism of isotonic water absorption and secretion. *Symp. Soc. Exp. Biol.* 19:392–47

25. Diamond, J. M., Wright, E. M. 1969. Biological membranes: the physical basis of ion and nonelectrolyte selectivity. *Ann. Rev. Physiol.* 31: 581–646

26. Dietz, T. H., Kirschner, L. B., Porter, D. 1967. The roles of sodium transport and anion permeability in generating transepithelial potential differences in larval salamanders. *J. Exp. Biol.* 46:85–96

27. Dörge, A., Nagel, W. 1970. Effect of amiloride on sodium transport in frog skin. II. Sodium transport pool

and unidirectional fluxes. *Pfluegers Arch.* 321:91–101

28. Doyle, W. L., Gorecki, D. 1961. The so-called chloride cell of the fish gill. *Physiol. Zool.* 34:81–8

29. Duval, M. 1925. Recherches physico-chimiques et physiologiques ser le milieu intérieur des animaux aquatiques. Modifications sous l'influence du milieu extérieur. *Ann. Inst. Oceanogr. Paris* 2:234–407

30. Ehrlich, E. N., Crabbé, J. 1968. The mechanism of action of amiprami-zide. *Pfluegers Arch.* 302 79–96

31. Eisenman, G. 1961. On the elementary atomic origin of equilibrium ionic specificity. *Membrane Transport and Metabolism*, ed. A. Kleinzeller, A. Kotyk. New York: Academic

32. Eisenman, G. 1962. Cation-selective glass electrodes and their mode of operation. *Biophys. J.* 2:259–323

33. Emilio, M. G., Machado, M. M., Menano, H. P. 1970. The production of a hydrogen ion gradient across the isolated frog skin. Quantitative aspects and the effect of acetazolamide. *Biochim. Biophys. Acta* 203:394–409

34. Engbaek, L., Hoshiko, T. 1957. Electrical potential gradients through frog skin. *Acta Physiol. Scand.* 39:348–55

35. Epstein, F. H., Cynamon, M., McKay, W. 1971. Endocrine control of Na-K ATPase and seawater adaptation in *Anguilla rostrata. Gen. Comp. Endocrinol.* 16:323–28

36. Epstein, F. H., Katz, A. I., Pickford, G. E. 1967. Sodium and potassium activated adenosine triphosphatase of gills: role in adaptation of teleosts to salt water. *Science* 156:1245–47

37. Epstein, F. H., Manitius, A., Weinstein, E., Katz, A. I., Pickford, G. E. 1969. Na-K ATPase in kidneys of *Fundulus heteroclitus* adapted to fresh and salt water. *Yale J. Biol. Med.* 41:388–93

38. Erlij, D. 1971. Salt transport across isolated frog skin. *Phil. Trans. Roy. Soc. London Ser. B.* 262:153–161

39. Essig, A., Leaf, A. 1963. The role of potassium in active transport of sodium by the toad bladder. *J. Gen. Physiol.* 46:505–15

40. Evans, D. H. 1967. Sodium chloride and water balance of the intertidal teleost *Xiphister atropurpureus.* III. The roles of simple diffusion, exchange diffusion, osmosis and active transport. *J. Exp. Biol.* 47:525–34

41. Evans, D. H. 1968. Measurements of drinking rates in fishes. *Comp. Biochem. Physiol.* 25:751–53

42. Evans, D. H. 1969. Sodium chloride and water balance of the intertidal teleost *Pholis gunnellus. J. Exp. Biol.* 50:179–90

43. Evans, D. H. 1969. Studies on the permeability to water of selected marine freshwater and euryhaline teleosts. *J. Exp. Biol.* 50:689–703

44. Farquhar, M. G., Palade, G. E. 1964. Functional organization of amphibian skin. *Proc. Nat. Acad. Sci. U.S.A.* 51:569–77

45. Farquhar, M. G., Palade, G. E. 1965. Adenosine triphosphatase in amphibian epidermis. *J. Cell Biol.* 30:359–79

46. Finn, A. L. 1971. The kinetics of sodium transport in the toad bladder. II. Dual effects of vasopressin. *J. Gen. Physiol.* 57:349–62

47. Finn, A. L., Rockoff, M. 1971. The kinetics of sodium transport in the toad bladder. I. Determination of the transport pool. *J. Gen. Physiol.* 57:326–48

48. Fontaine, M. 1964. Les mécanismes physiologiques du comportement migratoire amphibiotique catadrome des poissons téléostéens. *Verh. Int. Verein. Limnol.* 15:959–67

49. Frazier, H. S. 1962. The electrical potential profile of the isolated toad bladder. *J. Gen. Physiol.* 45:515–28

50. Frazier, H. S. 1964. Specificity of sodium transport and the biologically active form of sodium ion. *J. Clin. Invest.* 43:1265

51. Frazier, H. S., Leaf, A. 1963. The electrical characteristics of active sodium transport in the toad bladder. *J. Gen. Physiol.* 46:491–503

52. Frazier, H. S., Leaf, A. 1964. Cellular mechanisms in the control of body fluid. *Medicine Balt.* 43:281–89

53. Funder, J., Ussing, H. H., Wieth, J. O. 1967. The effects of CO_2 and hydrogen ions on active Na transport in the isolated frog skin. *Acta Physiol. Scand.* 71:65–76

54. Garcia-Romeu, F. 1971. Anionic and cationic exchange mechanism in skin of anurans, with special reference to Leptodactylidae in vivo. *Phil. Trans. Roy. Soc. London Ser. B.* 262:163–174

55. Garcia-Romeu, F., Maetz, J. 1964. The mechanism of sodium and chloride uptake by the gills of a freshwater fish, *Carassius auratus*. I. Evidence for an independent uptake of sodium and chloride ions. *J. Gen. Physiol.* 47:1195–1207

56. Garcia-Romeu, F., Motais, R. 1966. Mise en évidence d'échanges Na$^+$/NH$_4^+$ chez l'anguille d'eau douce. *Comp. Biochem. Physiol.* 17:1201–04

57. Garcia-Romeu, F., Salibian, A. 1968. Sodium uptake and ammonia excretion through the in vivo skin of the South American frog *Leptodactylus ocellatus* (L., 1758). *Life Sci.* 7:465–70

58. Garcia-Romeu, F., Salibian, A., Pezzani-Hernandez, S. 1969. The nature of the in vivo sodium and chloride uptake mechanisms through the epithelium of the Chilean frog *Calyptocephalella gayi* (Dum. et Bibr., 1841). *J. Gen. Physiol.* 53:816–35

59. Garrahan, P. J., Glynn, I. M. 1967. The behaviour of the sodium pump in red cells in the absence of external potassium. *J. Physiol. London* 192:159–74

60. Ferreira, K. T. 1968. Anionic dependence of sodium transport in the frog skin. *Biochim. Biophys. Acta* 150:587–98

61. Helfferich, F. 1962. *Ion exchange*. New York: McGraw

62. Herrera, F. C. 1968. Action of ouabain on sodium transport in toad urinary bladder. *Am. J. Physiol.* 210:980–86

63. Hickman, C. P., Trump, B. F. 1969. The kidney. *Fish Physiology*, ed. J. W. Hoar, D. J. Randall 1:91–239

64. Hirano, T. 1967. Effect of hypophysectomy on water transport in isolated intestine of the eel *Anguilla japonica*. *Proc. Jap. Acad.* 43:793–96

65. Hirano, T. 1969. Effect of hypophysectomy and salinity change on plasma cortisol concentration in the Japanese eel, *Anguilla japonica*. *Endocrinol. Jap.* 16:557–60

66. Hirano, T., Kamiya, M., Saishu, S., Utida, S. 1967. Effects of hypophysectomy on water and sodium transport in isolated intestine and gills of Japanese eels (*Anguilla japonica*). *Endocrinol. Jap.* 14:182–86

67. Hirano, T., Utida, S. 1968. Effects of ACTH and cortisol on water movement in isolated intestine of the eel *Anguilla japonica*. *Gen. Comp. Endocrinol.* 11:373–80

68. Hoshiko, T., Ussing, H. H. 1960. The kinetics of Na^{24} flux across amphibian skin and bladder. *Acta Physiol. Scand.* 49:74–81

69. House, C. R. 1963. Osmotic regulation in the brackish water teleost *Blennius pholis*. *J. Exp. Biol.* 40:87–104

70. Huf, E. G. 1935. Versuche über den Zusammenhang zwischen Stoffwechsel, Potentialbildung und Funktion der Froschhaut. *Pfluegers Arch.* 235: 655–73

71. Huf, E. G. 1936. Uber aktiven Wasser- und Salztransport durch die Froschhaut. *Pfluegers Arch.* 237:143–66

72. Huf, E., Doss, N. S., Wills, J. P. 1957. Effects of metabolic inhibitors and drugs on ion transport and oxygen consumption in isolated frog skin. *J. Gen. Physiol.* 41:397–417

73. Huf, E. G., Wills, J. 1951. Influence of some inorganic cations on active salt and water uptake by isolated frog skin. *Am. J. Physiol.* 167:255–60

74. Huf, E. G., Wills, J. 1953. The relationship of sodium uptake, potassium rejection, and skin potential in isolated frog skin. *J. Gen. Physiol.* 36:473–87

75. Huf, E. G., Wills, J. P., Arrighi, M. F. 1955. Electrolyte distribution and active salt uptake in frog skin. *J. Gen. Physiol.* 38:867–88

76. Jampol, L. M., Epstein, F. H. 1970. Na-K activated ATPase and osmotic regulation by fishes. *Am. J. Physiol.* 218:607–11

77. Jorgensen, C. B., Levi, H., Zerahn, K. 1954. On active uptake of sodium and chloride ions in anurans. *Acta Physiol. Scand.* 30:178–90

78. Kamiya, M. 1967. Changes in ion and water transport in isolated gills of the cultured eel during the course of salt adaptation. *Annot. Zool. Jap.* 40:123–29

79. Kamiya, M., Utida, S. 1968. Changes in activity of Na-K activated adenosine triphosphatase in gills during adaptation of the Japanese eel to sea water. *Comp. Biochem. Physiol.* 26:675–85

80. Kamiya, M., Utida, S. 1969. Sodium-potassium activated ATPase activity in gills of fresh water, marine

and euryhaline teleosts. *Comp. Biochem. Physiol.* 31:671–74

81. Kerstetter, T. H., Kirschner, L. B., Rafuse, D. D. 1970. On the mechanisms of sodium ion transport by the irrigated gills of rainbow trout (*Salmo gairdneri*). *J. Gen. Physiol.* 56:342–59

82. Keynes, R. D. 1969. From frog skin to sheep rumen: a survey of transport of salts and water across multicellular structures. *Quart. Rev. Biophys.* 2:177–281

83. Keys, A., Willmer, E. N. 1932. "Chloride secreting cells" in the gills of fishes, with special reference to the common eel. *J. Physiol. London* 76:368–78

84. Kirsch, R. 1971. *Echanges d'eau, de chlorures et de sodium au niveau des differents effecteurs de l'osmorégulation chez l'anguille* (Anguilla anguilla) *en eau douce et au cours de l'adaptation à l'eau de mer.* Thesis. Univ. Strasbourg. 257 pp.

85. Kirschner, L. B. 1969. ATPase activity in gills of euryhaline fish. *Comp. Biochem. Physiol.* 29:871–74

86. Kirschner, L. B. 1970. The study of NaCl transport in aquatic animals. *Am. Zool.* 10:365–76

87. Klahr, S., Bricker, N. S. 1964. On the electrogenic nature of active sodium transport across the isolated frog skin. *J. Clin. Invest.* 43:922–30

88. Koefoed-Johnsen, V., Levi, H., Ussing, H. H. 1952. The mode of passage of chloride ions through the isolated frog skin. *Acta Physiol. Scand.* 25: 150–63

89. Koefoed-Johnsen, V., Ussing, H. H. 1958. The nature of the frog skin potential. *Acta Physiol. Scand.* 42: 298–308

90. Koefoed-Johnsen, V., Ussing, H. H., Zerahn, K. 1952. The origin of the short-circuit current in the adrenaline stimulated frog skin. *Acta Physiol. Scand.* 27:38–48

91. Krogh, A. 1937. Osmotic regulation in the frog (*R. esculenta*) by active absorption of chloride ions. *Skand. Arch. Physiol.* 76:60–74

92. Krogh, A. 1938. The active absorption of ions in some freshwater animals. *Z. Vergl. Physiol.* 25:335–50

93. Krogh, A. 1939. *Osmotic regulation in aquatic animals.* Cambridge Univ. Press.

94. Lahlou, B. 1970. La fonction rénale des téléostéens et son rôle dans l'osmorégulation. *Bull. Inform. Sci.*

Tech. Commis. Energ. At. Fr. 144: 17–52

95. Lahlou, B., Giordan, A. 1970. Le contrôle hormonal des échanges et de la balance de l'eau chez le téléostéens d'eau douce, *Carassius auratus*, intact et hypophysectomisé. *Gen. Comp. Endocrinol.* 14:491–509

96. Lahlou, B., Sawyer W. H. 1969. Sodium exchanges in the toadfish, *Opsanus tau*, an euryhaline aglomerular teleost. *Am. J. Physiol.* 216: 1273–75

97. Lahlou, B., Sawyer, W. H. 1969. Adaptation des échanges d'eau en fonction de la salinité externe chez *Opsanus tau. J. Physiol. Paris* 61:143

98. Lam, T. J. 1969. Evidence of loss of C^{14}-Inuline via the head region of the threespine stickleback *Gasterosteus aculeatus*, form *Trachurus. Comp. Biochem. Physiol.* 28:459–63

99. Leloup, J. 1970. Les mécanismes de régulation de l'iodurémie et leur contrôle endocrinien chez les téléostéens d'eau douce. *Mem. Mus. Nat. Hist. Nat. Ser. A.* 62:1–108

100. Levinsky, N. G., Sawyer, W. H. 1953. Relation of metabolism of frog skin to cellular integrity and electrolyte transfer. *J. Gen. Physiol.* 36:607–15

101. Linderholm, H. 1953. The electrical potential across isolated frog skin and its dependence on the permeability of the skin to chloride ions. *Acta Physiol Scand.* 28:211–17

102. Mackay, W. C. 1969. Salt and water transport in coolated eel intestine. *Bull. Mt. Desert Isl. Biol. Lab.* 9:23–26

103. Mackay, W. C., Janicki, R. 1970. Water absorption by isolated eel intestine during seawater adaptation. *Bull. Mt. Desert Isl. Biol. Lab.* 10:42–44

104. MacRobbie, E. A. C., Ussing, H. H. 1961. Osmotic behaviour of the epithelial cells of frog skin. *Acta Physiol. Scand.* 53:348–65

105. Maetz, J. 1956. Les échanges de sodium chez le poisson *Carassius auratus* L. Action d'un inhibiteur de l'anhydrase carbonique. *J. Physiol. Paris.* 48:1085–99

106. Maetz, J. 1968. Salt and water metabolism. *Perspectives in endocrinology: Hormones in the lives of lower vertebrates*, ed. J. W. Barrington, C. B. Jorgensen. London and New York: Academic

107. Maetz, J. 1969. Seawater teleosts:

evidence for a sodium-potassium exchange in the branchial sodium excreting pump. *Science* 166:613–15

108. Maetz, J. 1970. Mechanisms of salt and water transfer across membranes in teleosts in relation to the aquatic environment. *Mem. Soc. Endocrinol.* 18:3–29

109. Maetz, J. 1971. Fish gills: mechanisms of salt transfer in fresh water and sea water. *Phil. Trans. Roy. Soc. London Ser.* B. 262:209–249

110. Maetz, J. 1971. Interaction of salt and ammonia transport in aquatic organisms. *Fed. Proc. Fed. Am. Soc. Exp. Biol.* In press

111. Maetz, J., Campanini, G. 1966. Potentiels transépithéliaux de la branchie d'anguille in vivo en eau douce et en eau de mer. *J. Physiol. Paris* 58:248

112. Maetz, J., Garcia-Romeu, F. 1964. The mechanism of sodium and chloride uptake by the gills of a freshwater fish, *Carassius auratus*. II. Evidence for NH_4^+/Na^+ and HCO_3^-/Cl^- exchanges. *J. Gen. Physiol.* 47:1209–27

113. Maetz, J., Lahlou, B. 1966. Les échanges de Na et de Cl chez un élasmobranche, *Scyliorhinus*, mesurés à l'aide des isotopes ^{24}Na et ^{36}Cl. *J. Physiol. Paris* 58:249

114. Maetz, J. Motais, R., Mayer N. 1969. Isotopic kinetic studies on the endocrine control of teleostean regulation. *Proc. Int. Cong. Endocrinol.* III Mexico, ed. C. Gual, 225–32. Amsterdam:Exerpta Med.

115. Maetz, J., Nibelle, J., Bornancin, M., Motais, R. 1969. Action sur l'osmorégulation de l'anguille de divers antibiotiques inhibiteurs de la synthèse des protéines ou du renouvellement cellulaire. *Comp. Biochem. Physiol.* 30:1125–51

116. Maetz, J., Rankin, J. C. 1969. Quelques aspects du rôle biologique des hormones neurohypophysaires chez les poissons. *Colloq. Int. Cent. Nat. Rech. Sci.* 177:45–55

117. Maren, T. H. 1967. Carbonic anhydrase: chemistry, physiology and inhibition. *Physiol. Rev.* 47:595–781

118. Martin, D. W., Curran, P. F. 1966. Reversed potentials in isolated frog skin. II. Active transport of chloride. *J. Cell. Comp. Physiol.* 67:367–74

119. Masoni, A., Garcia-Romeu, F. 1970. Sur la mise en évidence des cellules à chlorure de la branchie des poissons. *Arch. Anat. Microsc. Morphol. Exp.* 59:289–94

120. Mayer, N. 1970. Contrôle endocrinien de l'osmorégulation chez les téléostéens. Rôle de l'axe hypophyse-interrenal et de la prolactine. *Bull. Inform. Sci. Tech. Commis. Energ. At. Fr.* 146:45–75

121. Mayer, N., Nibelle, J. 1970. Evolution de la balance minérale de l'anguille, *Anguilla anguilla*, après modification de la salinité externe et infusion saline intravasculaire. *Comp. Biochem. Physiol.* 35:553–66

122. Mizuhira, V., Amakawa, T., Yamashina, S., Shirai, N., Utida, S. 1969. Electron microscopic studies on the localization of sodium ions and Na-K ATPase in chloride cells of eel gills. *Exp. Cell. Res.* 59:346–48

123. Morel, F., Jard, S. 1968. Actions of the neurohypophysial hormones and related peptides in lower vertebrates. *Handbook of Experimental Pharmacology*, ed. B. Berde, 23:655–716. Berlin: Springer

124. Motais, R. 1961. Cinétique des échanges de sodium chez un téléostéen euryhalin (*Platichthys flesus* L.) au cours de passages successifs eau de mer, eau douce, eau de mer, en fonction du temps de séjour en eau douce. *Compt. Rend. Acad. Sci.* 253:2609–11

125. Motais, R. 1967. Les mécanismes d'échanges ioniques branchiaux chez les téléostéens. *Ann. Inst. Oceanogr. Paris* 45:1–83

126. Motais, R. 1970. Les mécanismes branchiaux des échanges ioniques chez les téléostéens en rapport avec la salinité: aspect biochimique. *Bull. Inform. Sci. Tech. Commis. Energ. At. Fr.* 146:3–19

127. Motais, R. 1970. Effect of actinomycin D on the branchial Na-K dependent ATPase activity in relation to sodium balance of the eel. *Comp. Biochem. Physiol.* 34:497–501

128. Motais, R., Garcia-Romeu, F., Maetz, J. 1966. Exchange diffusion effect and euryhalinity in teleosts. *J. Gen. Physiol.* 50:391–422

129. Motais, R., Isaia, J. Temperature dependence of water and sodium permeabilities through the gill epithelium of the eel (*Anguilla anguilla*). Unpublished

130. Motais, R., Isaia, J., Rankin, J. C., Maetz, J. 1969. Adaptive changes of the water permeability of the teleostean gill epithelium in rela-

tion to external salinity. *J. Exp. Biol.* 51:529–46

131. Motais, R., Maetz, J. 1964. Action des hormones neurohypophysaires sur les échanges de sodium (mesurés à l'aide de radiosodium ^{24}Na) chez un téléostéen euryhalin *Platichthys flesus* L. *Gen. Comp. Endocrinol.* 4:210–24

132. Motais, R., Maetz, J. 1965. Comparaison des échanges de sodium chez un téléostéen euryhalin (le flet) et un téléostéen sténohalin (le serran) en eau de mer. Importance relative du tube digestif et de la branchie dans ces échanges. *Compt. Rend. Acad. Sci.* 261:532–35

133. Motais, R., Schmidt-Nielsen, B. 1970. In vivo ionic exchange through the skin of the frog *Rana clamitans.* *Bull. Mt. Desert Isl. Biol. Lab.* 10:51–6

134. Mullins, L. J. 1950. Osmotic regulation in fish as studied with radio isotopes. *Acta Physiol. Scand.* 21: 303–14

135. Nagel, W., Dörge, A. 1970. Effect of amiloride on sodium transport of frog skin. I. Action on intracellular sodium content. *Pfluegers Arch.* 317:84–92

136. Nagel, W., Dörge, A. 1971. A study of the different sodium compartments and the transepithelial sodium fluxes of the frog skin with the use of ouabain. *Pfluegers Arch.* 324:267–78

137. Nutbourne, D. M. 1968. The effect of small hydrostatic pressure gradients on the rate of active sodium transport across isolated living frog-skin membranes. *J. Physiol. London* 195:1–18

138. Oide, M. 1967. Effects of inhibitors on transport of water and ions in isolated intestine and Na$^+$-K$^+$ ATPase in intestinal mucosa of the eel. *Ann. Zool. Jap.* 40:130–35

139. Oide, H., Utida, S. 1968. Changes in intestinal absorption and renal excretion of water during adaptation to sea water in the Japanese eel. *Mar. Biol.* 1:172–77

140. Parry, G. 1966. Osmotic adaptation in fishes. *Biol. Rev.* 41:392–444

141. Parry, G., Hollyday, F. G. T., Blaxter, J. H. S. 1953. "Chloride secreting cells" in the gills of teleosts. *Nature (London)* 183:1248–49

142. Payan, P., Maetz, J. 1970. Balance hydrique chez les Elasmobranches: arguments en faveur d'un contrôle endocrinien. *Gen. Comp. Endocrinol.* In press

143. Pesente, L. 1969. Effetti della concentrazione idrogenionica sulla permeazione di alcuni ioni monovalenti attraverso la pelle di rana. *Bol. Soc. Ital. Biol. Sper.* 45:1161–64

144. Pesente, L. 1969. Analisi degli effetti della concentrazione idrogenionica sulla permeazione di alcuni ioni monovalenti. *Boll. Soc. Ital. Biol. Sper.* 45:1164–67.

145. Phillips, J. E. 1970. Apparent transport of water by insect excretory systems. *Am. Zool.* 10:413–36

146. Philpott, C. W. 1965. Halide localisation in the teleost chloride cell and its identification by selected area election diffraction. *Protoplasma* 60: 7–23

147. Philpott, C. W., Copeland, D. E. 1963. Fine structure of chloride cells from three species of *Fundulus.* *J. Cell. Biol.* 18:389–404

148. Pickford, G. E., Griffith, R. W., Torretti, J., Hendler, E., Epstein, F. H. 1970. Branchial reduction and renal stimulation of Na-K ATPase by prolactin in hypophysectomized killifish in freshwater. *Nature (London)* 228:378–79

149. Potts, W. T. W. 1968. Osmotic and ionic regulation. *Ann. Rev. Physiol.* 30:73–104

150. Potts, W. T. W., Evans, D. H. 1967. Sodium and chloride balance in the killifish *Fundulus heteroclitus.* *Biol. Bull.* 133:411–25

151. Potts, W. T. W., Foster, M. A., Rudy, P. P., Howells, G. P. 1967. Sodium and water balance in the cichlid teleost *Tilapia mossambica.* *J. Exp. Biol.* 47:461–70

152. Potts, W. T. W., Foster, M. A., Stather, J. W. 1970. Salt and water balance in salmon smolts. *J. Exp. Biol.* 52: 553–64

153. Prosser, C. L. 1955. Physioloigcal variation in animals. *Biol. Rev.* 30: 229–62

154. Rawlins, F., Mateu, L., Fragachan, F., Whittembury, G. 1970. Isolated toad skin epithelium: transport characteristics. *Pfluegers Arch.* 316: 64–80

155. Rothstein, A. 1968. Membrane phenomena. *Ann. Rev. Physiol.* 30:15–72

156. Rotunno, C. A., Vilallonga, F. A., Fernandez, M., Cereijido, M. 1970. The penetration of sodium into the epithelium of the frog skin. *J. Gen. Physiol.* 55:716–35

157. Salibian, A., Pezzani-Hernandez, S., Garcia-Romeu, F. 1968. In vivo ionic exchange through the skin of the South American frog, *Leptodactylus ocellatus*. *Comp. Biochem. Physiol.* 25:311–17

158. Salibian, A.. Preller, A., Robres, L. 1971. In vivo ionic uptake through the skin of the South American toad *Bufo arunco*. *Rev. Can. Biol.* In press

159. Schoffeniels, E. 1955. Influence du pH sur le transport actif de sodium à travers la peau de grenouille. *Arch. Int. Physiol. Biochem.* 63:513–30

160. Scott, W. N., Shamoo, Y. E., Brodsky, W. A. 1970. Carbonic anhydrase content of turtle urinary bladder mucosal cells. *Biochim. Biophys. Acta* 219:248–50

161. Shaw, J. 1960. The absorption of sodium ions by the crayfish, *Astacus pallipes* Lereboullet. II. The effect of the external anion. *J. Exp. Biol.* 37:534–47

162. Shaw, J. 1960. The absorption of sodium ions by the crayfish, *Astacus pallipes* Lereboullet. III. The effect of other cations in the external solution. *J. Exp. Biol.* 37:548–56

163. Shaw, J. 1960. The absorption of chloride ions by the crayfish, *Astacus pallipes* Lereboullet. *J. Exp. Biol.* 37:557–72.

164. Shaw, J. 1964. The control of salt balance in the crustacea. *Symp. Soc. Exp. Biol.* 18:237–56

165. Shirai, N. Utida, S. 1970. Development and degeneration of the chloride cell during seawater and freshwater adaptation of the Japanese eel, *Anguilla japonica*. *Z. Zellforsch.* 103:247–64

166. Skadhauge, E. 1969. The mechanism of salt and water absorption in the intestine of the eel (*Anguilla anguilla*) adapted to waters of various salinities. *J. Physiol. London* 204:135–58

167. Skadhauge, E., Maetz, J. 1967. Etude in vivo de l'absorption intestinale d'eau et d'électrolytes chez *Anguilla anguilla* adaptée à des milieux de salinités diverses. *Compt. Rend. Acad. Sci.* 265:347–50

168. Smith, H. W. 1932. Water regulation and its evolution in fishes. *Quart. Rev. Biol.* 7:1–26

169. Smith, P. G. 1969. The ionic relations of *Artemia salina* L. II. Fluxes of sodium, chloride and water. *J. Exp. Biol.* 51:739–57

170. Smith, T. C., Hughes, W. D., Huf, E. 1971. Movement of CO_2 and HCl_3^- across isolated frog skin. *Biochim. Biophys. Acta* 225:77–88

171. Steinbach, H. B. 1933. The electrical potential difference across living frog skin. *J. Cell Comp. Physiol.* 3:1–27

172. Stobbart, R. H. 1967. The effect of some anions and cations upon the fluxes and net uptake of chloride in the larva of *Aedes eagypti* (L.), and the nature of the uptake mechanisms for sodium and chloride. *J. Exp. Biol.* 47:35–57

173. Stobbart, R. H. 1971. Evidence for Na^+/H^+ and Cl^-/HCO_3^- exchanges during independent sodium and chloride uptake by the larva of the mosquito *Aëdes aegypti* (L.). *J. Exp. Biol.* 54:19–27

174. Teorell, T. 1953. Transport processes and electrical phenomena in ionic membranes. *Progr. Biophys. Biophys. Chem.* 3:305–69

175. Thuet, P., Motais, R., Maetz, J. 1968. Les mécanismes de l'euryhalinité chez le crustacé des salines *Artemia salina*. *Comp. Biochem. Physiol.* 26:793–818

176. Ussing, H. H., 1947. Interpretation of the exchange of radiosodium in isolated muscle. *Nature* 160:262–63

177. Ussing, H. H. 1949. The active ion transport through the isolated frog skin in the light of tracer studies. *Acta Physiol. Scand.* 17:1–37

178. Ussing, H. H. 1963–64. Transport of electrolytes and water across epithelia. *Harvey Lect.* 59:1–30.

179. Ussing, H. H., Windhager, E. E. 1964. Nature of shunt path and active sodium transport path through frog skin epithelium. *Acta Physiol. Scand.* 61:484–504

180. Ussing, H. H., Zerahn, K. 1951. Active transport of sodium as the source of electric current in the short-circuited isolated frog skin. *Acta Physiol. Scand.* 23:110–27

181. Utida, S., Hirano, T., Kamiya, M. 1969. Seasonal variations in the adjustive responses to seawater in the intestine and gills of the Japanese cultured eel, *Anguilla japonica*. *Proc. Jap. Acad.* 45:293–97

182. Utida, S., Isono, N., Hirano, T. 1967. Water movement in isolated intestine of the eel adapted to fresh water or sea water. *Zool. Mag.* 76:203–04

183. Utida, S., Kamiya, M., Shirai, N. 1971. Relationship between the ac-

tivity of Na-K activated ATPase and the number of chloride cells in eel gills with special reference to seawater adaptation. *Comp. Biochem. Physiol.* 38A:443–47

184. Utida, S., Oide, M., Saishu, S., Kamiya, M. 1967. Préétablissement du mécanisme d'adaptation à l'eau de mer dans l'intestin et les branchies isolées de l'Anguille argentée au cours de sa migration catadrome. *Compt. Rend. Soc. Biol. F.* 161: 1201–04

185. Vanatta, J. C., Bryant, L. A. 1970. Compartmentation of the sodium transport pool of the toad bladder. *Proc. Soc. Exp. Biol. Med.* 133:385–93

186. de Vooys, G. G. 1968. Formation and excretion of ammonia in Teleostei. I. Excretion of ammonia through the gills. *Arch. Int. Physiol. Biochim.* 76:628

187. Voûte, C. L., Ussing, H. H. 1968. Some morphological aspects of active sodium transport. *J. Cell. Biol.* 36:625–38.

188. Whittam, R., Wheeler, K. P. 1970. Transport across cell membranes. *Ann. Rev. Physiol.* 32:21–59

189. Whittembury, G. 1964. Electrical potential profile of the toad skin epithelium. *J. Gen. Physiol.* 47:795–808

190. Zadunaisky, J. A., Candia, O. A., Chiarandini, D. J. 1963. The origin of the short-circuit current in the isolated skin of the South American frog *Leptodactylus ocellatus*. *J. Gen. Physiol.* 47:393–402.

191. Zadunaisky, J. A., De Fisch, F. W. 1964. Active and passive chloride movements across isolated amphibian skin. *Am. J. Physiol.* 207:1010–14

192. Zerahn, K., 1969. Nature and localization of the sodium pool during active transport in the isolated frog skin. *Acta Physiol. Scand.* 77:272–81

THE PHYSIOLOGY OF SKIN

PAUL A. NICOLL AND THOMAS A. CORTESE, JR.

Departments of Physiology and Biochemistry
Indiana University Medical School
Indianapolis, Indiana

INTRODUCTION

Skin structure, both gross and microscopic, has traditionally served as the primary basis for the consideration of the role of skin in normal and pathological states. The introduction of new techniques in structural studies —with the development of electron microscopy and histochemistry—have yielded much information about normal skin and about many specific changes found in various skin diseases. The natural result of this emphasis on structure has been the use of descriptive terms in the discussion of skin function and dysfunction.

In many recent studies chemical and physical procedures have been introduced to the study of skin function. This has resulted in a gradual shift of emphasis from static to dynamic analysis in the discussion of various physiological activities of skin. This review, while clearly limited in scope, attempts to select from the large number of published studies those that particularly emphasize the dynamic aspect of skin physiology.

Skin function involves a considerable number of essentially independent activities. Most of these, in one way or another, fall into the broad category of protective actions. In many of these the dynamic aspect concerns the manner in which structural changes are brought about or how interrelationships of cellular units are achieved and maintained. In still other situations skin or skin appendages may play a major role in an activity, but because of the complexity of the skin and the involvement of other organs or systems, the phenomena are traditionally treated as entities in themselves. Good examples are body temperature regulation and whole body water balance.

In the last article on skin in the *Annual Review of Physiology*, Potter (75) primarily discussed the status of the cellular activities associated with many of those functions of skin that are of special interest in dermatology. Several of these will be considered again here and the new information uncovered in the intervening years will be reviewed. Included are the mechanism of keratinization, melanin production, skin response to actinic radiation, sebaceous glands and sebum production, and percutaneous absorption. In addition, we will examine the more recent studies on skin vascular behavior and involvement both in man and animals, including the microvascular elements.

Not all of the great array of interesting studies reported, even in the selected topics, can be considered in this brief review. To compensate partially for this lack, several interesting and more or less isolated investigations dealing with skin function will be included as "Briefly Noted" items.

CIRCULATION

Vascular phenomena associated with skin include both structural and dynamic aspects. The gross relationship of the vascular distribution in the skin of man and that of many animals has long been adequately described. Histological details, especially those revealed by use of the electron microscope, continue to appear. In the majority of the studies, changes associated with pathological states are involved (67). More recently, the scanning electron microscope has been used to explore the topographical details and orientations of skin microstructures (22, 100).

The dynamic involvement of skin circulation in the vascular adjustments of the individual and the nature of the physiological responses of skin vessels to particular situations are the subjects of several current studies. The availability of skin allows investigation of skin blood flow in conscious human subjects. The various techniques that have been used to study skin blood flow in man have been critically reviewed by Greenfield (41) who has discussed in considerable detail the prevalent knowledge of the nature of blood flow in skin vascular systems and how this flow is regulated. In the main, Greenfield restricted his review to cutaneous blood flow and its regulation in man. A more abbreviated summary of these concepts has been given by Frewin (37). Hyman (47) considered skin blood flow studies primarily from the viewpoint of microcirculation. He is rightly critical of much of the reported data on flow dynamics both in man and in other mammals. This caution stems from the almost invariable requirement that the studies be conducted either on a restricted region or in limited areas of the skin surface and frequently under poorly controlled conditions.

Fewings et al (32), using a combination of venous occlusion pletysmography and the study of A-V oxygen differences in the forearm of unanesthetized human subjects, concluded that skin blood vessels take an active part in the reactive hyperemia following arterial occlusion release. Although skin vessels probably contribute quantitatively less to the hyperemia than skeletal muscle vessels do, their response is qualitatively similar to that of other vascular beds. Beiser et al (6), using a variation of venous occlusion plethysmography—in which volume changes are measured by single strand mercury-in-rubber gauges, compared forearm flows in human subjects by applying catecholamine iontophoresis to the entire surface to be studied in one arm, while leaving the other arm in its normal state. The arteriolar inflow to skin was assumed to be blocked in the treated arm. The compensatory vascular adjustments following changes in baroreceptor activity in the carotid sinus were determined from the difference in flow changes in the two arms. The data indicated that skin responses occurred that were comparable to those shown by muscle blood flow. The significant pre-stress flow differences between the arm areas after epinephrine iontophoresis clearly showed that human skin vessels are responsive to the local application of adrenergic agents. Their responsiveness to adrenergic excitation was also shown by Alpert & Coffman (2) using ^{133}Xe and Na^{131}I plasma clearance and I.V. epinephrine infusion in unanesthetized normal human subjects.

In a complex study, Kontos et al (52) attacked the knotty problem of human skin vascular responses to changes in blood P_{CO_2}. Changes in blood CO_2 were measured directly from samples withdrawn by suitably placed venous catheters. The change in forearm blood flow or perfusion resistance was measured by venous occlusion plethysmography during breathing of different CO_2-air mixtures or following infusion of salt solutions saturated at various P_{CO_2}. They found a diphasic response to increased CO_2. Initially a slight but definite increased resistance (reduced flow) could be detected. This soon gave way to reduced resistance with vasodilation. They suggested that the initial constrictor response, which they think is probably maintained throughout the period of increased arterial P_{CO_2}, results from the action of augmented intra-arterial CO_2 level. However, the rapid buildup of interstitial CO_2 produces local responses that overwhelm the vasoconstriction and reduces resistance with increased flow. Neither alpha nor beta adrenergic blockage changed the results. This supports the theory that a local response to the interstitial increase in CO_2 is the primary mechanism involved.

Microcirculatory observations on superficial skin capillary form and function in man, especially as associated with a diseased state, continue to attract attention. Unfortunately, of necessity the observations are made at extremely low magnification using the "clinical capillary microscope." Davis & Landau (21) reviewed the basic techniques involved and emphasized Bosley's earlier conclusion (11) that the many pitfalls associated with the interpretation of capillary form and activity are indicative of specific clinical dermatoses. Their photographs are well done and the work certainly serves as essential background for any study in the field. Redisch et al (82) have stoutly defended the association of characteristic alertations of the papillary plexus with specific diseases, especially those that fall broadly into the auto-immune type. Maricq (56) has introduced a semiquantitative plexus visualization score (PVS) of the papillary plexus in her studies mainly with schizophrenic patients. She believes that the PVS scores provide a more reliable evaluation of the papillary plexus than do the measurements of the number and form of the nailbed end row capillary loops used by Davis & Landau (21). The PVS score, however, is basically subjective and provides at best only relative values of the number of visible capillary loops. Ryan and associates (87) have recently made much of clinical capillary microscopy and its usefulness to dermatologists. One would be more impressed, however, if fewer publications and more sound observations were involved. It is a rather frequent criticism of the studies using capillary clinical microscopy that too many articles based on too few observations tend to confuse the significance of the technique and its contribution to human skin microcirculatory physiology and pathology.

Zimmer & Demis (110) reviewed the character of nailbed capillaries and those in other skin sites exposed by cellophane stripping techniques and noted the changes in structure and flow seen with several diseases. They pointed out that, while the described changes are characteristic of the clinical conditions in which they were observed, they cannot be considered pathognomonic for the condition. They limited their data to total capillary loop counts per unit area and did not discuss abnormal forms. Redisch et al (83) believe that changes in capillary form, along with width and flow characteristics in individual segments of the loop, are quite specific diagnostically for several collagen diseases.

Recently published reviews of skin blood flow studies in experimental animals have concentrated mainly on the type of control mechanism involved and on the character of the vascular bed when subjected to essentially identical situations or to a common stress. Mellander & Johansson (64) in their review of peripheral vascular control, cited numerous observations on skin vessels but these observations are scattered throughout the paper since specific vascular beds are not treated as single entities. Green & Rapela (40) believe dog leg skin vasculature responds passively when pressure-flow relationships are determined and exhibit no autoregulation following sudden shifts up or down either of pressure during constant flow or of flow during constant pressure.

The question of what primary factors control physiological adjustments of dog skin vessels has been studied by several workers using different stress situations. In an analysis of peripheral response to hemorrhagic hypovolemia and shock, Bond et al (9, 10) concluded that skin vessels are primarily acted upon directly by catecholamines rather than indirectly by sympathetic nerve excitation. The adrenergic agents may either be locally produced or brought to the area via the blood. Denervation of skin vascular beds did not significantly modify their response to the severe stress, but infusion of phenoxybenzamine, an alpha receptor blocking agent, did inhibit the cutaneous responses. Schwinghamer et al (94) have confirmed humoral activation as the major excitor of skin vessels in the dog leg during prolonged hypovolemia. Zimmerman and co-workers (111, 112) found sympathetic transmitter release in dog skin less frequent than in skeletal muscle, but the vasoconstriction of skin vessels was as effective as in muscle. The transmitter release was increased and perfused catecholamines more active in skin vessels of dogs rendered hypertensive by renal artery constriction. Hammond, Davis & Dow (44), by carefully separating four segments of the skin circulation in the dog paw, showed that vein segments respond to sympathetic nerve stimulus more slowly and with longer duration than arterial segments. Vanhoutte & Shepherd (102), studying the response of isolated vein from dog skin vessels, found that the action of physiological humoral agents is increased by cooling and reduced by warming the perfusate. Since cold effects on activation by physical agents respond contrarily they believe that the temperature effect with the humoral excitors is on the transmitter-excitation mechanism and not on the mechanical response of the contraction system. One concludes from these studies that skin vessels are regulated primarily through the direct action of humoral agents—mainly catecholamines—acting on transmitter-excitation mechanisms, regardless of the immediate type of stress involved.

Although the structure and behavior of skin microvessels may reflect the physiological status of the skin, the limited metabolic demands of skin tissues have led to the belief that skin blood flow is associated primarily with body temperature regulation. Nevertheless since the microcirculation is fairly accessible to study in many skin sites, the minute blood and lymphatic vessels of skin have long been a favorite site for studies of the microcirculation. Two types of preparation are used. In the first type, the skin area of, for example, the bat wing (71) is naturally thin enough to permit direct examination at high magnifications without surgery or anesthesia. In the other type, some sort of window is inserted into the skin and, after stabilization, serves as a place for direct microscopic study of skin microcirculation (88). Several investigations using these preparations have appeared in the years here reviewed, but, since they deal primarily with the characteristics of both the structure and the function of the microcirculation itself rather than with microcirculation as a function of the skin, they will not be reviewed here in detail.

Zarem et al (108), using a window preparation, studied the revascularization of autogenous skin grafts in mice and showed that it depended on the ingrowth of new arterioles and venules from the adjacent tissue. The old existing vessels of the graft served only as guide lines for the revascularization. Cliff & Nicoll (17), using the bat wing after Berlin blue infusion into the large lymphatic capillary bulbs, demonstrated the existence of open gaps or pores of at least 2.5μ diameter in these structures. The graft revascularization studies are of special interest to dermatologists and the presence of the large pores in skin lymphatic capillaries helps to explain the ready entrance of foreign particulate matter into lymph as one of the major protective functions of skin.

EPIDERMAL KINETICS

It is generally accepted that the primary function of the basal cell layer is that of mitotic activity in which the cells pass through a series of physiological and biochemical events to constitute the so-called "cell mitotic cycle." Baserga (4, 5) reviewed the numerous investigations which made possible the schema of basilar cell mitotic division. The cycle consists essentially of four different phases: (a) the S phase, or stage of nuclear DNA synthesis; (b) the G2 phase, or premitotic growth stage; (c) the M phase or mitosis; (d) the G1 phase or postmitotic growth period. Epidermal cell regeneration time is therefore defined as the sum of the individual phases. The M and S phases can be recognized in histological sections, when the cells have been exposed to appropriately labeled radioactive material. Weinstein & Frost (105) determined that the duration of mitosis of epidermal cells in man was 60 minutes, in contrast to the 90 minutes reported by Fisher (33). The duration of the S phase was calculated to be 5.9 hours by Christophers & Schaumloffel (14); whereas, Weinstein & Frost (105) indicated that the duration was >8.5 hours. The length of the $G1$ phase, or postmitotic growth period, has a relatively high degree of variability within groups of similar cells and between species, and has been estimated to be between 16 to 146 hours or greater. The $G2$, or premitotic growth phase ranges from 6 to 8 hours in length.

The recent advanced technique in high resolution radioautography has permitted the direct analysis of the kinetics on selected epidermal cell populations (29, 105, 106). Cell renewal is measured directly by means of intradermally injected tritiated thymidine to label the deoxyribonucleic acid (DNA) synthesizing cell. The analysis of human epidermal cell turnover time is then made using serial biopsy specimens in order to observe the upward migration of the labeled cells. Epstein & Maibach showed that 24 hours after thymidine H³ injection, the labeled nuclei appeared above the basal cell layer. Four to seven days were required before any labeling appeared in the mid-epidermis. It was emphasized that a significant number of stratum germinativum cells were still labeled at the seven day period. It was not until after 10 to 14 days that labeled nuclei appeared in the granular cell layer. Labeled nuclei were still observed in the mid-epidermis as late as 36 to 48 days after initial injection. On the basis of these studies epidermal cell renewal time was calculated to be between 13 to 18 days.

These autoradiographic techniques have shed additional light on the manner in which cells move from the basal cell layer to the surface. Epstein & Maibach point out that although the prickle cells move to the surface, the individual cells (labeled) seem to move randomly and haphazardly. They do not migrate as soldiers in a row, but as "stragglers." They showed that some cells may take as little time as a week to reach the surface in contrast to those that reach the surface last—in a period of approximately six weeks. Consequently, under these circumstances, transit time does not define renewal time. Moreover, epidermal cells migrate at different speeds and are not rigidly bound to each other. It appears that the attachment plaques between the cells are not necessarily fixed structures, but may attach and detach from adjacent cells, allowing them to alter their size, shape, and movement.

KERATINIZATION PROCESS

Morphologically, keratinization begins in the stratum germinativum where, in the cytoplasm of the cell, ultrastructures or their modifications can be traced to all layers of the epidermis until desquamation begins. Lavker & Matoltsy (53) classified into two distinct phases the differentiation that epithelial cells undergo in their change to the horny cells of the stratum corneum. The first phase is the *synthetic phase*, during which the cells no longer divide but produce three major constituents necessary for keratinization. These cytoplasmic constituents include: (*a*) the filamentous bundles; (*b*) the membrane coating granules; and (*c*) the keratohyalin granules. After the epithelial cell has synthesized these products, the second or *transformation phase* begins. During this phase mature granular cells change into horny cells which contain chiefly a filament-amorphous matrix complex enveloped by a thickened plasma membrane (62, 72).

Many fine electron dense filaments measuring from 50 to 80 Å in diameter are the first constituents of keratinization to appear within the cytoplasm of the cells of the basal cell layer. As the cell undergoes further differentiation and growth in its upward migration, the filaments aggregate and form tonofibrils measuring in size to approximately 250 Å. Interspersed among the filaments in the cyptoplasm are numerous ribosomes, which many investigators, according to Matoltsy & Parakkal (62), have assumed to be responsible for the protein synthesis necessary for their formation. The composition of the filamentous protein remains to be determined; however, these filaments seen in electron micrographs are presumed to be the same as the larger tonofilaments identified with light microscopy in the epidermal cells of the granular layer.

The next new organelle that may be identified in the cells as they move into the stratum Malpighii was named by Matolsty & Parakkal (62) the *membrane coating granule*. These submicroscopic cytoplasmic particles, first noted by Selby (97) in the granular layer, are usually found about the Golgi apparatus. Whether they are formed within the cytoplasmic substance or in association with the Golgi apparatus is unknown. Each membrane coating granule is enveloped by a double-layered membrane and its internal structure consists of alternating dense and less dense lamellae imbedded in an amorphous matrix.

During cellular differentiation, analyses of electron micrographs indicate that the membrane coating granules move toward the plasma membrane, align in rows and subsequently discharge into the intercellular space (62). Matoltsy postulated that the membrane coating granules are attached to the plasma membrane and are pushed out of the cells into the intercellular space.

The chemical composition of the membrane coating granules is unknown, nor has there been any specific function firmly associated with these organelles. Matoltsy & Parakkal (57, 62) have suggested that they may possibly serve as an intercellular cement substance to keep the horny layer intact and that they may also act as a barrier to constituents moving in or about the intercellular space.

The keratohyalin granule, first noted by Auffhammer in 1869, is the third structural organelle to develop within the keratinizing epithelial cell. The granules are seen within the cytoplasm of the cell before membrane coating granules become numerous. They develop within the vicinity of the filament bundles and the latter appear to pierce or penetrate many of the keratohyalin granules (12). Rhodin & Reith (84) postulated that both tonofibrils and keratohyalin granules stem independently from ribosomes which surround these structures. Fukuyama & Epstein (38) later showed the presence of a "histidine-rich" protein that is added to the tonofibrils. The tonofibrils aggregate and, possibly in combination with lipid substance, result in the formation of keratohyalin granules. The keratohyalin granules could then increase in size due to the accumulation of this "histidine-rich" protein by the tonofibrils. The large granules are located in the cells of the outermost layer of the granular cell layer that are presumed to be the direct precursors of the cornified cell.

Based on the biochemical properties of the keratohyalin granules, Matoltsy (61) indicated that "the differentiating epidermal cells synthesized a highly insoluble amorphous protein, rich in proline and sulfur-containing amino acids. This protein accumulates in the cytoplasm as tightly packed amorphous particles and forms viscid inclusions varying in size from a few to several micra. Association of keratohyalin with filaments in the horny cell enveloped by a resistant membrane results in a complex structure." This structure significantly contributes to the structural stability and chemical resistance of the horny layer.

In the transformation phase, differentiation of the granular cell into a horny cell continues. The nucleus disrupts, and the synthetic organelles within the cell disappear. Lysosomes are present and may be responsible for the rapid process of nuclear and organelle destruction. Only the filamentous bundles and keratohyalin granules remain. Within the disintegrated contents of the cell, an accumulation of filaments occurs along the periphery of the cell where keratohyalin is forming. These events result in the thickening of the membrane of the transformation cell. Matoltsy (58, 61) stated that the microvilli which develop on the cell wall during the transformation phase could conceivably allow the horny cells, when fully formed, to interdigitate tightly with each other.

Thus, the process of keratinization involves the formation and elimination of various cellular products. Brody (12) applied the term "keratin pattern" to the filamentous and amorphous material contained within the horny cells. According to Matoltsy (59), keratin is a word that is difficult to define. Previous workers classified keratin with regard to both its protein structural basis (alpha pattern), as well as to the specific type of chemical bond present, principally, the disulfide linkage. Matoltsy (59) reviewed the earlier and recent concepts of keratin and emphasized that three variations of keratin can be distinguished structurally, as well as chemically. For example, keratin may be described as filaments, as filaments imbedded in an amorphous matrix, or as an amorphous mass of fused granules; whereas chemically, keratin may be represented as having either low sulfur fibrous protein, low sulfur fibrous protein plus high sulfur amorphous protein, or high sulfur amorphous protein. Because of the complexity of the structural and chemical nature of the various keratins, the term "keratin" can only be used in a broad sense. This is understandable since many studies on keratin were concerned with proteins extracted from wool fibers and it is not known whether the keratin of the stratum corneum of the epidermis contains the same structural and chemical properties as wool fibers.

The keratinizing sequence of epidermal cells is shown diagrammatically in Figure 1. Two major phases of differentiation occur. As it moves away from the basal cell layer it enters the synthetic stage of differentiation, during which the epidermal cells are no longer dividing but are concentrating on the formation of three major cellular constituents: the filamentous bundles, the membrane coating granules, and the keratohyalin granules. Of these, only the membane coating granules leave the cells. The other two products remain within the cell and are found within the horny cell of the stratum corneum. The second major phase of differentiation, the transformation phase, is the conversion of the granular cell into a cornified cell. The kerato-hyalin granules are believed to be the direct precursors of the filamentous amorphous protein complex contained within the cells of the stratum corneum. The amorphous interfilamentous matrix found in the horny cells and the thickened and resistant plasma membrane together give the protective properties afforded by the stratum corneum.

PERCUTANEOUS ABSORPTION

It is now generally accepted that the barrier layer of the skin resides almost exclusively in the stratum corneum, and that diffusion through this horny layer is a passive process. However, a controversy developed concerning the three potential pathways of absorption through the stratum corneum, namely the follicular route, the eccrine ducts, and the interappendageal area.

Van Kooten & Mali (103) studied the significance of the sweat ducts as a pathway for percutaneous penetration using isolated human cadaver skin. Using a model of resistances, they analyzed the different pathways of percutaneous penetration followed by strong electrolytes and water through the skin. They calculated that 70 % of the total quantity of strong electrolytes permeates the skin through the sweat ducts. The hairs and sebaceous glands served a small role in the diffusion of smaller electrolytes.

Wahlberg (104) studied the question of transfollicular vs transepidermal absorption of the skin using in vivo and in vitro studies on the percutaneous absorption of sodium (^{22}Na) and mercuric (^{203}Hg) chloride in hairy and non-hairy guinea pig skin. His results indicated that absorption in vivo occurred primarily by way of the transepidermal route. The author emphasized, however, that his in vitro studies showed that, to the contrary, absorption was greater through hairy skin. He concluded that "absorption in vitro occurs principally via the transepidermal route, . . . divergent results were obtained if in vivo or in vitro techniques were used."

Scheuplein's work (92, 93) offers a clearer understanding and reconciles

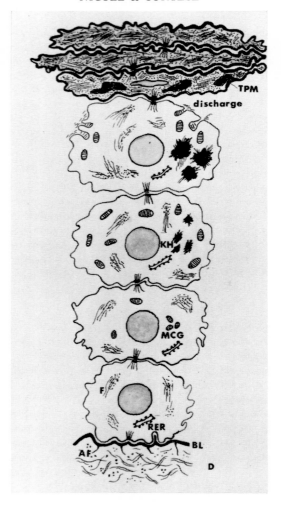

FIGURE 1. Schematic illustration of characteristic structural changes in mammalian cells. In the basal cell, rough-surfaced endoplasmic reticulum (*RER*) is scanty, filaments (*F*) are abundant. During differentiation many filament bundles are seen scattered throughout the cytoplasm. Membrane-coating granules (*MCG*) appear early; after migrating toward the cell periphery their lamellar content is discharged into the intercellular space. Keratohyalin (*KH*) is deposited later. During transformation the plasma membrane thickens (*TPM*), the major cell constituents disintegrate, except the filaments. The horny cells are filled with a filament-amorphous matrix complex. Note that collagen is randomly oriented in the dermis (*D*), and the basal lamina (*BL*) is bound to the dermis by numerous anchor fibrils (*AF*). (Taken from Matoltsy, A. G. 1969. Keratinization of the Avian Epidermis. An Ultrastructural Study of the Newborn Chick Skin. *J. Ultrastruct. Res.* 29:455. By permission of the publisher: Copyright Academic Press.)

the many investigations which have attempted to determine the predominant route of skin permeability. He found by using a mathematical analysis of skin diffusion that the penetration route via the appendages was quite active during the initial stage of diffusion. However, after a certain period of time, a steady-state diffusion through the substance of the stratum corneum became the most predominant route of penetration. Under appropriate conditions, therefore, any one of the above mentioned routes of penetration may be operable.

Buerger (13) reported that the penetration of many compounds through animal skins follows first order kinetics. Controversy still exists concerning whether the steady-state diffusion through the stratum corneum occurs transcellularly or intracellularly. Scheuplein (92) pointed out that the polarity and molecular weight of molecules undergoing percutaneous absorption determines the route of penetration. Moreover, Scheuplein (93) and Blank et al (8) showed that the major route of absorption of water and small molecular weight polar alcohols during steady-state diffusion is transcellular through "boundwater" regions in the hydrated stratum corneum.

A controversy initially arose as to the exact location of the barrier zone of the epidermis. At one time it was thought that the barrier layer resided between the stratum granulosum and stratum corneum (55, 86, 98). It is now generally accepted that the barrier layer of the skin resides in the stratum corneum. Kligman (50) implied that the impermeable properties of adult skin is attributed to its keratin layer. This statement is in agreement with the recent work of Parmley & Seeds (74). Using keratinized and unkeratinized human fetal skin and studying the in vitro diffusion of isotopic water (THO), the authors found that in the early stages of pregnancy, the skin is very permeable to tritiated water. They postulated that during this time the skin might serve as a major pathway for solute and water exchange between amniotic fluid and the fetus. However, as the fetus increased in age, (up to 24 weeks gestational age) a large decrease in skin permeability to tritiated water was found when early keratinization was demonstrable. They concluded that the development of the keratin layer imparts to the skin its relative impermeable properties.

Fredriksson (35) studied the influence of solvents and surfactants on the permeability of guinea pig skin. He found that pretreatment of the skin with water alone had little or no influence on the absorption of Sarin isopropoxymethylphosphoryl fluoride—an organophosphorus cholinesterase inhibitor. As absorption of this inhibitor resulted in respiratory arrest and death of the animal, the time rate of absorption was related to the length of time from application of the compound onto the skin until death occurs. Mere blotting of the skin did not produce any mechanical injury on the epidermal barrier. Pretreatment of skin for at least 30 minutes prior to Sarin exposure with acetone, ethanol, ether, chloroform, soap, cationic and anionic surfactants produced significant decreases in the survival time of the animals. He noted that prolonged contact is necessary in order to elicit the barrier destroying activity, and that once the barrier was disturbed its return to normal requires some time.

Feldmann & Maibach (31) studied the penetration of labeled ^{14}C-hydrocortisone through normal human skin when the stratum corneum had been stripped by adhesive tape or subjected to occlusive wrap. Using a logarithmic regression curve, they showed that the curve had the same slope after topical application of labeled hydrocortisone whether the stratum corneum had been stripped, occluded or both.

They proposed that the epidermis might possess two barriers to penetration. The first barrier would be the stratum corneum, because binding of the radiolabeled compound in large quantities prevented its distribution to the deeper layers. The second barrier would comprise the malpighian and basal cell layers. They noted that this second barrier zone may not have importance in intact skin because of the great efficiency of the stratum corneum barrier, but could have significance in diseased or injured skin. The rapid recovery of the upper barrier layer following cellophane stripping reported by Matoltsy et al (63) also suggests that there exists a secondary site besides the stratum corneum which limits skin permeability.

The biochemical and ultrastructural basis whereby horny cells are able to limit transepidermal diffusion is not yet completely understood. Matoltsy (60) reported on the biochemical analysis of the stratum corneum and indicated that the chief constituents are protein, lipids (7–9%), carbohydrates, and an unidentified material of low molecular weight. In his investigations of the chemical nature of the water barrier he noted that the cytoplasmic proteins of "keratin" were important for their barrier function and that the plasma membrane of the horny cell may also participate in limiting transepidermal permeability.

Malkinson (55) and Tregear (101) have listed in detail numerous factors that affect the permeability of the stratum corneum. For example, permeability is modified by species, age of the skin, region of the body, changes in the microcirculation, skin surface temperature, and surface sebum film. At the same time, the penetrability of the solvents into the stratum corneum is also determined by their physical and chemical properties and by the duration of their application.

Recently, dimethyl sulfoxide was shown to enhance percutaneous penetration. There resulted numerous in vitro and in vivo investigations to determine its therapeutic effectiveness as a topical medicament, as well as its effectiveness as a vehicle for dermatomedicaments which could be carried directly into diseased skin. The role that dimethyl sulfoxide may have in dermatology was recently reviewed in detail by Cortese (19).

MELANOGENESIS

Skin pigmentation in man has many facets both scientific and sociological that support the intense interest and considerable efforts of the numerous studies on the underlying systemic and cellular mechanisms involved. The last quarter century has seen amazing advances in knowledge of these mechanisms and the emergence of some understanding of how the chemical, cellular and systemic activities are integrated and regulated. But many details remain unresolved as Fitzpatrick et al (34) in their informative review of melanin biology clearly indicate in their lists of things that remain to be done.

The story of skin pigmentation begins with the study of the specialized cells where pigment is formed. The pioneering works of Rawales on their embryological origin in the neural crest and of Masson on their sole responsibility for melanin production have established as the center of focus for melanogenesis studies the dendritic cells in the basal layer of the epidermis. The characteristic dendritic structure of melanocytes is shared by the Langerhan cell, which is found in nearly equivalent numbers but concentrated more in the upper malpighian layer. The question of common origin and possible interconversion of these two cell types has been the subject of numerous studies (76). Their separate identity depends primarily on different histochemical responses. The Langerhan cell does not respond with melanin formation when incubated with dopa but does give a positive ATPase reaction. Melanocytes exhibit the opposite actions with these tests for enzymatic activity, which clearly indicates their cytoplasm contains the enzyme tyrosinase. Melanin, the pigment responsible for skin and hair color in man and animals, is formed through the action of tyrosinase on tyrosine. Details of the chemistry involved, including the final combination with a protein moiety, will not be reviewed here. The major aspects of melanin synthesis and distinguishing characteristics of the various melanins have been reviewed in considerable detail by Duchon et al (24).

Wolff & Winkelmann (107) studied with histochemical techniques the response of the dendritic cells in the epidermis of the guinea pig to ultraviolet irradiation. Their results showed no increase in either ATPase positive cells or aminopeptidase activity. Both of these enzymatic mechanisms are restricted to Langerhan cells in the epidermis. In contrast was the striking increase in both numbers and reaction intensity of dopa positive cells which indicates tyrosinase activity and the location of melanocytes. Quevedo et al (80) using similar techniques with human skin biopsies after uv irradiation but limiting their study to population and activity changes in dopa positive cells, confirmed the apparent increase in melanocytes with uv irradiation and discussed the possible origin of the increased cell numbers. Although recognizing the possibility that new melanocytes could be formed by increased mitosis similar to that reported for mouse skin by Quevedo et al (78), they believe that with human skin it is more probable that the increase in apparent melanocytes represents stimulation of melanin production in inactive melanocytes already present (79). Mishima & Widlan (65) have explored in considerable detail the existence of quiescent or dormant melanocytes in nonactivated skin. Their data indicates that such cells can be identified in skin by a staining technique employing ammoniacal silver nitrate and gold chloride.

The formation of melanin within the cytoplasm of the melanocyte, with regard both to the cell organelles involved and to its correlation with the chemical transformations concerned has been studied in great detail. The now classical sequence of events has been reviewed by Fitzpatrick et al (34). This schema proposes that tyrosinase originates with the ribosomes. It is then associated with the rough and smooth surface membranes and finally appears in smooth-walled vacuoles that arise from Golgi vesicles. These vacuoles increase in size and acquire a characteristic inner protein structural organization prior to the appearance of melanin. As these vacuoles or premelanosomes grow in size and migrate toward the cell periphery, they gradually exhibit increasing accumulation of the black pigment, melanin. Eventually they become fully packed with melanin and lose their tyrosinase activity. These then are the fully formed melanosomes and may be called melanin granules. They migrate into the dendritic extensions of the melanocyte and are transferred into the protoplasm of the associated cluster of malpighian cells.

The classical picture of melanogenesis was largely based on studies of melanoma cells from the Harding-Possey mouse melanomas (95). Hunter et al (46) recently reported on their investigation of melanin formation in normal human epidermis. To ensure maximal melanogenesis the area was first irradiated with a 6X M.E.D. (minimum erythema dose) level of ultraviolet light. Biopsies of irradiated skin were subjected either to dopa, or to tyrosine incubation. As controls, biopises from unirradiated adjacent sites were treated similarly except that no tyrosine of dopa was added to the incubation buffer. Electron micrographs from biopsies taken 72 hours after irradiation from both the tyrosine and the dopa incubations clearly showed considerable accumulation of what they term "reaction product" within the cytoplasm. Linear reaction product concentrations were associated with both rough and smooth endoplasmic reticulum. The concentration of smooth membrane structures lying closely adjacent to the Golgi apparatus was the most active site. Vesicular concentrations of reaction product appeared to arise from the Golgi apparatus. They also identified other fair sized vacuoles empty of any reaction product that were identical to premelanosomes. Their data does not provide any evidence of vacuoles filled with coalescing reaction product or of how reaction product became associated within the premelanosome to form the mature melanosome. Their interpretation of melanogenesis in human skin melanocytes is shown in Figure 2.

Skin color is primarily determined by the number and type of distribution of the mature melanosomes or melanin granules. As Szabo (99) points out most investigators report essentially equal numbers of melanocytes in the basal cell layer in both Caucasoid and Negroid skin. Cochran (18) has recently studied the relative distribution of melanocytes to keratinocytes in the adult epidermis. He finds the ratio to be approximately 1:10. Mitchell (66) reports a higher melanocyte to keratinocyte ratio of 1:6 in the epidermis of the Australian aborigine. The aborgine's melanosomes are both larger,

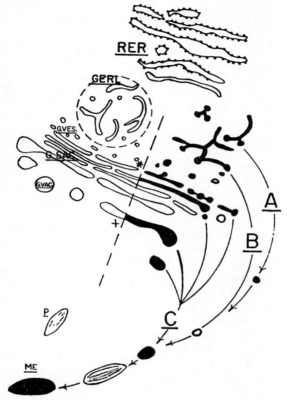

FIGURE 2. Composite diagram of the Golgi region in a melanocyte. To the left of the interrupted line the Golgi apparatus has been labelled according to the terminology used in this text: *G. VES*: Golgi vesicles; *G. SAC*: Golgi saccules; *G. VAC*: Golgi vacuoles: *GERL*: Golgi associated system of smooth endoplasmic reticulum; *RER*: Rough endoplasmic reticulum. * Vesicular face of the apparatus. + Vacuolar face of the apparatus. The subcellular localization of reaction product is illustrated at the right of the interrupted line. The arrows indicate suggested pathways in the development of the melanosome (*ME*): *A* From smooth endoplasmic reticulum. *B* From smooth endoplasmic reticulum associated with the Golgi complex (*GERL*). *C* From all parts of the Golgi apparatus. Of these, *B* pathway appears to be the most common. Note the structures resembling the matrix of premelanosomes (*P*) which contains no reaction product, even though it is present in surrounding vesicles. [From (46). By permission of the publisher: Copyright The Williams and Wilkins Company.]

exhibit greater melanin activity and are less fragile than those of Caucasoid skin. The greater stability of the aborigine's melanosomes within the keratinocyte is similar to that found in Negroid skin. This stability of melanosomes after their incorporation into the cytoplasm of the malpighian cells along with their absolute increase in numbers are the major causes of the marked difference in skin color between "black" and "white" populations.

The control of melanogenesis in various types of skin, especially in mice, rats, and guinea pigs, where sharply delineated patterns of skin color are commonly found have been studied in considerable detail. Genetic determination of such patterns have been investigated by several workers (77). Moyer (68) studied mice that possessed genes at six different allelic series known to act within the melanoblast. He demonstrated that the genes alter melanin formation by changing the patterns of subunit aggregation within the protein structure developed within the melanosomes. In addition, he noted that they also alter the intracellular sites where matrix protein is formed. He also reported that another gene locus acts by altering the immediate chemical environment where the melanocyte is differentiating and can thus modify the type of enzymatic action that developed later within the melanosome. In his experiments this resulted in a significant alteration in the character of the pigment eventually formed.

The marked variation in melanogenic activity observed in melanocytes in different skins and the speed with which ultraviolet light irradiation evokes increased melanogenesis has given rise to the theory that an inhibitory system exists in melanocytes that blocks melanogenesis. Halprin and Ohkawara (43) reviewed the data supporting reduced glutathione as the major inhibitor. They found that a glutathione reductase system within the melanocytes ordinarily keeps 90% of the glutathione present in the reduced state. They further reported ultraviolet irradiation blocks the reductase system, allowing much of the glutathione to be shifted into the oxidized or $-S-S$ condition. In the reduced or $-SH-$ state glutathione can inhibit melanin formation either by blocking tyrosinase directly or by combining to form a stable complex with some product in the tyrosine-tyrosinase reaction (96). Halprin & Ohkawara further reported that the glutathione reductase system in Negroid skin is both different from and much less efficient than that in Caucasoid skin—resulting in a significant lowering of reduced glutathione levels in Negroid melanocytes. This, they suggested, might account at least in part for the greater melanogenesis activity in Negroid skin. However, other factors must also be responsible for skin color. Melanosomes in the granular layer cells of Negroid skin retain their intact form, while in Caucasoid skin the melanin granules are destroyed and the melanin is dispersed throughout the cell's cytoplasm.

PHOTOPHYSIOLOGY

Closely associated with the protective action of skin against the harmful effects of various portions of the radiant energy spectrum are the cellular changes induced by ultraviolet irradiation. Unfortunately, most of the responses of skin to uv irradiation seem to fall into the category of pathological physiology. Indeed even a casual perusal of skin responses to actinic radiation of wavelengths between 280 and 320 nm soon evokes wonderment at the current cult of sun worship among Caucasians. One is reminded of the popular ballad of some years ago that was entitled "Mad Dogs and Englishmen Go Out in the Mid-Day Sun." The justification for the inclusion in this review of a consideration of the various studies on the skin response to uv irradiation is its ubiquitous nature and the accepted belief that the various shades of tan on Caucasian skin are both beautiful and healthful. Beauty is, of course, in the eyes of the beholder, but the only healthful result of the uv irradiation of any normal skin is the production of vitamin D. Johnson & Daniels (49) in their discussion of this subject, point out that the current food fortification with vitamins makes solar irradiation of skin no longer a necessary condition for health. But even if for some reason it is necessary to satisfy one's vitamin D requirements through solar action on skin, very slight amounts of irradiation of limited areas of skin are sufficient.

That increased pigmentation of skin results from adequate exposure to solar uv radiation has long been appreciated. Hunter et al (46) took advantage of this fact in their recent study of melanogenesis in normal human melanocytes. Quevedo et al, (79) investigating the cellular source and distribution of the increased pigmentation in human skin with uv irradiation, could find no evidence in the basal epidermal layer of either increased melanocyte mitosis or immigration. Rather, their data showed intensification of melanogenesis in the dopa-positive melanocytes. They also noted an increase of melanin in keratinocytes following irradiation, which indicates increased transfer of melanosomes from the dendrites of the melanocytes. In a later study Quevedo et al (80) confirmed the decrease with age of epidermal melanocytes in human buttock skin at about 20% per 10 years of age but also found that uv irradiation of buttock skin at any age level markedly increased melanogenesis and dopa-positive melanocytes.

Freeman et al (36) have discussed the nature of the solar uv radiation that actually acts on human skin. It is, of course, well established that little radiation of wavelengths shorter than 290 nm penetrates the atmosphere at any time or place. However, the effective amount and character of the radiation that reaches a given person at a given time depends on the air mass thickness and on the sun ray's angle of incidence at the time. Even at noon in the tropics, increased air mass thickness decreases the intensity of the shorter wavelengths, thereby decreasing the sunburn effectiveness of the radiation. With an air mass of 1, only 10% of the rays effective for sunburn are longer than 314 nm, while with an air mass of 3 in otherwise equivalent conditions, some 34% of the effective rays are longer than 314 nm.

The pathological changes associated with uv irradiation are both transitory and long lasting. The typical sunburn response, so fully appreciated at one time or another by most hypopigmented individuals, consists of a series of short lasting responses listed succinctly by Johnson & Daniels (49) as erythema, edema, blistering, altered barrier function, and desquamation. Recovery usually brings with it increased skin pigmentation which along with epidermal thickening is of course the body's attempt to alleviate these responses to additional exposures. As elaborated in their review, Johnson & Daniels (49) indicated that the long term changes in skin subjected to repeated solar irradiation are largely due to alterations in the collagen bundles and elastic tissue structures of the dermis. Numerous investigations both with man and with experimental animals provide evidence that carcinoma, sarcoma, and even melanoma can result from solar irradiation.

Since solar uv radiation is extremely variable and difficult to use in experimental work, most studies of the mechanisms involved either in physiological adjustments or in pathological-physiological changes following uv irradiation use artificial light sources. Sayre et al (91) described an efficient uv light and later (90) reported quantitative data concerning its use in biological studies. Their data also supports the theory of the simple additive action of the various wavelengths of the incident rays in producing skin responses. Recently Berger (7) described a uv light source especially suited to simulate solar radiation.

The great number of important pathological-physiological skin studies cannot be reviewed in detail here. These have shown that nearly every cellular and subcellular mechanism of epidermal cells can be affected. Johnson & Daniels (49) have suggested that when injury to subcellular lysosomes occurs there is a subsequent release of proteolytic enzymes into the cell cytoplasm. Grice et al (42) found that uv irradiation in some way blocks the normal fibrinolytic system associated with the dermal vasculature. They have suggested that the untoward effects of uv irradiation is somehow related to this loss of fibrinolytic activity. Since vascular blockage is not usually associated with mild erythematous conditions it is unclear how blockage of fibrinolytic activity could underlie most pathological responses to uv irradiation. Several investigators have explored the changes in protein synthesis (30) while others have suggested that inherent protective mechanisms such as the GSH inhibition of tyrosinase are blocked by the action of uv light (46).

Several studies have been directed primarily toward the vascular responses in the dermal layer in attempts to explain the initial and delayed erythema that occurs. Since it is doubtful that much solar uv irradiation—at least of wavelengths shorter than 320 nm—penetrates into even the upper layer of the dermis, the vascular responses, particularly of the larger vessels, may be secondary in nature. Epstein & Winkelmann (28) reported that kinins in the perfusate of irradiated human skin reached a maximum within 20 minutes after irradiation and then disappeared. They thought this might be associated with an initial transitory erythema response. However, Greaves & Søndergaard (39) using similar techniques, although finding that several physiological-pharmacological substances could be identified at times in the perfusate, could not confirm Epstein & Winkelmanns' findings. No really satisfactory description of the mechanism underlying the delayed erythema has yet been advanced.

SEBACEOUS GLANDS AND SEBUM PRODUCTION

Cell renewal and differentiation in human sebaceous glands were elucidated by Epstein & Epstein (27), employing autoradiographic analysis of biopsy specimens of sebaceous glands whose cells had been labeled with tritiated thymidine-H³. Labeled nuclei were demonstrated at the perimeter of the sebaceous glands and in the germinative layer within 40 minutes after interdermal injection of the radioisotope. Not until 7 to 9 days after injection did most of the labeled cells appear in the center of the gland. By the 14th day, all of the labeled cells had begun to differentiate and only an occasional central cell remained labeled at 21 to 28 days. On the basis of average labeled cell counts the authors calculated the renewal time at 7.4 days—i.e. the time required for the number of new cells produced to equal the total number of cells present in the gland. Their study indicated that new acini seemed to develop continuously, undergo differentiation and then disappear.

Zelickson (109) reviewed the current concepts in ultrastructural anatomy and in the physiology of the sebaceous gland cells. He categorized the life cycle of sebaceous cells into three distinct cell types: (a) the *peripheral cells* which are rich in ribosomes and are generally found against the basement membrane that surrounds the acinus; (b) the *partially differentiated cells*, which are actively synthesizing and storing sebum droplets within the cell, and (c) the *fully differentiated cells*, which contain a multitude of tightly packed sebum vacuoles ready to be released upon rupture of the cell. Sebaceous gland cell differentiation progresses in a centripetal direction (from periphery to central) and occurs, as mentioned above, in about seven days. The specific electron microscopic details of the ultrastructural contents of the cells are excellently covered in that review.

The specific events in the cellular maturation of sebaceous gland cells and sebum lipogenesis represent a dynamic biologic process. Much of our understanding and appreciation of this process has been made possible by refined electron photomicrographic analysis of "captured" living events. In brief, glycogen, smooth endoplasmic reticulum, and ribosomes predominate in the cytoplasm of cells engaged in the early phase of lipogenesis. Later in the cellular maturation, numerous mitochondria, along with smooth surface vesicles, ribosomes, glycogen, and Golgi membranes, fill the cytoplasmic substance of the cell. As maturation is completed, numerous lipid vacuoles, smooth membranes, and a minimal number of ribosomes and mitochondria are seen within the cells. The early work of Rogers (85) and Palay (73) suggested that it is the smooth surface membranes of the cell's endoplasmic reticulum which are primarily involved in lipogenesis. The mitochondria may play a role in providing the necessary energy for lipid synthesis. Hibbs (45) and Ellis & Henrikson (25) found that the sebaceous glands of man have prominent Golgi cisternae from which the lipid storage vacuoles are possibly derived.

The sebum contained within the sebaceous gland cell consists of a complex mixture of lipid substances whose specific chemical compositions are not completely known. The difficulty in obtaining an accurate and detailed biochemical analysis of sebum stems from the fact that pure sebum samples are not readily obtainable directly from within the gland substance. Consequently, analyses have in general been performed on the skin surface lipid film, which consists of a mixture of sebum and epidermal lipids. Nicholaides (69) reviewed the origin, composition and possible function of human skin surface lipids. The various classes of compounds identified include fatty acids, triglycerides, sterols, sterol esters, wax esters and other aliphatic components. In a biochemical analysis of human skin surface lipids compared with those of eighteen other species of animals, Nicholaides (70) showed that the surface lipids of man are unique. Only man produces a surface lipid which consists predominantly of triglycerides, their breakdown products, and squalene. Free fatty acids comprise approximately 30% of the human skin surface lipid. More than half of these fatty acids consist of saturated and unsaturated C_{16} and C_{18} acids. In addition, a wide range of branched and unbranched C_{17}, C_{15}, and C_{14} and some shorter carbon chain fatty acids have also been identified (69). Downing et al (23) showed in their studies that the concentration of free fatty acids in the skin surface lipid differed widely between subjects but showed little variation between samples collected successively from the same subject over an extended period of time. Their studies also supported the findings of previous investigators that the free fatty acids appear to be derived exclusively from the triglycerides originating primarily from the sebaceous glands.

Endocrine control and dietary effects on sebaceous gland activity have been discussed elsewhere (54, 67). Briefly, the sebaceous glands are primarily under the control of androgens. It has not yet been resolved whether progesterone affects the sebaceous glands in physiological doses. Estrogens have been shown to decrease the size of the sebaceous glands of animals, as well as to reduce sebum production in man. Current evidence indicates that sebum production is stimulated primarily by androgens originating either in the testes, adrenal glands, or ovaries. Estrogen has been found to be the only gonadal hormone capable of inhibiting sebum production. The role of the pituitary gland to facilitate sebum production is in question. There is insufficient data at present to show the composition of sebum to be influenced by dietary factors.

The physiologic concepts of sebum delivery to the skin surface has been an intriguing subject. Starling earlier suggested that the contraction of the arrectores pyloris muscle played a role in sebum delivery. Emanuel (26) advanced the feedback theory which was later repudiated. Kligman & Shelley (51) stated that ". . . the sebaceous gland functions continuously without regard to what is on the surface." He concluded that sebum is delivered to the skin surface by the capillary wick action of the stratum corneum.

The recent studies of Cortese & Nicoll (20) have introduced a new consideration to the study of the mechanism of sebum delivery in mammalian skin. In vivo observations of the pilosebaceous unit in the bat wing demonstrated that a contractile tissue sheath surrounds the sebaceous glands. The sheath exhibited normal rhythmical contractions of approximately four per minute. Each contraction distorted and produced kneading effect on the sebaceous glands. Both the duration of the individual phases of the contraction cycle and the strength of the contractions were readily modified by changes in the chemical composition of the immediate environment. As sebum does not appear in liquid drops on the skin surface at any time, the authors were unable to observe the direct delivery of sebum droplets to the skin surface in response to contraction of the sheath. In addition, the in vivo observations on maturing glands revealed the development and accumulation of serum droplets within the gland. In more mature glands, large sebum droplets were present which were thought to represent a coalescense of the smaller droplets, while in some glands the sebum was found to fill the gland completely.

In regard to the biological significance of this activity Cortese and Nicoll suggest that "the functional significance of the sheath's contractile action . . . could aid in the rupture of individual sebaceous gland cells as they disintegrate to release sebum. The contractions may assist in sebum expulsion by pressing on the entire sebaceous structure to produce brief transitory gradients toward the skin surface. It is also possible that the sheath is associated with some developmental phase of the pilosebaceous unit and is, then, essentially vestigial in character in mature units. Finally, the contractile tissue elements might be homologous to the piloerector muscle of other mammals."

BRIEFLY NOTED

In an intriguing article very well documented both from historical and research points of view, Jenkinson (48) suggests the term "apocrine" should be dropped to describe the sweat gland. As he notes, the original concept that "apocrine" sweat was formed by shedding the outer portion of the secretory cell is now known to be incorrect.

Cleaver (15, 16) in a brilliant investigation showed that the normal enzymatic repair system which is responsible for the removal and replacement of the uv damaged DNA base is lacking in the fibroblasts in the skin of patients with xeroderma pigmentosum. The cells can repair other types of DNA damage. This finding may prove useful in resolving carcinogenesis in prone individuals.

Abe et al (1) used a radio-immune assay technique to clarify regulation of B-melanocyte stimulating hormone (B-MSH) in normal subjects and in those with pituitary-adrenal disorder. They concluded the B-MSH secretion is controlled by the same factors that regulate ACTH.

Baden & Bonar (3) isolated α-fibrous protein from the insoluble residue of stratum corneum of human palms and soles and defined its physical and chemical properties. The protein has a characteristic alpha pattern, an apparent molecular weight of 25 million, and yielded a carboxymethyl derivative which showed a helical content of 50%.

Sato & Dobson (89) demonstrated the equal enzyme activity of sodium-potassium-magnesium activated adenosine triphosphatase (N+K-ATPase) in the duct and the secretory coil of Rhesus monkey palm sweat glands. This finding suggested that sodium is actively transported in both areas. The probable mechanism of formation of the secretory fluid depends on active sodium transport by the secretory cells followed by the passive diffusion of water and chloride. Sodium is actively reabsorbed in the duct in an excess of water giving a hypotonic fluid.

Ramasastry et al (81) studied the change in chemical composition of skin surface lipids in humans from age 5 days to 15 years old. Cholesterol concentrations were low at birth, maximum at age 6, and low at age 9, corresponding to the adult level. Wax esters were high at birth, low between ages 3–6 and returned to the higher adult level by age 9. No difference between age groups were found for triglyceride and free fatty acid levels. Squalene concentrations were highly variable.

LITERATURE CITED

1. Abe, K., Nicholson, W. E., Liddle, G. W., Orth, D. N., Island, D. P. 1969. Normal and Abnormal Regulation of B-MSH in Man. *J. Clin. Invest.* 48:1580-85

2. Alpert, J. S., Coffman, J. D. 1969. Effect of Intravenous Epinephrine on Skeletal Muscle, Skin, and Subcutaneous Blood Flow. *Am. J. Physiol.* 216:156-60

3. Baden, H. P., Bonar, L. 1968. The α-Fibrous Proteins of Epidermis. *J. Invest. Dermatol.* 51:478-83

4. Baserga, R. 1968. Biochemistry of the Cell Cycle: A Review. *Cell Tissue Kinet.* 1:167-91

5. Baserga, R. 1965. The Relationship of the Cell Cycle to Tumor Growth and Control of Cell Division. A Review. *Canc. Res.* 25:581-95

6. Beiser, G. D., et al. 1970. The Role of Skin and Muscle Resistance Vessels in Reflexes Mediated by the Baroreceptor System. *J. Clin. Invest.* 49:225-31

7. Berger, D. S. 1969. Specification and Design of Solar Ultraviolet Simulators. *J. Invest. Dermatol.* 53:192-99

8. Blank, I. H., Scheuplein, R. J., MacFarlane, D. J. 1967. Mechanism of Percutaneous Absorption. III. The Effect of Temperature on the Transport of Non-Electrolytes Across the Skin. *J. Invest. Dermatol.* 49:582-89

9. Bond, R. F., Manley, E. S., Green, H. D. 1967. Cutaneous and Skeletal Muscle Vascular Responses to Hemorrhage and Irreversible Shock. *Am. J. Physiol.* 212:488-97

10. Bond, R. F., Lackey, G. F., Taxis, J. A., Green, H. D. 1970. Factors Governing Cutaneous Vasoconstriction During Hemorrhage. *Am. J. Physiol.* 219:1210-15

11. Bosley, P. G. H. J. 1961. A Consideration of Pathological Morphology in the Nailbed Capillary Network of Human Subjects. *Bibl. Anat.* 1:229-38

12. Brody, I. 1959. The Keratinization of Epidermal Cells of Normal Guinea Pig Skin as Revealed by Electron Microscopy. *J. Ultrastruct. Res.* 2:482-511

13. Buerger, A. A. 1967. A Theory of Integumental Penetration. *J. Theor. Biol.* 14:66-73

14. Christophers, E., Schaumloffel, E. 1967. Zer DNS-Synthesizeit in der Menschlichen Epidermis. *Arch. Klin. Exp. Dermatol.* 228:57-64

15. Cleaver, J. E. 1969. Xeroderma Pigmentosum. A Human Disease in which an Initial Stage of DNA Repair is Defective. *Proc. Nat. Acad. Sci.* 63:428-35

16. Cleaver, J. E. 1970. DNA Damage and Repair in Light-Sensitive Human Skin Disease. *J. Invest. Dermatol.* 54:181-95

17. Cliff, W. J., Nicoll, P. A. 1970. Structure and Function of Lymphatic Vessels of the Bat's Wing. *Quart. J. Exp. Physiol.* 55:112-21

18. Cochran, A. J. 1970. The Incidence of Melanocytes in Normal Human Skin. *J. Invest. Dermatol.* 55:65-70

19. Cortese, T. A., Jr. 1971. DMSO in Dermatology. *Dimethyl Sulfoxide*, ed. S. W. Jacob, E. E. Rosenbaum, D. C. Wood, Vol. 1. New York: Marcel Dekker. 479 pp.

20. Cortese, T. A., Jr., Nicoll, P. A. 1970. In Vivo Observations of Skin Appendages in the Bat Wing. *J. Invest. Dermatol.* 54:1-10

21. Davis, E., Landau, J. 1966. *Clinical Capillary Microscopy.* Springfield: Thomas. 231 pp.

22. Dawber, R., Shuster, S. 1971. Scanning Electron Microscopy of Dermal Fibrous Tissue Networks in Normal Skin, Solar Elastosis and Pseudo-Xanthoma Elasticum. *Brit. J. Dermatol.* 84:130-34

23. Downing, D. T., Strauss, J. S., Pochi, P. E. 1969. Variability in the Chemical Composition of Human Skin Surface Lipids. *J. Invest. Dermatol.* 53:322-27

24. Duchon, J., Fitzpatrick, T. B., Seiji, M. 1968. *The Year Book of Dermatology*, ed. A. W. Kopf, 6-33. Chicago: Yearb. Med.

25. Ellis, R. A., Henrikson, R. C. 1963. The Ultrastructure of the Sebaceous Glands of Man. *Advan. Biol. Skin* 4:94-109

26. Emanuel, S. 1938. Mechanism of the Sebum Secretion. *Acta Dermato Venereol.* 19:1-18

27. Epstein, E. H., Jr., Epstein, W. L. 1966. New Cell Formation in Human Sebaceous Glands. *J. Invest. Dermatol.* 46:453-58

28. Epstein, J. H., Winkelmann, R. K. 1967. Ultraviolet Light Induced

Kinin Formation in Human Skin. *Arch. Dermatol.* 95:532-36

29. Epstein, W. L., Maibach, H. I. 1965. Cell Renewal in Human Epidermis. *Arch. Dermatol.* 92:462-68

30. Epstein, W. L., Fukuyama, K., Epstein, J. H. 1969. Early Effects of Ultraviolet Light on DNA Synthesis in Human Skin *In Vivo. Arch. Dermatol.* 100:84-89

31. Feldmann, R. J., Maibach, H. I. 1965. Penetration of ¹⁴C Hydrocortisone Through Normal Skin. *Arch. Dermatol.* 91:661-66

32. Fewings, J. D., Hyman, C., Walsh, J. A., Whelan, R. F. 1970. The Role of Forearm Skin and Muscle Vessels in Reactive Hyperaemia. *Aust. J. Exp. Biol.* 48:179-86

33. Fisher, L. B. 1968. Determination of the Normal Rate and Duration of Mitosis in Human Epidermis. *Brit. J. Dermatol.* 80:24-28

34. Fitzpatrick, T. B., Miyamoto, M., Ishikawa, K. 1967. The Evolution of Concepts of Melanin Biology. *Advan. Biol. Skin* 8:1-30

35. Fredriksson, T. 1969. Influence of Solvents and Surface Active Agents on the Barrier Function of the Skin Towards Sarin. *Acta Dermato Venereol.* 49:55-58

36. Freeman, R. G., Owens, D. W., Knox, J. M., Hudson, H. T. 1966. Relative Energy Requirements for an Erythemal Response of Skin to Monochromatic Wave Lengths of Ultraviolet Present in the Solar Spectrum. *J. Invest. Dermatol.* 47:586-92

37. Frewin, D. B. 1969. The Physiology of the Cutaneous Circulation in Man. *Aust. J. Dermatol.* 10:61-74

38. Fukuyama, K., Epstein, W. L. 1967. Ultrastructural Autoradiographic Studies of Keratohyalin Granule Formation. *J. Invest. Dermatol.* 49:595-604

39. Greaves, M. W., Søndergaard, J. 1970. Pharmacologic Agents Released in Ultraviolet Inflammation Studied by Continuous Skin Perfusion. *J. Invest. Dermatol.* 54:365-67

40. Green, H. D., Rapela, C. E. 1964. Blood Flow in Passive Vascular Beds. *Cir. Res.* Suppl. 1, 14, 15:11-16

41. Greenfield, A. D. M. 1963. The Circulation Through the Skin. *Handb. Physiol.* 2:1325-51

42. Grice, K., Ryan, T. J., Magnus, I. A. 1970. Fibrinolytic Activity in

Lesions Produced by Monochromator Ultraviolet Irradiation in Various Photodermatoses. *Brit. J. Dermatol.* 83:637-49

43. Halprin, K., Ohkawara, A. 1968. Human Pigmentation: The Role of Glutathione. *Advan. Biol. Skin* 8:241-51

44. Hammond, M. C., Davis, D. L., Dow, P. 1969. Rate of Development of Constrictor Responses of the Dog Paw Vasculature. *Am. J. Physiol.* 216:414-20

45. Hibbs, R. J. 1962. Electron Microscopy of Human Axillary Sebaceous Glands. *J. Invest. Dermatol.* 38:329-38

46. Hunter, J. A., Mottaz, J. H., Zelickson, A. S. 1970. Melanogenesis: Ultrastructural Histochemical Observations on Ultraviolet Irradiated Human Melanocytes. *J. Invest. Dermatol.* 54:213-21

47. Hyman, C. 1968. *Microcirculation as Related to Shock*, ed. D. Shepro, G. Fulton, 69-78. New York: Academic. 276 pp.

48. Jenkinson, D. M. 1967. On the Classification of the Existence of an Apocrine Secretory Process. *Brit. Vet. J.* 123:311-16

49. Johnson, B. E., Daniels, F. 1969. Lysosomes and the Reaction of Skin to Ultraviolet Radiation. *J. Invest. Dermatol.* 53:85-94

50. Kligman, A. M. 1964. *The Epidermis,* ed. W. Montagna, W. C. Lobitz, Jr., 387-433. New York: Academic. 649 pp.

51. Kligman, A. M., Shelley, W. B. 1958. An Investigation of the Biology of the Human Sebaceous Gland. *J. Invest. Dermatol.* 30:99-125

52. Kontos, H. A., Richardson, D. W., Patterson, J. L., Jr. 1967. Effects of Hypercapnia on Human Forearm Blood Vessels. *Am. J. Physiol.* 212: 1070-80

53. Lavker, R. M., Matoltsy, A. G. 1970. Formation of Horny Cells. *J. Cell Biol.* 44:501-12

54. Macdonald, I. 1968. Effects of a Skimmed Milk and Chocolate Diet on Serum and Skin Lipids. *J. Sci. Food Agr.* 19:270-72

55. Malkinson, F. D. 1964. *The Epidermis,* ed. W. Montagna, W. Lobitz, New York: Academic. 649 pp.

56. Maricq, H. R., Jarvik, L. F., Rainer, J. D. 1968. Chronic Schizophrenia, Lymphocyte Growth, and Nailfold

Plexus Visualization Score. *Dis. Nerv. Syst.* 29:659–67

57. Matoltsy, A. G. 1967. *Ultrastructure of Normal and Abnormal Skin,* ed. A. S. Zelickson, 76–104. Philadelphia: Lea & Febiger. 481 pp.

58. Matoltsy, A. G. 1967. The Envelope of Epidermal Horny Cells. *Congr. Int. Dermatol.* 13:1014–15

59. Matoltsy, A. G. 1969. What is Keratin? *Advan. Biol. Skin* 9:559–68

60. Matoltsy, A. G., Downes, A. M., Sweeney, T. M. 1968. Studies of the Epidermal Water Barrier. II. Investigation of the Chemical Nature of the Water Barrier. *J. Invest. Dermatol.* 50:19–26

61. Matoltsy, A. G., Matoltsy, M. N. 1970. The Chemical Nature of Keratohyalin Granules of the Epidermis. *J. Cell Biol.* 47:593–603

62. Matoltsy, A. G., Parakkal, P. F. 1965. Membrane Coating Granules of Keratinizing Epithelia. *J. Cell Biol.* 24:297–307

63. Matoltsy, A. G., Schragger, A., Matoltsy, M. N., 1962. Observation on Regeneration of the Skin Barrier. *J. Invest. Dermatol.* 38:251–53

64. Mellander, S., Johansson, B. 1968. Control of Resistance, Exchange, and Capacitance Functions in the Peripheral Circulation. *Pharm. Rev.* 20:117–96

65. Mishima, Y., Widlan, S. 1967. Enzymatically Active and Inactive Melanocyte Populations and Ultraviolet Irradiation: Combined DOPA Premelanin Reaction and Electron Microscopy. *J. Invest. Dermatol.* 49:273–81

66. Mitchell, R. E. 1969. The Skin of the Australian Aborigine: A Light and Electron Microscopical Study. *Aust. J. Dermatol.* 9:314–28

67. Montagna, W. 1962. *The Structure and Function of Skin,* 268–311. New York: Academic. 454 pp.

68. Moyer, F. 1966. Genetic Variations in the Fine Structure and Ontogeny of Mouse Melanin Granules. *Am. Zool.* 6:43–66

69. Nicolaides, N. 1963. Human Skin Surface Lipids—Origin, Composition and Possible Function. *Advan. Biol. Skin* 4:167–87

70. Nicolaides, N., Fu, H. C., Rice, G. R. 1968. The Skin Surface Lipids of Man Compared with Those of Eighteen Species of Animals. *J. Invest. Dermatol.* 51:83–89

71. Nicoll, P. A., Webb, R. L. 1946. Blood Circulation in the Subcutaneous Tissue of the Living Bat's Wing. *Ann. N Y Acad. Sci.* 46:697–711

72. Odland, G. F., Reed, T. H. 1967. *Ultrastructure of Normal and Abnormal Skin,* ed. A. Zelickson, 54–75. Philadelphia: Lea & Febiger. 481 pp.

73. Palay, S. L. 1958. *Frontiers of Cytology,* 305–310. New Haven: Yale Univ. Press

74. Parmley, T. H., Seeds, A. E. 1970. Fetal Skin Permeability to Isotopic Water (THO) in Early Pregnancy. *Am. J. Obstet. Gynecol.* 108:128–31

75. Potter, B. 1966. The Physiology of the Skin. *Ann. Rev. Physiol.* 28:159–76

76. Prunieras, M. 1969. Interactions Between Keratinocytes and Dendritic Cells. *J. Invest. Dermatol.* 52:1–16

77. Quevedo, W. C., Bienieki, T. C., McMorris, F. A., Hepinstall, M. J. 1968. Environmental and Genetic Influences on Radiation-Induced Tanning of Murine Skin. *Advan. Biol. Skin* 8:361–77

78. Quevedo, W. C., Brenner, R. M., Kechijian, P. 1963. Melanocyte Performance During Radiation-Induced Tanning of Murine Skin. *Proc. Int. Congr. Zool., 16th* 2:306–15

79. Quevedo, W. C., Szabo, G., Virks, J., Sinesi, S. J. 1965. Melanocyte Populations in U.V. Irradiated Human Skin. *J. Invest. Dermatol.* 45:295–98

80. Quevedo, W. C., Szabo, G., Virks, J. 1969. Influence of Age and U.V. in the Populations of DOPA-Positive Melanocytes in Human Skin. *J. Invest. Dermatol.* 52:287–90

81. Ramasastry, P., Downing, D. T., Pichi, P. E., Strauss, J. S. 1970. Chemical Composition of Human Skin Surface Lipids from Birth to Puberty. *J. Invest. Dermatol.* 54:139–44

82. Redisch, W., Messina, E. J., Hughes, G., McEwen, C. 1970. Capillaroscopic Observations in Rheumatic Diseases. *Ann. Rheum Dis.* 29:244–53

83. Redisch, W., Terry, E. N., Messina, E. J., Clauss, R. H. 1970. Clinical Implications of Microcirculatory Disturbances. *Angiology* 21:63–69

84. Rhodin, J. A. G., Reith, E. J. 1962. *Fundamentals of Keratinization,* ed. E. O. Butcher, R. F. Sognnaes, 61–

94. Washington, D.C.: AAAS. 189 pp.

85. Rogers, G. E. 1957. Electron Microscopic Observations on the Structure of Sebaceous Glands. *Exp. Cell Res.* 13:517–20

86. Rothman, S. 1954. *Physiology and Biochemistry of the Skin.* Chicago: Chicago Univ. Press. 741 pp.

87. Ryan, T. J. et al. 1970. Capillary Microscopy and the Skin. *Brit. J. Dermatol.* Suppl. 5 82:74–76

88. Sandison, J. C. 1924. A New Method for the Microscopic Study of Living Growing Tissue by the Introduction of a Transparent Chamber in the Rabbit's Ear. *Anat. Rec.* 28: 281–87

89. Sato, K., Dobson, R. L. 1970. Enzymatic Basis for the Active Transport of Sodium in the Duct and Secretory Portion of the Eccrine Sweat Gland. *J. Invest. Dermatol.* 55:53–56

90. Sayre, R. M., Olson, R. L. Everett, M. A. 1966. Quantitative Studies on Erythema. *J. Invest. Dermatol.* 46:240–44

91. Sayre, R. M., Straka, E. R., Anglin, J. H., Everett, M. A. 1965. A High Intensity U.V. Light Monochromator. *J. Invest. Dermatol.* 45:190–93

92. Scheuplein, R. J. 1965. Mechanism of Percutaneous Absorption. I. Routes of Penetration and the Influence of Solubility. *J. Invest. Dermatol.* 45: 334–46

93. Scheuplein, R. J. 1967. Mechanism of Percutaneous Absorption. II. Transient Diffusion and the Relative Importance of Various Routes of Skin Penetration. *J. Invest. Dermatol.* 48:79–88

94. Schwinghamer, J. M., Grega, G. J., Haddy, F. J. 1970. Skin and Muscle Circulatory Responses During Prolonged Hypovolemia. *Am. J. Physiol.* 219:318–26

95. Seiji, M. 1968. Subcellular Particles and Melanin Formation in Melanocytes. *Advan. Biol. Skin* 8:189–222

96. Seiji, M., Yoshida, T., Itakura, H., Irimajiri, T. 1969. Inhibition of Melanin Formation by Sulfhydryl Compounds. *J. Invest. Dermatol.* 52:280–86

97. Selby, C. C. 1957. An Electron Microscope Study of Thin Sections of Human Skin. *J. Invest. Dermatol.* 29:131–49

98. Stoughton, R. B. 1959. *The Human Integument,* ed. S. Rothman, Publ. No. 54 Washington, DC:AAAS 260 pp.

99. Szabo, G. 1968. Photobiology of Melanogenesis Cytological Aspects With Special Reference to Differences in Racial Coloration. *Advan. Biol. Skin* 8:379–96

100. Tosti, A., Villardita, S., Fazzini, M. L., Scalici, R. 1970. Contributions to the Knowledge of Dermatophytic Invasion of Hair. *J. Invest. Dermatol.* 55:123–34

101. Tregear, R. T. 1966. Physical Functions of the Skin, 1–52. New York: Academic, 185 pp.

102. Vanhoutte, P. M., Shepherd, J. T. 1970. Effect of Cooling on Beta-Receptor Mechanisms in Isolated Cutaneous Veins of the Dog. *Micro. Vasc. Res.* 2:454–61

103. Van Kooten, W. J., Mali, J. W. H. 1966. The Significance of Sweat Ducts in Permeation Experiments in Isolate Cadaverous Human Skin. *Dermatologica* 132:141–51

104. Wahlberg, J. E. 1968. Transepidermal or Transfollicular Absorption? *In Vivo* and *In Vitro* Studies in Hairy and Non-Hairy Guinea Pig Skin with Sodium (^{22}Na) and Mercuric (^{203}Hg) Chlorides. *Acta Dermato Venereol.* 48:336–44

105. Weinstein, G. D., Frost, P. 1968. Abnormal Cell Proliferation in Psoriasis. *J. Invest. Dermatol.* 50:254–59

106. Weinstein, G. D., Van Scott, E. J. 1965. Autoradiographic Analysis of Turnover Times of Normal and Psoriatic Epidermis. *J. Invest. Dermatol.* 45:257–62

107. Wolff, K., Winkelmann, R. K. 1967. The Influence of Ultraviolet Light on the Langerhan Cell Population and Its Hydrolytic Enzymes in Guinea Pigs. *J. Invest. Dermatol.* 48:531–39

108. Zarem, H. A., Zweifach, B. W., McGehee, J. M. 1967. Development of Microcirculation in Full Thickness Autogenous Skin Grafts in Mice. *Am. J. Physiol.* 212:1081–85

109. Zelickson, A. S. 1967. *Ultrastructure of Normal and Abnormal Skin,* ed. A. S. Zelickson, 144–53. Philadelphia: Lea & Febiger. 481 pp.

110. Zimmer, J. G., Demis, D. J. 1962. Studies on the Microcirculation of the Skin in Disease. *J. Invest. Dermatol.* 39:501–9

111. Zimmerman, B. G., Whitmore, L.

1967. Transmitter Release in Skin
and Muscle Blood Vessels During
Sympathetic Stimulation. *Am. J.
Physiol.* 212:1043–54

112. Zimmerman, B. G., Rolewicz, T. F.,

Dunham, E. W., Gisslen, J. L. 1969.
Transmitter Release and Vascular
Responses in Skin and Muscle of
Hypertensive Dogs. *Am. J. Physiol.*
217:798–804

ROBERT WINSLOW BULLARD

On June 24, 1971, Robert Winslow Bullard suffered a fatal fall from the slopes of Mt. McKinley, while conducting a study of the physiological effects of work and stress at high altitudes.

Dr. Bullard had begun his teaching career in the fall of 1956 in the Physiology Department at Indiana University, Bloomington. In 1958 he transferred to the Physiology Department of the Medical School on the Indianapolis campus, returning to the Bloomington campus in 1962 as Associate Professor of Physiology in the Anatomy and Physiology Department. In 1964 he became Professor of Physiology and chairman of the department. He was a visiting Professor of Epidemiology and a Research Fellow at the John B. Pierce Foundation at Yale University in 1969–70.

Dr. Bullard was a member of the Physiology Committee of the National Board of Medical Examiners, and served also on the Editorial Board of the American Physiological Society.

Dr. Bullard's unusually broad and comprehensive knowledge enabled him to move with ease within the the fields of medicine and environmental and comparative physiology. He was an exciting teacher who continually led his students to examine the basic evidence for the hypotheses of physiology. His smiling casual demeanor eased the rigorous intellectual journey his students were taking: they felt he was "their great friend and teacher."

Environmental physiologists throughout the world recognized Dr. Bullard for his achievements in elucidating the controlling mechanism of heat adaptation in man. These elegant studies were made possible by his development of the use of the resistance hygrometer which revolutionized the scientific approach to the problem of heat stress. Dr. Bullard was also held in esteem for his work on the phenomena of adaptation to hypothermia including hibernation. In recent years he had developed a great interest in the responses of the heart to altitude, which led to the expedition on Mt. McKinley and to his untimely death.

PHYSIOLOGICAL PROBLEMS OF SPACE TRAVEL 1078

ROBERT W. BULLARD

Department of Physiology,
Indiana University,
Bloomington, Indiana

On April 12, 1961, Cosmonaut Gagarin first orbited the earth, to be followed 23 days later by the suborbital flight of Astronaut Sheppard. Thus ten years have elapsed since man's first experience in a true space environment. In these ten years we have witnessed a tremendous surge of interest and conjecture on the physiological effects of space flight, followed by the emergence of a new investigative science. At this writing, the USSR has announced the establishment of a large manned orbiting laboratory (June 10, 1971). Such an accomplishment may begin a new era in controlled physiological testing in space. This then is a propitious time to review the research efforts in space physiology, and to take stock of what has been done and of what has need of further investigative effort.

A rather formidable array of journal articles, books, and technical reports has appeared in the last five years. This author has reviewed with varying degrees of interest and intensity approximately 800 articles, of which 89 are cited in this review. Most effort has been directed toward reports published in established scientific journals, since many of the hundreds of technical reports are repetitious or nonscientific.

Page limitations have forced the omission of many aspects of space physiology. I have tried to select subject matter which is applicable yet fits into the general scheme of physiology as seen from my own bias. Many areas such as neurophysiology, sensory deprivation, radiation biology, biorhythms and human engineering are omitted because, in some cases, applications to actual space physiology are not well documented. Most of this review deals with the investigation of increased gravitational effects, in which a sophisticated level of research has been reached, and with the effects of decreased gravity, where greater sophistication is required.

ACCELERATION

General concepts.—Several worthwhile reviews have appeared presenting in precise fashion the important concepts of increased gravitational effects. Rather complete treatises by Wunder, Duling, & Bengele (1) and Wunder (2) summarize the history and concepts concerning gravity as a biological determinant. The latter article also contains an excellent review of the physics of field force and gravity and, along with the treatments by Howard (3) and Von Gierke (4), presents a worthwhile introduction to this field.

As Hardy (5) has pointed out, the space traveler is concerned with two

205

acceleration problems: overall tolerance and ability to perform in the acceleration environment. There are several types of acceleration which are of concern not only in space flight but in accident prevention and in work performance. These are vibration or oscillation, impact accelerations, and sustained linear or angular acceleration. This last type will be considered here in greatest detail.

Weight is equal to the product of mass times acceleration. It is the increase in weight that alters any performance when muscle movement or skeletal loading is required; the increase in weight also produces several secondary effects in the acceleration environment. The hydrostatic or fluid pressure gradients that depend on change in weight are of physiological importance because of marked alterations in local and overall vascular pressures and in local pressures of extravascular fluids. Such changes can evoke compensatory mechanisms of physiological import and greatly alter hemodynamics, vascular pools, and capillary filtration and absorption processes. Secondly, the distortion or displacement of mobile or elastic tissue structures of the body, because of both the change in weight or the structure and its contained fluids, can produce physiological impairment (5).

It appears that acceleration could greatly alter the process of convection and thereby change thermal transfer at the skin, although this has not yet been a serious problem (6).

STANDARDIZATION AND ENDPOINTS

The earlier literature on acceleration is somewhat confusing in the terminology and descriptions used. Throughout this paper the symbol for accelerative forces will be the symbol G which is a dimensionless expression for the ratio of gravitational or accelerative forces divided by the force of earth's gravity symbolized by g (6). Clark, Hardy, & Crosbie (7) have proposed a system of nomenclature based on the direction of heart displacement by inertial forces. This has been adopted by the Advisory Group for Aerospace Research and Development Space Medical Panel and is now used universally in United States literature but not always in the Russian and European reports. In their system, the length of the body is designated by subscript z, the distance through the body from front to back by x, and that across the body from side to side by y. Figure 1 shows these acceleration modes. It must be remembered that acceleration forces and resulting inertial forces are always opposite in direction, whether velocity is increasing or decreasing. Heart displacement downward, towards the back, or towards the left, is indicated by +G; heart displacement upward, forward or to the right as −G. Table 1 adapted from Von Gierke summarizes terminology of interest to physiologists (4).

Accurate means are needed to determine both the tolerance of an organism to acceleration and the ability of that organism to perform or function in the acceleration environment. There are three primary determinants of tolerance: (a) the time function, which includes the rate of onset to peak ac-

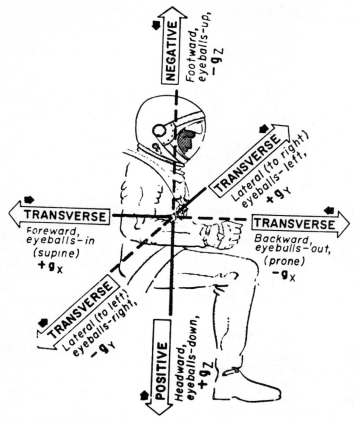

FIGURE 1. Acceleration direction is shown by the solid arrow, inertial forces in the opposite direction by the open arrows. Terminology is that used in this chapter. (From Wunder, 1966. Reprinted with permission.)

celeration and the total time of G exposure; (*b*) the orientation of the subject with respect to acceleration (primarily the angle between the spinal axis and the acceleration vector; (*c*) the magnitude of the applied G forces (4, 5).

The actual limits or endpoints, defined as the points at which the centrifuge test must be stopped or at which a pilot or astronaut is approaching traumatic hazard, are not satisfactorily standardized. The blackout response with decreased retinal circulation in the $+G$ vector is perhaps an ideal endpoint, although there is much individual variation. Loss of peripheral vision may be useful, but is also a variable endpoint (8). Redout can be used in $-G_z$ acceleration but this also appears to be variable.

Tolerances to G_x acceleration are much higher than those to G_z accelera-

TABLE 1. G Vector Notations and Descriptions

Vector	Linear motion	Classic physiological description	Pilot description	Direction relative to body
$+G_x$	Forward	Supine G	Eyeballs in	Chest-to-back: toward spine
$-G_x$	Backward	Prone G	Eyeballs out	Back-to-chest: toward sternum
$+G_y$	To right	Lateral G	Eyeballs left	Lateral: toward left
$-G_y$	To left	Lateral G	Eyeballs right	Lateral: toward right
$+G_z$	Upward	Positive G	Eyeballs down	Head-to-feet: toward feet
$-G_z$	Downward	Negative G	Eyeballs up	Foot-to-head: toward head

tion, but limits are clearly delineated. Coburn (9) has reviewed some possible endpoints, including visual and auditory phenomena, electroencephalographic changes, cardiorespiratory effects, and altered states of consciousness and performance. To this list could be added chest pain, which has been reported for G_x accelerations (10). None of the above has proven to be really consistent or objective enough to be considered a really useful criterion. Perhaps a direct means of monitoring either arterial O_2 saturation or some other factor will provide useful objective endpoints.

Acceleration Exposure

In manned space flight the vehicle and crew, starting from rest, must attain a velocity of 8000 m/sec to enter earth orbit or attain an escape velocity of 11,600 m/sec to leave the earth's gravitational field. Using the convenient expression of G-seconds, which as the product of time and G forces refers to the area under an acceleration profile (plot of acceleration vs time), 828 G-sec are required for orbit and 1152 G-sec for escape.

Acceleration profiles for the US program have been published. Earlier Mercury flights had two peaks of about 7 and 8 $+G_x$ over a 6 minute period and a single peak of 8 $+G_x$ with a base of longer duration upon reentry (11). In the more recent Apollo flights with more powerful engines the acceleration profile is much smoother, with an initial plateau at about $4-G_x$ and a secondary plateau at 2 $-G_x$ until sufficient velocity is attained. Peak accelerations at reentry from lunar missions reach 6.7 $+G_x$ with the brief impact of 6 to 8 $+G_x$ (12).

A proposed acceleration profile for a flight to Mars with postulated physiological responses and discussion has been published. There appears to be no serious problems as earth lift off and reentry will impose about 6 $+G_x$. Martian activity as in the case of lunar activity with lower gravitational forces will present minimal G stress. Acceleration problems appear to have been very much ameliorated with the present engine characteristics, and physiological problems are not serious for routine missions. However, with extended planetary exploration or mission difficulties, very high G forces may be experienced (6).

CARDIOVASCULAR SYSTEM

Because fluid columns and elastic tissues are greatly affected by changes in gravity, the cardiovascular system is one of the main bodily components to bear the brunt of acceleration. The pressure and organ alterations are, in themselves, of great physiological importance and they also secondarily activate interesting compensatory responses. A general review of these effects has been published (3).

Cardiac excitability and the electrocardiogram.—Because of the simplicity of the instrumentation the electrocardiogram has proven to be a most commonly used test in acceleration studies. In several studies an increased incidence of cardiac arrhythmias has been reported, particularly with both $+G_z$ and $+G_x$ acceleration. Torphy and co-workers (13) working with $+G_x$ acceleration have reported a high incidence of premature ventricular contractions. (PVC). In further pursuit of this problem Rogge et al (14) compared in 51 men the incidence of arrhythmias during treadmill exercise, tilt table tests, and $+G_x$ acceleration. The acceleration program was as follows: 5.5 $+G_x$ for 110 sec, 7.4 $+G_x$ for 170 sec and 8.0 $+G_x$ for 100 sec. Of the 51 subjects, 20 had arrhythmias during at least one part of the centrifuge run while the treadmill exercise produced PVCs in 10 subjects and the tilt test produced PVCs in 17 subjects. There appeared to be no correlation with physical fitness as judged by the time the man endured the treadmill test and the incidence of PVCs.

The most common electrocardiographic alteration was in the T wave in both $+G_z$ and G_x accelerations. These changes were usually a flattening of the T wave in leads II, III, AVF, V_4–V_6 which developed 5 to 6 sec after reaching a peak acceleration; they persisted for 11 to 30 sec after return to 1 G. This has been interpreted as due to a positional change of the heart (15, 16); since the ST segment depression occurred only very rarely, these investigators believed that the effect was not due to myocardial ischemia. P waves in most subjects also were affected and showed increased peaks in leads II, III, V, and AVF (17) which returned to normal in about 30 sec. After acceleration no changes in atrioventricular or intraventricular conduction have been reported. The brachycardias or tachycardias reported appear to be of sinus origin (18).

Extension of these studies using spatial vectorcardiography as a primary probe combined with analog to digital computer techniques has been made for a more thorough analysis (19) with acceleration runs to 10 $+G_x$. Rather small but significant changes occurred which were not G dependent as they did not progressively increase with increasing G. These authors conclude that up to 10 G_x the alterations were minor; this conclusion agrees with earlier studies using comparable approaches (20).

Cohen and Brown (16) have made an effort to uncover the mechanism of the electrocardiographic changes induced by $+G_z$ acceleration. Subjects rode the centrifuge under control conditions, either while breathing 100% oxygen or after receiving the beta receptor blocking agent, propranolol. This latter drug depressed the heart rate response and eliminated abnormalities in the electrocardiograms, particularly the T wave changes during $+G_z$ acceleration. Breathing 100% oxygen had no apparent effect. These results are interpretable on the basis of previous suggestions (21). Myocardial ischemia was not a factor. The propranolol effect is explained on the following basis: sympathomimetic drugs produce T wave changes as heart rate increases; the changes in the P and T waves were quite similar during acceleration, orthostasis, or epinephrine administration; the beta block of beta receptors reversed changes with orthostasis. Orthostasis, like acceleration in the $+G_z$ axis, produces hemodynamic alterations which reduce pressures at the carotid sinus level and result in compensatory mechanisms of increased sympathetic activity and tachycardia. This concept thus explains the five to six second delay in initiation of electrocardiographic changes and the delay of reversal upon return to 1 G. Of interest here would be the extensive analysis of the incidence of premature contractions in acceleration tests following propranolol treatment where increased sympathetic activity has been suggested as a causative factor (22). In contrast, Chimoskey reports that with $+G_z$ acceleration the decrease in T wave may be of ischemic origin at 6 $+G_z$, as the greatest T wave changes coincided with the greatest decrease in coronary blood flow (23).

Heart rate changes with acceleration have been repeatedly described. During moderate increase in G increase consistently occurs. The US Gemini Astronauts had large increases in heart rate, (to 120 to 180 beats/min) in the acceleration stress of launch and reentry (11). Positive accelerations of dogs produced an increase in heart rate of 37% at 10 $+G_x$; at 15 $+G_x$ the heart rates increased less but were still higher than those of the dogs at 1 G. These results contrast with those of Stone et al who reported that at 15 $+G_x$ a marked bradycardia occurred consistently in dogs; in their experiments the heart rate changed very little from 1 G to 5 G but dropped from a control rate of 108 beats at 1 G to approximately 60 beats/min at 10 and 15 $+G_x$ (24). One possible explanation for the discrepancy is the difference in anesthetic used or in body position.

The contrasting results emphasize that it is somewhat difficult to generalize the relationship between heart rate and gravitational stress. Michie, in an effort to reconcile these differences, has studied conscious dogs at 10 G. He changed the angle of the spine to the axis of inertial forces and the results indicated a marked dependency of the heart rate responses to the angle between body and the direction of acceleration. Between $+10°$ and $-10°$ there appeared to be a minimal disturbance of cardiovascular function. At $0°$ the heart rate increased up to 6 G and decreased between 6 and 10 G, while at $10°$ little change occurred. At $+30°$ marked increases were seen and at $-30°$

marked decreases occurred (25). If these results prove to be correct, they would indicate that modest changes in orientation to the G forces can call forth markedly different physiological responses.

With greater G stress a decrease in heart rate seems to result. With accelerations up to 400 $+G_x$ all 24 squirrel monkeys used had bradycardia and 12 showed a complete absence of any cardiac electrical activity (26). Further studies suggest that this marked bradycardia may result from a massive parasympathetic discharge. This evidence comes from experiments in which squirrel monkeys were treated with atropine which delayed the fall in heart rate at 200 $+G_x$ for 200 sec (27). Hexamethonium treatment delayed somewhat the slowing of the heart in comparison to that of control untreated monkeys. After the initial marked bradycardia heart rate rose in the controls; the heart rates between 70 and 200 sec were approximately the same in both groups. Since the rates in the hexamethonium treated monkeys were so similar to those in the control, it is untenable to attribute the responses to extrinsic sympathetic influences. Thus the increase must result from intrinsic stimulation, which in these experiments would have been equivalent in monkeys treated with hexamethonium or atropine treatments and in the controls. An 83% mortality rate in these experiments indicates the severity of this G_x stress.

Three possible alternative mechanisms exist which could result in increased vagal impulses to the heart: (a) direct stimulation of the dorsal motor nucleus of the vagus; (b) stimulation of afferent nerves because of compression of lungs and other viscera; (c) or mechanical distortion and stretch of baroreceptors in the carotid sinus and aortic arch. The latter possibility is the most likely (27).

A very interesting paper by Yuganov et al indicates that animals with intact labyrinthine systems and vagus nerves had bradycardia during a period of weightlessness. The bradycardia disappeared with removal of the labyrinth system and the heart rate was then unchanged during weightlessness (28). This is an experiment which should be repeated during the stress of acceleration. It has also been reported that tachycardia appearing with acceleration can be suppressed when oxygen is breathed under high pressure. The explanation is not apparent but the results suggest that there may be hypoxic drives involved (29).

Hemodynamics.—The hemodynamic alterations with increased gravitational force vary greatly with the direction, magnitude and duration of the applied force. Excellent technical progress has been made in the last few years and rather precise data is now available. What appear to require further study are the details of the physiological mechanisms involved in both the direct reactions to stress and in the compensatory responses (30).

In several reports on experimental animals, $+G_x$ acceleration has been shown to decrease cardiac output. In studies on mongrel dogs with 5, 10, and 15 $+G_x$ accelerations, the stroke volume was decreased approximately

50% at 15 $+G_x$ (31, 32). Both the dye dilution technique and angicardio-graphic analysis showed marked decreases in stroke volume as the cardiac index decreased 20% at 5 $+G_x$, 20.5% at 10 $+G_x$ and 37% at 15 $+G_x$. The most interesting aspect of these studies is that heart rate increased from a mean of 83 beats/min to 114 beats/min at 5 $+G_x$; at higher G_x forces, mean heart rates were lowered but were still higher than at the 1 G control level. Thus the decrease in cardiac output was due to a decrease in stroke volume. An analysis of X-ray motion pictures showed that end diastolic and end systolic volumes decreased in all animals studied. This study also showed a marked posterior displacement of the heart in the dog's chest; this displacement appeared to be much greater than that seen in a few similar studies made on humans during similar accelerations.

Stone et al, on the other hand, have found that stoke volume is main-tained and that the decreased cardiac output is due to a decreased heart rate (24). This discrepancy in results is not explicable from the published reports.

A marked increase in arterial pressure occurs with increasing $+G_x$. This increase in mean arterial pressure was from 130 to 220 mm Hg at 15 $+G_x$, to 180 at 10 $+G_x$ and to 140 at 5 $+G_x$ (31). In another study using the same G stress the results were similar but not quite as marked (24). Both reports agree in finding increased blood pressure coincident with a falling cardiac output—a result which can be explained only on the basis of marked increase in resistance in some peripheral vascular beds. In neither study were venous pressures measured; quantification of the overall peripheral resistance change is thus not possible.

Banchero et al have introduced an interesting concept concerning high intraventricular pressures during acceleration (32). They found that pleural and pericardial pressures recorded at contiguous sites in the thorax were not significantly different and they suggested that the pleural pressure in regions juxtaposed to the heart must have a pressure gradient of 1 cm H_2O/cm of vertical distance in the thorax (just as within the pericardial sac). Stone et al have calculated in dogs that the pericardial pressures would be approxi-mately 18, 40, and 60 mm Hg (24) during 5, 10, and 15 $+G_x$ acceleration. They conclude that the transmural left ventricular end diastolic and end systolic pressures are not greatly increased during acceleration exposure. Banchero et al point out that the heart appears to exist in a hydrostatic com-pensating system. Since it is relatively flaccid and fluid filled, the mainte-nance of proper function is more certain if this system automatically applies perfectly compensating hydrostatic pressure to all of its external surfaces whenever the gravitational or inertial forces acting on this organ are altered. This is a concept of interest to the cardiovascular physiologist studying the heart in any dynamic environment.

Venous and atrial pressures.—More data are required on central venous pressure, right atrial pressure, and right ventricular pressures in the various acceleration vectors. Stone et al (24) and Sandler (33) have discussed the problems that can be encountered here if there is even a slight error in estimating the zero reference level, which is magnified by the applied G force. The zero reference level can also be altered with varying G forces, which further complicates any measurements of venous and atrial pressures.

The response to transverse acceleration is generally an increase in these pressures as well as in left atrial pressure. Again referring to the study of Banchero et al, at 7 G there is a sevenfold increase in effective weight of the blood. After the recorded atrial pressures were corrected to the height in the chest—which is about 12 cm in the dog, an estimation of transmural atrial pressure could then be made. When this was done, no changes in the transmural left and right atrial pressures were obtained at accelerations to either plus or minus 7 G_x. Thus, the pressure created by any fluid pushed into the atrium was counterbalanced by external forces acting on the outside. However, in dependent parts of the lung, effective counter pressures may not be applied, and there exists evidence for increased fluid loss and formation of pulmonary edema in these areas (34).

Offerhaus and Dejongh (35) were concerned with the overall homeostatic regulation of blood volume during gravitational stress of 3 $+G_z$ acceleration maintained for 30 minutes. Their studies indicated an 80% increase in peak urinary excretion of norepinephrine and a 220% increase in excretion of epinephrine. However, the absolute amount of epinephrine excreted was only about $\frac{1}{5}$ as much as the amount of norepinephrine. These authors have proposed that increased sympathetic activity primarily constricts the capacitance vessels and thus maintains venous return to the heart (35).

In a high G environment the usual decrease in stroke volume was prevented by leg exercise. This was attributed to the muscle pump and the maintenance of venous return (36, 37).

Regional blood flows.—Although not yet thoroughly studied, some rather marked alterations in regional blood flows have been reported during acceleration. Kesselman has reviewed the physical principles involved in gravitational effects on blood distribution (38). One series of experiments using implanted ultrasonic flow meters in unanesthetized dogs showed that during positive acceleration renal blood flow decreased in proportion to the increased acceleration; at 6 $+G_z$ it reached a minimal level of 16% of control values. Since systemic arterial blood pressure rose in these experiments, the decrease in flow or velocity was due to a decreased cardiac output and to sympathetically induced renal vasoconstriction (39).

Blood flow in $+G_x$ acceleration has been studied on nine anesthetized dogs using the hydrogen ion electrode (40). Tissue blood flows were shown to decrease in the renal cortex, in the adrenal gland, and in the small intestine At 0°—or pure $+G_x$ acceleration—the flow decreased with increasing acceleration in a fairly linear fashion. At 12 $+G_x$ renal and adrenal flow had decreased to 60% of that at 1 G, while the intestinal blood flow dropped to 43% of the control value. As the angle of the spine and G vector approached 30° off the pure G_x axis, the blood flows further decreased. In these experiments, starting with zero angle, mean arterial pressure fell from 100 to 60 mm Hg at 12 $+G_z$, while in a 30° position it fell to 60 mm Hg at 3 $+G_x$. Heart rates did not change consistently, but it is assumed here that a fall in cardiac output of 20–30% occurs at 10–15 $+G_x$. Thus the more pronounced drop of local blood flow is probably due to sympathetic vasoconstriction.

Stone et al have attempted to determine the vascular beds in which flow changes with increased gravitational stress (34). Flow in the left circumflex coronary artery and common carotid artery were measured with Doppler ultrasonic flow transducers in intact but anesthetized dogs. After 20 seconds of $+15$ G_x acceleration, the coronary flow increased to 173 ml/min (control at 1 G was 83 ml/min). At 5 $+G_x$ and 10 $+G_x$ the increases in flow were slight but nonsignificant. Coincident with these changes mean aortic flow and common carotid flow decreased. The authors attribute the change in coronary flow to a hypoxic response concomitant to decreased arterial oxygen saturation. Studies using polarographic electrodes implanted in dogs indicated that early in moderate acceleration myocardial tissue Po_2 tends to rise but later falls, particularly with 6, 8, 10, and 12 $+G_x$ accelerations, and that Po_2 fell more in the G_z than in the G_x vector (41).

Glaister has used the ⁸⁶Rb technic of Sapirstein to determine the functional distribution of cardiac output in greyhounds at 4.2 $+G_x$. The tissues studied included skin, skeletal muscle, diaphragm, heart, lung, kidney, adrenals, liver, spleen, gut, and pancreas. Blood flow increased in heart, diaphragm, and adrenals; it decreased in skeletal muscle and kidney (42).

A field of investigation which appears fruitful lies in the compensating mechanisms that regulate regional blood flow and in determining the effector and affector sides of the control loop. Such mechanisms are very definitely called into play but most of the literature concerned with these responses is somewhat conjectural. Interesting experiments could be done using various denervation technics and pharmacologic blocking agents.

RENAL FUNCTION AND BODY FLUID REGULATION

Increased gravitational fields can produce marked effects on systems that regulate body water content and ionic concentrations. As reported above, high G forces at least in animal experiments markedly alter renal blood flow (39).

Studies have been completed on trained unanesthetized dogs in plus and minus G_z acceleration. At 6 $+G_z$, arterial pressure diminished, renal flow decreased disproportionately, and oliguria resulted. After perfusion of phenoxybenzamine into the renal artery, renal blood flow was reduced less, while systemic hemodynamics were not altered. Therefore the reduction was attributed to intrarenal vasoconstriction mediated by alpha receptors. At 3 $-G_z$, renal blood flow initially decreased to 50% with only small decreases in renal arterial pressure or renal arterial to venous pressure differences and returned toward normal after 16 seconds. In this case decrease in renal perfusion was attributed to the pronounced bradycardia presumably due to elevated carotid sinus and aortic arch pressures (43).

When humans were centrifuged in the $+G_z$ axis, changes in hematocrit ratio and plasma protein concentration have been reported (35). Any receptors that have been proposed for blood volume regulation also appear to be affected by the distortions of gravitational stress. Several interesting reports have appeared dealing with this problem. Piemme, McCally and Hyde (44), studying the $+G_z$ vector in short axis centrifugation with a gradient from 0 G_z at the head to 3 $+G_z$ at the feet, found little change in the glomerular filtration rate. However, the ability to excrete a water load was markedly impaired. Free water clearance decreased from 2.8 to -0.5 ml/min with increasing G load to 3 $+G_z$. Because of the time lag this response appeared to be hormonal and mediated by the action of the antidiuretic hormone. Its secretion in this case was probably mediated by shifts of blood to the periphery and activation of volume receptors (44).

A study by Rogge et al (45), using a bioassay method for measuring antidiuretic hormone in peripheral venous blood, compared both $+G_z$ and $+G_x$ accelerations in humans. With 30 min of 2 $+G_z$ acceleration a mean rise in ADH of 2.97 μU/ml of blood was observed. Presumably this increased concentration was due to enhanced secretion caused by a shift in blood from the thorax to extremities. With the use of an anti-G suit inflated to 10 mm Hg in an effort to decrease the volume shift, a nonsignificant decrease in ADH concentration of 0.86 μU/ml of blood was observed, which again suggests that activation of central volume receptors had initiated the secretion. With transverse accelerations of 2 $+G_x$ a significant decrease of 0.89 μU/ml occurred. In this case central pooling of blood could act through volume receptors to effect a change in ADH, as proposed by Gauer et al (46). Urine flow decreases when intrathoracic blood volume falls due either to a reduction in total blood volume or, in the case of centrifugation, to a shift of blood to the lower extremities.

Bengele has reported that in rats centrifuged for 2 weeks in a G_x vector, which would tend to increase the intrathoracic volume, urine flow increased, ADH production decreased, and dehydration occurred (47). The interesting point here is that neither the ADH nor the volume receptor mechanism nor the circulatory system showed any evidence of adaptation in this time period.

Offerhaus and Dejongh have proposed that $+G_z$ acceleration may also involve augmented aldosterone secretion (35). They noted that excess ADH does not account for all of the antidiuresis due to blood pooling in tilt table procedures. They found that when a salt load was administered prior to acceleration the ability to excrete this was greatly impaired, but creatinine excretion indicated little decrement of glomerular filtration. Their results also showed an increased urinary excretion of aldosterone. Their theory is further supported by experiments indicating that renin release by the kidney is augmented in $+G_z$ acceleration, which thus suggests a mechanism for aldosterone secretion (48). The reduction in renal blood flow, the increased firing of sympathetic nerves to the kidney, and catecholamine release would thus be responsible for the stimulation of renin secretion.

RESPIRATION

If cerebral circulation is maintained either by body position or by some other means, the final limit of G tolerance is determined by the failure of respiratory function (34). Not only does the respiratory structure suffer from all of the displacement or distortions of the circulatory system, but, because of the differences in weight and compressibility of air and blood, the changes are augmented. Results of these stresses are atelectasis, airway closure, increased transudation of fluids from capillaries, and marked variations in ventilation-perfusion ratios.

Physical displacements.—Acceleration in several vectors has been shown to increase the weight of the chest wall and to displace the abdominal viscera, thus altering the dimensions of the thorax (49, 50). Subjects appear to attempt to counteract compression of the thorax during acceleration by contracting both the diaphragm and the external intercostal muscles (51). Barer et al have presented a diagram of the X-ray changes in $+G_x$ acceleration (10). Expressed in percentages of the area of lung field at 1 G, the following changes were observed: 95% at 2 G_x, 93% at 4 G_x, 93% at 6 G_x, and 79% at 12 G_x.

In following the anterior-posterior dimension of the thorax in $+G_x$ acceleration, Sandler has reported a mean decrease of 8.6% at 5 G_x and 15.4% at 10 G_x. Changes are greater at the xiphisternum than at midsternum (52). These alterations could produce the commonly reported chest pains as well as the change in respiratory function.

More serious are weight alteration and displacement of elastic and flaccid structures with increased G force. Measurable regional differences in pleural pressures along the lung are generally believed to be caused by the weight of the thoracic contents. Centrifugation experiments provide an advantage in that such weights can be varied in a controlled fashion. Rutishauser et al (53), in an excellent study on dogs, have used acceleration for testing the hypothesis above. Pleural pressures decreased at ventral or superior regions, while markedly increasing in areas which are dependent or dorsal in the $+G_x$ vector. At 6–7 G_x pleural pressures of -40 cm H_2O were obtained during inspiration in superior regions of the thorax while in dorsal or dependent regions pressures reached $+40$ cm H_2O. These pressure changes matched the estimated weight and thus support the above hypothesis.

The low pressures at nondependent lung regions tend to produce alveolar distension and the high pressures in dependent areas may produce alveolar or airway closure. Glazier & Hughes (54), were able to measure the regional differences in alveolar size of dogs after 8 hours at 3 and 5 $+G_x$ by freezing whole and intact dog carcasses while still subjecting them to these accelerations. With the G_x accelerations the average volume of ventral alveoli was twice that of alveoli in the supine dog at 1 G. At 4 cm lower into the thorax, many air spaces were obliterated by apposition of alveolar walls or were filled with blood.

In the $+G_z$ vector the normal gradient of alveolar size from apex to base was 3.7:1, but changed with acceleration. By adding an abdominal binder as a makeshift antigravity suit the ratio increased to 11:1 as the basal alveoli then became compressed. Thus, antigravity correction attempts can present serious hazards of physiological import.

Glazier & Hughes (54) have presented the simple concept that the lung is like a hanging loosely coiled spring in which the alveoli are analogous to each coil. At 1 G the upper coils are somewhat stretched while the lower portions remain tightly coiled. If exposed to 3 G this difference would become exaggerated if the lower end were fixed. This appears to be what happens when an anti-G appliance is used during $+G_z$ stress or when the dependent portion of the lung is held in position by the back of the thorax in $+G_x$ acceleration. Without support for the lower end, the entire spring would stretch and the ratio of upper and lower coil size would remain near constant at increased G_z. In spite of its simplicity this model appears to fit the experimental observations. Wood has presented models showing similar effects (34).

Increased respiratory dead space has also been reported during $+G_x$ accelerations. This may be due to mechanical distortion combined with the bronchodilating effects of increased sympathetic activity (55).

Ventilation.—Needless to say the marked distortion of pulmonary structures has a marked effect upon ventilation. Up to 4–6 G it is concluded that the respiratory musculature has sufficient strength to lift the increased weight of the thoracic cage and the abdominal viscera (10). The most obvious effect is an increased rate of respiration to roughly 30 breaths/min, usually associated with a decreased tidal volume. Hyperventilation has been reported, as well as apnea (56).

Figure 2 presents a graph of respiratory measurements from 2–12 min at $+G_x$ at a 65° angle to the acceleration vector and from 12–22 min at $+G_x$ at an 80° angle.

Considering displacements due to weight changes and possibly to surface and elastic forces, the complexities of ventilation inhomogeneities are augmented. Bryan et al used ^{133}Xe to compare the distribution of regional lung volumes and ventilations at 1 $+G_z$ to that at 2 and 3 $+G_z$ (57). Scintillation counters mounted in front of the chest at three different positions showed that in the $+G_z$ vector differences in ventilation between the apex and the base of the lung were greatly magnified. This resulted from the augmented gradient of pleural pressure described above, even though the shape of the pressure volume curve did not change. With higher accelerations the results show greater expansion of upper lung zones and closing of airways in dependent portions.

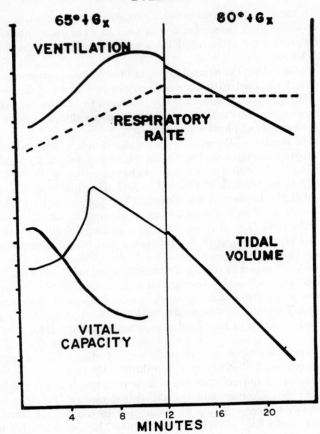

FIGURE 2. Respiratory response to acceleration. Angle represents that between acceleration vector and long axis of body. (Data redrawn from Barer et al 10)

Alterations such as these effectively reduce ventilatory exchange. Using a test which followed the time course of the expiration of a single breath of nitrogen after breathing argon and oxygen, Jones et al found evidence for gas trapping at 4 $+G_z$ acceleration (58). This was indicated by an increase in nitrogen concentration over the last liter or so of the vital capacity. With augmented expiratory rates the trapping was presumably increased in the basal airways. At 0 G there was virtually no gas trapping, while at 9 $+G_z$ there was a large volume of gas trapping. Thus regional inhomogeneities of ventilation are mostly gravity dependent.

The increase in ventilation, reported by several authors (10, 59), is not fully explained. The observed decrease in arterial Po_2 and in hemoglobin saturation, and the change in pH do not appear to be sufficient for this stimulus. For $+G_z$ acceleration Barr (59) has discussed possible respiratory stimuli. A direct influence on the medullary centers by changes in the local blood flow, combined with a decrease in arterial pressure, hypotension at the carotid sinus region and local ischemia at the carotid bodies, could provide strong stimulation. Some credence can be placed in this latter possibility as Barr, Bjurstedt & Coleridge (60) found that respiration decreased during $+G_z$ acceleration after denervation of the carotid chemoreceptors. Barr (59) has shown a mean increase in the oxygen consumption of humans at 5 $+G_z$ to 410 ml/min from a control level of 269 ml/min. This increased oxygen consumption presumably results from the extra work of respiration, contraction of trunk muscles for maintenance of posture, and perhaps a generalized increased muscle tone or voluntary contraction.

A fall in the arterial O_2 saturation level from a control of 96% to 87% after 70 seconds of 5 $+G_z$ acceleration has been demonstrated in man (59). The alveolar-arterial Po_2 difference increased approximately twofold. Concomitant with this change was a marked increase in mean pulmonary ventilation from 9 l/min to 19 l/min. Ventilation appeared to be quite adequate even though metabolism was elevated 52%. Thus, the mean alveolar to mean arterial Po_2 difference was greatly increased in this situation.

Blood flow and ventilation perfusion relationships.—Overall pulmonary blood flow is, of course, dependent on the cardiac output which may decrease or increase with acceleration. Some of the resulting pressure changes will increase transudation of fluid into alveolar sacs, creating a greater decrement in gas exchange. The major problem with blood flow appears to be in the establishment of marked inequalities of blood flow and ventilation in different regions of the lungs.

Permutt (6) has reviewed the effect of increased gravitational forces in ventilation and perfusion relationships through the Starling resistor concept. In simplified terms, three zones exist in the lung. In zone 1 the alveolar pressure is greater than the pulmonary arterial pressure and the pulmonary venous pressure. This is a zone of no flow, the result of the collapse of small vessels exposed to alveolar pressure. Zone 2 is that portion in which pulmonary arterial pressure exceeds alveolar pressure and pulmonary venous pressure but alveolar pressure is greater than venous pressure. Here flow increases linearly toward the more dependent regions because the arterial pressure, but not the alveolar pressure, also increases linearly. In zone 3 pulmonary arterial pressure exceeds pulmonary venous pressure, which exceeds alveolar pressure. Here flow remains constant at any vertical distance because pulmonary arterial and venous pressure are equally effected by gravity and the driving pressure remains constant.

Assuming that the lungs act as Starling resistors under conditions of increased G_z, and assuming minimal changes in cardiac dynamics, the height (h) in centimeters above the heart level at which the lungs can be perfused is expressed as:

$$h = (P_{PA'} - P_{alv})/G$$

where $P_{PA'}$ is the pulmonary arterial pressure at the heart level. If $P_{PA'}$ stayed at 20 cm H_2O, at 5 G_z, acceleration lung perfusion would not reach more than 4 cm above the heart. Superior to this level would be zone 1. Extension of this reasoning can be used for the calculation of the vertical distance of zone 2.

$$h_{zone\ 2} = (P_{PA} - P_{LA})/G$$

Where P_{LA} equals left atrial pressure. When $P_{PA} - P_{LA} = 10$ cm H_2O, the vertical distance of zone 2 would be reduced from 10 cm at 1 G_z to only 2 cm at 5 G_z. Permutt points out that the overall effect of augmented G would thus be to form an increasingly sharp division between upper portions of the lung with no flow (zone 1) and the lower portions of the lungs with relatively even blood flow (zone 3).

The inhomogeneities in blood flow and in ventilation over the various lung regions are not parallel in acceleration environments. Vandenburg et al (61), working with anesthetized dogs accelerated in the G_y vector or decubitus position, measured superior and dependent venous oxygen saturations while dogs breathed 99.6% oxygen. In the dependent pulmonary veins blood oxygen levels decreased and matched the level found in the pulmonary arterial blood. In the superior pulmonary veins, blood O_2 levels were unchanged with acceleration, while the oxygen saturation of aortic blood was between that of the superior and the dependent pulmonary venous levels.

The experimental results indicate that there was considerable venous admixture, due not to flow through anatomical shunts, but to perfusion of alveoli that were not exchanging respiratory gases—because of compression, atelectasis, airway closure, or edema. Experiments estimating the fall in alveolar acetylene previously added to the inspired gas mixture show a 35% decrease in calculated pulmonary capillary blood flow in G_x accelerations (62). In this type of measurement flow through poorly ventilated or nonventilated alveoli is not measured and thus accounts for the marked decrease. Other studies using ^{133}Xe have demonstrated a ratio of blood flow between lower and upper portions of the lung from 2.7:1 at 1 $+G_z$ to 5.9:1 at 3 $+G_z$. Ventilation changed in the opposite direction (63).

Acceleration can thus markedly alter the ventilation perfusion relationships. A report by Hoppin et al (64) indicates that with transverse accelerations, reasonably even perfusion is maintained in superior and dependent portions of the lung; the macroaggregated albumin these authors used has been criticized (61), but their finding—of uniform distribution of blood flow in the anterior posterior direction—suggests that future work is necessary.

Rosenhamer (36) in computing a ratio of shunt blood flow to total blood flow has found little difference between 1 and 3 $+G_z$. This contrasts with the work of Barr who estimated that at least a 20% physiological shunt flow occurs at 5 $+G_z$. Studies with 3 $+G_z$ acceleration showed that with exercise measured shunt flow increased markedly. This may have been because venous blood returned with a lower Po_2 and admixture would thus be calculated as higher. The measured central blood volume decreased by an average of 0.7 liters in $+G_z$ acceleration. With exercise, the muscle pump action presumably restores this central blood volume and may increase flow through poorly ventilated areas.

Power et al (62) have studied pulmonary diffusing capacity (DL) and capillary blood flow in humans during 8 $+G_x$ acceleration. DL measured by the carbon monoxide technique, decreased by 35% during acceleration—from a mean control value of 33.7 to 21.5 ml/min/mm Hg. This decrease can be attributed in part to alterations of pulmonary membranes and to diminished quantity of pulmonary capillary blood available to gas exchange, but primarily to an uneven distribution of ventilation and perfusion. Thus a simple change in diffusion characteristics could not adequately account for the marked decrease in arterial O_2 saturation, since adequate or augmented A-a differences existed. The venous admixture was probably responsible.

During acceleration, arterial desaturation occurs even though ventilation may be augmented. The primary effects are marked distortions of tissues and hydrostatic pressures adjacent to the air filled cavities. These effects cause mismatching of ventilation and perfusion, and reduction in arterial O_2 saturation (65). Because it is in the thorax that the most distortion can occur, the lung is the most susceptible to high acceleration forces and the least capable of being protected.

TRAINING STATUS

Scientists and laymen alike have always labored under the belief that intense physical training, in addition to increasing aerobic work capacity, augments resistance or tolerance to a wide variety of imposed stresses. The physical fitness programs of the United States astronauts have been described in rather glowing commentary. Parin of the USSR suggests that Alpine acclimatization be used to condition and train cosmonauts, and advocates it as cross acclimatization to combat stress in general and to improve stress tolerance (66). A point of interest here is that Klein et al have found no improvement in the highly trained athlete over the nonathlete in tolerance to increased G forces (67). The tests used consisted of a $+G_z$ acceleration which was increased 1.0 G every fifteen seconds. The attained G at the point of loss of visual acuity was 6.84 for the nonathlete and 6.89 for the athlete—not a significant difference. Also related to this was the lack of difference in tilt test responses (90° tilt for 20 min) between athletes and nonathletes. The authors did not specify the type of training activity the athletes experienced, but from their rather high aerobic capacity they must have been participants in running or some similar endurance activity. Jethon (68) has pointed out that only training involving acceleration or rapid changes in direction such as might be encountered in gymnastics or tumbling (e.g. looping exercises) improve the acceleration tolerance. Thus we again see that a specific adaptation regimen does not yield a generalized nonspecific increase in tolerance to various stress. Klein et al (67) conclude that "we do not see a great advantage in the improvement of physical fitness by dynamic muscular exercise training regarding the tolerance to the environmental extremes of space."

Similarly direct attempts to train rats by exercise in an effort to increase G tolerance have met with failure (69). A six-week program of treadmill running improved exercise capacity under normal and reduced atmospheric pressure (7000 m, simulated altitude) or following a 15 min exposure to 10 $+G_x$. The training did not affect the comparative survival time of experimental to control rats when exposed to an acceleration of 15 $+G_x$. Training which consisted of centrifugation routines, however, did improve acceleration tolerance. Thus in both humans and rats very similar results were obtained. This does not usually happen with experiments in exercise physiology, but it may have certain strong implications regarding a specific adaptation and tolerance to another specific stress.

WEIGHTLESSNESS

The evolution of terrestrial life in a constant 1 G field, combined with the impossibility of adequately simulating or producing a weightless environment for any great duration on earth, has made weightlessness a rather provocative subject for speculation and this in turn has led to prediction of many sorts of hazards. These include nausea, anorexia, disorientation, sleeplessness, fatigue, restlessness, euphoria, hallucinations, decreased G tolerance, gastrointestinal disturbances, urinary retention, diuresis, muscular atrophy and bone demineralization. Most of these effects have proven not to be serious. Some appear to be self limiting. Others have been quickly adapted to by flight crews who have attained normal performance capabilities (70).

Considerable experience has now been accumulated on the weightless state by both the United States astronauts and the Russian cosmonauts. Data are available for the 18-day manned flight in the Soyuz 9 spacecraft (71). The United States experience now totals over 6000 man hours through Apollo 13 (12). In addition, considerable experience has been obtained through the various Biosatellite efforts (72–74).

The mission orientation of space flights and the limitations imposed by weight and cabin configuration have superseded the goals of obtaining precise physiological data. Much of the information only comes from preflight and postflight experiments. All of the data on weightlessness obtained thus far comes from exceedingly complicated multivariable situations. The effects are compounded by disturbed circadian rhythms, altered cabin environments, confinement and changes in physical activity, and work routines, dietary regimens, as well as emotional factors and general fatigue. It is hoped that the advent of the orbiting laboratory—spacious to the extent of eliminating confinement—may be able to provide truly controlled physiological data on weightlessness.

CARDIOVASCULAR DECONDITIONING

Perhaps the best-documented alteration of weightlessness is the so-called cardiovascular deconditioning which results in a marked decrease in orthostatic tolerance. Some of the significant findings, summarized by the United States Space programs (11, 12, 75), indicate that even after the Mercury flight of only six hours orthostatic intolerance occurs, consisting of increased lability of blood pressure, increased pulse pressure, and pulse rates reaching 100 beats/min.

Astronaut Cooper provides perhaps the best example for orthostatic intolerance in his egress from the Mercury 9 capsule when he had no detectable blood pressure and a pulse rate of 188 beats/min. Profound sensitivity to tilt board procedures was demonstrated for 16 hours following the flight as heart rate in these procedures increased by 60 beats/min (75). Consistently in Apollo flights 7 through 11, the nine crewmen tested showed very marked increases in heart rate upon passive standing at 90°. The control values expressed as Δ beats/min ranged from −2 to +11, and immediately following reentry this increased to +13 to +47. The application of negative pressure to the lower part of the body revealed similar changes and the Δ beat/min rose from control values of −1 to +9 to the post flight values of +13 to +66.

Again it must be emphasized that many factors leading to orthostatic intolerance or syncope are not completely understood (76). Both the physical and emotional impact of prolonged space flight and the excitement of capsule recovery and disembarkation hopelessly confuse the experimental data. Within the framework of rational physiology it is possible to review the mechanisms which may be responsible. It appears that even in the weightless state cardiodynamic factors such as the systolic pressure attained, the stroke volume expected, and the inertial factors imposed are not greatly altered. Therefore one must look to the vascular bed, the blood volume, and the mechanisms for compensating for gravitational influences with positional changes.

BLOOD VOLUME

The immobility of bed rest, water immersion, and weightlessness have all resulted in a decrease in blood volume, with a decrease in both the plasma and red cell volumes. Apparently under these conditions the volume loss occurred early, perhaps within the first 24–48 hours, and then leveled off or reversed. The decrease in plasma volume usually amounted to about 500 ml, or about 7% of the body weight. In several well conducted studies of prolonged bed rest for 14, 30, and 42 days the obtained data indicated a return toward normal levels after a typical initial decrease. Hemoconcentration does occur in the bed rest situation, but this is reversed, presumably because of a suppression of red cell production (77).

In the Gemini programs blood volume decreased 7 to 15% in the 4–8 day missions (75). In this brief period the loss of red cell volume appeared to be greater than that which would be expected from studies of bed rest. Quite possibly the almost pure oxygen environment at 258 torr used in these flights augmented arthrocyte destruction and inhibited production. Red cell volume did not decrease in the Russian flights; these flights utilized a cabin atmosphere almost equivalent to that normally breathed at sea level. The later Apollo flights in which at least 7% nitrogen was present did not appear to suppress erythropoiesis (10) or enhance lysis (12). An examination of the Gemini program data reveals that there is no correlation between flight duration and blood volume changes. In the 14-day Gemini flight the pre- and postflight blood volumes were the same. If the decrease reported for shorter flights truly represents a valid phenomenon then in longer flights some other influence must have intervened to restore red cell and plasma volume (75, 77).

The mechanisms for the decrease in plasma volume under the conditions of bed rest or weightlessness have been reviewed recently (46, 77, 78). It appears that the regulatory system described above as altering body fluid loss with increased gravity is here brought to the fore. It is supposed there is a pooling of blood in the thorax under these conditions. Weightless and bed rest states have been studied in the monkey (74). In a monkey that changes from the vertical to the horizontal position, it is estimated that about 500 of the 650 ml of blood that had been pooled in the leg vascular bed is shifted to the thorax (77). Forces that pool blood in the lower extremities are absent in weightlessness as well as in the horizontal position, and the distribution of blood is similar in the two states (79). A second factor is that with the very marked decrease in hydrostatic pressures of the fluid column reabsorption in capillaries will surpass filtration.

Any addition of blood to the thorax thus increases venous volume, resulting in some distension of central veins and a stimulation of central blood volume receptors. This addition also initiates the mechanisms described by Gauer & Henry (46) that decrease ADH secretion.

Piemme has reviewed the vast literature concerning the hazards of applying this concept to weightlessness (78). Briefly, this literature indicates that an increase in central blood volume above homeostatic levels induces inhibition both of ADH release through left atrial receptors and of aldosterone production through right atrial receptors. This results in both a salt and water diuresis. Ordinarily ADH production has its own diurnal variation and thus the recumbency of sleep does not produce a great increase in free water clearance even though pooling of blood in the thorax takes place.

Unfortunately, thorough and consistent excretory measurements have not been made of astronauts. It would be extremely interesting to know the abilities of an astronaut to handle either a salt or water load, and to determine free water clearance or aldosterone excretion. Disturbed ability to excrete has been reported by the Voshkod cosmonauts (80).

The problems encountered in the ill-fated flight of Bonny, monkey #470, in the 8.8-day flight of Biosatellite III, launched in June 1969, represents what appears to be a documented case of central venous pooling with resulting compensations in the weightless state (74). Monitoring of central venous pressures revealed an increase of 2–3 cm H_2O, perhaps due to the reversal of pooling in the extremities. This is of the order of magnitude sufficient to activate the Gauer-Henry mechanism and to lead to loss of body fluids. This pressure elevation was maintained until the eighth day of flight, but by the third day the cumulative water loss had exceeded 10% of the body weight in spite of water taken in by drinking. In the entire flight the percentage weight loss was 20%. Undoubtedly there was also serious electrolyte disturbance, as well as emotional disturbance, which probably compounded the difficulties.

Duomarco and Rimini (79) have presented a theoretical discussion of venous pressures in the weightless state. In accord with the above, they conclude that systemic and pulmonary veins are distended by a rather small pressure of 2 cm of water.

A correlation has been established between the loss of blood volume and orthostatic intolerance (81). Changes could be seen in the response of heart rate to tilting after an addition of as little as six hours of bed rest to normal sleeping time. After several days the intolerance was as severe as it would have been with weightlessness. When the subject assumed an upright posture blood in the thorax drained into empty lower extremity capacitance vessels. Hydrostatic pressure greatly surpassed colloid pressure and tissue pressure which had been lowered by previous withdrawal of fluid. In the upright position venous return to the heart was decreased, resulting in impaired stroke volume and the observed orthostatic hypotension.

An interesting point concerning the United States astronauts is that their physical training regimens complicate any conclusions drawn concerning changes in weightlessness. It is well confirmed that the trained athlete possesses a blood volume of about 20–25% greater than average. Even relatively short training periods of 10 days can increase volume 10–20%. When investigators place a healthy human in bed for six weeks or in the confinement of a space capsule, blood volume change is either simply a physical deconditioning or an actual effect of loss of gravity stress (78).

GENERAL CARDIOVASCULAR ALTERATIONS

With the mechanisms of volume control mentioned above it is readily understandable why the decrement in plasma volume is self limiting. Once a certain volume is eliminated the stimulus forcing the response disappears. Why a reversal takes place is more difficult to establish. An interesting possibility is that a decrease occurs in constrictor activity or in tone of the venous capacitance vessels of the extremities after several days of weightlessness with lack of normal gravitational stimuli and hydrostatic compensations. This decrease in tone of the capacitance vessels tends to drain blood from the thorax, lower the pulmonary blood volume, and again through alteration of stimuli to atrial receptors, restore production or release of ADH and aldosterone to establish the normal preflight blood volume (77, 78).

An alteration in venous tone is an attractive hypothesis in accounting for the return of blood volume while orthostatic intolerance is continued. There is little direct evidence for the phenomenon in either weightlessness or bed rest. This is perhaps unfortunate since rather precise techniques now exist for such measurements.

Stevens et al (82), in a most interesting report, compared two groups of subjects in bed rest experiments, one receiving daily treatment with 9 fluorohydrocortisone (9 FF) and the other utilizing a procedure ("LBNP") in which negative pressure was applied to the lower portion of the body. Each of these procedures tended to restore blood volume to normal levels by the end of five weeks: the first by endocrine regulation and the second by challenging the vascular system as body positional changes would do. However, the 9 FF group clearly showed a greater decrement in orthostatic tolerance, whereas the LBNP group showed tolerances similar to those obtained prior to bed rest. Thus even though blood volumes were similar, marked differences were present in tolerance, which suggests that venous tone was altered.

Following the Gemini flights abnormal tilt table responses were noted for periods up to 50 hours. The time required to return to normal preflight responses to tilt did not correlate either with the duration of the space flight or with blood volume decreases which occurred. The Gemini astronauts demonstrated orthostatic intolerance for many hours after their blood volumes returned to preflight levels, which suggests a true venous deconditioning (75).

Following bed rest and weightlessness, there is an increased tendency for blood pooling when assuming an upright posture (77). The Gemini astronauts all showed definite pooling of blood in lower extremities over that period of time in which tilt tests were abnormal.

It is easy to extrapolate from the skeletal muscle, which loses tone, strength, and mass when inactive, to the smooth muscle of the blood vessel walls, which could show similar losses as the result of inactivity in the weightless state. But this is pure speculation and further investigation is needed. It is probably too simplistic to ask how much exercise a vascular smooth muscle needs to keep fit. The activity required to keep the central regulating mechanisms of the orthostatic compensations in optimal working order must also be ascertained. Unpublished studies by J. G. Oulete, who worked with competitive gymnasts, report what appears to be improved orthostatic tolerance after several years practicing dynamic postural changes over a 360° range. Whether this is a difference in vascular tone or central vasoconstrictor activity remains to be tested.

RESPIRATION

Inadequate experimental data have been obtained on respiratory variables in the weightless state. The reasons for this are obvious in that carrying a pulmonary testing laboratory aloft has been prohibitive. As indicated, there is a marked dependency upon gravity for observed characteristics of regional inhomogeneities of ventilation as well as of perfusion. Permutt (6) has extended the analysis described above for the Starling resistor concept in increased gravitation to the weightless state and has concluded that all parts of the lung will be in either zone 2 or zone 3, if one assumes that left atrial pressure is positive in this state. Although this latter assumption may not be entirely true and although left atrial pressure drops below alveolar pressure particularly with inspiration, the lungs would tend to be evenly ventilated. It is noted that all factors tending to produce atelectasis and inhomogeneities would be at a minimum were it not for the complexities imposed by cabin atmosphere of oxygen.

When the studies of Bryan were extrapolated to the 0 G state regional lung expansion and regional ventilation were found to be uniform throughout the thorax. Problems such as trapping disappeared and the ventilation perfusion ratios throughout the lung approached unity (57).

Although it appears that weightlessness can only improve pulmonary perfusion and ventilation, Permutt warns that the subject in the weightless state has considerably higher transmural pressure in the lung apex than he does upright at 1 G (6). The subject then resembles the patient with mitral stenosis and thus Permutt concludes, "it is not inconceivable that this would result in reflex changes and structural alterations."

An increased transudation of fluid from the capillaries is also likely, since the restraints of the Starling resistor are removed in weightlessness. Those capillaries which at 1 G are surrounded by a fluid pressure equivalent to alveolar pressure exist in a near state of collapse with a very low transmural pressure. When this situation changes and those capillaries in the zone 2 and 3 condition are fully distended, capillary filtration is augmented (6).

No problems have arisen to date with manned space flight experiences. Even in the extended 18 day mission of the Russian Soyuz 9 spacecraft, in which respiration was monitored and expired air samples were collected, no respiratory impairment occurred (71). It must be remembered that the respiratory system is one with a large reserve and that the impairment noted must be of considerable magnitude, particularly when the cosmonaut or astronaut is not required to perform at even near full aerobic capacity.

BONE AND ELECTROLYTE METABOLISM

This is an area which has not had vigorous investigation. It appears that after the Gemini VII flight US investigators gave scant attention to what appeared to be some interesting phenomena (75, 83). Pooled samples of urine for each 48 hours of flight from the Gemini VII flight of almost 14 days indicated some sodium retention paralleled by a similar decrease in chloride secretion. Aldosterone excretion in the urine was not detectable in the first four days of flight but increased to a higher than preflight value for the remaining 10 days. This observation is of considerable interest in the self-limiting nature of the decrease in blood volume as described above. Potassium excretion was reduced during the entire flight. There appeared to be no relationship between potassium and the observed changes in aldosterone secretion. Attempts to assay for ADH were difficult to interpret, since it appeared high only in postflight determination. Here again its output may have been too low during flight for detection. This entire area needs further investigation. The marked decreases in food intake may be a major factor in the observed changes in excretion.

With the Apollo flights 8 through 11 similar changes in potassium, sodium, and chloride were observed (12). Unfortunately only pre- and immediate postflight urine samples were analyzed. Calcium excretion was increased in Apollo 9, a 10 day flight, and decreased in Apollo 8, 10, and 11, all flights of shorter duration.

Measurements of blood electrolytes were variable in the Apollo mission and again only pre- and immediate postflight samples were available (12).

Bone demineralization had earlier been predicted for prolonged weightlessness. This is a reasonable prediction based on Wolf's law which states that "every change in the form of and function of bones, or in their function alone, is followed by certain definite changes in their internal architecture, and equally definite changes in their external configuration" (77). Since its formulation in 1868 this law has proven to be one of the most immutable in biology. Quite definitely the function of the entire skeleton is greatly altered in the weightless state. Busby (77) has presented an excellent review of demineralization problems occurring with prolonged bed rest. Some of this is applicable to spaceflight, but it must be recalled that both Russian and US crewmen indulged in exercise regimens during long flights, which may have reduced the demineralization process (71, 75).

In Gemini VII a marked increase in bound hydroxyproline, the amino acid unique to collagen, was found in the plasma in the first postflight blood sample (75). This is explicable in that demineralization may be accompanied by dissolution of the bone matrix. Hydroxyproline excretion was also in-increased in the postflight urine sample, when compared to the preflight samples in Apollo 8 crew members (12). Increased calcium excretion, however, was not a consistent finding and further evaluation is needed.

The Gemini program included the measurement of bone density in the heel and little fingers, a procedure that was apparently eliminated in the Apollo program. Decreases in density in the heel were about 8 to 16% in 4- and 8-day flights of Gemini V and VI, but only about 2 to 3% in the 14-day Gemini VII mission. Finger density decreased from 7 to 24% in Gemini IV and V and from 6 to 8% in Gemini VII. The difference in flights is noteworthy. In Gemini VII calcium intake was maintained at 1000 mg/day while in VI and V at 600 to 700 and 300 mg/day respectively. The changes appear greater than those during bed rest, but apparently can be ameliorated with exercise and calcium supplements (75).

ALTERATION OF WORK CAPACITY

An extensive review on muscle function and structure and their alterations under various gravitational conditions such as bed rest and immersion has been made by Bourne et al (84). These authors point out that the essential requirement of muscle in maintaining its structure and strength is that it be used, and when not used—as in conditions of weightlessness, bed rest, immersion, immobilization, or denervation disuse, atrophy occurs. Both Russian and US manned space programs evidence an awareness of this in the exercise programs which have been included in all missions of any duration.

This is an area which requires controlled nonexercising crewmen to compare with exercising counterparts. This has not been done, and it appears that there is little interest in actually comparing the physiological differences resulting from different exercise intensities among crew members.

Manned space flight operations including those of the Gemini (85) and Apollo (86) programs and the Soyuz 9 (71) have not indicated any marked occurrence of muscle atrophy and weakness, incoordination, or undue fatigue. However, decreases in exercise tolerance have occurred. In the 14-day flight of Gemini VII an experiment was done to examine day-to-day changes in physical fitness as assessed by the maximal heart rate attained during exercise, and by the pattern of heart rate recovery following exercise requiring a force of 70 pounds, (11, 75). The exercise consisted of stretching rubber cords 12 inches, once per second for 30 seconds. Heart rates attained and recovery patterns showed no alterations during the course of the 14-day mission, indicating little change in exercise tolerance.

When preflight and postflight exercise tolerance has been compared, marked decrements in exercise capacity after prolonged space flight have been reported (12, 75). Six Gemini astronauts underwent procedures which consisted of Balke tests with a gradually increasing work load until a heart rate of 180 beats/min was attained. Of the six crewmen tested, five showed decreased tolerance in that the work test was stopped earlier in postflight tests. A definite decrease in maximum oxygen consumption was also recorded. In the Apollo experiences 12 of the 15 crewmen tested demonstrated a significant decrease in work performed and in oxygen consumed at submaximal heart rate levels in the postflight tests. Oxygen consumption at 4 levels of heart rate in all 15 men ranged from 68.8 to 77.8% with a mean of 73.8% of the preflight level.

From one brief report, on the 18-day flight of Soyuz 9 the prolonged weightlessness resulted in subjective feelings of heaviness of head, limbs, and body, similar to that felt at 2 to 2.5 G (71). Muscle tone of the legs was reduced to a greater extent than was that of the arms. Walk and posture was not normal until 10 days after flight. The cosmonauts had used specially designed elasticized exercise garments and spring devices attached to the

floor with a tension of "several dozen Kf" enabling cosmonauts to simulate
walking, running, and jumping in place. With such devices a rather rigorous
program of exercises was followed in a four-day program of two hours each
day. The first day activities were designed to maintain muscular strength
and speed, the second day for measurement of physical and physiological
variables. Cardiac responses measured inflight showed no substantial
changes.

Although exercise programs were followed changes were apparent in
postflight tests. Again this is a situation complicated by moderate fatigue
and emotional stress. Inflight testing must be expanded with additional
emphasis placed on muscle metabolism.

METABOLIC PROBLEMS

Considerable effort has been placed in the Apollo program on measuring
various concentrations of blood constituents (12). To this reviewer the rationale for some measurements remains obscure. Perhaps the most striking
and consistent finding was hyperglycemia in the postflight blood samples.
This is interpreted as a result of "reentry stress" and augmented secretion of
catecholamines, although the latter were not measured. Serum cholesterol
and uric acid levels were reduced, a reduction attributed to the altered diets
of the crewmen. The observed decrease in M forms of the serum lactic dehydrogenase and the increase in H forms is of interest but is as yet unexplained. This again may be a result of the oxygen environment rather than
of weightlessness. Further documentation is required.

The general experience of United States crewmen has been one of negative nutritional balance. Diets are now set up to provide 2300 kcal of
energy per man per day. Estimated food intakes have ranged from about
1200 to 2100 kcal per day with an average in the Apollo flights of 1600 kcal.
Again, before any conclusions are established, controlled experiments in a
space station without confinement are required (12).

CONCLUDING REMARKS

So many subject areas of the physiological aspects of space flight have
been omitted that I feel some guilt. However, in defense of my selections, I
should like to point out that comprehensive reviews have appeared on
biological rhythms (87), thermal problems (88), and radiobiological problems (89).

ACKNOWLEDGMENTS

The author is especially indebted to Elisabeth Sherrill for her devoted
attention to the preparation of this manuscript, to the Aerospace Research
Applications Center of Indiana University for assistance in the literature
search, and to the U.S. Air Force for funds for the incidental expenses.

LITERATURE CITED

1. Wunder, C. C., Duling, B., Bengele, H. 1968. Gravity as a biological determinant. *Hypodynamics and Hypogravics. The Physiology of Inactivity and Weightlessness*, p. 1–62. New York: Academic

2. Wunder, C. C. 1966. *Life Into Space: An Introduction to Space Biology.* Philadelphia: Davis

3. Howard, P. 1965. Accelerations: Introduction. *A Textbook of Aviation Physiology*, ed. J. A. Gillies, p. 517–50. Oxford: Pergamon

4. Von Gierke, H. E. 1964. Transient acceleration, vibration and noise problems in space flight. *Bioastronautics*, p. 27–75. New York: Macmillan

5. Hardy, J. D. 1964. Acceleration. *Physiological Problems in Space Exploration*, p. 152–195. Springfield: Thomas

6. Permutt, S. 1968. Pulmonary circulation and the distribution of blood and gas in the lungs. *Physiology in the Space Environment*, Vol. 1 *Circulation*. National Academy of Sciences, National Research Council. Publ. 1485A. Wash, DC: NAS

7. Clark, C. C., Hardy, J. D., Crosbie, R. J. *A Proposed Physiological Acceleration Terminology with an Historical Review*. Johnsville, Pa: Aviation Medical Acceleration Laboratory, US Naval Air Development Center. Unpublished report

8. Lipman, R. L. et al 1970. Metabolic response to acceleration in man. *Aerosp. Med.* 41:905–8

9. Coburn, K. R. 1970. Physiological endpoints in acceleration research. *Aerosp. Med.* 41:5–11

10. Barer, A. S. et al 1966. Physiological reactions of the human body to transverse accelerations and some means of increasing the organism's resistance to these effects. *Aerosp. Med.* 37:127–33

11. National Aeronautics and Space Administration 1966. *Gemini Midprogram Conf.*, SP-121, *Manned Spacecraft Center, Houston.* Wash, DC: NASA

12. Berry, C. A. 1970. Summary of medical experience in the Apollo 7 through 11 manned spaceflights. *Aerosp. Med.* 41:500–19

13. Torphy, D. E., Leverett, S. D., Lamb,

L. E. 1966. Cardiac arrhythmias occurring during acceleration. *Aerosp. Med.* 37:52–58

14. Rogge, J. D., Meyer, J. F., Brown, W. K. 1969. Comparison of the incidence of cardiac arrhythmias during $+G_x$ acceleration, treadmill exercise and tilt table testing. *Aerosp. Med.* 40:1–5

15. Cohen, G. H., Brown, W. K. 1969. Changes in ECG contour during prolonged $+G_z$ acceleration. *Aerosp. Med.* 40:874–79

16. Cohen, G. H., Brown, W. K. 1969. Electrocardiographic changes during positive acceleration. *J. Appl. Physiol.* 27:858–62

17. Vacca, C., Causa, L., Aurucci, A. 1965. On the variations of the P wave of the electrocardiogram in relation to changes of body position in space. *Riv. Med. Aeronaut. Spaz.* 28:407–22

18. Tikhomirov, Ye. P. 1969. Chronotropic cardiac reaction accompanying exposure to accelerations. *Space Biol. Med.* 3(3):110–18

19. Cohen, G. H., Brown, W. K., Stowe, D. E., Fitzpatrick, E. L., Threatt, D. 1970. Analysis of the Frank orthogonal vectorcardiogram during gravitational stress. *Aerosp. Med.* 41:891–96

20. Bondurant, S., Finney, W. 1958. The spatial vectorcardiogram during acceleration. *Wright Air Develop. Center (NASA) Tech. Rep.*, p. 58–263

21. Robinson, B. F., Epstein, S. E., Beiser, G. D., Braunwald, E. 1966. Control of heart rate by the autonomic nervous system. *Circ. Res.* 19:400–11

22. Sandberg, L. 1961. Studies on electrocardiographic changes during exercise tests. *Acta Med. Scand.* 169:Suppl. 365

23. Chimoskey, J. E., 1970. Coronary blood flow during headward acceleration in unanesthetized dogs. *Aerosp. Med.* 41:1028–30

24. Stone, H. L., Stegall, H. F., Kardon, M. B., Sandler, H., Payne, R. M. 1971. Changes in aortic, coronary, and carotid flows during $+G_x$ acceleration. *J. Appl. Physiol.* 30:21–26

25. Michie, D. D. 1967. Hemodynamic responses of conscious dogs during

exposure to various $+G_x$/back angle combinations. *Aerosp. Med.* 38:883–89

26. Pince, B. W., Barr, M. L. 1963. Some responses of squirrel monkeys to high G brief duration profiles. *Aerosp. Med.* 34:752–57

27. Life, J. S., Pince, B. W. 1969. Role of autonomic nervous system in the control of heart rate in acceleratively stressed monkeys. *Aerosp. Med.* 40:44–48

28. Yuganov, Ye. M. et al 1969. Efferent pulses from the vagus nerve in intact animals and in animals whose labyrinths were removed during weightlessness. *Probl. Space Biol.* 6:180—84

29. Babushkin, V. I., Usachev, V. V. 1964. The efficiency of man exposed to radial acceleration and breathing of oxygen at an excess pressure. *Aviat. Space Med.* Dec:36–38

30. Gauer, O. H., Zuidema, G. D. 1961. *Gravitational Stress in Aerospace Medicine.* Boston: Little, Brown. 278 pp.

31. Sandler, H. 1966. Angiocardiographic and hemodynamic study of transverse (G_x) acceleration. *Aerosp. Med.* 37:901–10

32. Banchero, N., Rutishauser, W. J., Tsakiris, A. G., Wood, E. H. 1967. Pericardial pressure during transverse acceleration in dogs without thoracotomy. *Circ. Res.* 20:65–77

33. Sandler, H. 1964. *Hemodynamic and Cine-radiographic Study of Transverse ($+G_z$) Acceleration.* Rep. NADC-ML-6413. Johnsville, Pa: Aviation Medical Acceleration Laboratory, US Naval Air Development Center

34. Wood, E. H. 1967. Some effects of gravitational and inertial forces on the cardiopulmonary system. *Aerosp. Med.* 38:225–33

35. Offerhaus, L., Dejongh, J. C. 1967. Homeostatic regulation of the circulation during prolonged gravitational stress ($+G_z$). *Aerosp. Med.* 38:468–75

36. Rosenhamer, G. 1967. Influence of increased gravitational stress on the adaptation of cardiovascular and pulmonary function to exercise. *Acta Physiol. Scand.* 68:Suppl. 276, 5–61

37. Gjurstedt, H., Rosenhamer, G., Wigertz, O. 1968. High-G environment and responses to graded exercise. *J. Appl. Physiol.* 25(6):713–19

38. Kesselman, R. H. 1968. Gravitational effects on blood distribution. *Aerosp. Med.* 39:162–65

39. Chimoskey, J. E. 1970. Effect of positive and negative centrifugal acceleration on renal blood flow of unanesthetized dogs. *Fluid Dynamics of Blood Circulation and Respiratory Flow,* Advisory Group for Aerospace Research and Development. Johnsville, Pa: US Naval Air Development Center

40. Stone, H. L. 1968. Abdominal blood flow changes during acceleration stress in anesthetized dogs. *Aerosp. Med.* 39:115–19

41. Kovalenko, Ye. A., Korol'kov, V. I. 1965. Change in oxygen pressure in the heart muscle during ascent and acceleration. *Fiziol. Zh. SSSR Sechenova,* Engl. Transl. 51(8):966–73

42. Glaister, D. H. 1968. The effect of positive acceleration upon cardiac output and regional blood flow in the dog. *Aviat. Space Med., Proc. Int. Cong., 17th, Oslo, Aug. 5–8,* ed. B. Hannisdahl, C. W. Sem-Jacobsen. p. 333–38

43. Chimoskey, J. E. 1969. Renal blood flow of trained unanesthetized dogs under positive acceleration. *Fed. Proc.* 28:716

44. Piemme, T. E., McCally, M., Hyde, A. S. 1966. Renal response to $+G_z$ gradient acceleration in man. *Aerosp. Med.* 37:1253–56

45. Rogge, J. D., Moore, W. W., Segar, W. E., Fasola, A. F. 1967. Effect of $+G_z$ and $+G_x$ acceleration on peripheral venous ADH levels in humans. *J. Appl. Physiol.* 23:870–74

46. Gauer, O. H., Henry, J. P., Behn, C. 1970. The regulation of extracellular fluid volume. *Ann. Rev. Physiol.* 32:547–94

47. Bengele, H. H. 1969. Water intake and urine output of rats during chronic centrifugation. *Am. J. Physiol.* 216:659–65

48. Rogge, J. D., Fasola, A. F., Martz, B. L. 1967. *Aerospace Medical Association, Annual Scientific Meeting, 1967, Wash., DC.* American Medical Association, p. 259–60

49. Murakhovskii, K. I. 1968. Mechanics of the respiratory act during prolonged exposure to accelerations. *Environ. Space Sci.* 2:389–92

50. Murakhovskiy, K. I. 1969. X-ray photography of the human chest during accelerations varying in magnitude and direction. *Probl. Space Biol.* 6:283–90

51. Jacquemin, C., Varene, P. 1966. Recent aspects of respiratory physiology during transverse acceleration. *Rev. Corps Sante Armees Terre, Mer, Air.* 7:335–58

52. Sandler, H. 1966. Cineradiographic observations of human subjects during transverse accelerations of $+5$ G_x and $+10$ G_x. *Aerosp. Med.* 37:445–48

53. Rutishauser, W. J., Banchero, N., Tsakiris, A. G., Wood, E. H. 1967. Effect of gravitational and inertial forces on pleural and esophageal pressures. *J. Appl. Physiol.* 22:1041–52

54. Glazier, J. B., Hughes, J. M. B. 1968. Effect of acceleration on alveolar size in the lungs of dogs. *Aerosp. Med.* 39:282–92

55. Demange, J., Jacquemin, C., Timbal, J., Varene, P. 1965. Respiratory dead space during transverse acceleration. *Rev. Med. Aeronaut.* 4:4–7

56. National Academy of Sciences, National Research Council. 1967. *Physiology in the Space Environment*, Vol. 2, *Respiration*. Publ. 1485G. Wash, DC: NAS

57. Bryan, A. C., Milic-Emili, J., Pengelly, D. 1966. Effect of gravity on the distribution of pulmonary ventilation. *J. Appl. Physiol.* 21:778–84

58. Jones, J. G., Clarke, S. W., Glaister, D. H. 1969. Effect of acceleration on regional lung emptying. *J. Appl. Physiol.* 26:827–32

59. Barr, P. O. 1963. Pulmonary gas exchange in man as affected by prolonged gravitational stress. *Acta Physiol. Scand.* 58:Suppl. 207.

60. Barr, P. O., Bjurstedt, H., Coleridge, J. C. G. 1959. Blood gas changes in the anesthetized dog during prolonged exposure to positive radial acceleration. *Acta Physiol. Scand.* 47:16–27

61. Vandenberg, R. A., Nolan, A. C., Reed, J. H., Wood, E. H. 1968. Regional pulmonary arterial-venous shunting caused by gravitational and inertial forces. *J. Appl. Physiol.* 25:516–27

62. Power, G. G., Hyde, R. W., Sever, R. J., Hoppin, F. G., Nairn, J. R. 1965. Pulmonary diffusion capacity and capillary blood flow during forward acceleration. *J. Appl. Physiol.* 20:1199–1204

63. Glaister, D. H. 1965. Regional ventilation and perfusion in the lung during positive acceleration measured with ^{133}Xe. *J. Physiol. London* 177:738–48

64. Hoppin, F. G., Jr., York, E., Kuhl, D. E., Hyde, R. W. 1967. Distribution of pulmonary blood flow as affected by transverse $(+G_x)$ acceleration. *J. Appl. Physiol.* 22:469–74

65. Dowell, A. R., Shropshire, S., McCally, M. 1968. Ventilation and pulmonary gas exchange during headward $(+G_z)$ gradient acceleration. *Aerosp. Med.* 39:926–34

66. Parin, V. V. 1969. Some important problems of space physiology. *Aerosp. Med.* 40:1009–13

67. Klein, K. E., Wegmann, H. M., Brüner, H. Vogt, L. 1969. Physical fitness and tolerances to environmental extremes. *Aerosp. Med.* 40:998–1001

68. Jethon, Z. 1967. Elevation of tolerance by means of physical fitness improvement. *International Congress on Aviation and Space Medicine, 16th Lisbon, September 11–15.*

69. Soysiak, J. 1968. Effect of physical training on the work capacity and resistance in rats to hypoxia and acceleration stress. *Acta Physiol. Pol.* 19:703–11

70. Berry, C. A., Catterson, A. D. 1967. *Gemini Sum. Conf.* p. 197–218. Manned Spacecraft Center, Houton. Wash., DC: NASA

71. Mandrovsky, B. N. 1971. Soyuz-9 flight, a manned biomedical mission. *Aerosp. Med.* 42:172–77

72. Hanby, J., Adez, W. R. 1971. Sleep and wake states in the Biosatellite III monkey. Visual and computer analysis of telemetered electroencephalographic data from earth orbital flight. *Aerosp. Med.* 42:304–13

73. Walter, D. O. et al 1971. Digital computer analysis of neurophysiological data from Biosatellite III. *Aerosp. Med.* 42:314–21

74. Meehan, J. P., Rader, R. D. 1971. Cardiovascular observations of the Macaca nemestrina monkey in Biosatellite III. *Aerosp. Med.* 42:322–36

75. National Aeronautics and Space Administration 1967. *Gemini Sum.*

Conf., SP-138. *Manned Spacecraft Center, Houston.* Wash., DC: NASA

76. Mayerson, H. S., Burch, G. E. 1939. Relationship of tissue (subcutaneous and intramuscular) and venous pressure to syncope induced in man by gravity. *Am. J. Physiol.* 128: 258–69

77. Busby, D. E. 1968. Space Clinical Medicine. Dordrecht, Holland: Reidal. 276 pp.

78. Piemme, T. E. 1968. Body fluid volume and renal relationship to gravity. *Hypodynamics and Hypogravics.* Chapt. 5. New York: Academic

79. Duomarco, J. R., Rimini, R. 1970. Venous pressure of man in space. *Aerosp. Med.* 41:175–78

80. Natochin, Yu. N., Sokolova, M. M., Vasil'eva, V. F., Balakhovskii, I. S. 1965. Investigation of the renal function of the crew of the cosmic ship "Voskhod." *Cosmic Res.* 3:775–79

81. McCally, M., Piemme, T. E., Murray, R. H. 1966. Tilt table responses of human subjects following application of lower body negative pressure. *Aerosp. Med.* 37:1247–49

82. Stevens, P. M., Lynch, T. N., Johnson, R. L., Lamb, L. E. 1966. Effects of 9-alphafluorohydrocortisone and venous occlusive cuffs on orthostatic deconditioning of prolonged bed rest. *Aerosp. Med.* 37:468–74

83. Whedon, G. D., Lutwack, L., Newman, W. F., LaChance, P. A. 1966. *Gemini MidProgram Conf.*, SP-121: 417–22, *Manned Spacecraft Center, Houston.* Wash, DC: NASA

84. Bourne, G. H., Kalidas, M., de Bourne, M. 1968. Muscle in the weightless state. *Hypodynamics and Hypographics*, p. 187–212. New York: Academic

85. Dietlin, L. F., Rapp, R. M. 1966. *A Review of Medical Results of Gemini and Related Flights*, p. 36. *Manned Spacecraft Center, Houston.* Wash, DC: NASA

86. Myers, S. J., Sullivan, W. P., McCally, M. 1969. Measurement of muscle function in astronauts. *Aerosp. Med.* 40:1002–5

87. Halberg, F. 1969. Chronobiology. *Ann. Rev. Physiol.* 31:675–726

88. Lambertsen, C. J., Bullard, R. W., Eds. 1970. Temperature limitations in manned undersea and aerospace operations. *Aerosp. Med.* 41:1265–88

89. Langham, W. H., Brooks, P. M., Grahn, D. 1965. Radiation biology and space environmental parameters in manned spacecraft design and operations. *Aerosp. Med.* 36:1–55

REGULATION OF BODY FLUIDS 1079

Leonard Share and John R. Claybaugh

Department of Physiology and Biophysics, University of
Tennessee Medical Units, Memphis, Tennessee

The subject of the regulation of the body fluids is indeed complex, including elements of the endocrine, renal, nervous and cardiovascular systems. Because of the difficulty of the experimental methods, most of us have had tunnel vision in our research and reviews, although there have been some notable exceptions with respect to the latter (e.g., 58, 59, 121, 123). However, limitations of space and of our competence and a voluminous literature compel us to confine the scope of this review to a single topic: the control of the secretion of hormones involved in the regulation of extracellular volume, osmolarity, and concentrations of sodium and potassium. In this context, we shall then review vasopressin, the renin-angiotensin-aldosterone system, and the still hypothetical natriuretic hormone. Only those papers in these three areas which relate to the topic outlined above and which appeared within the period of about June 1969 to June 1971 have been reviewed. Some exceptions to the latter limitation have been made in order to present a coherent picture. We have resisted the temptation to cite abstracts, since they usually contain insufficient information for critical evaluation. Even within these limits we have undoubtedly overlooked some important, relevant papers. This was unintentional, and we apologize to the authors.

Vasopressin

The primary physiological stimuli for vasopressin release are plasma osmolarity which acts via osmoreceptors in or near the hypothalamus, and blood volume which acts via stretch or baroreceptors in the left atrium, carotid sinus, and aortic arch. Little has occurred in the past several years to change this overview, but work has continued to enhance our understanding of the components of this control system.

Volume receptors.—Left atrial receptors have recently been given considerable attention. Of particular importance is the report by Johnson et al (71) that small increases in left atrial transmural pressure, which are within physiological range, can inhibit vasopressin release. The plasma vasopressin concentration decreased linearly with increases in atrial transmural pressure

235

of up to 7 cm H_2O. Although there is no question that distention of the left atrium will inhibit vasopressin release, there has been no conclusive demonstration that a decrease in left atrial volume per se will result in an increased release of this hormone. Goetz et al (61) have attempted to provide such a demonstration in dogs prepared with a pericardial pouch around the atria. In the conscious animal, an increase in pressure within this pouch, decreasing atrial transmural pressure, failed to result in the expected increase in the plasma vasopressin concentration, although urine flow and urinary sodium excretion were decreased. The reabsorption of solute free water was unchanged. As the authors point out, one explanation for this apparently anomalous finding is that the receptors which function in the control of vasopressin release may be located along the edges of the pericardial pouch and would thus be little affected by the atrial tamponade. An alternate explanation is that the atrial receptors are not tonically active in the control of vasopressin secretion in the conscious dog. The possibility that atrial receptors play no role in the control of vasopressin release is most unlikely in view of the overwhelming evidence that distention of the left atrium can inhibit the release of this hormone (58, 59, 116). Baratz et al (13) reported that intermittent positive pressure respiration failed to increase the plasma vasopressin concentration. These experiments are difficult to interpret in the absence of measurements of left atrial pressure. Although it might be presumed that atrial transmural pressure decreases during the positive phase of respiration, the opposite might be true, because of the forcing of blood out of the lungs into the left atrium by the increased transpulmonary pressure.

Evidence continues to accumulate that changes in intrathoracic blood volume, presumably acting via atrial receptors, affect the plasma vasopressin concentration. Six hours after comatose patients with severe lesions of the central nervous system were changed from a 15° to 20° head-up position to a 5° to 10° head-down position, the blood vasopressin concentration fell an average of 0.8 microunits/ml (11). When the patients were returned to the head-up position, the vasopressin concentration rose again. Similar findings were obtained in a normal volunteer. Although these changes in plasma vasopressin levels were attributed to changes in left atrial filling, it is unfortunate that measurements of arterial blood pressure were not reported and that suitable controls were not obtained to rule out effects due to diurnal variations. Bengele et al (16) found that when rats were subjected to prolonged centrifugation, the blood vasopressin concentration fell to a minimum level in five days and then returned to control values over the next four days. One explanation for the fall in vasopressin concentration is a pooling of blood in the chest, the result of the position of the rats in the centrifuge. Should this be the case, then a prolonged volume stimulus can maintain a prolonged effect on vasopressin release.

Although there is little doubt that the arterial baroreceptors play an important role in the control of vasopressin release, the bulk of the currently available experimental evidence is consistent with the view, originally expressed by Gauer & Henry (58), that a reduction in the activity of the atrial receptors is primarily responsible for the increase in the plasma vasopressin concentration which follows small to moderate reductions in blood volume. On the other hand, Rocha e Silva & Rosenberg (107) have suggested, as have several other groups of investigators (for review, see 116), that the arterial baroreceptors play a dominant role in the hemorrhage-induced release of vasopressin. Rocha e Silva & Rosenberg (107) felt they had achieved a maximal release of vasopressin when anesthetized dogs were bled a volume sufficient to reduce diastolic pressure below 60 mm Hg, a level below which the arterial baroreceptors become silent. This seems a tenuous argument, and it is not at all certain that a maximal release of vasopressin was actually attained in these experiments. Some of the apparently contradictory views concerning the relationship between vasopressin release and arterial pressure following hemorrhage may result from the anesthetic used. Conscious dogs and dogs anesthetized with chloralose or a mixture of chloralose and urethane seem better able to maintain arterial pressure in the face of hemorrhage than do dogs anesthetized with sodium pentobarbital, the anesthetic Rocha e Silva & Rosenberg used (107). In the dog anesthetized with chloralose and urethane, the vasopressin response to hemorrhage can occur independently of a fall in arterial blood pressure (e.g. 116).

Osmoreceptors.—The work of Verney (130) establishing that small increases in the osmotic pressure of the plasma stimulate vasopressin secretion is truly classic in that it has withstood the test of time with little modification. The great sensitivity of this neuroendocrine reflex is typified by the observation by Johnson et al (72) that in the conscious sheep, a decrease in the plasma osmolality of 1.2% resulted in a reduction in the plasma vasopressin concentration from 2 to 1 microunits/ml, a change sufficient to bring about a water diuresis. There has been no corresponding clear-cut study on the relationship between an acute increase in plasma osmolality, divorced from blood volume changes, and the plasma vasopressin concentration. Saito et al (109), however, reported that short term infusions of hypertonic saline in the dog increase the concentration of vasopressin in jugular vein plasma. These responses were variable. There was no clear-cut dose-response relationship, and it was not possible to relate changes in the plasma vasopressin concentration to changes in the plasma osmolality since these last data were not given.

The possibility of hepatic osmoreceptors which function in the control of the renal excretion of water and sodium remains controversial. Haberich et al (65) have extended their earlier observations that the infusion of hypertonic sodium chloride solution into the portal vein of the conscious rat resulted in decreased urine flow rate, whereas the intraportal infusion of water resulted in a diuresis. These effects were presumably due to changes in vasopressin secretion. Further support for the existence of osmoreceptors in the liver is provided by Niijima's observation (93) that perfusion of the guinea pig liver in vitro with hypertonic solution resulted in an increased afferent impulse activity in vagal fibers supplying the liver. However, a minimum of a 6% increase in the osmotic pressure of the perfusate was required to elicit this response.

Schneider et al (110), using the same experimental design employed by Haberich et al (65), found, on the other hand, that in the conscious dog the renal responses to the infusion of either hypertonic saline or water were independent of whether the infusion was into the vena cava or portal vein. The obvious cause for the differences in findings by these two groups of investigators is species difference. This may, however, be too facile an explanation.

Interactions between extracellular fluid volume and osmolality.—Since it is widely held that extracellular fluid volume is conserved at the expense of concentration under extreme circumstances, it is of interest to examine the interrelationships between the volume and osmotic elements of the vasopressin control system. Moore and his associates have attempted this in the conscious sheep. In water deprivation, both elements of this control system act together to stimulate vasopressin release. There is an increase in the plasma osmolality and a reduction in blood volume which is reflected by a reduction in left atrial pressure (136). Hypotonic or isosmotic expansion of extracellular fluid volume in either the normally hydrated or dehydrated sheep resulted in a reduction in the plasma vasopressin concentration, regardless of the direction of changes in plasma osmolality (136). Certainly these data show that changes in left atrial pressure may play an important physiological role in the control of vasopressin release, but the authors' suggestion that such changes may play a major role in this regard does not seem warranted. Indeed, in a subsequent paper (72), these workers come to the more soundly based conclusion that with small changes in plasma osmolality and blood volume neither receptor system appears to dominate the other in the control of vasopressin release. In these well designed experiments, comparisons were made of the effects of an isovolemic reduction in plasma osmolality, isosmotic changes in blood volume, and combinations of osmotic and volume stimuli. The stimuli applied individually resulted in the expected changes in the plasma vasopressin concentration. When volume and osmotic stimuli were combined, the effects on the plasma vasopressin concentration were roughly additive. Thus, the plasma vasopressin concentration was unchanged when a 1.2% reduction in plasma osmolality was combined with a hemorrhage of 10% of the estimated blood volume. Similarly, in hydrated human subjects, the plasma osmolality at which the water diuresis was inhibited was higher when the increase in the osmotic pressure of the plasma was achieved by infusing hypertonic saline, increasing extracellular fluid volume, than by water deprivation, decreasing extracellular volumes (89).

Olsson & McDonald (97) reported the intriguing observation that the injection of hypertonic solutions of sodium chloride or sucrose into the arterial supply to the head in the ewe did not inhibit a water diuresis until approximately 30% of the administered water load was excreted. This was not due to a lack of responsiveness of the kidney to vasopressin. The authors suggested that it may have been due to a volume effect overriding an osmotic stimulus. Since the water load was given into the rumen, it is not clear that the expansion of extracellular volume was any greater in the early stages of the water diuresis than at the time when the effects of the hypertonic solutions could be demonstrated.

The rate of depletion of pituitary vasopressin was virtually identical in rats deprived of water for 5 days and in rats given 2% saline to drink during this same interval (73), although one would expect that these two procedures would have different effects on extracellular fluid volume. However, conclusions about the rate of release of vasopressin in these experiments cannot be drawn, since the rate of hormone synthesis may not have been the same in these two different experimental situations.

Central nervous system.—A number of studies have been concerned with the further characterization of the central nervous system components in the reflex control of vasopressin release, but great progress does not seem to have been made. Saito et al (109) have shown that dogs with diencephalic islands can respond to the infusion of hypertonic saline with an increased release of vasopressin. Consistent with this observation is the finding (52) that an isolated block of rat brain tissue, containing the supraoptic nuclei and the posterior lobe of the pituitary, released vasopressin at an increased rate when incubated in hypertonic medium. It was, however, necessary to raise the osmotic concentration of the medium to unphysiologically high levels to achieve this response.

Andersson and his colleagues (4) have extended their earlier observations that the injection of small volumes of hypertonic saline into the third ventricle of the brain inhibits a water diuresis in the conscious goat. This effect can also be produced by the injection of an isotonic ammonium chloride solution into the third ventricle (95), presumably the result of stimulation of adjacent nerve cells by the ammonium ion. These responses are probably due to the release of vasopressin, since they could not be produced after the induction of experimental diabetes insipidus. Although vasopressin release was stimulated by the injection of a hypertonic sucrose solution into the cerebral arterial supply of the dog (130) and sheep (97), the injection of hypertonic sucrose into the third ventricle of the goat was without effect on water diuresis (95). Could the ventricular osmoreceptors be different from those stimulated via the arterial supply to the brain?

It is generally accepted that the osmoreceptors are located in or near the supraoptic nucleus of the hypothalamus. This view is supported by the work summarized above and by much electrophysiological evidence. The injection of hypertonic solutions of sodium chloride, sucrose, or glucose into the carotid artery of the rabbit produced slow negative potentials in the region of the supraoptic nucleus (49). These changes are characteristic of stimulated receptors. Hayward & Vincent (66), recording the activity of single neurones in conscious monkeys, identified "specific" osmosensitive cells in the immediate perinuclear zone of the supraoptic nucleus. They suggested that these cells could be Verney's osmoreceptors.

Synaptic excitation of neurosecretory cells in the supraoptic and paraventricular nuclei of the hypothalamus appears to be requisite for the release of vasopressin. There are continuing efforts to substantiate this hypothesis experimentally. Dyball & Koizumi (51) found that stimuli which were previously shown (e.g. 50) to increase vasopressin release, i.e. the intracarotid injection of calcium chloride, carbachol, and acetylcholine and stimulation of the central end of the sectioned vagus, increased, decreased or had no effect on the rate of discharge of units in the supraoptic and paraventricular nuclei. Increased activity occurred more frequently than decreased activity. Barker et al (14), studying only units in the supraoptic nucleus which could be identified antidromically by stimulation of the posterior pituitary, reported an increased discharge frequency of these units when the central ends of the sectioned vagi and right carotid sinus nerve were electrically stimulated. It is not clear whether all of the identified units responded. The conclusion of both groups of workers that these data substantiate a causal relationship between increased activity of hypothalamic neurones and vasopressin release seems tenuous. The vagi and carotid sinus nerves carry, in addition to chemoreceptor afferents, baroreceptor afferents which should inhibit vasopressin release. Furthermore, in dealing with the heterogeneous cell population of the supraoptic and paraventricular nuclei, there is no assurance that a given cell under study is directly concerned with vasopressin release.

Neural connections between the diencephalon and the midbrain are necessary for an increased release of vasopressin in response to hemorrhage (109). This provides further evidence that peripheral receptors are required for the increased release of vasopressin following hemorrhage, and that cerebral ischemia and a reduction in the rate of removal of vasopressin from the circulating blood do not contribute appreciably to this immediate response (see 116 for review). Saito et al (109) also found that neither decortication nor section of the spinal cord at the level of C-1 interfered with the hemorrhage-induced release of vasopressin.

Cholinergic and monoaminergic synapses in or near the hypothalmus appear to be involved in the release of vasopressin (see 60 for review). In keeping with this view are several reports that the injection of cholinergic drugs into the third ventricle (76, 96) or into the common carotid artery (29) inhibits a water diuresis—presumably as a consequence of an increased release of vasopressin. More direct evidence for this role of acetylcholine is provided by the observation by Eggena & Thorn (52) that acetylcholine stimulated the supraoptico-neurohypophysial complex to release vaso-pressin in vitro. The inhibition of a water diuresis by an osmotic stimulus can be prevented by anti-adrenergic drugs, ganglionic blocking agents and atropine; inhibition of a water diuresis by acetylcholine can be prevented by pempidine but not reserpine (29). Based on these findings, Bridges & Thorn (29) suggested that a monoaminergic and a cholinergic synapse lie between the osmoreceptor and the supraoptic neurosecretory cell. However, most of the drugs used in this study themselves caused an initial antidiuresis, pre-sumably because of the release of a substantial quantity of vasopressin. This may have contributed to the subsequent impaired ability to release vaso-pressin. Further support for a role of a monoaminergic synapse in the control of vasopressin release is provided by the observation that the injection of catecholamines into the third ventricle of the goat inhibits a water diuresis (96).

Some further insight into the complicated nature of the synaptic control of the hypothalamic neurosecretory cells is provided by the work of Barker et al (15), who applied drugs microelectrophoretically to supraoptic neuro-secretory cells identified antidromically by stimulation of the posterior pituitary. Acetylcholine depressed the electrical activity of 84% of the re-sponsive cells and stimulated the remainder. It was thought that the former was a muscarinic effect and the latter a nicotinic effect. Norepinephrine depressed all of the responsive cells.

Metabolism.—In acute experiments, it is generally assumed that changes in the plasma vasopressin concentration provide an index of changes in se-cretion rate. This is a reasonable assumption if the changes in the plasma vasopressin concentration are rapid and large. On the other hand, in long term experiments, changes in the concentration of the hormone in plasma might just as well reflect changes in rate of removal from the blood as changes in secretion rate. There is, however, little information concerning the physi-ological control of vasopressin metabolism. Studies in this area still are con-cerned largely with questions of volume of distribution, half-life and plasma protein binding. An extensive investigation of these factors in man has been made by Fabian et al (53). In general agreement with earlier work by others, arginine vasopressin was found to have a half-life of 5.6 min and an apparent volume of distribution of approximately $\frac{2}{3}$ the extracellular fluid volume. The pitfalls in measurements of this sort have been discussed by Brook & Share (30) and by Lauson (77). Thirty percent of the vasopressin was bound to plasma proteins (53), but this is a controversial area and may reflect species differences as well as technical difficulties (60, 77). Approximately 8.5% of the injected dose of vasopressin appeared in the urine, and it was calculated that all of urinary hormone was filtered. The whole body clearance for vasopressin was 1 liter/min.

Pliška et al (104) have reported an anomolous behavior of the plasma vasopressin concentration in dogs which were infused with vasopressin at a constant rate for 1.5 to 2 hours. When the infusion was stopped, the plasma vasopressin concentration fell rapidly for 7 to 10 min, but then rose within 15 to 20 min after cessation of the infusion to a peak which was 45 to 100% of the level just preceding the cessation of the infusion. The plasma vasopressin concentration then fell again. The authors suggested that the secondary peak was due to the release of vasopressin which had been actively accumulated in some tissue, possibly the neurohypophysis, during the infusion phase of the experiment. This intriguing observation obviously needs further study.

NATRIURETIC HORMONE

The question of the existence of a hormonal natriuretic factor continues to generate a large number of pages in the journals. A definitive answer remains elusive, although the preponderance of recent reports seem to favor a natriuretic hormone.

Recent evidence for a natriuretic hormone.—One of the standard approaches to this problem is to determine whether volume expansion in a donor animal will provoke a natriuresis in a cross-circulated recipient. As in the past, this technique continues to yield conflicting results. Bonjour & Peters (26) reported that expansion of extracellular fluid volume or of blood volume alone provoked a natriuresis and diuresis in donor rats, but not in recipient cross-circulated animals. Since the half-life of the natriuretic factor may be so short that an effective concentration of the factor cannot be achieved in the recipient at the exchange rate for blood between donor and recipient, negative findings with this experimental approach cannot be considered conclusive. Thus, Blythe et al (24) found that expansion of extracellular fluid volume with saline resulted in a marked increase in sodium excretion in a donor dog, but only a small natriuresis in the cross-circulated recipient. Modification of the cross-circulation circuit, so that the kidneys of the recipient were perfused primarily by blood from the donor and the kidneys of the donor perfused largely by blood from the recipient, resulted in an enhanced response by the recipient and a diminished response by the donor. These responses were not due to dilution of the blood per se. Expansion of blood volume alone had only a modest effect on sodium excretion by the donor and no effect on sodium excretion by the recipient.

Another approach to this problem is to attempt to extract the natriuretic factor from blood, concentrate it, and identify it by bioassay. Finding an appropriate bioassay is obviously of critical importance. Sealey and her associates (112, 113), working with the urine and plasma of humans and sheep maintained on a high salt intake and of humans subjected to volume expansion, were able to isolate a factor which increased sodium excretion and sometimes urine flow and potassium excretion in an assay rat, independently of changes in glomerular filtration rate. This material appears to have a molecular weight between 10,000 and 50,000, is not dialyzable, and is inactivated by trypsin and trichloroacetic acid. However, the extract has two different natriuretic activities. When it was given to the assay rat intravenously, the natriuresis had a delayed onset and a long duration (112, 113). When the extract was injected into the renal arteries of the assay animal, there was only an abrupt natriuresis associated with an increased blood pressure. The activity of the material causing this second response was not related to the state of the sodium balance in the experimental subject from which it was derived. Thus, the first, delayed response reported by these investigators may not have been due to a hormone which acts on the kidney, but to an agent which elicits the appearance of a natriuretic factor in the assay animal. It does not appear that the natriuretic factor isolated by Sealey and colleagues is secreted by a brain structure, since they could find no gross differences in activity when comparing femoral vein blood with jugular vein blood obtained from the sheep. Krück (75) has also found a nondialyzable natriuretic factor in urine from normal, hydrated human subjects.

Sedláková et al (114) have reported quite different physical and chemical properties for a natriuretic factor, which they isolated by gel filtration from blood draining from the head in volume-expanded cows and dogs. This factor is claimed to have a molecular weight of approximately 1000, to be inactivated by chymotrypsin, and to be stable in trichloroacetic acid.

The mechanism of action for a presumed natriuretic hormone is inhibition of sodium reabsorption by the nephron. Thus, several investigators have found in plasma obtained from volume-expanded animals a factor which inhibits sodium transport in vitro. When renal tubule fragments were incubated in plasma from dogs in which blood volume had been increased, there was an increased intracellular sodium concentration and a decreased intracellular potassium concentration (39). The ability of these fragments to concentrate p-aminohippurate was also impaired. Nutbourne et al (94) incorporated a frog skin into an external blood circulation circuit in the dog. An increase in blood volume without changing blood composition resulted in a decreased short circuit current and potential across the frog skin. Similarly, dialyzates and ultrafiltrates of plasma from dogs which were expanded with saline reduced the short circuit current and potential difference in toad bladders in vitro (32). This material has a molecular weight less than that of the substance extracted by Sealey et al (112, 113). Clearly these observations on renal tubule fragments and amphibian epithelial tissue are consistent with the existence of a natriuretic hormone in the plasma of animals in which blood volume has been increased. It is equally clear that the ultimate proof of the occurrence of a natriuretic hormone will require the isolation and characterization of a circulating factor which can inhibit sodium reabsorption by the kidney, and whose concentration in the plasma varies with the individual's extracellular fluid volume.

Extrarenal receptors and the control of renal sodium excretion.—Evidence continues to accumulate that receptors in the brain may participate in the control of sodium excretion by the kidney. The injection of small volumes of hypertonic saline into the third ventricle of the brain (5, 46) or superfusion of the third ventricle with hypertonic saline (47) results in an increased renal excretion of sodium, potassium and water. It was considered that these changes were not the primary consequence of changes in renal hemodynamics, but this conclusion is not as firmly supported by the experimental evidence as one would like. In experiments in the dog by Dorn et al (46), glomerular filtration rate and effective renal plasma flow did not change, but these measurements were made in only three animals. In the experiments by Andersson et al (5) in the goat, glomerular filtration rate increased. However, the fraction of filtered sodium reabsorbed decreased, and the changes in glomerular filtration rate and sodium excretion did not coincide temporally. Since the natriuresis was not necessarily associated with changes in renal hemodynamics, was not prevented by exogenous aldosterone, and was induced in animals with diabetes insipidus (5), it was presumed that it was due to a change in secretion of a natriuretic or antinatriuretic factor. These experiments have not, however, ruled out a possible contribution by changes in renal nerve activity.

There appears to be a cholinergic link in this centrally mediated natriuresis. The injection of carbachol into the third ventricle of water-loaded conscious rats resulted in an increased urinary excretion of sodium and potassium and a decreased urine volume (45). This response was blocked by atropine, but not by hypophysectomy.

These studies of the effects of intraventricular hypertonic saline leave unanswered several important questions. What is the relationship of these observations to the observation that an isotonic increase in extracellular fluid volume increases renal sodium excretion? Does intraventricular hypertonic saline stimulate a specific receptor, which responds to an increase in the sodium concentration in the cerebrospinal fluid, in the plasma, or in both?

If there is a natriuretic hormone, reasonable candidates for the requisite "volume receptors" are receptors in the heart, since left atrial receptors are known to play an important role in the control of vasopressin secretion. Thus, Goetz et al (62) investigated the effects of changes in atrial transmural pressure in dogs prepared with a pericardial pouch around the atria. In one set of experiments in which blood volume was expanded acutely, atrial tamponade blunted the diuresis, but had no effect on the natriuresis. In a second set of experiments in which the dogs were hydrated with isotonic saline, atrial tamponade decreased urine flow rate and sodium excretion. The effects of the tamponade could not be attributed to changes in mean arterial blood pressure, cardiac output, glomerular filtration rate, or the plasma vasopressin concentration (61).

However, the role of receptors in the thorax in the renal response to volume expansion is far from clear. McDonald et al (82) reported that cord section at C-6, but not T-6, reduced the natriuresis in response to the intravenous infusion of isotonic saline. The blunting of the natriuresis by cervical cord section was due to a loss of efferent rather than afferent impulse activity, since section of the dorsal roots from C-6 to T-6 and vagal blockade were without effect. The authors presented the possibility that the impaired natriuresis in response to volume expansion following high cord section may be due to a reduction in circulating cathecholamines or angiotensin, as a result of a loss of sympathetic tone. The possible importance of the sympathetics is supported by the work of Michaelis & Gilmore (85). They reported that in the anesthetized dog, interruption of the thoracic and lower cervical sympathetic ganglia attenuated the diuresis and natriuresis which follow expansion of blood volume. However, their finding that these surgical procedures were without effect on the renal response to an increased blood volume in the unanesthetized dog is puzzling.

There have been attempts to implicate hepatic receptors in the control of sodium excretion by the kidney. Strandhoy & Williamson (122) reported confirmation of earlier work that a natriuresis could be produced in the dog by the infusion of hypertonic saline into the portal vein at a rate which was ineffective when administered via the femoral vein. This effect was not found either by Schneider et al (110) or by Potkay & Gilmore (105). Since both of these latter groups used unanesthetized dogs, there is the possibility that the natriuretic effect of intraportal hypertonic saline is in some way the consequence of the anesthetic agent. Thus, at the present time the physiological role of hepatic receptors in water and electrolyte metabolism is questionable.

The prostaglandins.—Several known humoral agents have been considered for the role of a natriuretic hormone. The prostaglandins are among the candidates (e.g. 78). This is based on the observations that prostaglandins of the E and A series are natriuretic, are found in the renal medulla, inhibit transport of a p-aminohippurate by the renal tubule, and have a chromophore at 280 mμ. The last two are properties which Bricker et al (28) have attributed to a humoral natriuretic factor. Evidence consistent with a physiological natriuretic role for prostaglandins continues to appear.

The prostaglandins impair the uptake of p-aminohippurate by slices of rabbit kidney cortex (79). The effectiveness of the E and A series compounds was greater than that of the F series, and it is claimed that compounds in this last series are not natriuretic.

Although prostaglandins had been earlier identified in the rabbit renal medulla (see 78 for review), PGA_2, PGE_2, and $PGF_{2\alpha}$ have now also been identified in dog renal medulla (41). Stimulation of the renal nerves and the infusion of norepinephrine result in an increased secretion of prostaglandin-like material by the kidney of the anesthetized dog (48). This material was tentatively identified as prostaglandins of the E type. Since the kidney was auto-perfused at constant flow, this response was not dependent upon a change in total renal blood flow, although the possible effect of a redistribution of renal blood flow could not be ruled out. No statement could be made about the possible secretion of prostaglandins of the A and F series, since the authors felt that their methods might not be adequate to detect these compounds. Fujimoto & Lockett (57) reported the appearance of a material, which they identified as PGE_1, in the renal lymph following the infusion of norepinephrine in the anesthetized cat. Neither blockade of the α and β receptors nor atropine interfered with this response.

Reports continue to accumulate that PGE_1 increases the renal excretion of sodium, potassium, and water although it is not agreed whether these urinary changes are accompanied by changes in glomerular filtration rate and renal plasma flow. Shimizu et al (118) have provided a particularly clear demonstration that the effects of PGE_1 on the urinary excretion of water and electrolytes is due to a direct action of the prostaglandin on the kidney. These workers infused small amounts of PGE_1 into one renal artery of the anesthetized dog. On the side of the infusion, the excretion of sodium, potassium, and water increased, glomerular filtration rate decreased, and renal plasma flow increased. Thus, the effects on water and electrolyte excretion were due either to a direct action on the tubule or to a redistribution of renal blood flow. Since the urine excreted by the infused kidney became hypotonic (the urine excreted by the control kidney remained hypertonic), and the free water clearance changed from negative to positive, the authors suggested that one of the actions of the prostaglandin is to block the action of vasopressin on the renal tubule. This concept is supported by the observation that PGE_1 inhibited the vasopressin-stimulated osmotic water flow across the toad bladder in vitro (81). In the experiments by Werning et al (134), the prostaglandin-induced natriuresis was not accompanied by changes in glomerular filtration rate or in effective renal plasma flow.

Although it is the general consensus that prostaglandins of the E and A series increase renal sodium and water excretion, it is perhaps not surprising in this complex field that there are several opposing reports. Thus, Murphy et al (92) reported that PGE_1 and PGA_1 at a dose of 1 $\mu g/kg$ caused a reduction in the renal excretion of sodium and water in the anesthetized dog. This response may have been related to changes in arterial blood pressure and renal hemodynamics. Vilhardt & Hedqvist (132) found an antidiuresis when the large dose of 1 to 4 μg of PGE_2 was injected into the carotid artery of the water-loaded, inactin-anesthetized rat. Sodium excretion was not reported. This response was not due to a direct action of the prostaglandin on the kidney, since the injection of the same dose of PGE_2 into the abdominal aorta above the origin of the renal arteries was without effect on urine flow or urine osmolality. The authors suggested that the antidiuresis resulting from the injection of PGE_2 into the cerebral circulation was the consequence of an increased release of vasopressin. However, the data are insufficient to rule out the possibility that the response was neurally mediated via the renal nerves. Since these authors found that the addition of PGE_2 to the medium in which rat posterior pituitary lobes were incubated was without effect either on the basal rate of vasopressin release or on the potassium-stimulated vasopressin release, they postulated that the prostaglandin influenced vasopressin secretion in vivo by an action on the hypothalamus or some higher central nervous system structure.

As Lee has pointed out (78), it is unlikely that PGE and PGF compounds function as systemic humoral factors, since they are almost completely cleared from the blood in its passage through the lungs. Since PGA_2 escapes this fate, it could function systemically, although it has not yet been identified in the circulating blood. However, it is possible that the PGE compounds can act intrarenally to affect sodium excretion. Consistent with this concept is the finding that prostaglandin-like material appears in the renal lymph in greater quantity when urinary sodium excretion is stimulated by norepinephrine (57). In any event, a definitive understanding of the role of the prostaglandins in sodium and water metabolism is still lacking.

Calcitonin—In the past several years a number of reports have confirmed the original observation by Rasmussen et al (106) that calcitonin increases renal sodium and water excretion (2, 9, 17, 74), although one report has failed to confirm such an effect (38). It seems unlikely that the natriuretic and diuretic activities of this hormone are due to a contaminant, since these responses have been produced with porcine (2, 9, 17), salmon (2, 74) and synthetic human (17) calcitonin. Nor do these effects appear to be due to changes in glomerular filtration rate (9). Although calcitonin may be a very potent natriuretic factor, it is questionable whether it plays an important role in the control of the renal handling of sodium. The dose which is minimally effective on sodium excretion in the rat is considerably higher than that required to lower the plasma calcium concentration in the young rat (2, 74). In addition, thyroparathyroidectomized rats show no impairment in their ability to excrete sodium (74).

α-MSH.—Orias and McCann (99) have reported that α-MSH increased sodium and water excretion in the water-loaded, conscious rat. However, this hormone does not appear to be a particularly potent natriuretic factor, and at this time the physiological significance of this finding is not apparent.

Conclusive evidence for a natriuretic hormone is still lacking. Even among the proponents of a natriuretic hormone, there is disagreement concerning the chemical properties of such a hormone and the organ from which it is secreted. Some of the assays for this hormone test phenomena which seem somewhat far removed from its supposed role. Certainly, the renal effects which are usually attributed to a natriuretic hormone may be due in large measure to changes in intrarenal physical factors, but this does not preclude the possibility of an important physiological role for a humoral natriuretic factor. It is our opinion that the preponderance of evidence favors the existence of a natriuretic hormone, or indeed of several such hormones.

RENIN-ANGIOTENSIN-ALDOSTERONE SYSTEM

Changes in body fluid volume and composition are known to affect plasma renin activity. The exact means by which these changes are sensed and ultimately control renin release is still not clear. It is generally accepted, however, that these changes are detected by both intrarenal and extrarenal receptors which can affect renin release (126). A major effect of the renin released from the kidney is via the well known relationship in which it acts on renin substrate to produce angiotensin I which is converted to angiotensin II by converting enzyme. The angiotensin II then stimulates the release of aldosterone from the adrenal cortex which will increase sodium reabsorption from the renal tubules. However, the renin-angiotensin-aldosterone system may be interrelated with other systems, and its components may have independent actions. For example, there is evidence of a renin-angiotensin-vasopressin system (e.g. 8, 25, 115), which will be discussed later, and a control system for aldosterone secretion which is partially independent of the renin-angiotensin system or adrenocorticotrophic hormone (21, 37, 86, 103). Recent evidence also further substantiates the proposed (42, 133) existence and functional role of angiotensin II, generated intrarenally.

Intrarenal control of renin release.—Two theories have been advanced, in which changes in extracellular volume and sodium balance are sensed by intrarenal receptors, the baroreceptor and macula densa theories (see review, 126). Proof of the baroreceptor theory has been difficult since changes in arterial pressure are often accompanied by parallel changes in the intrarenal handling of sodium. Skinner et al (119) hypothesized a baroreceptor system based on the observation that renin release occurred with very slight reductions in blood pressure, within the limits of the kidney to autoregulate blood flow, a finding recently confirmed by Imbs et al (70). However, with reductions of arterial blood pressure within the range of autoregulation, Fojas & Schmid (55) found an increased renin secretion only when urinary sodium and potassium concentration and excretion were decreased. This suggests that the increase in renin secretion that has been observed when blood pressure is lowered within renal autoregulatory limits could have been due to macula densa stimulation as well as to baroreceptor stimulation.

A different approach may give the baroreceptor theory more support. Blaine et al (20) have recently developed a method which attempts to eliminate the influence of the macula densa on the secretion of renin. Ligation of the ureter combined with two hours of total renal ischemia results in tubular degeneration and cessation of glomerular filtration. Hemorrhage and suprarenal aortic constriction result in elevated plasma renin activity in such dogs with "nonfiltering" kidneys. However, it would be desirable to know if this model can respond to hyponatremia with an increased renin release.

There is considerable support for a receptor, presumably the macula densa, which is responsive to changes in tubular sodium load or concentration (see 108, 126). Additional support for this mechanism is provided by Cooke et al (40) who administered ethacrynic acid to dogs in order to inhibit sodium reabsorption in the ascending limb of Henle's loop. When urine flow was stopped by ureteral occlusion, no change was observed in renal venous renin concentration. However, upon release of the occlusion a prompt rise in renal venous renin occurred; when ethacrynic acid was not given, this maneuver caused a reduction in renal venous renin concentration. A reduction in body fluid volume and electrolyte depletion were prevented in these experiments by returning urine via the femoral veins. Like responses have been obtained with a similarly acting drug, furosimide (70, 84, 129). However, the interpretation of these findings is controversial. Vander & Carlson (129) concluded that furosimide inhibits the reabsorption of sodium by the macula densa cells, reducing the sodium transport across these cells, and that therefore a decrease in sodium delivery to the macula densa increases renin release. Cooke et al (40) and Meyer et al (84), on the other hand, interpreted their results to indicate that increased tubular sodium delivery to the macula densa caused the increased renin secretion. Precisely what does occur at the level of the macula densa is yet to be resolved.

The role of sodium in the control of renin secretion has been studied under a wide range of experimental conditions and appears to be significant. The role of potassium in the regulation of renin release has also been supported by recent investigations. It has been shown that in humans, decreases in dietary potassium intake stimulate renin release (1, 31) in the face of elevated plasma sodium concentration (1); an increase in dietary potassium intake decreases plasma renin activity (31, 44) despite a fall in plasma sodium concentration (31). These studies have been extended in the rat, employing wider ranges of sodium and potassium diets (111). In the dog, infusions of potassium chloride into the renal artery inhibited renin release in that kidney (128). These acute effects of potassium chloride were not accompanied by changes in renal hemodynamics nor do they appear to be dependent on changes in sodium balance since there was a slight increase in urinary sodium excretion. Unfortunately, as these authors have pointed out, the possibility remains that the inhibitory effect of the potassium chloride infusion in these experiments may have been due to the systemic increase in potassium concentration since the renin release from the contralateral kidney was not determined. Taken all together, these reports indicate, however, that potassium can alter renin release via a mechanism independent of changes in sodium balance. The possibilities of a direct action on the juxtaglomerular apparatus or of an indirect action by influencing the tubular handling of sodium remain to be investigated.

Since there is evidence for a renal angiotensinogen (54), since angiotensin I can be converted to angiotensin II in the kidney (35, 56, 98), and since both renin (69, 80) and angiotensin II (12) are abundantly present in renal lymph and therefore present in the interstitium, it seems very plausible that an intrarenal renin-angiotensin system operating in the interstitium may play a role in the regulation of extracellular fluid volume and content. Two recent reviews have included such a mechanism in their discussions of the renin-angiotensin system (42, 133). Both reviewers advanced the hypothesis that increased delivery of sodium to the macula densa shifts the direction of renin secretion from the circulatory system to the interstitium, where a local increase in angiotensin II results. Speculation as to the function of the interstitially released renin is probably premature; however, the effects of intravascular angiotensin II on intrarenal blood flow may be important in sodium regulation (36).

Extrarenal control of renin release.—There is little question that sympathetic stimulation via the renal nerves can alter renin synthesis and release (see reviews 59, 126), but what are the extrarenal stimuli that result in changes in efferent impulses in the renal nerves? One such stimulus appears to be a change in blood volume. The increase in plasma renin activity (34) or in angiotensin II concentration (68) after a small hemorrhage can be prevented by anesthesia of the renal nerves. At least some of the afferent nerve fibers for this response may be carried in the vagi, since vagotomy or cooling of the vagi result in increased circulating angiotensin, despite elevated blood pressure (67). Hodge et al (67), however, were able to obtain a further increase in circulating angiotensin levels when the animals were bled following blockade of the vagi by cooling, confirming the presence of baroreceptors other than those with afferent fibers in the vagus.

In addition to the influence of extrarenally detected volume changes on renin release, Mouw & Vander (91) have shown that ventriculocisternal perfusion of hyposmotic, low-sodium solutions increases renin release from the kidney. Central control of renin release has also been shown by experiments in which stimulation of pressor areas in the mesencephalon (125) and medulla oblongata (101) resulted in an increased renin release, which was inhibited by denervation of the kidneys. The intrarenal adrenergic receptors involved in the release of renin brought about by stimulation of the medulla (100), hypoglycemia, epinephrine infusions (10), and physostigmine (3) have been reported to be β receptors. The involvement of α receptors in the release of renin resulting from hemorrhage-induced hypotension has been suggested by Birbari (18). The increase in renin release observed after change in posture to an upright position or after ethacrynic acid administration, on the other hand, has been reported to be inhibited by both α- and β-adrenergic blocking agents (135).

How essential is this neural influence on "normal" renin synthesis and release? It has been proposed by Blaufox and his colleagues (23) that the denervated kidney is able to handle sodium normally, because renal responses of patients with transplanted kidneys were indistinguishable from those of their respective donors, when they were subjected to increased sodium intake. It has also been suggested, however, that the nerve supply to the kidneys may be essential for sodium depletion to stimulate the secretion of renin (87, 88). Using the absence of renal cortical norepinephrine as an index of complete renal sympathectomy, Mogil et al (87) found that sodium depletion did not result in an increased renin release until approximately 2 mos after sympathectomy, a time when there was evidence of reinnervation of the kidney. The earliest date after renal transplantation studied by Blaufox's group (23) was 1½ mos, so that reinnervation of these kidneys may have occurred. Thus, the ability of the denervated kidney to handle sodium "normally" is still questionable. That volume stimuli affect the denervated kidney is well documented and recently confirmed by the work of Blaine & Davis (19) in which hemorrhage, or suprarenal aortic constriction in dogs with denervated, "nonfiltering" kidneys resulted in increased renin release (see also review 43).

Thus, changes in extracellular volume, sodium, and potassium, detected by intrarenal or extrarenal receptors, result in appropriate changes in renin secretion. Volume stimuli can override sodium stimuli (63) in some cases, and the reverse can occur in other situations (33). This supports the concept that both types of stimuli are important in the control of renin. The functional significance and the control of renin released into the interstitium of the kidney obviously require additional investigation as does the mechanism whereby potassium controls renin release.

The control of aldosterone.—Important recent observations suggest that the secretion of aldosterone may be partially independent of the control of the renin-angiotensin system, adrenocorticotrophic hormone, and the plasma potassium concentration (120). Thus, during fasting, elevated plasma aldosterone levels occur in the absence of detectable increases in plasma concentrations of renin, adrenocorticotrophic hormone, sodium. or potassium (37). During sodium repletion of a previously sodium-depleted animal, an elevated plasma renin activity concurrent with rapidly falling plasma aldosterone levels has been reported (21). This suppression of aldosterone secretion does not appear to be a result of direct action of sodium on the adrenal gland (22). Other results obtained by Boyd et al (27) indicate that the increase in plasma aldosterone concentration resulting from sodium depletion cannot be duplicated by infusing angiotensin II at rates sufficient to produce even higher concentrations of circulating angiotensin II than were present during the sodium deficiency.

Whether an additional aldosterone controlling factor of renal origin (103) or factors already known but not fully investigated are responsible for the dissociation remains to be determined.

HORMONAL INTERRELATIONSHIPS

It is perhaps stating the obvious to point out that the hormonal regulation of water and electrolyte metabolism depends upon the integrated control of all of the hormones which affect the renal handling of water and electrolytes. It should, therefore, be particularly profitable to explore the interrelations among these various hormones.

Vasopressin and the adrenocortical hormones.—One such area of long standing interest concerns a possible interrelationship between vasopressin and the hormones of the adrenal cortex. This interest has centered around the controversy whether the plasma vasopressin concentration is elevated in adrenal insufficiency. Share & Travis (117) have shown that in the dog, circulating levels of vasopressin can increase in adrenal insufficiency. Since this increase could be prevented by maintaining the dogs on a high salt intake, they concluded that it was the consequence of a reduction in blood volume and pressure, rather than of a loss of an inhibitory action of the glucocorticoids on the neural mechanism which controls vasopressin release. Vilhardt (131), on the other hand, has reported that prednisolone inhibited the potassium-stimulated release of vasopressin from isolated rat neural lobes. Although he concluded that glucocorticoids can play a role in the control of vasopressin release in vivo, a more physiological test of this hypothesis would be desirable.

Green et al (64) have found in studies of the effects of adrenalectomy in rats with hereditary diabetes insipidus, that the impaired ability to excrete a water load in adrenal insufficiency is not entirely due to vasopressin. Both gluco- and mineralocorticoids were necessary for full restoration of water diuresis in the adrenalectomized animal.

Vasopressin and the renin-angiotensin system.—Recently, considerable attention has been directed to the possibility of an interrelationship between vasopressin and the renin-angiotensin system. The injection of a small dose of angiotensin II into the third ventricle of the conscious, hydrated goat potentiated the ability of intraventricular hypertonic saline to inhibit a water diuresis, presumably by stimulating vasopressin release (8). Andersson and his associates (7) subsequently showed that a more prolonged infusion of angiotensin II in isotonic solutions of sodium chloride as well as nonelectrolytes will also inhibit a water diuresis. They suggested that angiotensin may stimulate vasopressin release by facilitating either the transport of sodium into brain cells involved in the control of vasopressin release or the transependymal transport of sodium. Severs et al (115) also reported evidence which is consistent with a stimulatory effect of angiotensin on vasopressin release. The injection of large doses of angiotensin into the lateral ventricle of the conscious rat resulted in a pressor response which could be partially blocked by hypophysectomy and lesions in the supraoptic nucleus.

If angiotensin is to function physiologically in the control of vasopressin release, the angiotensin must be able to act via the systemic circulation. That this may indeed be the case is suggested by the work of Bonjour &

Malvin and their associates. The intravenous infusion of pressor doses of either renin or angiotensin in the conscious dog was found to increase the plasma vasopressin concentration (25). This response was small (10 ng of angiotensin II/min/kg for 40 min resulted in an increased plasma vasopressin concentration of 0.9 microunits/ml), and a dose-response relationship could not be obtained consistently. Subsequently, in experiments on anesthetized dogs these investigators attempted to show that angiotensin acts centrally to stimulate vasopressin release (90). In experiments on three dogs, the intravenous infusion of angiotensin at the rate of 10 ng/kg/min, was ineffective, whereas, this same dose of angiotensin increased the plasma vasopressin concentration when given into a common carotid artery. However, the intra-arterial injection always preceded the intravenous injection, so that the possibility that the response to the first infusion modified the response to the second could not be ruled out. In a second series of experiments, perfusion of the ventricular-cisternal system of the brain with solutions containing angiotensin increased the plasma vasopressin concentration. Particularly puzzling is the observation that there was no dose-response relationship between the concentration of angiotensin in the perfusate and the increment in the plasma vasopressin concentration. This report and those from the laboratories of Andersson (7, 8) and Severs (115) suggest that angiotensin may act centrally to increase the release of vasopressin, but additional study of this point would be desirable.

There appears to be a negative feedback relationship between vasopressin and the renin-angiotensin system, since the intravenous infusion of Pitressin resulted in a fall in plasma renin activity in unanesthetized, sodium-deprived dogs (124). That this response may be of physiological importance is indicated by the observation that an increase in the plasma vasopressin concentration of only 1.2 microunits/ml resulted in almost a 30% reduction in plasma renin activity.

What is the physiological function of the negative feedback loop involving vasopressin, renin, and angiotensin? Bonjour & Malvin (25), citing the many situations in which there are parallel changes in vasopressin and the renin-angiotensin system, suggest that in these situations renin secretion may play a role in controlling vasopressin release. We think that this is unlikely, at least with respect to volume and osmotic stimuli. First, a reduction in blood volume elicits an increase in the plasma vasopressin concentration which is many times the maximum effect produced by exogenous angiotensin or renin. Second, the negative feedback relationship between vasopressin on the one hand and renin and angiotensin on the other would tend to throttle an increase in these three humoral agents when blood volume is reduced. Third, an increase in the plasma sodium concentration increases the secretion of vasopressin (as a result of the increased plasma osmolality), but decreases renin release. However, the interrelationships between vasopressin, renin, and angiotensin may serve to minimize fluctuations in their plasma concentrations under resting conditions. Changes in blood volume or composition, activating appropriate receptors, would then override this negative feedback relationship, bringing about appropriate changes in the secretion of vasopressin and renin.

Natriuretic hormone and the renin-angiotensin system.—There is evidence that the renin-angiotensin system may participate in the control of the secretion of the still hypothetical natriuretic hormone. Andersson and his colleagues (6, 7, 8) have shown that the infusion of antiotensin II into the third ventricle of the brain in the conscious goat increased the renal excretion of sodium. The effect was greater when the angiotensin was dissolved in isotonic or slightly hypotonic sodium chloride solutions than in solutions of nonelectrolytes (7). The angiotensin also potentiated the natriuretic action of intraventricular hypertonic sodium chloride (8). Larger doses of angiotensin intravenously enhanced sodium excretion in two of the four goats studied (6).

Pearce et al (102) reported that in the rat, chronic salt depletion, presumably increasing renin secretion, diminished the natriuretic response to acute expansion of blood volume. On the other hand, chronic treatment with deoxycorticosterone and supplemental sodium chloride, presumably depleting renin, enhanced the response. This difference in responsiveness appeared to be humorally mediated, since isovolemic cross-circulation between a sodium-depleted rat and a sodium-loaded rat partially restored the response of the sodium-depleted rat to subsequent volume expansion. The relationship of the renin-angiotensin system to these observations remains to be determined.

Prostaglandins and the renin-angiotensin system.—The ubiquitous prostaglandins may not only directly affect the renal handling of sodium and water, but may also be involved with vasopressin, angiotensin, and renin. McGiff et al (83) reported that the infusion of angiotensin II into the renal artery of the dog resulted in the appearance in the renal venous blood of a prostaglandin-like material, which was tentatively identified as PGE_2. The threshold dose of angiotensin in most cases was 0.5 to 5 ng/kg/min. There is conflict over whether the prostaglandins increase renin secretion. Vander (127) could find no effect on renin release when PGE_1 and PGE_2 were infused into a renal artery of the anesthetized dog at rates of 0.2 to 0.5 μg/min for 20–30 min. However, Werning et al (134), using the much larger dose of 25 μg of PGE_1 in 2 min into the aorta just above the origin of the renal arteries in anesthetized dogs, reported a large increase in plasma renin activity in blood taken from the vena cava just above its junction with the renal veins. The dose of prostaglandin in these experiments seems unphysiologically high. If prostaglandins can increase renin release under physiological conditions, we are then faced with a positive feedback loop, involving prostaglandin, renin, and angiotensin. This seems unlikely.

Prostaglandins and vasopressin.—There seems little need to postulate that the diuresis induced by the PGE and PGA compounds is due in part to a reduction in the plasma vasopressin concentration. However, it might be worth while to investigate the possibility of interrelationships between the prostaglandins and vasopressin, particularly in view of the report by Vilhardt & Hedqvist (132) that large doses of PGE_2 may act centrally to to inhibit vasopressin release.

Conclusion

Water and electrolyte homeostasis in mammals is dependent upon a complex, multifaceted system. To date, most of our efforts have been directed toward the study, in isolation, of the individual components of this system. Hopefully, we are now entering an era in which improved methodology will make it possible to study the ways in which these components are related one to the other.

LITERATURE CITED

1. Abbrecht, P. H., Vander, A. J. 1970. Effects of chronic potassium deficiency on plasma renin activity. *J. Clin. Invest.* 49:1510–16
2. Aldred, J. P., Kleszynski, R. R., Bastian, J. W. 1970. Effects of acute administration of porcine and salmon calcitonin on urine electrolyte excretion in rats. *Proc. Soc. Exp. Biol. Med.* 134:1175–80
3. Alexandre, J. M., Menard, J., Chevillard, C., Schmitt, H. 1970. Increased plasma renin activity induced in rats by physostigmine and effects of alpha- and beta-receptors blocking drugs thereon. *Eur. J. Pharmacol.* 12:127–31.
4. Andersson, B., Dallman, M. F., Olsson, K. 1969. Observations on central control of drinking and of the release of antidiuretic hormone (ADH). *Life Sci.* 8:425–32
5. Andersson, B., Dallman, M. F., Olsson, K. 1969. Evidence for a hypothalamic control of renal sodium excretion. *Acta Physiol. Scand.* 75:496–510
6. Andersson, B., Eriksson, L. 1971. Conjoint action of sodium and angiotensin on brain mechanisms controlling water and salt balances. *Acta Physiol. Scand.* 81:18–29
7. Andersson, B., Eriksson, L., Oltner, R. 1970. Further evidence for angiotensin sodium interaction in central control of fluid balance. *Life Sci.* 9:1091–96

8. Andersson, B., Westbye, O. 1970. Synergistic action of sodium and angiotensin on brain mechanisms controlling fluid balance. *Life Sci.* 9:601–8
9. Ardaillou, R. et al 1969. Renal excretion of phosphate, calcium and sodium during and after a prolonged thyrocalcitonin infusion in man. *Proc. Soc. Exp. Biol. Med.* 131:56–60
10. Assaykeen, T. A., Clayton, P. L., Goldfien, A., Ganong, W. F. 1970. Effect of alpha- and beta-adrenergic blocking agents on the renin response to hypoglycemia and epinephrine in dogs. *Endocrinology* 87:1318–22
11. Auger, R. G., Zehr, J. E., Siekert, R. G., Segar, W. E. 1970. Position effect on antidiuretic hormone. *Arch. Neurol. Chicago* 23:513–17
12. Bailie, M. D., Rector, F. C., Seldin, D. W. 1971. Angiotensin II in arterial and renal venous plasma and renal lymph in the dog. *J. Clin. Invest.* 50:119–26
13. Baratz, R. A., Philbin, D. M., Patterson, R. W. 1970. Urinary output and plasma levels of antidiuretic hormone during intermittent positive-pressure breathing in the dog. *Anesthesiology* 32:17–22
14. Barker, J. L., Crayton, J. W., Nicoll, R. A. 1971. Supraoptic neurosecretory cells: autonomic modulation. *Science* 171:206–7.

15. Barker, J. L., Crayton, J. W., Nicoll, R. A. 1971. Supraoptic neurosecretory cells: adrenergic and cholinergic sensitivity. *Science* 171:208–10

16. Bengele, H. H., Moore, W. W., Wunder, C. C. 1969. Decreased antidiuretic activity measured in the blood of chronically centrifuged rats. *Aerosp. Med.* 40:518–20

17. Bijvoet, O. L. M., Veer, J. V. S., de Vries, H. R., Van Koppen, A. T. J. 1971. Natriuretic effect of calcitonin in man. *N. Engl. J. Med.* 284:681–88

18. Birbari, A. 1971. Effect of sympathetic nervous system on renin release. *Am. J. Physiol.* 220:16–18

19. Blaine, E. H., Davis, J. O. 1971. Evidence for a renal vascular mechanism in renin release: new observations with graded stimulation by aortic constriction. *Circ. Res.* 29: Suppl. II. 118–26

20. Blaine, E. H., Davis, J. O., Witty, R. T. 1970. Renin release after hemorrhage and after suprarenal aortic constriction in dogs without sodium delivery to the macula densa. *Circ. Res.* 27:1081–89

21. Blair-West, J. R. et al 1971. The dissociation of aldosterone secretion and systemic renin and angiotensin II levels during the correction of sodium deficiency. *Acta Endocrinol.* 66:229–47

22. Blair-West, J. R. et al 1971. The effect of adrenal arterial infusion of hypertonic NaHCO₃ solution on aldosterone secretion in sodium deficient sheep. *Acta Endocrinol.* 66:448–61

23. Blaufox, M. D. et al 1969. Physiologic responses of the transplanted human kidney. *N. Eng. J. Med.* 280: 62–66

24. Blythe, W. B., D'Avilla, D., Gitelman, H. J., Welt, L. G. 1971. Further evidence for a humoral natriuretic factor. *Circ. Res.* 29:Suppl. II. 21–31

25. Bonjour, J. P., Malvin, R. L. 1970. Stimulation of ADH release by the renin-angiotensin system. *Am. J. Physiol.* 218:1555–59

26. Bonjour, J. P., Peters, G. 1970. Nonoccurrence of a natriuretic factor in circulating blood of rats after expansion of the extracellular or the intravascular space. *Pfluegers Arch.* 318:21–34

27. Boyd, G. W., Adamson, A. R., James, V. H. T., Peart, W. S. 1969. The role of the renin-angiotensin system in the control of aldosterone in man. *Proc. Roy. Soc. Med.* 62:1253–54

28. Bricker, N. S. et al 1968. *In vitro* assay for a humoral substance present during volume expansion and uraemia. *Nature London* 219:1058–59

29. Bridges, T. E., Thorn, N. A. 1970. The effects of autonomic blocking agents on vasopressin release *in vivo* induced by osmoreceptor stimulation. *J. Endocrinol.* 48:265–76

30. Brook, A. H., Share, L. 1966. On the question of protein binding and the diffusibility of circulating antidiuretic hormone in the dog. *Endocrinology.* 78:779–85

31. Brunner, H. R., Baer, L., Sealey, J. E., Ledingham, J. G. G., Laragh, J. H. 1970. The influence of potassium administration and of potassium deprivation on plasma renin in normal and hypertensive subjects. *J. Clin. Invest.* 49:2128–38

32. Buckalew, V. M., Jr., Martinez, F. J., Green, W. E. 1970. The effect of dialysates and ultrafiltrates of plasma of saline-loaded dogs on toad bladder sodium transport. *J. Clin. Invest.* 49:926–35

33. Bull, M. B., Hillman, R. S., Cannon, P. J., Laragh, J. H. 1970. Renin and aldosterone secretion in man as influenced by changes in electrolyte balance and blood volume. *Circ. Res.* 27:953–60

34. Bunag, R. D., Page, I. H., McCubbin, J. W. 1966. Neural stimulation of release of renin. *Circ. Res.* 19:851–58

35. Carrière, S., Biron, P. 1970. Effect of angiotensin I on intrarenal blood flow distribution. *Am. J. Phyisol.* 219:1642–46

36. Carrière, S., Friborg, J. 1969. Intrarenal blood flow and PAH extraction during angiotensin infusion. *Am. J. Physiol.* 217:1708–15.

37. Chinn, R. H. et al 1970. The natriuresis of fasting: relationship to changes in plasma renin and plasma aldosterone concentrations. *Clin. Sci.* 39:437–55

38. Clark, J. D., Kenny, A. D. 1969. Hog thyrocalcitonin in the dog: urinary calcium, phosphorus, magnesium and sodium responses. *Endocrinology* 84:1199–205

39. Clarkson, E. M., Talner, L. B., de Wardener, H. E. 1970. The effect of plasma from blood volume expanded dogs on sodium, potassium

and PAH transport of renal tubule fragments. *Clin. Sci.* 38:617–27

40. Cooke, C. R., Brown, T. C., Zacherle, B. J., Walker, W. G. 1970. The effect of altered sodium concentration in the distal nephron segments on renin release. *J. Clin. Invest.* 49:1630–38

41. Crowshaw, K., McGiff, J. C., Strand, J. C., Lonigro, A. J., Terragno, N. A. 1970. Prostaglandins in dog renal medulla. *J. Pharm. Pharmacol.* 22:302–4

42. Davis, B. B., Jr., Knox, F. G. 1970. Current concepts of the regulation of urinary sodium excretion—a review. *Am. J. Med. Sci.* 259:373–82

43. Davis, J. O. 1971. What signals the kidney to release renin? *Circ. Res.* 28:301–6

44. Dluhy, R. G., Underwood, R. H., Williams, G. H. 1970. Influence of dietary potassium on plasma renin activity in normal man. *J. Appl. Physiol.* 28:299–302

45. Dorn, J., Antunes-Rodrigues, J., McCann, S. M. 1970. Natriuresis in the rat following intraventricular carbachol. *Am. J. Physiol.* 219:1292–98

46. Dorn, J. B., Levine, N., Kaley, G., Rothballer, A. B. 1969. Natriuresis induced by injection of hypertonic saline into the third cerebral ventricle of dogs. *Proc. Soc. Exp. Biol. Med.* 131:240–42

47. Dorn, J., Porter, J. C. 1970. Diencephalic involvement in sodium excretion in the rat. *Endocrinology* 86:1112–17

48. Dunham, E. W., Zimmerman, B. G. 1970. Release of prostaglandin-like material from dog kidney during nerve stimulation. *Am. J. Physiol.* 219:1279–85

49. Durham, R. M., Novin, D. 1970. Slow potential changes due to osmotic stimuli in supraoptic nucleus of the rabbit. *Am. J. Physiol.* 219:293–98

50. Dyball, R. E. J. 1968. Stimuli for the release of neurohypophysial hormones. *Brit. J. Pharmacol. Chemother.* 201:319–28

51. Dyball, R. E. J., Koizumi, K. 1969. Electrical activity in the supraoptic and paraventricular nuclei associated with neurohypophysial hormone release. *J. Physiol. London* 201:711–22

52. Eggena, P., Thorn, N. A. 1970. Vasopressin release from the rat supra-optico-neurohypophysial system *in vitro* in response to hypertonicity and acetylcholine. *Acta Endocrinol.* 65:442–52

53. Fabian, M., Forsling, M. L., Jones, J. J., Prior, J. S. 1969. The clearance and antidiuretic potency of neurohypophysial hormones in man and their plasma binding and stability. *J. Physiol. London* 204:653–68

54. Finkielman, S., Nahmod, V. E. 1969. *In vitro* production of angiotensin I by renal glomeruli. *Nature London* 222:1186–88

55. Fojas, J. E., Schmid, H. E. 1970. Renin release, renal autoregulation, and sodium excretion in the dog. *Am. J. Physiol.* 219:464–68

56. Franklin, W. G., Peach, M. J., Gilmore, J. P. 1970. Evidence for the renal conversion of angiotensin I in the dog. *Circ. Res.* 27:321–24

57. Fujimoto, S., Lockett, M. F. 1970. The diuretic actions of prostaglandin E_1 and of noradrenaline and the occurrance of a prostaglandin E_1-like substance in the renal lymph of cats. *J. Physiol. London* 208:1–19

58. Gauer, O. H., Henry, J. P. 1963. Circulatory basis of fluid volume control. *Physiol. Rev.* 43:423–81

59. Gauer, O. H., Henry, J. P., Behn, C. 1970. The regulation of extracellular fluid volume. *Ann. Rev. Physiol.* 32:547–95

60. Ginsburg, M. 1968. Production, release, transportation and elimination of the neurohypophysial hormones. Neurohypophysial hormones and similar polypeptides. *Handbook of Experimental Pharmacology.* ed. B. Berde, 23:286–371. Berlin: Springer. 967 pp.

61. Goetz, K. L., Bond, G. C., Hermreck, A. S., Trank, J. W. 1970. Plasma ADH levels following a decrease in mean atrial transmural pressure in dogs. *Am. J. Physiol.* 219:1424–28

62. Goetz, K. L., Hermreck, A. S., Slick, G. L., Starke, H. S. 1970. Atrial receptors and renal function in conscious dogs. *Am. J. Physiol.* 219:1417–23

63. Gordon, R. D., Pawsey, C. G. K. 1971. Relative effects of serum sodium concentration and the state of body fluid balance on renin secretion. *J. Clin. Endocrinol.* 32:117–19

64. Green, H. H., Harrington, A. R., Valtin, H. 1970. On the role of antidiuretic hormone in the inhibition

of acute water diuresis in adrenal insufficiency and the effects of gluco- and mineralocorticoids in reversing the inhibition. *J. Clin. Invest.* 49:1724–36

65. Haberich, F. J., Aziz, O., Nowacki, P. E., Ohm, W. 1969. Zur Spezifität der Osmoreceptoren in der Leber. *Pfluegers Arch.* 313:289–99

66. Hayward, J. N., Vincent, J. D. 1970. Osmosensitive single neurones in the hypothalamus of unanaesthetized monkeys. *J. Physiol London* 210: 947–72

67. Hodge, R. L., Lowe, R. D., Ng, K. K. F., Vane, J. R. 1969. Role of the vagus nerve in the control of the concentration of angiotensin II in the circulation. *Nature London* 221:177–79

68. Hodge, R. L., Lowe, R. D., Vane, J. R. 1966. The effects of alteration of blood-volume on the concentration of circulating angiotensin in anesthetized dog. *J. Physiol. London* 185: 613–26

69. Hosie, K. F. et al 1970. The release of renin into the renal circulation of the anaesthetized dog. *Clin. Sci.* 38:157–74

70. Imbs, J. L., Velly, J., Fontaine, J. L., Schwartz, J. 1970. Contrôle de la sécrétion de rénine. *Nephron* 7:499–511

71. Johnson, J. A., Moore, W. W., Segar, W. E. 1969. Small changes in left atrial pressure and plasma antidiuretic hormone titers in dogs. *Am. J. Physiol.* 217:210–14

72. Johnson, J. A., Zehr, J. E., Moore, W. W. 1970. Effects of separate and concurrent osmotic and volume stimuli on plasma ADH in sheep. *Am. J. Physiol.* 218:1273–80

73. Jones, C. W., Pickering, B. T. 1969. Comparison of the effects of water deprivation and sodium chloride inhibition on the hormone content of the neurohypophysis of the rat. *J. Physiol. London* 203:449–58

74. Keeler, R., Walker, V., Copp, D. H. 1970. Natriuretic and diuretic effects of salmon calcitonin in rats. *Can. J. Physiol. Pharmacol.* 48: 838–41

75. Krück, F. 1969. Influence of humoral factors on renal tubular sodium handling. *Nephron* 6:205–16

76. Kühn, E. R., McCann, S. M. 1970. Injections of carbachol into third ventricle and release of oxytocin and vasopressin in the lactating rat.

Arch. Int. Pharmacodyn. 186:192–93

77. Lauson, H. D. 1970. Fate of the neurohypophysial hormones. Pharmacology of the endocrine system and related drugs: the neurohypophysis. *International Encyclopedia of Pharmacology and Therapeutics.* ed. H. Heller, B. T. Pickering, 1:Sec. 41, 377–97 Oxford: Pergamon. 486 pp.

78. Lee, J. B. 1969. Hypertension, natriuresis, and the renal prostaglandins. *Ann. Intern. Med.* 70:1033–38

79. Lee, J. B., Ferguson, J. F. 1969. Prostaglandins and natriuresis: the effect of renal prostaglandins on PAH uptake by kidney cortex. *Nature London* 222:1185–86

80. Lever, A. F., Peart, W. S. 1962. Renin and angiotensin-like activity in renal lymph. *J. Physiol. London* 160:548–563

81. Lipson, L. C., Sharp, G. W. G. 1971. Effect of prostaglandin E_1 on sodium transport and osmotic water flow in the toad bladder. *Am. J. Physiol.* 220:1046–52

82. McDonald, K. M., Rosenthal, A., Schrier, R. W., Galicich, J., Lauler, D. P. 1970. Effect of interruption of neural pathways on renal response to volume expansion. *Am. J. Physiol.* 218:510–17

83. McGiff, J. C., Crowshaw, K., Terragno, N. A., Lonigro, A. J. 1970. Release of a prostaglandin-like substance into renal venous blood in response to angiotensin II. *Circ. Res.* 26, 27: Suppl. I. 121–30

84. Meyer, P., Menard, J., Papanicolaou, N., Alexandre, J. M., Devaux, C., Milliez, P. 1968. Mechanism of renin release following furosemide diuresis in rabbit. *Am. J. Physiol.* 215:908–15.

85. Michaelis, L. L., Gilmore, J. P. 1970. Cardiac Sympathetics and control of sodium excretion. *Am. J. Physiol.* 218:999–1002

86. Michelakis, A. M., Horton, R. 1970. The relationship between plasma renin and aldosterone in normal man. *Circ. Res.* 27:Suppl. I. 185–94

87. Mogil, R. A., Itskovitz, H. D., Russell, J. H., Murphy, J. J. 1969. Renal innervation and renin activity in salt metabolism and hypertension. *Am. J. Physiol.* 216:693–97

88. Mogil, R. A., Itskovitz, H. D., Russell, J. H., Murphy, J. J. 1970. Plasma renin activity and blood

pressure before and after renal denervation. *Invest. Urol.* 7:442–47

89. Moses, A. M., Miller, M. 1971. Osmotic threshold for vasopressin release as determined by saline infusion and by dehydration. *Neuroendocrinology.* 7:219–26

90. Mouw, D., Bonjour, J. P., Malvin, R. L., Vander, A. 1971. Central action of angiotensin in stimulating ADH release. *Am. J. Physiol.* 220:239–42

91. Mouw, D. R., Vander, A. J. 1970. Evidence for brain Na receptors controlling renal Na excretion and plasma renin activity. *Am. J. Physiol.* 219:822–32

92. Murphy, G. P. et al 1970. The renal and cardiodynamic effects of prostaglandins (PGE_1, PGA_1) in renal ischemia. *J. Surg. Res.* 10:533–41

93. Niijima, A. 1969. Afferent discharges from osmoreceptors in the liver of the guinea pig. *Science* 166:1519–20

94. Nutbourne, D. M. et al 1970. The effect of expanding the blood volume of a dog on the short-circuit current across an isolated frog skin incorporated in the dog's circulation. *Clin. Sci.* 38:629–48

95. Olsson, K. 1969. Studies on central regulation of secretion of antidiuretic hormone (ADH) in the goat. *Acta Physiol. Scand.* 77:465–74

96. Olsson, K. 1970. Effects on water diuresis of infusions of transmitter substances into the third ventricle. *Acta Physiol. Scand.* 79:133–35

97. Olsson, K., McDonald, I. R. 1970. Lack of antidiuretic response to osmotic stimuli in the early stages of a water diuresis in sheep. *J. Endocrinol.* 48:301–2

98. Oparil, S., Sanders, C. A., Haber, E. 1970. *In-vivo* and *in-vitro* conversion of angiotensin I to angiotensin II in dog blood. *Circ. Res.* 26:591–99

99. Orias, R., McCann, S. M. 1970. Natriuretic effect of α-MSH in the water-loaded rat. *Proc. Soc. Exp. Biol. Med.* 133:469–74

100. Passo, S. S., Assaykeen, T. A., Goldfien, A., Ganong, W. F. 1971. Effect of α- and β-adrenergic blocking agents on the increase in renin secretion produced by stimulation of the medulla oblongata in dogs. *Neuroendocrinology* 7:97–104

101. Passo, S. S. et al 1971. Effect of stimulation of the medulla oblongata on renin secretion in dogs. *Neuroendocrinology.* 7:1–10

102. Pearce, J. W., Sonnenberg, H., Veress, A. T., Ackermann, U. 1969. Evidence for a humoral factor modifying the renal response to blood volume expansion in the rat. *Can. J. Physiol. Pharmacol.* 47:377–86

103. Peart, W. S. 1970. Renin and angiotensin in relation to aldosterone. *Am. J. Clin. Pathol.* 54:324–30

104. Pliška, V., Heller, J., Tata, P. S. 1970. Anomalous changes in the plasma antidiuretic activity of hydrated dogs after the cessation of intravenous infusion of arginine vasopressin. *Experientia* 26:1108–9

105. Potkay, S., Gilmore, J. P. 1970. Renal responses to vena caval and portal venous infusions of sodium chloride in unanesthetized dogs. *Clin. Sci.* 39:13–20

106. Rasmussen, H., Anast, C., Arnaud, C. 1967. Thyrocalcitonin, EGTA, and urinary electrolyte excretion. *J. Clin. Invest.* 46:746–52

107. Rocha e Silva, M., Jr., Rosenberg, M. 1969. The release of vasopressin in response to haemorrhage and its role in the mechanism of blood pressure regulation. *J. Physiol. London* 202:535–57

108. Romero, J. C., Hoobler, S. W. 1970. The renin-angiotensin system in clinical medicine. *Am. Heart J.* 80:701–8

109. Saito, T., Yoshida, S., Nakao, K. 1969. Release of antidiuretic hormone from neurohypophysis in response to hemorrhage and infusion of hypertonic saline in dogs. *Endocrinology* 85:72–78

110. Schneider, E. G. et al 1970. Lack of evidence for a hepatic osmoreceptor mechanism in conscious dogs. *Am. J. Physiol.* 218:42–45

111. Sealey, J. E., Clark, I., Bull, M. B., Laragh, J. H. 1970. Potassium balance and the control of renin secretion. *J. Clin. Invest.* 49:2119–27

112. Sealey, J. E., Kirshman, J. D., Laragh, J. H. 1969. Natriuretic activity in plasma and urine of salt-loaded man and sheep. *J. Clin. Invest.* 48:2210–24

113. Sealey, J. E., Laragh, J. H. 1971. Further studies of a natriuretic substance occurring in human urine and plasma. *Circ. Res.* 29:Suppl. II. 32–43

114. Sedláková, E., Lichardus, B., Cort, J. H. 1969. Plasma saluretic activity: its nature and relation to

oxytocin analogs. *Science* 164: 580–82

115. Severs, W. B., Summy-Long, J., Taylor, J. S., Connor, J. D. 1970. A central effect of angiotensin: release of pituitary presser material. *J. Pharmacol. Exp. Ther.* 174:27–34

116. Share, L. 1969. Extracellular fluid volume and vasopressin secretion. *Frontiers in Neuroendocrinology*, ed. W. F. Ganong, L. Martini, 183–210. New York: Oxford Univ. Press. 442 pp.

117. Share, L., Travis, R. H. 1970. Plasma vasopressin concentration in the adrenally insufficient dog. *Endocrinology* 86:196–201

118. Shimizu, K., Kurosawa, T., Maeda, T., Yoshitoshi, Y. 1969. Free water excretion and washout of renal medullary urea by prostaglandin E₁. *Jap. Heart J.* 10:437–55

119. Skinner, S. L., McCubbin, J. W., Page, I. H. 1964. Control of the renin secretion. *Circ. Res.* 15:64–76

120. Slater, J. D. H. 1969. The role of the renin-angiotensin system in the control of aldosterone secretion. *Proc. Roy. Soc. Med.* 62:1251–53

121. Smith, H. W. 1957. Salt and water volume receptors. An exercise in physiologic apologetics. *Am. J. Med.* 23:623–52

122. Strandhoy, J. W., Williamson, H. E. 1970. Evidence for an hepatic role in the control of sodium excretion. *Proc. Soc. Exp. Biol. Med.* 133:419–22

123. Strauss, M. B. 1957. *Body Water in Man.* Boston: Little, Brown. 286 pp.

124. Tagawa, H., Vander, A. J., Bonjour, J. P., Malvin, R. L. 1971. Inhibition of renin secretion by vasopressin in unanesthetized sodium-deprived dogs. *Am. J. Physiol.* 220:949–51

125. Ueda, H. et al 1967. Increased renin release evoked by mesencephalic stimulation in the dog. *Jap. Heart J.* 8:498–506

126. Vander, A. J. 1967. Control of renin release. *Physiol. Rev.* 47:359–82

127. Vander, A. J. 1968. Direct effects of prostaglandin on renal function and renin release in anesthetized dog. *Am. J. Physiol.* 214:218–21

128. Vander, A. J. 1970. Direct effects of potassium on renin secretion and renal function. *Am. J. Physiol.* 219:455–59

129. Vander, A. J., Carlson, J. 1969. Mechanism of the effects of furosemide on renin secretion in anesthetized dogs. *Circ. Res.* 25:145–52

130. Verney, E. B. 1947. The antidiuretic hormone and the factors which determine its release. *Proc. Roy. Soc. Ser. B.* 135:25–106

131. Vilhardt, H. 1970. Influence of corticosteroids and chlorpromazine on the release of vasopressin from isolated neural lobes of rats. *Acta Endocrinol.* 65:490–96

132. Vilhardt, H., Hedqvist, P. 1970. A possible role of prostaglandin E₂ in the regulation of vasopressin secretion in rats. *Life Sci.* 9:825–30

133. Werning, C., Siegenthaler, W. 1969. Das Renin-Angiotensin-Aldosteron-System in pathophysiologischer Sicht. *Klin. Wochenschr.* 47:1247–55

134. Werning, C. et al 1971. Effect of prostaglandin E₁ on renin in the dog. *Am. J. Physiol.* 220:852–56

135. Winer, N., Chokshi, D. S., Yoon, M. S., Freedman, A. D. 1969. Adrenergic receptor mediation of renin secretion. *J. Clin. Endocrinol.* 29:1168–75

136. Zehr, J. E., Johnson, J. A., Moore, W. W. 1969. Left atrial pressure, plasma osmolality and ADH levels in the unanesthetized ewe. *Am. J. Physiol.* 217:1672–80

DIGESTION: MOTILITY

ALEXANDER BORTOFF[1]

*Department of Physiology, State University of New York,
Upstate Medical Center, Syracuse, New York*

In keeping with recent editorial policy, the editors have asked that each review for this volume represent a critical discussion of current research in the field, "rather than encyclopedic coverage of many papers." I have attempted to comply with the editors' request; this review covers chiefly those papers written between January 1968 and May 1971 that present some of the more controversial aspects of current research in gastrointestinal motility. Because of my somewhat biased approach to the subject, however, this review deals primarily with neural and myogenic regulation of gastrointestinal motility, rather than with patterns of motility per se. Fortunately, many of the areas not discussed here have been given extensive coverage in related reviews, the most comprehensive of which are found in the volume on motility in the alimentary section of the *Handbook of Physiology* (36a). A second, highly informative volume on smooth muscle, written by former students and collaborators of Edith Bülbring has also recently appeared (19). Other pertinent review articles include the exhaustive, two-part review of vascular smooth muscle by Somlyo & Somlyo (100, 101), a compilation of the opening addresses to the 2nd International Symposium on Gastrointestinal Motility,[2] and a short review dealing with the electrical activity of the intestine (9).

ESOPHAGEAL MOTILITY

There is little doubt that esophageal motility is under both central and peripheral control. Much of the current research in this area is concerned with the nature and mode of peripheral control mechanisms, and with the relative importance of central and peripheral neural control. Doty, in his recent review of the neural control of deglutition (48), cites evidence for the classical view that the mechanical events of swallowing are controlled by centers in the medulla and consequently can "proceed in a preordained manner . . . without benefit of afferent support," although he points out that the normal pattern of esophageal motility can be modified by afferent feedback. The concept of "preordained" central control of esophageal motility

---

[1] Preparation of this review was aided by USPHS Grant AM-06958 from the National Institute of Arthritis and Metabolic Diseases.

[2] *Rendic. R. Gastroenterol.* 1970, 2:1–80.

is supported by experiments such as those of Siegel & Hendrix (99) in which they showed that secondary and, supposedly, primary esophageal peristalsis in the dog is unaffected by high cervical esophageal section, followed by immediate anastomosis. In these experiments, secondary peristalsis could be initiated above the level of anastomosis in response to distension below the level of transection. In other experiments on humans, Siegel & Hendrix showed that rapid distension and deflation of a balloon in the upper esophagus elicited a secondary peristaltic wave beginning above the level of the balloon and continuing down to the lower esophageal sphincter. The mechanical events of secondary peristalsis, including relaxation of both upper and lower esophageal sphincters, were indistinguishable from those of normal swallowing. The authors thus concluded that both primary and secondary peristalsis are mediated by common central reflex centers and efferent pathways, the only difference being in the afferent input.

Somewhat different results were obtained in more recent experiments (81) in which primary peristalsis was studied in conscious dogs before and after diverting the water bolus to the exterior by means of a cervical esophageal cannula. With the cannula closed, the water bolus traversed the entire esophagus and peristalsis was found to occur in the lower esophagus 90% of the time. With the esophageal cannula open, the water bolus was diverted to the exterior immediately after entering the esophagus, and no peristaltic activity could be detected in the lower esophagus. These data indicate that primary as well as secondary peristalsis requires sequential afferent input from the esophagus, and is thus contrary to the concept of preordained central control. Another challenge to this concept comes from work of Vantrappen & Hellemans (108) indicating that transection of the smooth muscle portion of the esophagus in the monkey interferes with normal peristaltic activity. Furthermore, stimulation of the peripheral end of the vagus nerve following bilateral cervical vagotomy in monkeys occasionally elicited a coordinated peristaltic wave in the lower esophagus. Thus, it appears that in the smooth muscle portion of the monkey esophagus intramural elements are involved in the coordination of primary and secondary peristaltic activity. Furthermore, the fact that stimulation of the peripheral cervical vagal trunk could elicit peristaltic contractions in the lower monkey esophagus raises the question whether peristaltic activity in this region of the esophagus normally requires sequential efferent impulses originating in the medullary swallowing center.

Coordination, by intramural elements, of peristalsis in the smooth muscle portion of the esophagus has been also demonstrated in vitro. Especially interesting are some of the studies from Christensen's laboratory of opossum esophagus (31, 32, 35, 84). In the esophagus of this animal, like that of the human, striated muscle is limited to the rostral third; the distal portion contains only smooth muscle. The opossum thus differs from the more common laboratory animals, such as the cat, dog and rabbit, in which the musculature of the body of the esophagus is almost exclusively striated. Distension of the opossum esophagus, either in vivo or in vitro, produced three types of response (35). Inflation of a distending balloon was followed by a brief circumferential contraction just rostral to the point of stimulation, the so-called *on* response. If distension was maintained, the esophagus underwent sustained shortening, the *duration* response. Following deflation of the stimulating balloon a circumferential contraction occurred distal to the point of stimulation and appeared to propagate aborally; this was called the *off* response, and has been likened to secondary peristalsis as seen in man. Essentially the same responses were obtained by localized, repetitive electrical stimulation of the isolated esophagus, except that the on response was not elicited as frequently as it was with distension. In subsequent papers (31, 84) the same workers provided pharmacological and electrophysiological evidence indicating that the on response is purely myogenic, while the off response and the duration response are neurally mediated. Furthermore, the duration response appears to be limited to longitudinal muscle, while the on and the off responses are apparently due to circular contractions. A puzzling finding was that the off response was not affected by hexamethonium, nicotine, propranolol, tolazoline, d-tubocurarine, methysergide or atropine. Hence, although it appears to be neurally mediated (blocked by tetrodotoxin), neither cholinergic nor adrenergic motor neurons seem to be involved; furthermore, transmission in the synapses of this particular reflex appear not to be cholinergically mediated. The authors were left no alternative but to suggest that the off response may be a rebound contraction following excitation of the currently ubiquitous nonadrenergic inhibitory nerves.

Lower esophageal sphincter (LES).—According to the classical view of the central origin of deglutition, relaxation and the subsequent contraction of the gastroesophageal sphincter are the terminal mechanical events of the swallowing reflex, which is controlled almost exclusively by medullary centers without the aid of new afferent stimuli (88; see also 48). According to this view the relaxation-contraction sequence of the LES involves central mediation whether the accompanying esophageal peristalsis is of the primary or secondary type (48, 99). That the vagus may certainly be involved in relaxation of the LES is indicated by experiments such as those of Vantrappen & Hellemans (108), in which electrical stimulation of the peripheral stump of the vagus in monkeys, following bilateral cervical vagotomy, produced relaxation of the LES even though esophageal peristalsis did not regularly occur. Furthermore, in patients with extensive resection of the esophagus, but with an intact LES, the sphincter regularly relaxes during swallowing (30).

There is more recent evidence, however, indicating that the relaxation-contraction cycle of the LES may be at least partly controlled by local intramural processes. Thus, in cats that have been totally pithed distension of the midthoracic esophagus inhibited mechanical activity of the most caudal segment of the esophagus, including the LES (104). In isolated preparations of guinea pig esophagus which included the cardiac region of the stomach, distension of the lower half of the body of the esophagus produced sphincteric relaxation followed, in some cases, by contraction (86). Distension of the upper esophagus had no effect on the LES. These results clearly indicate that the lower, but not the upper, esophagus is intrinsically capable of co-ordinated mechanical activity similar to that which occurs in situ, regardless of whether it consists of striated muscle as in the guinea pig, or of smooth muscle as in the opossum (35). Mann et al (86) suggest that autonomy may reside in the intramural plexuses of the lower esophagus, although in more recent experiments these investigators indicate that the responses to distension are not affected by the more common ganglion blocking agents (85). Hence, the contraction-relaxation cycle in the LES of the isolated guinea pig preparation resembles in some respects the off response of the opossum esophagus described above (84).

Except during the relatively brief time when it relaxes at the end of a swallow, the pressure within the LES is normally greater than that of either the upper stomach or esophagus. This is true even of isolated preparations of this portion of the gut (85, 86). The precise mechanism or mechanisms responsible for the maintenance of high pressure within the LES, as well as for its relaxation during deglutition, have yet to be clearly defined. One of the first questions to be resolved is whether the LES is tonically contracted in the absence of esophageal peristalsis. Several years ago Hellemans & Vantrappen (61) studied this question by recording with their bipolar technique the electrical activity from the LES of unanesthetized dogs at rest and during swallowing. They were not able to detect electrical activity at the distal portion of the LES either during deglutition or during its absence. Bursts of spike activity were found to accompany peristalsis in the body of the esophagus and in the proximal portion of the sphincter, however.

A more recent attempt to record from the canine LES may have proved more successful (5). According to these investigators, they were able to record from the distal segment of the LES a continuous, slow, phasic change of potential which oscillated at frequencies from 1.4 to 2.1 cycles/sec. These phasic potentials were nearly always diminished or abolished by swallowing (during the period of reduced pressure in the LES). Whether these potentials represent tonic activity of the LES in the absence of deglutition is not clear, however. In the first place, contractile activity in other parts of the gastrointestinal tract is normally associated with spike potentials rather than with phasic potentials. Secondly, as pointed out by the authors themselves, these potentials were recorded with the amplifier set at time constants of 0.1 to 0.01 sec, some 10 to 100 times shorter than the period of the recorded phasic potentials, conditions which would produce considerable distortion of the potentials actually picked up by the electrodes. Nevertheless, such potentials are clearly evident in some of the records, especially those taken from the cardiac region of the stomach, and they are modified by esophageal and gastric distension. Further studies, perhaps utilizing intracellular microelectrodes in vitro, are needed to clarify both the nature and the significance of these potentials.

The pressure within the LES has been shown to be an accurate index of the strength of the sphincter, which in turn is directly related to its ability to prevent gastric reflux (38). A number of control systems, originating within the stomach, increase the efficiency of the LES in preventing reflux. One of these is related to an increase in intragastric pressure, such as moderate gastric distension, which has been shown to increase the tone of the LES in decerebrate cats. The increase in sphincter tone may be mediated by long vago-vagal reflexes, since it is abolished by bilateral vagotomy (36, 104), even though vagotomy per se has little effect on the resting pressure within the sphincter (5, 36). Similar increases in sphincter pressure have been shown to accompany increases in intragastric pressure due to gastric contractions in unanesthetized dogs (44).

The presence of acid in the stomach has also been related to an increase in sphincter pressure. This was first demonstrated by Cannon (27) who found that the intragastric pressure required to produce regurgitation in spinal cats increased when the gastric contents were made acidic. Similar results were obtained by Clark & Vane (36) during perfusion of the LES with 0.1 N HCl. In both cases the increase in sphincteric tone was unaffected by bilateral vagotomy. Slightly different results were obtained by Titchen & Wheeler (104) following the introduction of acid into the stomachs of decerebrate cats, and also by Giles et al (54) following irrigation of the cardiac mucosa in humans with HCl. Although both groups of investigators found sphincteric pressure to increase in response to gastric acidification, the response was virtually abolished after bilateral vagotomy in the one case and after injection of atropine in the other. The apparent discrepancy may have been resolved by Titchen & Wheeler (104) who showed that increased sphincteric tone may be produced by acid perfusion of both the caudal esophagus and the cardiac mucosa. Only the latter is vagally mediated however, so that the earlier results may have been due to acid reflux from the stomach into the lower esophagus.

Instillation of 0.1 N HCl into the fundic area of the human stomach has been found to decrease LES pressure, while alkalinization of the same region has the opposite effect (29). This is apparently due to the effect of gastric pH on the release of gastrin by the gastric antrum, the third mechanism by which gastric activity controls LES pressure. Both gastrin and pentagastrin have been shown to stimulate contractions of isolated longitudinal and circular muscle of the LES (13). Both these hormones, in physiological doses, have also been shown to increase lower sphincteric pressure in man (29, 39, 55). Hence, procedures which increase the release of endogenous gastrin, such as alkalinization of the stomach (presumably distal to the cardiac area), administration of betazole (29), or introduction of meat extract into the stomach (55), increase LES pressure; procedures which inhibit gastrin release, such as antral acidification, would be expected to have the reverse effect.

In addition to gastrin and pentagastrin a number of other substances have been shown to stimulate contraction of sphincteric muscle (32, 34). More interestingly, however, is the observation that circular muscle strips taken from the sphincter have a lower excitation threshold to certain drugs than do circular strips taken from other portions of the lower esophagus of the opossum (32). This includes responses to such drugs as acetylcholine, dimethylphenylpiperazinium (DMPP), and, especially, norepinephrine. Thus it appears that the intrinsic neuromuscular apparatus of the LES is quantitatively different from that of the adjacent lower esophagus, i.e. that "the sphincter is defined, at least in part, by differences within the wall of the esophagus rather than in the central nervous system" (32).

GASTROINTESTINAL MOTILITY

Accurate descriptions of gastrointestinal motility patterns are important not only per se, but also because prevailing concepts of these patterns profoundly influence the types of questions asked about their control mechanisms. Unfortunately, although the study of gastrointestinal motility has had a long and distinguished history, many of its basic features have not yet been clearly elucidated. For example, with respect to peristalsis several fundamental questions remain unresolved, such as: (a) is it strictly an excitatory phenomenon, or is active inhibition of mechanical activity also involved; (b) do the two muscle layers contract synchronously, or out of phase with one another; (c) does it differ from "segmentation" qualitatively or only quantitatively? During the past few years a number of papers have appeared which deal specifically with different aspects of these questions. Although none of them may provide universally acceptable answers, a few raise some intriguing points which should certainly influence future concepts of control mechanisms, if only by provoking a more critical approach to these concepts.

Most in vitro studies of intestinal peristalsis involve the use of some modification of the Trendelenburg method (106), in which isolated segments of guinea pig ileum are perfused with Tyrode solution, and longitudinal and circular contractions are measured as changes in length and volume, respectively. Based on such studies, Trendelenburg and later Kosterlitz and others (74) concluded that during intestinal peristalsis the longitudinal muscle contracts first, followed 90° later by a contraction wave of circular muscle travelling aborally. It is generally maintained that coincident with circular contraction, longitudinal muscle actively relaxes (74). Kottegoda (75, 76), using a modified Trendelenburg preparation, studied the peristaltic reflex in nonterminal guinea pig ileum. The sequence of events following either an increase in radial distension or transmural electrical stimulation (frequency 1 Hz, pulse duration 0.1 msec), consisted first of a "powerful contraction of the longitudinal muscle" followed by circular contraction and longitudinal relaxation. At the end of the 5 sec stimulation period the circular layer relaxed while the longitudinal layer again showed a slight contraction. During ganglionic blockade longitudinal muscle contraction persisted throughout the stimulation period, while the initial circular contraction failed to occur. All responses to electrical stimulation were blocked by tetrodotoxin, which indicates that they were neurally mediated. Kottegoda interpreted these results on the assumption that the two muscle layers are reciprocally innervated, so that when one muscle layer contracts the other is inhibited. The observed phase difference between the two contractions was explained by assuming that the nerves to the circular muscle have a higher frequency threshold than those to the longitudinal layer. Thus at low frequencies of transmural stimulation or in response to radial distension, longitudinal muscle would be excited first. Circular muscle would contract when the longitudinal muscle contraction has raised the intraluminal pressure to threshold, thereby presumably causing high-frequency firing from sensory receptors. Kosterlitz (74) has explained the recorded phase difference between contractions of the two muscle layers in essentially the same way.

In an earlier paper Hukuhara & Fukuda (67) presented an intriguing challenge to the concept that longitudinal contractions precede circular contractions during peristalsis. In a series of experiments they showed that longitudinal shortening in response to a rise in intraluminal pressure depends on the initial tension existing in the preparation, in this case guinea pig ileum. When tension was initially low, distension, produced by filling the lumen with physiological saline, produced lengthening of the preparation. When initial tension was high, an increase in intraluminal pressure produced shortening in the longitudinal direction. Inasmuch as the same phenomena could be produced by using a slender rubber balloon in place of the intestinal segment, the authors concluded that the initial longitudinal shortening associated with an increase in intraluminal pressure is a physical, rather than a physiological phenomenon. Furthermore, they pointed out that in their records of peristaltic activity the initial longitudinal shortening can be distinguished from active contraction by an inflection point. According to their records, then, the two muscle layers appear to contract in phase with one another.

Although the conclusions of these experiments provide a reasonable alternative explanation for the initial longitudinal shortening due to radial distension, they do not explain the phase difference obtained by Kottegoda during transmural stimulation. Either transmural stimulation does not produce the same sequence of events occurring during the response to radial distension, or the two layers do indeed contract out of phase, or a common artifact is introduced by the several variations of the Trendelenburg method. It would appear that a solution to this problem might be found by examining the temporal relationships of the two muscle layers obtained by other recording methods, on the assumption that if a phase difference exists it should be detected by other recording methods of adequate sensitivity.

One such method may be that involving the use of implanted extraluminal strain gauge force transducers. When two strain gauges are sewn into the wall at right angles to one another, mechanical activity can be detected simultaneously in the longitudinal and transverse directions. Based on results obtained by this technique, Reinke et al (96) came to the conclusion that the contractile activity of the longitudinal muscle layer preceded that in the circular layer. This is difficult to determine from their records, at least for individual contractions, but it certainly seems to be the case for tonus changes associated with ileal "burst activity" and also for the so-called P wave. The latter consists of a large tonus change, lasting approximately 1 min and occurring 2 to 4 times during a twelve hour recording period. On the other hand, Bass & Wiley show quite clearly in Figure 4 of their paper (11), that individual contractions of longitudinal and circular muscle, recorded from the dog duodenum with similar type strain gauges, can indeed occur in phase with one another.

Similarly arranged transducers implanted on the stomach again indicated that contraction of the longitudinal muscle precedes that of the circular layer (94, 96). In all of these studies, however, the transducers were arranged in the form of a "T," with the cross bar oriented longitudinally. Thus, the advancing front of a peristaltic wave would be expected to affect the longitudinal transducer before affecting the transverse transducer, assuming for the moment that both layers contract synchronously. In the study of Papazova et al (94) the propagation velocity of the gastric contraction wave was found to be 4.3 mm/sec along the lesser curvature and 5.8 mm/sec along the greater curvature. Thus, if the end of the longitudinal transducer extended 5 mm beyond the oral edge of the circular transducer, the longitudinal contraction would appear to precede the circular contraction by about 1 sec, even if the two in fact contracted synchronously. Although Papazova et al do not indicate the dimensions of their transducers, they do state that after injecting carbacholine into their animals the circular layer began to contract one second after the longitudinal layer. For purposes of comparison, the longitudinal strain gauge used by Bass & Wiley (11) measured 17 mm in length; the transverse transducer measured 6 mm in width. Corresponding values for the transducers used by Reinke et al (96) were 8.5 mm and 6.5 mm, respectively. Obviously, the smaller and the closer together the strain gauges, the more accurately they record the temporal sequence of contractions from corresponding points of the two muscle layers. Equally important, however, is the orientation of the strain gauges with respect to one another. An appropriately oriented "L" rather than a "T" type of arrangement may yield more reliable data regarding the time of onset of contractile activity in corresponding areas of the two muscle layers.

Another approach to this problem has been to record contractions in the longitudinal and transverse directions from restricted regions of intestinal wall in vitro (14, 16). This has been accomplished by recording circular contractions from a number of discrete points along one edge of a segment of intestinal wall while simultaneously recording longitudinal contractions from localized areas at either end of the preparation. In cat preparations circular contractions were found to be initiated at any point within the tissue and to propagate aborally at a velocity of 6–8 mm/sec, i.e. the contractions were peristaltic. Circular contractions recorded at either end of the preparation tended to be in phase with longitudinal contractions recorded from the same end, but were rarely in phase with each other (14). Thus, contractions recorded from corresponding points of the two muscle layers appeared to be in phase with one another during peristaltic activity, at least according to this method of recording.

This question is obviously not yet completely resolved. Its importance, however, is more than simply academic, for if the muscle layers do in fact contract in phase, there would be no need to implicate reciprocal inhibition as a mechanism for sequential activation (or inhibition) of the two muscle layers. Indeed, the very possibility of simultaneous rather than sequential contraction raises questions regarding (a) the role of the myenteric plexus in peristalsis and (b) whether or not active neural inhibition is really involved as part of the sequence of events in peristalsis.

That the myenteric plexus plays a role in peristalsis in undeniable. However, whether its role is primary, as it would be if it initiates and governs the mechanical events of peristalsis, or whether it is secondary, functioning essentially as the autonomic nerves in the heart, is still open to question. A primary role of the myenteric plexus is certainly indicated by the work of Kosterlitz (74) and of Kottegoda (75, 76). However, neither of these investigators has considered the functional role of the myogenic slow waves in peristalsis. Slow waves have been strongly implicated as a major, if not the prime, factor involved in the control of rhythmicity in gastrointestinal muscle, by virtue of the fact that they alternately increase and decrease the probability of spike discharge and, consequently, contractile activity. Furthermore, both gastric and intestinal slow waves propagate aborally, thereby conceivably accounting for progressive waves of contractile activity, i.e. peristalsis. Finally, slow waves have been shown to spread electrotonically from the longitudinal muscle layer to the underlying circular layer, where they again apparently serve to increase and decrease alternately the excitability of circular muscle in phase with that of longitudinal muscle (16). Thus there appears to be an electrophysiological precedent for simultaneous contraction of the two layers, which is myogenic in nature. Although a glance at the references will quickly reveal the bias of this reviewer on this particular subject, it is difficult, in view of the evidence, to escape the conclusion that both myogenic and neurogenic factors are involved in the control of peristaltic activity. In the past peristalsis was considered to be predominantly under neural control; the pendulum may now be swinging toward the other direction (see also 56).

Returning now to the question of whether active inhibition is involved in peristalsis, two papers have recently appeared which indicate, at the very least, that more critical evaluation should be made of records of mechanical activity which appear to show active relaxation of either muscle layer. Wood and Perkins (114) studied tension changes in both the longitudinal and circular axes of isolated cat jejunum elicited by transmural stimulation. Responses to stimulation at frequencies of 10 Hz (1 msec duration) consisted of both phasic and tonic contractions of circular muscle, with no active contraction of longitudinal muscle being apparent. On the contrary, records of tension changes in the longitudinal axis showed apparent relaxations, occurring simultaneously with, and resembling mirror images of the circular contractions. Wood and Perkins concluded that "the relaxation in the longitudinal axis is not due to nervous inhibition of longitudinal muscle . . . , but rather that the apparent relaxation is a passive elongation as a consequence of circular muscle contraction." They based their conclusion on the following observations: (a) longitudinal elongation was exhibited in preparations treated with tetrodotoxin, procaine, or ganglion blocking agents—and hence in the absence of nervous activity; (b) longitudinal elongation indistinguishable from that of intact preparations was exhibited by segments of jejunum completely devoid of longitudinal muscle and treated with procaine, and hence, was not due to relaxation of longitudinal muscle per se; (c) in experiments in which the decrease in radius of intestinal segments was controlled by inserting glass rods of various known diameters into the lumen before eliciting potassium contracture, they found that the extent of longitudinal elongation approximated that predicted by simply decreasing the radius of a cylinder while maintaining constant surface area.

Essentially the same conclusion was reached by Gregory & Bentley (58) who studied the effect of circular contractions on longitudinal lengthening in isolated guinea pig ileum. They found that the lengthening of a segment of ileum was always associated with contractions of circular muscle, when the tone of longitudinal muscle was initially high. When shortening of circular muscle was mechanically limited, the amount of lengthening was found to decrease correspondingly. Gregory & Bentley interpreted these results as indicating that the observed lengthening of the ileum is a direct mechanical consequence of the contraction of the circular muscle layer. Thus in two species, cat and guinea pig, contraction of circular muscle has been shown to be directly responsible for elongation of isolated segments of intestine.

In view of these experiments, results of motility studies showing "inhibition" of longitudinal muscle occurring concurrently with circular contractions should be viewed with no small degree of skepticism, especially since circular muscle in most species is several times thicker than longitudinal muscle. On the other hand, there seems to be a growing body of evidence for the presence in the myenteric plexus of post-ganglionic nonadrenergic inhibitory neurons (see below). The unresolved question then is whether longitudinal relaxation can be accounted for entirely on the basis of circular contraction, or whether inhibitory neurons are also involved.

NEURAL REGULATION OF GASTROINTESTINAL MOTILITY

Evidence for nonadrenergic neural inhibition.—Since the last review of gastrointestinal motility additional evidence has accumulated for the presence in the gut of nonadrenergic inhibitory neurons. Crema et al (41) found that transmural stimulation of atropinized strips of human colon produced inhibition of spontaneous mechanical activity. Since the inhibition was blocked by tetrodotoxin, but not by dibenamine plus propranolol, it was thought to be mediated by nonadrenergic neurons. In another study involving isolated segments of guinea pig and rabbit colon single shocks of less than 1 msec duration applied through platinum electrodes held against the tissue resulted in the appearance of inhibitory junctional potentials (*IJP*s) in muscle cells of both layers (51). Since the IJPs could be blocked by procaine, they were probably neurally mediated. The fact that they were unaffected by guanethidine, a drug which blocks release of adrenergic transmitter, indicates that the nervous elements responsible for the IJPs were nonadrenergic. Single stimuli applied to either the periarterial or the pelvic nerves had no detectable inhibitory effect, although high frequency stimulation of the periarterial nerves did evoke guanethidine-sensitive IJPs. The author concluded from these studies that nonadrenergic inhibitory nerves are present in the colon, and that they are entirely intrinsic in nature, i.e. they are independent of both the pelvic and periarterial innervation. In this respect the nonadrenergic inhibitory nerves of the colon seem to differ from those of the upper gastrointestinal tract, since the latter are thought to form part of the vagal inhibitory system (25, 68, 87), and thus are not entirely intrinsic.

Perhaps the most convincing evidence for a physiological role for nonadrenergic inhibition comes from the work of Abrahamsson & Jansson (2), who showed that distension of the esophagus in the cat causes reflex relaxation of the stomach, an effect which is not blocked by concentrations of guanethidine sufficient to block reflex adrenergic inhibition of gastric motility. The reflex relaxation persisted after administration of atropine, and hence was not due to inhibition of cholinergic excitatory fibers. Relaxation was abolished by bilateral vagotomy, even though the tone of the gastric musculature was higher following vagotomy than during esophageal distension. Similar reflex relaxation was obtained by mechanically stimulating the mucous membrane of the pharynx, or by inducing deglutition. The importance of this work is that it represents one of the few examples—indeed perhaps the only example—of reflex inhibition of gut motility by a nonadrenergic mechanism. Most other demonstrations of nonadrenergic inhibition involve either massive stimulation of the gut wall or "efferent" stimulation of vagal trunks, usually in the presence of one or more blocking drugs (see below).

In an interesting and provocative paper evidence has been presented which indicates that the transmitter released by nonadrenergic inhibitory nerves may be adenosine triphosphate or a related nucleotide (24). The method of study essentially consisted of stimulating the nonadrenergic inhibitory nerve supply to a perfused organ, and then extracting and identifying the active substance in the perfusate. Since nonadrenergic inhibitory fibers had been demonstrated in the vagal nerves to the stomachs of both guinea pig (25) and toad (26), these organs were selected for the perfusion studies. By means of paper chromatography and bioassay techniques, the active fraction of the perfusate was identified as adenosine. In subsequent experiments the effects of electrical stimulation on the release of purine compounds from Auerbach's plexus were studied. Turkey gizzard was used, since in this organ the plexus is concentrated in a single thick layer just beneath the serosa, and can thus be easily isolated. Following intermittent electrical stimulation for 30 min, the bathing medium contained an appreciable amount of AMP and also traces of ATP and ADP; that of the nonstimulated plexus contained no detectable amounts of purine compounds. Based on these findings, the authors concluded that ATP or a related nucleotide may be the transmitter released by stimulation of the nonadrenergic inhibitory neurons. Such a conclusion is supported by the fact that ATP and ADP are the most potent of a number of naturally occurring purine and pyrimidine compounds causing relaxation of the guinea pig taenia-coli (24; see also 8). The absence of ATP from the stomach perfusates may have been due to the rapid degradation of ATP to adenosine, inosine and adenine which occurs when the nucleotide is perfused through the gastric vasculature (24).

The authors have provided a rather convincing case for the participation of ATP (or a related nucleotide) in the type of nonadrenergic inhibition described in their paper. The case would be much stronger, however, if it could be demonstrated that sufficient quantities of nucleotide are released during reflex inhibition of the type described by Abrahamsson & Jansson (2). Unfortunately, electrical stimulation of the vagal trunk, such as that described by Burnstock et al (24) stimulates afferent as well as efferent fibers. As shown by Holton (64), antidromic stimulation of sensory nerves is associated with liberation of ATP at the dendritic terminals. Since 90% of the fibers in the vagus are afferent (3), at least some of the ATP found in the perfusate may have come from this source. Although Burnstock et al (24) consider this possibility, they reject it on the ground that "the fibers in the vagal trunk mediating gastric inhibition are preganglionic and therefore efferent." The evidence for involvement of efferent nerves in the vagal nonadrenergic pathway is based primarily on the effect of pentolinium, a ganglionic blocking agent that acts on nicotinic receptors (20, 26). However, the results obtained with pentolinium are not completely unequivocal. For example, Bülbring & Gershon (20) found that, in the presence of hyoscine, vagal stimulation or the administration of the nicotinic ganglion stimulant DMPP produced relaxation of the guinea pig stomach. In the presence of pentolinium, although the response to DMPP was abolished, that to vagal stimulation was only reduced. In similar experiments on toad stomach, Campbell (26) found that "the effects of ganglion blockade on inhibitory responses of the stomach were difficult to assess because of the fall in tone induced by pentolinium. In many preparations, the tone fell to such an extent that no further relaxation was possible. In one such preparation . . . stimulation of the vagus nerve no longer caused inhibition of the spontaneous movements. In another . . . stimulation of the vagus roots caused a relaxation of decreased absolute amplitude." Thus, it appears that in both the toad and the guinea pig stomach inhibition produced by vagal stimulation is not completely abolished by ganglionic blockade, i.e. at least some of the vagal fibers involved may not be efferent preganglionic. Furthermore, there is abundant evidence that acetylcholine and nicotinic compounds depolarize sensory nerve terminals and sensory receptors (6, 50, 57). The depolarizing effect of acetylcholine is antagonized by blocking drugs such as hexamethonium (6, 50). Thus, it is conceivable that some of the inhibitory effects of vagal stimulation or of DMPP may be due to the release of ATP brought about by depolarization of afferent nerve terminals. Depolarization could be both direct, via antidromic stimulation, and indirect, via the action of acetylcholine on dendritic nicotinic receptors, especially when the latter are unmasked by muscarinic blocking agents such as hyoscine or atropine. In many cases the inhibitory effects of transmural stimulation (41, 51, 62) or intraluminal distension (63) could be similarly explained since atropine or hyoscine have been routinely used in such experiments to prevent the muscarinic excitatory effects of the acetylcholine which is released by these procedures.

Three things are apparent from these experiments: (a) nonadrenergic inhibition can be reflexly elicited; (b) nonadrenergic inhibition can be demonstrated by massive electrical stimulation of either the peripheral vagal trunks or the intestinal wall; (c) such massive stimulation results in the liberation of a nucleotide which has potent inhibitory effects on gastrointestinal motility. What has yet to be substantiated is the equivalence of (a) and (b), and a direct relationship between (a) and (c).

Evidence for noncholinergic neural excitation.—Ambache & Freeman (4) using preparations of longitudinal muscle from guinea pig ileum, recorded two types of contractile responses to transmural electrical stimulation. The first, a twitch response evoked by a single electrical shock of 0.1 to 0.2 msec duration, was abolished by atropine or hyoscine, and was therefore probably due to excitation of cholinergic motor neurons. The second response was described as a "tetanic spasm" and occurred 2–3 sec after delivery of a 1 sec train of 50 pulses/sec. The tetanic spasm was abolished by tetrodotoxin, but not by atropine, and hence was probably due to stimulation of noncholinergic neurons. Based on results obtained with specific blocking agents, the authors excluded such compounds as 5-hydroxytryptamine, histamine and prostaglandins as possible mediators of the response. They suggested that the neural structures involved may be either afferent nerve endings or interneurons within Auerbach's plexus.

Similar experiments were performed by Furness (52) using sections of guinea pig colon. After the initial contraction was blocked with hyoscine, an inhibitory response was usually found to precede the secondary contraction, the latter probably identical to that described by Ambache & Freeman (4) since it was hyoscine-resistant and occurred with a delay of 3–4 sec. Intracellular recording of muscle membrane potentials indicated that the initial contractions were associated with spikes elicited by excitatory junction potentials, while the secondary contractions were associated with spikes which occurred following membrane hyperpolarization. The author therefore concluded that the secondary contraction was not due to noncholinergic excitatory nerves, but rather to rebound excitation of the muscle following inhibitory nerve stimulation (see also 25).

Electrical activity of single units in Auerbach's plexus.—This reviewer is aware of only two attempts to record from single units of Auerbach's plexus. In the first of these studies (115), spike potentials were recorded with metal microelectrodes inserted through the serosal side of intact segments of rabbit intestine, or with the tip of the electrode in contact with ganglion cells which adhered to a strip of longitudinal muscle after it had been peeled away from the rest of the segment. In this study spontaneous action potentials occurred in bursts, each burst apparently associated with a rhythmic, segmental type of contraction.

More recently (112) metal-filled glass capillaries or steel microelectrodes were used to record single unit activity from intact segments of cat jejunum by advancing the electrode through the serosa into the plexus, or by stripping away the longitudinal layer and directly exposing the plexus, which in this case adhered to the circular muscle. Electrical recording was facilitated by staining the exposed plexus with methylene blue so that the individual neurons could be observed microscopically. Unlike the earlier study, no consistent relationship was found between spontaneous spike bursts and rhythmic contractions, nor was there any apparent relationship between any type of neuronal spike bursts and myogenic slow wave activity. In addition to the units with spontaneous bursts, other units were found in which spiking could be evoked by mechanical deformation. Some responded by discharging only during the time they were distorted by the electrode tip (phasic type mechanoreceptors); others continued to discharge even after withdrawal of the mechanical stimulus (tonic mechanoreceptors). Perhaps the most surprising finding in this study was the apparent lack of a positive correlation between neuronal spike discharge and mechanical activity. If anything, there was a negative correlation. Thus, during neuronal discharge of either the spontaneous or the induced type, mechanical activity of the circular layer appeared to be minimal. Also, application of local anesthetics always produced immediate cessation of nervous activity and increased circular muscle activity. Thus, Wood suggests that circular muscle in isolated segments of intestine may be in a state of tonic neural inhibition (see also 113).

Another pertinent finding in this study was that the neurons exhibited a high resistance to hypoxia in contrast to the results reported earlier by Yokoyama (115). The electrical activity from segments of intestine stored overnight in unaerated Tyrode solution at 5–8°C, or up to seven hours at 37°C, did not appear to differ from that of freshly dissected preparations. Similar results were recently obtained by Kyi Kyi & Daniel (79), who showed that in chronic dog preparations, following recovery from intestinal ischemia, functional intramural neurons were still present, as evidenced by responses to ganglion stimulating drugs and transmural stimulation. Reflex activity was grossly impaired in the post-ischemic sections of intestine, however. Both these studies indicate that although prolonged hypoxia may abolish reflex activity in the intestine, it does not appear to damage intramural ganglion cells to the extent previously supposed (66). On the other hand, once reflexes have been irreversibly abolished, what valid criteria remain for determining whether a given neuron is functioning "normally"?

MYOGENIC REGULATION OF GASTROINTESTINAL MOTILITY

Intestinal slow waves.—The relationship of intestinal slow waves to motility is now quite well established and was covered in some detail in the last review of this subject (42). Since that time a number of papers have appeared which deal with the frequency gradient of intestinal slow waves (37, 45–47, 59, 60, 103). In an earlier work, Bunker et al (23) had shown that intestinal slow waves recorded from unanesthetized dogs with chronically implanted electrodes ranged in frequency from 19 cycles/min in the duodenum to 13–14 cycles/min in the distal ileum. The authors noted that the frequency remained essentially constant over the duodenum and proximal jejunum, but then decreased in apparently "step-wise fashion" from this point to the terminal ileum. The "step-wise" nature of the frequency gradient was later confirmed by studies in which intestinal slow waves were recorded by a series of closely spaced (1 to 2 cm apart) electrodes, from several species of animals, all under sodium pentobarbital anesthesia (45). These studies revealed that various lengths of intestine in situ have the same frequency, and that each frequency plateau is separated from the next by an area in which the amplitudes of the slow waves periodically wax and wane. When the intestine was cut into small segments (1 to 2 cm in length) it was found that the slow wave frequency of each consecutive segment decreased aborally as a function of distance. The explanation of these phenomena was based on the concept that intestinal smooth muscle can behave electrically as if it consists of a series of coupled oscillators, with each successive oscillator having a lower intrinsic frequency than that preceding it. According to this concept individual slow wave oscillators in a frequency plateau would be driven by that oscillator having the highest intrinsic frequency. A frequency plateau would be terminated at that point where coupling between adjacent oscillators is inadequate, or where the driving frequency is simply too high for the next oscillator to follow.

Other experiments indicated, however, that although this concept of the frequency gradient is essentially correct, it is oversimplified. Bunker et al (23) had shown that transection of the intestine along the initial frequency plateau (in the distal duodenum) caused a drop in the frequency distal to the transection to approximately that recorded from the terminal ileum prior to transection, i.e. the gradient along the entire intestine appeared to be abolished. Subsequent transection experiments, both acute (46) and long-term (37, 60) corroborated these findings, although in experiments extending over more than 3 months the slow wave frequency distal to a transection showed a tendency to return to pre-operative levels (60). Most investigators have attempted to explain the results of transection experiments on the basis of a pacemaker or pacemaking area situated somewhere in the upper duodenum (23, 60), although the presence of such a pacemaker certainly could not account for the normal slow wave frequency gradient. An alternative explanation is that each frequency plateau is normally pulled to a frequency above the intrinsic frequency of its pacemaking oscillator by the faster slow wave activity of the plateau immediately proximal to it (46). The temporal waxing and waning patterns commonly recorded between adjacent plateaus may be reflection of such frequency pulling between the terminal oscillators of each plateau (47). The driving influence of each plateau upon its distal neighbor would explain why a succession of transections from duodenum to mid-ileum results in a decrease in slow wave frequency distal to each transection (37, 46). It also explains why artificially increasing the frequency of a proximal slow wave oscillator, e.g. by local heating, raises the slow wave frequency of several plateaus distal to it (46). Frequency pulling between adjacent plateaus does not, however, explain why the in situ frequency of the initial plateau appears to be higher than the intrinsic frequency of its fastest oscillator. The process by which this is achieved is unknown.

Many of the phenomena occurring in vivo have been simulated by a digital computer model consisting of a series of resistively coupled Van der Pol oscillators having successively decreasing frequencies (47). With 5–25 oscillators forward coupled in series with one another a steplike frequency gradient was obtained in which the oscillators in each frequency plateau were driven or entrained by the oscillator having the highest intrinsic frequency. Furthermore, the frequency of the initial or driving oscillator in each plateau could be raised above its intrinsic frequency by the driving influence of the higher frequency plateau adjacent to it. The authors suggest that waxing and waning occurs when higher frequency oscillators in one plateau attempt to drive or entrain the lower frequency oscillators in the next plateau. The degree of waxing and waning was related to the degree of coupling between oscillators in adjacent cells. When coupling was reduced to zero, both waxing and waning and frequency pulling were abolished, similar to the situation in vivo following intestinal transection. Another important finding in these experiments was that during frequency entrainment a time delay or phase shift occurred between successive oscillations, i.e. the recorded slow waves appeared to be propagated at a velocity which was found to be directly related to the magnitude of coupling between successive oscillators. The only characteristic of the in situ slow wave frequency gradient which could not be simulated by this model was the high frequency of the initial plateau. What the model clearly shows, however, is that the major characteristics of the in situ frequency gradient can be adequately accounted for by a series of resistively coupled relaxation oscillators having successively decreasing intrinsic frequencies.

What is the nature of the biological slow wave oscillator and how are these oscillators coupled to one another? Addressing themselves to the first of these questions, Job and his associates undertook to determine the ionic basis of the intestinal slow waves and to explore possible mechanisms for the ionic movements (69, 70, 80). In the first of this series of studies, labelled ionic fluxes associated with slow wave activity were studied in isolated segments of cat jejunum from which mucosa and submucosa had been removed. By means of a revolving collecting carousel, 15 radioactive fractions could be collected per slow wave, while recording the wave monophasically with a pressure electrode. Although the method has several inherent weaknesses that limit its usefulness as a quantitative tool, the results nevertheless indicate that slow wave depolarization is associated with Na influx, and repolarization with Na efflux. Job attributed the repolarization phase of the slow wave to the activity of an electrogenic Na pump, since it had been shown that slow waves can be blocked by metabolic inhibitors, and since Job's data indicated that the rate of repolarization exhibits both a high Q_{10} and an optimum at 37°C.

Pursuing the Na pump hypothesis further, Job and his associates studied the effects on slow waves of various procedures which are known to affect Na flux (80). In support of the hypothesis they found that replacement of Na in the organ bath by Tris or lithium virtually abolished slow wave activity. Ouabain, in concentrations less than 10^{-6} M, reduced slow wave amplitude, but tetrodotoxin, even at concentrations as high as 2.4×10^{-6} M, had no observable effect either on slow waves or on spikes. According to the authors, iontophoretic injection of Na into longitudinal muscle cells increased slow wave amplitude some 3.5 times, but similar injections of K had no such potentiating effect. However, in the figure illustrating the effects of iontophoresis, the slow wave amplitude appears to have increased and decreased instantaneously at the beginning and end, respectively, of Na injection; furthermore, slow wave amplitude appears to have remained constant during the entire 20–25 sec period during which current was applied. One would predict a more gradual change in slow wave amplitude both at the beginning and the end of ion injection (see, for example, 73). During injection of K, the slow waves appear to have diminished in amplitude and there also appears to have been a continuous depolarization. Unfortunately the authors did not show what happened to the membrane potential upon termination of K iontophoresis. It is hoped that such experiments will be repeated and perhaps extended, since they are obviously quite crucial to the electrogenic Na pump hypothesis.

In the last of this series of papers, Job (70) described the effects of several antibiotics and metabolic inhibitors on slow wave frequency and amplitude, in an attempt to elucidate the relationship between the generation of slow waves and ATP production. Antibiotics, such as valinomycin, which stimulates mitochondrial uptake of K, and monensin, which inhibits such uptake, did not significantly alter slow wave frequency and had variable and unpredictable effects on slow wave amplitude. On the other hand, anoxia or metabolic inhibitors, such as dinitrophenol and cyanide, profoundly depressed slow wave amplitude, while affecting frequency to a much more limited extent. Following total inhibition of slow waves by antimycin A, addition to the bath of TMPD (tetramethyl-p-phenylenediamine dihydrochloride) followed by ascorbic acid, led to the transient appearance of oscillatory potentials suggestive of the spontaneously occurring slow waves. Job suggests that the combination of TMPD and ascorbic acid may have led "electrons into the cytochrome chain artificially resulting in ATP synthesis." In Fig. 7 of his paper (70), the initial decrease in slow wave amplitude seems to be associated with a gradual membrane depolarization, while the transient appearance of slow waves following addition of ascorbic acid is apparently associated with repolarization. It would have been interesting therefore to have tested the effects of electrical hyperpolarization on slow wave induction following inhibition, especially since slow wave amplitude is directly related to membrane potential, as can be demonstrated by electrical displacement of the membrane potential (Specht & Bortoff, unpublished data).

Job interprets these data as indicating that both slow wave amplitude and frequency are dependent on the level of ATP present at the membrane, but that frequency is significantly decreased only when ATP levels are very low. He suggests that the increased Na influx presumably responsible for slow wave depolarization is triggered by an increase in the level of membrane ATP. Repolarization would then occur as a result of increased activity of the Na pump together with the consequent decrease in ATP concentration. Although this is a rather novel and interesting idea, there is little evidence to support the suggestion that increasing intracellular ATP can increase Na influx without concomitantly increasing Na efflux. On the contrary, Brinley & Mullins (18) have shown that in perfused squid axons Na influx and Na permeability do indeed increase when ATP is added to the perfusing solution, but whereas mean Na influx increased from 43 to 71 p moles/cm^2 sec, Na efflux increased from 2 to 48 p moles/cm^2 sec, so that net Na influx was actually reduced by 44 percent. Brinley & Mullins suggest that the increase in Na permeability may be due to the activity of the Na pump.

A less serious criticism of Job's model is that it does not provide for being driven, or entrained, although it could certainly be appropriately modified to do so. What Job has attempted to do is to explain the ionic basis for the inherent rhythmicity—the pacemaker function—of intestinal muscle. Equally important to intestinal motility, however, is the fact that the slow waves can be entrained, for it is probably by this means that slow waves are circumferentially synchronized and aborally propagated. The potential for entrainment probably exists by virtue of the fact that slow waves (a) represent the output of relaxation oscillators, (b) are generated by units which are electrically coupled to one another, and (c) can be electrically triggered by an appropriately applied electrical stimulus. Although it has not been experimentally demonstrated, the smallest oscillating unit probably resides within the cell membrane of single muscle cells in the longitudinal layer of the intestine. Individual cells are electrically coupled to one another, presumably via nexuses (10), so that current entering one cell can pass outward through the cell membranes of adjacent cells. Information concerning the electrical properties of the nexus, as well as the gastrointestinal smooth muscle cells themselves, has been provided by studies of the cable properties of gastrointestinal smooth muscle (1, 91, 105).

Tomita (105) measured the absolute value of the tissue impedance of various lengths of guinea pig taenia coli after soaking the tissue in isosmotic sucrose in order to reduce the shunting effect of the external solution. At any given frequency there was a linear relationship between recorded impedance and distance from the current-supply electrode, but the impedance at any distance decreased with frequency, and the curves, when extrapolated to zero distance, showed a deviation from the origin which was inversely related to the frequency. The deviation at the origin could be explained by the reactive properties of the tissue membrane at the recording electrodes, and was cited as evidence by the author for the cable-like properties of the tissue. The frequency dependence along the tissue, which differed somewhat from that at the recording electrodes, was thought to be due to the reactive properties of the junctional membrane (nexus ?). By measuring the tissue impedance of fixed lengths of tissue at various current frequencies, Tomita found that below 100 Hz and above 5000 Hz the absolute value of the impedance was nearly independent of current frequency. At the low frequencies the impedance per unit volume of tissue averaged 370 ohm-cm; at high frequencies it was reduced to 190 ohm-cm. The difference between these values, 180 ohm-cm, was taken to be the impedance of the cell junctions, and the lower value, 190 ohm-cm, was assumed to represent myoplasmic resistance, the rationale being that the junctional resistance is shunted by a parallel capacitance. Thus the total junctional resistance appears to be similar in magnitude to that of the myoplasmic resistance in a cylinder of tissue.

In a related study Abe & Tomita (1) investigated the passive electrical properties of taenia coli to determine how the cable properties of intestinal smooth muscle can be affected by the junctional resistance. Cable constants were obtained experimentally by studying the electrotonic spread of current introduced at one end of a taenia coli preparation and recorded with micro-electrodes from several points along the tissue. The average value of the space constant obtained by this method was found to be 1.45 mm, i.e. current traversed approximately 15 cells before the recorded steady-state electro-tonic potential fell to 37% of its original value. The membrane time constant was obtained both experimentally and by inserting the previously obtained space constant into cable equations originally derived for core conductors such as nerve and skeletal muscle. The close agreement between the experi-mental and theoretical curves indicates that the muscle of the taenia coli exhibits cable properties which are not qualitatively different from those of nerve or skeletal muscle. Similar cable-like properties have been demon-strated for the longitudinal muscle of guinea pig fundus (91) and circular fibers of the antrum (77). Thus, it appears that bundles of smooth muscle cells from various parts of the gastrointestinal tract exhibit cable-like proper-ties similar to those of skeletal muscle and nerve. This implies that potential changes occurring in one cell can directly influence the membrane potentials of adjacent cells, but that this influence probably does not extend beyond several cell lengths, 1–2 mm at most.

Several years ago it was suggested that entrainment of slow waves in a frequency plateau is achieved by current, flowing from actively depolarized cells through the nexus and outward across the membranes of adjacent cells, where it serves to trigger slow wave depolarization (45). The idea that slow waves may be triggered by local circuit currents was based on the observa-tion that slow waves as recorded in volume were usually initiated by a posi-tive deflection, indicating that the initial depolarization was associated with outward flowing membrane current (95). If this is true, it should be possible to drive intestinal slow waves electrically, but until recently, this had not been achieved. It was finally accomplished by passing depolarizing pulses of current into one end of a narrow longitudinal strip of cat intestinal muscle (102), which was set up in a recording chamber similar to that used by Abe & Tomita (1). By means of either cathodal- or anodal-break stimulation it was possible to raise the slow wave frequency of cat jejunal strips signifi-cantly above their intrinsic frequency. Thus, it appears that local circuit cathodal current, passing through the nexus from the actively depolarized cell, may serve to drive adjacent cells in a frequency plateau. In this fashion slow waves may propagate from one end of the plateau to the other. If the level of excitability in a given plateau is sufficient to generate spike poten-tials, propagated waves of contraction, i.e. peristalsis, may result.

Assuming that slow waves are propagated by local circuit currents, sev-eral problems remain to be resolved. In most electrically excitable tissue the application of cathodal current produces an increase in Na permeability which allows rapid entry of Na ions into the cells down their concentration gradient, thereby further depolarizing the cell membrane. It is tempting to postulate that slow wave depolarization in the intestine occurs by the same mechanism, especially in view of the evidence indicating that Na influx is maximal during the depolarization phase (69). However, such a mechanism is incompatible with the observation that tetrodotoxin has no effect on either slow wave amplitude or slow wave frequency (80). Therefore, if sodium influx is involved in slow wave depolarization, it must enter the cells by a channel other than that which is blocked by tetrodotoxin. One possibility is that longitudinal muscle cell membranes contain a pathway for sodium, similar to the "slow channel" which has recently been described for frog atrium (97). This pathway allows both sodium and calcium to enter the atrial cells, and is selectively blocked by manganese. Although Liu et al (80) indicate that manganese has no effect on slow waves, the maximum concentrations used by these investigators were in the range of 10^{-4} to 10^{-3} M. Rougier et al (97) used 1 to 2×10^{-3} M to block the "slow channel" in heart muscle, and Bülbring & Tomita (21) found that 2.5×10^{-3} M manganese was required to abolish evoked spike activity in taenia coli. Obviously, this problem requires further investigation.

It is generally accepted that intestinal slow waves are generated by the longitudinal muscle layer and spread electrotonically into the underlying circular layer where they regulate the phasic changes in excitability associated with rhythmic contractions. Additional support for the electrotonic nature of slow wave transmission has been provided by studies of volume-conducted slow waves recorded simultaneously from both muscle layers under a variety of conditions (16). These studies corroborated an earlier finding that in intact segments of intestine slow waves occur synchronously in corresponding points of the two muscle layers, and went on to show that the membrane current associated with the slow wave is quite different in each layer. Whereas the current is largely inwardly directed in longitudinal muscle, it is apparently exclusively outwardly directed in circular muscle, which indicates that slow wave depolarization in the latter is entirely passive. The authors suggest that synchronized depolarization of both muscle layers may account for the apparently synchronized contractile activity described above.

Electrotonic transmission of slow waves from longitudinal to circular muscle has been assumed to occur via the interconnecting muscle bridges which exist between the layers. However, for electrotonic spread to occur in these bridges, the constituent muscle cells must be electrically coupled. Recent electron microscopic data indicates that junctions do indeed exist between muscle cells of the circular and longitudinal layers of the guinea pig ileum (53), some of which are true nexuses (Gabella, personal communication, 1971). Intimate contact of circular and longitudinal fibers has also been reported to occur in human colon (92) although true nexal contacts have not yet been described. Thus, anatomical evidence for electrical coupling between cells of the two muscle layers seems to be forthcoming.

It is difficult to reconcile the proposed reciprocal innervation of the two muscle layers (76) with the physiological and anatomical evidence indicating that they are electrically coupled to one another.

Gastric slow waves.—The relationship of gastric slow waves to gastric motility is perhaps even more striking than the corresponding relationship in the small intestine. Gastric slow waves occur regularly in the antral musculature of the stomach and are probably absent from the cardiac and fundic portions (40, 56, 71, 89, 109). In strips of muscle taken from guinea pig antrum spontaneously occurring slow waves give rise to spike potentials which in turn trigger contractions at a frequency of 4–5 per minute (56). Since antral motility is characteristically peristaltic, and since in their experiments neither the electrical nor the mechanical activity recorded from such muscle strips was affected by tetrodotoxin, Golenhofen et al (56) concluded that gastric peristalsis is myogenic, rather than neurogenic.

In contrast to the intestine, the slow wave frequency in the stomach is the same in all regions from which slow waves can be recorded (40, 71, 109), which indicates that a single frequency plateau normally exists in the stomach. However, complete transverse transection of the muscle layers in the antral region, results in decreased frequency of slow waves aboral to the cut (12, 109) which indicates that an intrinsic frequency gradient does exist in the stomach. The intrinsic frequency gradient probably accounts for the fact that gastric slow waves normally propagate in an aboral direction. In both acute (109) and long term (71) experiments in dogs transverse transections just distal to the fundus had no effect on slow wave frequency in the rest of the stomach, but oblique sections, separating the greater and lesser curvatures produced a decrease in frequency of the lesser curvature without altering the rate in the greater curvature. It has been suggested therefore, that the gastric pacemaker is located on the greater curvature near the proximal body of the stomach.

Bedi & Kelly (12) found that transverse transection of the entire gastric wall 5 cm from the pylorus, followed by immediate suturing, resulted in a decreased slow wave frequency distal to the transection that lasted between one and two weeks. During this period of time the frequency gradually returned to its original level. As pointed out above, most investigators have reported that intestinal transection results in permanent reduction of slow wave frequency distal to the anastomosis, although it has been reported that in some cases after three months the distal frequency approached that of the intestine proximal to the anastomosis (59, 60). Complete recovery of coupling may have occurred in the stomach because the current which crossed the anastomosis was of sufficient magnitude to drive the slow wave oscillators just distal to it. "Sufficient" current may have been produced either because of the comparatively large amplitude of gastric slow waves, or because these slow waves have a comparatively low triggering threshold, or, most likely, because of both these factors.

The gastric slow wave of the guinea pig differs from that of the dog, cat, and probably human (89), in that it lacks an initial fast component (56, 77); in this respect it resembles the intestinal slow wave. However, it appears to differ from the latter in its ionic requirements. Whereas the intestinal slow wave of the cat has been reported to be insensitive to manganese and tetrodotoxin (80), the gastric slow wave of the guinea pig is completely blocked by either manganese (1 to 2×10^{-3} M) or tetrodotoxin (10^{-6} g/ml) (77).

It has been suggested that antral slow waves may play a role in coordinating the activity at the gastroduodenal junction during gastric emptying (15). Antral slow waves of diminished amplitude have been recorded from the proximal duodenum of several species of animals (15), most recently from man (49). It has been proposed that antral slow waves propagate across the gastroduodenal junction along longitudinal muscle bundles which pass from antrum to duodenum, and then spread electrotonically into adjacent duodenal muscle where they periodically augment the depolarization of duodenal slow waves. Such a mechanism could account for the coordination of spike activity and contractions which occur in this region during gastric emptying or when the junction is influenced by high vagal tone (see also 7).

Electrical activity of the colon.—Studies of gut motility, whether of its electrical, neural or mechanical aspects, have traditionally been both intriguing and controversial. The recent studies dealing with electrical activity of the colon promise to continue in this tradition. A case in point is the study by Christensen and his colleagues (33) of spontaneous electrical activity in cat and opossum colon. These investigators, using both surface electrodes and intracellular microelectrodes, recorded slow waves and bursts of spike potentials from various types of in vitro preparations, including whole segments and muscle strips. One curious feature of these potentials was their origin; slow waves not only appeared to be generated by circular muscle, but they appeared to be limited to circular muscle as well. On the other hand, spike potentials were rarely recorded from circular muscle, but occurred regularly in longitudinal muscle in association with the rhythmical contractions recorded from this layer. Thus, the genesis of slow waves differs from that in the small intestine, where they are generated in the longitudinal layer and spread electrotonically into the circular layer. Another rather curious finding was that the slow wave frequency was found to increase aborally, rather than to decrease as it does in the small intestine. In more recent experiments slow wave frequency in the cat colon in vitro was found to increase from 2.1 cycles/min in the proximal colon to 5.5 cycles/min in the distal colon (110).

In a related study Caprilli et al (28) recorded electrical and mechanical activity simultaneously from isolated strips of circular and of longitudinal muscle from cat colon. They corroborated the earlier findings of the circular muscle origin of slow waves, and showed in addition that rhythmic contractions of circular muscle are closely correlated, on a one-to-one basis, with slow waves over a wide range of frequencies.

Controversy has reared its head, however, in the form of a recent study by Vanasin et al (107) involving human colon both in vitro and in vivo. First, these investigators maintain that when the muscle layers are separated from one another, electrical activity—including slow waves—could be recorded only from the taenia coli, since both intervening longitudinal and circular muscle were quiescent. Second, the slow wave frequency was found to diminish from cecum to proximal transverse colon, then to increase from transverse colon to rectum.

The apparent discrepancy regarding the origin of colonic slow waves cannot be resolved in the light of currently available information. The evidence for the circular origin in the cat appears to be well founded. On the other hand the data on humans are appealing in view of the similar slow wave origin in small intestine. The possibility of true species differences should not be rejected, since there are anatomical differences between man and cat in the arrangement of longitudinal muscle in the colon, and species differences do apparently exist with respect to the genesis of antral slow waves. In the cat slow waves are absent from isolated circular muscle of the antrum (93), while in the guinea pig they can be recorded from isolated circular muscle of both antrum and pylorus (77). The reported difference in the direction of the slow wave frequency gradient may not be so difficult to resolve since Wienbeck et al (111) have recently reported the existence of an almost negligible gradient in the cat in vivo, with the frequency in the proximal colon sometimes exceeding that of the distal colon.

The relationship of the colonic slow wave to motility is not so clear as it is in the upper gastrointestinal tract. Christensen et al (33) suggest that it may be related to segmentation, since in the cat it appears to be limited to the circular layer—in which it propagates comparatively rapidly in the direction of the long axis of the cells, but spreads only for short distances in the other direction. The latter observation, coupled with reverse frequency gradient of the colonic slow wave makes it rather unlikely that it is involved in peristalsis, and even less likely that it is involved in "mass movement."

Muscle spike potentials.—There is little doubt that the rhythmic contractile activity of gastrointestinal muscle is normally triggered by spike potentials. A considerable amount of evidence has accumulated during the past two or three years which supports the idea that calcium is the major ion involved in the generation of spike potentials of the guinea pig taenia coli (17, 21, 22, 78), the guinea pig antrum (77) and cat jejunum (80). Much of the evidence for the involvement of calcium can be summarized as follows. When calcium is removed from the solution bathing a strip of taenia coli, the membrane depolarizes and spiking is abolished (17, 22). If sodium is now removed from the bathing medium, the membrane repolarizes, but spiking is still absent. Addition to the bath of as little as 10% of the normal calcium concentration produces spontaneous spike activity which is suppressed by further increasing the calcium concentration, although in this condition spikes can be elicited by electrical stimulation (17). Thus, when sodium is absent, spiking can occur if calcium is present in the bathing medium. In low sodium solution (10–15 mM) the amplitude, overshoot, and rate of rise of the spike are actually greater than they are in normal bathing media (17, 22, 78). The same effect can be obtained by increasing the calcium concentration of Kreb's solution (17). Such results have prompted the suggestion that calcium and sodium may compete for certain membrane sites where the presence of calcium is essential for spike production (22). Finally, the sensitivity of the spike to manganese (21, 77, 80) and its insensitivity to tetrodotoxin (77, 80), together with the apparent increase in calcium influx accompanying spike activity (69), are further evidence that calcium, not sodium, is the dominant ion required for spike generation in gastrointestinal muscle.

Both strontium and barium can substitute for calcium in its role as current carrier for the action potential (65, 78, 98), although under these conditions contractile activity is not maintained (65, 98). According to Ebashi (cited by Hotta & Tsukui, 65), strontium and barium are respectively only 1/20 and 1/200 as effective as calcium in the superprecipitation of chicken gizzard actomyosin. This has prompted Hotta & Tsukui (65) to suggest that the calcium that carries the inward current for the action potential may also be directly involved in excitation-contraction coupling.

In calcium-free Locke solution containing the normal amount of sodium, spike potentials, but no contractions, could be elicited, if a small amount (0.5 mM) of magnesium was present (22). Spike potentials could not be elicited when the concentration of magnesium was raised above 1 mM, or in the absence of sodium, but they were insensitive to tetrodotoxin. Thus, it appears that under certain conditions sodium may utilize the same channels normally used by calcium, again reminiscent of the "slow channel" in cardiac muscle (97).

Although barium and strontium can substitute for calcium in the generation of spike activity, they suppress both the normal excitatory effects of acetylcholine (65) and the inhibitory effect of epinephrine (21, 65) on guinea pig taenia coli in the absence of calcium. Furthermore, manganese abolishes both the inhibition and the accompanying increase in membrane conductance produced by epinephrine in the presence of calcium (21). Bülbring & Tomita (21) have interpreted these data as indicating that calcium is important to the control of membrane conductance.

Thus, it appears that in gastrointestinal smooth muscle, calcium may be directly involved in: (a) the regulation of membrane permeability; (b) the transfer of current across the membrane during the action potential; and (c) the triggering of the contractile process itself.

Organization of smooth muscle contractile proteins.—No review of gastrointestinal motility can be complete without some reference to the functional organization of the constituent contractile proteins. Although both actin and myosin have been extracted from visceral smooth muscle, the intracellular localization of these contractile proteins is not completely resolved. Most observers agree that actin is probably located on the 50–70 Å filaments which have been seen in most smooth muscle preparations, but there is no general agreement as to the existence of thick filaments similar to those associated with myosin in striated muscle (see 90 for earlier references). Kelly & Rice (72), on the basis of their studies of glutaraldehyde-fixed preparations of taenia coli, both in the relaxed and contracted states, concluded that both thick (150–200 Å) and thin (50–70 Å) filaments are present in smooth muscle, but that thick filaments can be found only in the contracted state. More recently, however, Devine & Somlyo (43) and Lowy et al (82, 83) have provided evidence for the presence of thick and thin filaments both in the contracted and the relaxed states, thick (myosin ?) filaments being more labile during fixation procedures than their counterparts in striated muscle. A major point of contention between the Somlyo and the Lowy groups concerns the structure of the thick filaments, one group (Lowy) contending that they are "ribbon-like," the other (Somlyo) that they are more cylindrical in form. These papers should be consulted for further details.

LITERATURE CITED

1. Abe, Y., Tomita, T. 1968. Cable properties of smooth muscle. *J. Physiol. London* 196:87–100
2. Abrahamsson, H., Jansson, G. 1969. Elicitation of reflex vagal relaxation of the stomach from pharynx and esophagus in the cat. *Acta Physiol. Scand.* 77: 172–78
3. Agostoni, E., Chinnock, J. E., Daly, M. De B., Murray, J. G. 1957. Functional and histological studies of the vagus nerve and its branches to the heart, lungs and abdominal viscera in the cat. *J. Physiol. London* 135:182–205
4. Ambache, N., Freeman, M. A. 1968. Atropine-resistant longitudinal muscle spasms due to excitation of non-cholinergic neurones in Auerbach's plexus. *J. Physiol. London* 199:705–27
5. Arimori, M., Code, C. F., Schlegel, J. F., Sturm, R. E. 1970. Electrical activity of the canine esophagus and gastroesophageal sphincter. *Am. J. Dig. Dis.* 15:191–208
6. Armett, C. J., Ritchie, J. M. 1961. The action of acetylcholine and some related substances on conduction in mammalian nonmyelinated nerve fibres. *J. Physiol. London* 155:372–84
7. Atanassova, E. 1970. On the mechanism of correlation between the spike activities of the stomach and duodenum. *Bull. Inst. Physiol. Bulg. Acad. Sci.* 13:229–242

8. Axelson, J., Holmberg, B. 1969. The effects of extracellularly applied ATP and related compounds on electrical and mechanical activity of the smooth muscle taenia coli from the guinea pig. *Acta Physiol. Scand.* 75:149–56
9. Baker, R. D. 1969. Electrical activity of small intestinal smooth muscle. *Am. J. Surg.* 117:781–97
10. Barr, L., Dewey, M. M. 1968. Electrotonus and electrical transmission in smooth muscle. *Handb. Physiol. Sec. 6, Aliment. Canal.* IV, *Motility*, 1733–42
11. Bass, P., Wiley, J. N. 1965. Electrical and extraluminal contractile-force activity of the duodenum of the dog. *Am. J. Dig. Dis.* 10:183–200
12. Bedi, B. S., Kelly, K. A. 1971. Propagation of the canine gastric pacesetter potential. *Gastroenterology* 60: 640
13. Bennett, A., Misiewicz, J. J., Waller, S. L. 1967. Analysis of the motor effects of gastrin and pentagastrin on the human alimentary tract in vitro. *Gut* 8:470–74
14. Bortoff, A. 1971. Temporal relationship between contractions of longitudinal and circular muscle during intestinal peristalsis. *Gastroenterology* 60:766
15. Bortoff, A., Davis, R. S. 1968. Myogenic transmission of antral slow waves across the gastroduodenal

junction in situ. *Am. J. Physiol.* 215:889–97

16. Bortoff, A., Sachs, F. 1970. Electrotonic spread of slow waves in circular muscle of small intestine. *Am. J. Physiol.* 218:576–81

17. Brading, A., Bülbring, E., Tomita, T. 1969. The effect of sodium and calcium on the action potential of the smooth muscle of the guinea-pig taenia coli. *J. Physiol. London* 200: 637–54

18. Brinley, F. J., Mullins, L. J. 1968. Sodium fluxes in internally dialyzed squid axons. *J. Gen. Physiol.* 52: 181–211

19. Bülbring, E., Brading, A. F., Jones, A. W., Tomita, T., Eds. 1970. *Smooth Muscle.* Baltimore: Williams and Wilkins. 676 pp.

20. Bülbring, E., Gershon, M. D. 1967. 5-hydroxytryptamine participation in the vagal inhibitory innervation of the stomach. *J. Physiol. London* 192:823–46

21. Bülbring, E., Tomita, T. 1969. Effect of calcium, barium and manganese on the action of adrenaline in the smooth muscle of the guinea-pig taenia coli. *Proc. Roy. Soc. London Ser. B.* 172:121–36

22. Bülbring, E., Tomita, T. 1970. Effects of Ca removal on the smooth muscle of the guinea-pig taenia coli. *J. Physiol. London* 210:217–32

23. Bunker, C. E., Johnson, L. P., Nelsen, T. S. 1967. Chronic in situ studies of the electrical activity of the small intestine. *Arch. Surg. Chicago* 95: 259–68

24. Burnstock, G., Campbell, G., Satchell, D., Smythe, A. 1970. Evidence that adenosine triphosphate or a related nucleotide is the transmitter substance released by non-adrenergic inhibitory nerves in the gut. *Brit. J. Pharmacol.* 40:668–88

25. Campbell, G. 1966. The inhibitory nerve fibres in the vagal supply to the guinea-pig stomach. *J. Physiol. London* 185:600–12

26. Campbell, G. 1969. The autonomic innervation of the stomach of a toad (*Bufo Marinus*). *Comp. Biochem. Physiol.* 31:693–706

27. Cannon, W. B. 1908. The acid closure of the cardia. *Am. J. Physiol.* 23: 105–114

28. Caprilli, R., Onori, L., Tonini, M., Zapponi, G. 1970. Slow waves and mechanical activity in cat colon circular muscle. *Rendic. R. Gastroenterol.* 2:83–89

29. Castell, D. O., Harris, L. D. 1970. Hormonal control of gastroesophageal-sphincter strength. *N. Eng. J. Med.* 282:886–89

30. Chrispin, A. R., Friedland, G. W. 1966. A radiological study of the neural control of oesophageal vestibular function. *Thorax* 21: 422–27

31. Christensen, J. 1970. Patterns and origin of some esophageal responses to stretch and electrical stimulation. *Gastroenterology* 59:909–16

32. Christensen, J. 1970. Pharmacologic identification of the lower esophageal sphincter. *J. Clin. Invest.* 49: 681–91

33. Christensen, J. Caprilli, R., Lund, G. F. 1969. Electric slow waves in circular muscle of cat colon. *Am. J. Physiol.* 217:771–76

34. Christensen, J., Daniel, E. E. 1968. Effects of some autonomic drugs on circular esophageal smooth muscle. *J. Pharmacol. Exp. Ther.* 159:243–49

35. Christensen, J., Lund, G. F. 1969. Esophageal responses to distension and electrical stimulation. *J. Clin. Invest.* 48:408–19

36. Clark, C. G., Vane, J. R. 1961. The cardiac sphincter in the cat. *Gut* 2: 252–62

36a. Code, C. F., Heidal, W., Eds. 1968. *Handbook of Physiology, Sec. 6, The Alimentary Canal,* IV, *Motility.* Baltimore: Williams and Wilkins

37. Code, C. F., Szurszewski, J. H. 1970. The effect of duodenal and mid small bowel transection on the frequency gradient of the pacesetter potential in the canine small intestine. *J. Physiol. London* 207: 281–89

38. Cohen, S., Harris, L. D. 1970. Lower esophageal sphincter pressure as an index of lower esophageal sphincter strength. *Gastroenterology* 58:157–62

39. Cohen, S., Lipshutz, W. 1971. Hormonal regulation of human lower esophageal sphincter competence: Interaction of gastrin and secretin. *J. Clin. Invest.* 50:449–54

40. Couturier, D., Rozé, C. Paolaggi, J., Debray, C. 1970. Activité electrique de l'estomac humain normal; variations topologiques. *Compt. Rend. Acad. Sci. Paris* 270:2817–20

41. Crema, A., Del Tacca, M., Frigo, G. M., Lecchini, S. 1968. Presence

of a non-adrenergic inhibitory system in the human colon. *Gut* 9:633–37

42. Daniel, E. E. 1969. Digestion: Motor Function. *Ann. Rev. Physiol.* 31: 203–26

43. Devine, C. E., Somlyo, A. P. 1971. Thick filaments in vascular smooth muscle. *J. Cell. Biol.* 49:636–49

44. Diamant, N. E., Akin, A. N. 1970. Response of the lower esophageal sphincter to gastric contractile activity. *Gastroenterology* 58:940

45. Diamant, N. E., Bortoff, A. 1969a. Nature of the intestinal slow-wave frequency gradient. *Am. J. Physiol.* 217:301–7

46. Diamant, N. E., Bortoff, A. 1969b. Effects of transection on the intestinal slow-wave frequency gradient. *Am. J. Physiol.* 217:734–43

47. Diamant, N. E., Rose, P. K., Davison, E. J. 1970. Computer simulation of intestinal slow-wave frequency gradient. *Am. J. Physiol.* 219:1684–90

48. Doty, R. W. 1968. Neural organization of deglutition. *Handb. Physiol., Sec. 6, Aliment. Canal.* IV, *Motility,* 1861–1902

49. Duthie, H. L., Kwong, N. K., Brown, B. H., Whittaker, G. E. 1971. Pace-setter potential of the human gastroduodenal junction. *Gut* 12: 250–56

50. Eyzaguirre, C., Zapata, P. 1968. The release of acetylcholine from carotid body tissues. Further study on the effects of acetylcholine and cholinergic blocking agents on the chemosensory discharge. *J. Physiol. London* 195:589–607

51. Furness, J. B. 1969. An electrophysiological study of the innervation of the smooth muscle of the colon. *J. Physiol. London* 205:549–62

52. Furness, J. B. 1970. An examination of nerve-mediated hyoscine-resistant excitation of the guinea-pig colon. *J. Physiol. London* 207:803–21

53. Gabella, G. 1970. Electron microscopical examination of the junction between the myenteric plexus and the longitudinal muscle of the guinea-pig ileum *Brit. J. Pharmacol.* 40: 588P

54. Giles, G. R., Humphries, C., Mason, M. C., Clark, C. G. 1969. Effect of pH changes on the cardiac sphincter. *Gut* 10:852–56

55. Giles, G. R., Mason, M. C., Humphries, C., Clark, C. G. 1969. Action of gastrin on the lower

oesophageal sphincter in man. *Gut* 10:730–34.

56. Golenhofen, K., Loh, D. V., Milenov, K. 1970. Elektrophysiologische Untersuchungen zur Spontanaktivität isolierter Muskelpräparate aus verschiedenen Abschnitten des Meerschweinchen-magens. *Pfluegers Arch.* 315:336–56

57. Gray, J. A. B., Diamond, J. 1957. Pharmacological properties of sensory receptors and their relation to those of the autonomic nervous system. *Brit. Med. Bull.* 13:185–88

58. Gregory, J. E., Bentley, G. A. 1968. The peristaltic reflex in the isolated guinea pig ileum during drug-induced spasm of the longitudinal muscle. *Aust. J. Exp. Biol. Med.* 46:1–16

59. Grivel, M. L., Ruckebusch, M., Ruckebusch, Y. 1970. Basal electrical rhythm of the intestine after section or transposition. *Compt. Rend. Soc. Biol. Paris* 164:447–54

60. Grivel, M. L., Ruckebusch, Y. 1971. A study in the dog and cat of the electrical activity of the small intestine some months after transection and transplantation of the gut. *Life Sci.* 10:241–50

61. Hellemans, J., Vantrappen, G. 1967. Electromyographic studies on canine esophageal motility. *Am. J. Dig. Dis.* 12:1240–55

62. Holman, M. E., Hughes, J. R. 1965. Inhibition of intestinal smooth muscle. *Aust. J. Exp. Biol. Med. Sci.* 43:277–90

63. Holman, M. E., Hughes, J. R. 1965. An inhibitory component of the response to distension of rat ileum. *Nature London* 207:641–42

64. Holton, P. 1959. The liberation of adenosine triphosphate on antidromic stimulation of sensory nerves. *J. Physiol. London* 145:494–504

65. Hotta, Y., Tsukui, R. 1968. Effect on the guinea-pig taenia coli of the substitution of strontium or barium ions for calcium ions. *Nature London* 217:867–69

66. Hukuhara, T., Sumi, T., Kotani, S. 1961. The role of the ganglion cells in the small intestine taken in the intestinal intrinsic reflex. *Jap. J. Physiol.* 11:281–88

67. Hukuhara, T., Fukuda, H. 1965. The motility of the isolated guinea-pig small intestine. *Jap. J. Physiol.* 15:125–139

68. Jansson, G. 1969. Vago-vagal reflex

relaxation of the stomach in the cat. *Acta Physiol. Scand.* 75:245–52

69. Job, D. D. 1969. Ionic basis of intestinal electrical activity. *Am. J. Physiol.* 217:1534–41

70. Job, D. D. 1971. Effect of antibiotics and selective inhibitors of ATP on intestinal slow waves. *Am. J. Physiol.* 220:299–306

71. Kelly, K. A., Code, C. F., Elveback, L. R. 1969. Patterns of canine gastric electrical activity. *Am. J. Physiol.* 217:461–70

72. Kelly, R. E., Rice, R. V. 1969. Ultrastructural studies on the contractile mechanism of smooth muscle. *J. Cell Biol.* 42:684–94

73. Kerkut, G. A., Thomas, R. C. 1965. An electrogenic sodium pump in snail nerve cells. *Comp. Biochem. Physiol.* 14:167–83

74. Kosterlitz, H. W. 1968. Intrinsic and extrinsic nervous control of motility of the stomach and the intestines. *Handb. Physiol., Sec. 6, Aliment. Canal*, IV, *Motility*, 2147–71

75. Kottegoda, S. R. 1969. An analysis of possible nervous mechanisms involved in the peristaltic reflex. *J. Physiol. London* 200:687–712

76. Kottegoda, S. R. 1970. Peristalsis of the small intestine. *Smooth Muscle*, ed. E. Bülbring, A. F. Brading, A. W. Jones, T. Tomita, 525–541. Baltimore: Williams and Wilkins

77. Kuriyama, H., Osa, T., Tasaki, H. 1970. Electrophysiological studies of the antrum muscle fibers of the guinea pig stomach. *J. Gen. Physiol.* 55:48–62

78. Kuriyama, H., Tomita, T. 1970. The action potential in the smooth muscle of the guinea pig taenia coli and ureter studied by the double sucrose-gap method. *J. Gen. Physiol.* 55:147–62

79. Kyi, J. K. K., Daniel, E. E. 1970. The effects of ischemia on intestinal nerves and electrical slow waves. *Am. J. Dig. Dis.* 15:959–81

80. Liu, J., Prosser, C. L., Job, D. D. 1969. Ionic dependence of slow waves and spikes in intestinal muscle. *Am. J. Physiol.* 217:1542–47

81. Longhi, E. H., Jordan, P. H., Jr. 1971. Necessity of a bolus for propagation of primary peristalsis in the canine esophagus. *Am. J. Physiol.* 220:609–12

82. Lowy, J., Poulsen, F. R., Vibert, P. J. 1970. Myosin filaments in vertebrate smooth muscle. *Nature London* 225:1053–54

83. Lowy, J., Small, J. V. 1970. The organization of myosin and actin in vertebrate smooth muscle. *Nature London* 227:46–51

84. Lund, G. F., Christensen, J. 1969. Electrical stimulation of esophageal smooth muscle and effects of antagonists. *Am. J. Physiol.* 217:1369–74

85. Mann, C. V., Code, C. F., Ellis, F. H., Jr. 1969. Intrinsic mechanisms controlling the mammalian gastroesophageal sphincter. *Rendic. R. Gastroenterol.* 1:126

86. Mann, C. V., Code, C. F., Schlegel, J. F., Ellis, F. H., Jr. 1968. Intrinsic mechanisms controlling the mammalian gastro-oesophageal sphincter deprived of extrinsic nerve supply. *Thorax* 23:634–39

87. Martinson, J. 1965. Vagal relaxation of the stomach. *Acta Physiol. Scand.* 64:453–62

88. Meltzer, S. J. 1899. On the causes of the orderly progress of the peristaltic movements in the oesophagus. *Am. J. Physiol.* 2:266–72

89. Monges, H., Salducci, J., Roman, C. 1969. Étude électromyographique de la motricité gastrique chez l'homme normal. *Arch. Fr. Mal. l'Appar. Dig.* 58:517–30

90. Needham, D. M., Shoenberg, C. F. 1968. Proteins of the contractile mechanism in vertebrate smooth muscle. *Handb. Physiol., Sec. 6, Aliment. Canal*, IV, *Motility*, 1793–810

91. Osa, T., Kuriyama, H. 1970. The membrane properties and decremental conduction of excitation in the fundus of the guinea-pig stomach. *Jap. J. Physiol.* 20:626–39

92. Pace, J. L. 1968. The interconnexions of the muscle layers of the human colon. *J. Anat.* 103:289–96

93. Papasova, M. P., Nagai, T., Prosser, C. L. 1968. Two-component slow waves in smooth muscle of cat stomach. *Am. J. Physiol.* 214:695–702

94. Papazova, M. P., Atanassova, E., Boev, K. 1969. On the contractile activity of the longitudinal and circular muscular layers of the stomach. *Bull. Inst. Physiol.* Bulg. Acad. Sci. 12:103–13

95. Prosser, C. L., Bortoff, A. 1968. Electrical activity of intestinal muscle under in vitro conditions. *Handb.*

Physiol., Sec. 6, Aliment. Canal, IV, *Motility*, 2025–50

96. Reinke, D. A., Rosenbaum, A. H., Bennett, D. R. 1967. Patterns of dog gastrointestinal contractile activity monitored in vivo with extraluminal force transducers. *Am. J. Dig. Dis.* 12:113–41

97. Rougier, O., Vassort, G., Garnier, D., Gargouil, Y. M., Coraboeuf, E. 1969. Existence and role of a slow inward current during the frog atrial action potential. *Pfluegers Arch.* 308:91–110

98. Sakamoto, Y., Kuriyama, H. 1970. The relationship between the electrical and mechanical activity of the guinea-pig stomach. *Jap. J. Physiol.* 20:640–56

99. Siegel, C. I., Hendrix, T. R. 1961. Evidence for the central mediation of secondary peristalsis in the esophagus. *Bull. Johns Hopkins Hosp.* 108:297–307

100. Somlyo, A. P., Somlyo, A. V. 1968. Vascular smooth muscle. I. Normal structure, pathology, biochemistry, and biophysics. *Pharmacol. Rev.* 20:197–272

101. Somlyo, A. P., Somlyo, A. V. 1970. Vascular smooth muscle. II. Pharmacology of normal and hypertensive vessels. *Pharmacol. Rev.* 22:249–353

102. Specht, P., Bortoff, A. 1971. Electrical entrainment of intestinal slow waves. *Fed. Proc.* 30(2):609

103. Szurszewski, J. H., Elveback, L. R., Code, C. F. 1970. Configuration and frequency gradient of electric slow wave over canine small bowel. *Am. J. Physiol.* 218:1468–73

104. Titchen, D. A., Wheeler, J. S. 1971. Contractions of the caudal region of the oesophagus in the cat. *J. Physiol. London* 215:119–37

105. Tomita, T. 1969. The longitudinal tissue impedance of the smooth muscle of guinea-pig taenia coli. *J. Physiol. London* 201:145–59

106. Trendelenburg, P. 1917. Physiologische und pharmakologische Versuche über die Dünndarmperistaltik. *Arch. Exp. Pathol. Pharmakol.* 81:55–129

107. Vanasin, B., Schuster, M. M. 1971. Motor and electrical activity in human colon in vitro and in vivo. *Gastroenterology* 60:728

108. Vantrappen, G., Hellemans, J. 1970. Esophageal motility. *Rendic. R. Gastroenterol.* 2:7–19

109. Weber, J., Jr., Kohatsu, S. 1970. Pacemaker localization and electrical conduction patterns in the canine stomach. *Gastroenterology* 59:717–26

110. Wienbeck, M., Christensen, J. 1970. Autonomic drug effects on the cat colon slow wave. *Fed. Proc.* 21:262

111. Wienbeck, M., Weisbrodt, N., Christensen, J. 1971. The electrical activity of the cat colon *in vivo*. *Gastroenterology* 60:809

112. Wood, J. D. 1970a. Electrical activity from single neurons in Auerbach's plexus. *Am. J. Physiol.* 219:159–69

113. Wood, J. D. 1970b. Effects of atropine and local anesthetics on mechanical and electrical activity of circular muscle in the small bowel of cat and guinea pig. *The Physiologist* 13:347

114. Wood, J. D., Perkins, W. E. 1970. Mechanical interaction between longitudinal and circular axes of the small intestine. *Am. J. Physiol.* 218:762–68

115. Yokoyama, S. 1966. Aktionspotentiale der Ganglienzelle des auerbachschen plexus im Kaninchendünndarm. *Pfluegers Arch.* 288:95–102.

CENTRAL VISION: VISUAL CORTEX AND SUPERIOR COLLICULUS

JAMES T. MCILWAIN

Neurosciences Section, Division of Biological and Medical Sciences, Brown University, Providence, Rhode Island

This review considers selected aspects of recent research on the physiology of the visual cortex and the optic tectum. Attention is directed in particular to studies relating single unit responses to mechanisms of pattern vision, stereoscopy and visual orienting behavior. I have limited discussion to these aspects of central visual physiology so that I might consider them in some detail. Other areas of research on the visual system are reviewed in several recent books and articles (49, 68, 71, 94, 106, 107).

VISUAL CORTEX

Receptive field organization.—Current notions about the nature and structure of receptive fields of visual cortex neurons derive largely from the pioneering studies of Hubel & Wiesel (60, 61, 63), who established that many cells in this area respond best to oriented lines and edges. These investigators classified cells in area *17* as simple or complex—on the basis of spatial properties of the receptive fields—and noted that the behavior of complex cells could not be predicted from the distribution of on- and off-zones mapped with a small light spot. Recent studies have demonstrated that area *17* of the cat and monkey also contains hypercomplex cells (63) previously thought to be restricted to areas *18* and *19* (61). Hypercomplex units respond selectively to patterns which are more elaborate and constrained than those which activate complex cells. An important feature of the hypercomplex receptive field is the presence of inhibitory regions, which flank the activating zones and require that an edge or line be "stopped" at one or both ends to stimulate the unit effectively. Cells exhibiting simple and complex receptive fields occur in the striate cortex of the unanesthetized rhesus monkey (143–146), so these field patterns are not attributable to the effects of anesthesia. Wurtz (144) did not find hypercomplex units in area *17*, but the difficulty of controlling eye movements in experiments using unanesthetized animals precluded an adequate search. An earlier report (109) that orientation specificity changes under anesthesia was not confirmed by Lee (80), who did find substantial effects on directional properties and on distributions of excitatory and inhibitory regions within the cortical receptive fields.

Pettigrew et al (101, 102) adopted the receptive field classification of Hubel & Wiesel in their study of neurons in the cat's striate cortex. They confirmed that, in a single electrode penetration, one may record units with quite narrow (1° or less) orientation specific receptive fields, and other units with much wider (over 3°) fields, which still exhibit orientation preference. These authors also noted differences in spontaneous discharge rates and in optimal stimulus velocities for the two general classes. A striking difference between the findings of the two laboratories was the observation by Pettigrew et al (101) of directional selectivity in fields which by geometrical criteria appeared to be of the simple type. The directional selectivity was independent of stimulus contrast and could not be predicted from the configuration of on- and off-zones in the receptive field.

Another observation by Pettigrew et al (102) indicated further complexity in the organization of simple fields. When the monocular (right and left eye) receptive field components of binocular cortical cells were not in exact correspondence on the tangent screen, monocular stimulation with a single slit was usually more effective in activating the unit than was binocular stimulation. One interpretation of this finding is that, with the two fields separated on the tangent screen, a stimulus moving through the activating zone of one field is moving through the surround of the other. If the surrounds are inhibitory, one would expect the suppressive effects seen by Bishop's group (102). Such inhibitory surrounds have been identified in simple fields by Henry et al (55) and comparable findings are reported by Jones (74) and by Spinelli & Barrett (122). This explanation is less satisfactory in those cases where complex cells show substantial decreases in activation when their binocular fields are only slightly out of correspondence (102). These findings blur the distinction between simple, complex and hypercomplex fields to some extent, but there remain important differences, even with regard to the inhibitory surrounds. The "stopped-edge" properties of hypercomplex cells are reported to result from inhibitory flanks which have trigger features similar—if not identical—to those of the activating regions (61). The inhibitory surrounds of simple fields do not share the directional properties of the activating central regions (55) and therefore may represent a less specific type of mechanism. It is not possible to say from present evidence whether the inhibitory surrounds of simple fields exhibit orientation or other preferences. The total extent of the inhibitory surround is unknown and the data of Henry et al (55) suggest that it does not always completely encircle the central activating regions. Yet more complex lateral interactions, some of them inhibitory, have been examined in several recent studies on visual cortex neurons (22, 74) and parallel phenomena have been studied psychophysically (16, 84, 85).

Spinelli & Barrett (122) took issue with the scheme of receptive field classification proposed by Hubel & Wiesel for striate neurons and offered alternative groupings: disc-shaped, diffuse, bar and edge, composite, and unclassified. These authors were able to relate 20% of their cells to the simple type and 10% to the complex type of Hubel & Wiesel, who originally reported 70% of their sample to be simple field cells and the rest complex.

Thus, 70% of the cells examined by Spinelli & Barrett (122) are said to fall outside the simple-complex classification. The principal sources of discrepancy appear to be differences in stimulus technique and interpretive emphasis. Whereas Spinelli & Barrett mapped with a small (0.5°) disc, continuously scanning the receptive field, Hubel & Wiesel (60, 61) and Pettigrew et al (101, 102) employed moving and stationary line segments and edges as their basic stimuli. Spinelli & Barrett emphasized any consistent change in firing pattern produced by their stimulus disc, while the other groups sought the stimulus which gave a maximal response, i.e. the stimulus which seemed to be "preferred" by the unit. When Spinelli & Barrett stimulated their bar-shaped fields with rectangular stimuli, the results could resemble simple fields (122, Figure 5) or complex fields (122, Figure 6). Directional selectivity in diffuse fields suggests that they might exhibit complex or hypercomplex properties if examined with line segment stimuli (61). It is, however, the disc-shaped fields of Spinelli & Barrett, constituting 44% of their sample, which pose the largest puzzle. If they do not represent a new class of receptive fields, it is most likely that they are complex or hypercomplex, because simple fields would appear bar-shaped in the scan maps, with on- and off-zones separated. The crucial test is that of orientation preference, because this characterized all of the "cortical sample" of Hubel & Wiesel (60), including those simple field cells which were uncategorized as to disposition of on- and off-zones (see also 22). Orientation preference is reported absent in some cells with peripheral receptive fields (73), but Spinelli & Barrett studied fields close to the visual axis. These investigators scanned the disc-shaped receptive fields with "bars and edges and other stimuli" and found that "this type of analysis did not reveal any more than could have been predicted by taking spatial summation and direction sensitivity (for those units that showed it) into account" (122 p. 91). It is unfortunate that the authors did not describe in detail the scan paths and stimulus angles used, for they gave the impression that the search for orientation preference was not systematic.

Spinelli & Barrett (122) asked "whether units with line-shaped receptive fields are to be considered 'detectors of lines' and nothing else," and since such fields can be mapped with small spots, they decided the answer to this is "no". The question points up an interesting ambiguity in the term "receptive field" and it is perhaps useful to make note of it here. "Receptive field," as used in studies of vision, comprises at least two concepts. The first, or "peripheral" concept, embodies the functional connections of a unit which determine its responses to retinal stimulation. It is an analytic concept in the sense that the response properties of a sensory cell should be reducible to the pattern and nature of its neural connections with the sensory surface. However, this analytic quality does not apply to the "central" concept of receptive field. A complete description of a unit's response properties (or its peripheral connections) does not reveal unequivocally what information it is passing on to other parts of the nervous system. For instance, the structure

and specificities of cortical receptive fields are not deducible from the properties of lateral geniculate neurons. It is clear, then, why calling a neuron a detector of something has a certain frustrating imprecision about it. On the one
hand, the statement is a thumbnail sketch of the operational geometry of the
cell's peripheral connectivity and, on the other hand, it is a guess about the
stimulus information actually extracted by units in the projection field of the
cell's axon. To avoid confusion, it would seem necessary and worthwhile to
establish explicit rules of evidence for the identification of detectors in the
"central" sense, a task which has yet to receive the attention it needs. Additional facets of the receptive field concept are dealt with by Jacobs in a recent review (71).

Receptive field ontogeny.—The properties of cortical neurons depend substantially on the visual experience of the organism in the first few months of
life. Hubel & Wiesel (65), have pinpointed the most crucial period in kittens
as the fourth and fifth weeks after birth. Unilateral eye closure for as little
as 3–4 days during this period produces a marked decline in the number of
cells driven from both eyes, as well as a decline in the relative influence of
the previously occluded eye. Behavioral experiments on monocularly deprived kittens reveal that susceptibility to permanent functional deficit is
also greatest during the second month after birth (28, 140). Covering the
normal eye results in improvement of behavior guided by the deprived eye,
particularly after prolonged testing. This contrasts with the finding that
similar training leads to no such improvement in cortical neuronal responses
to stimulation of the deprived eye (141). Deprivation amblyopia in the
rhesus monkey is most severe and irreversible when the lids are closed in the
first month of life (96).

The nature of visual deprivation in early life appears to have important
consequences for the receptive field geometry of cortical neurons which remain functional. Hirsch & Spinelli (57) exposed kittens to controlled monocular stimulation until the tenth or twelfth week. One eye saw a series of
vertical, the other a series of horizontal lines. At the end of the deprivation
period, receptive fields of neurons in the striate cortex were found to be either
of the diffuse or of the bar type, as defined by Spinelli & Barrett (122). The
bar type receptive fields were oriented either vertically or horizontally and
were activated only from the eye previously exposed to the corresponding
grid orientation. These findings are corroborated by the experiments of
Blakemore & Cooper (17) who reared kittens in darkness, except for daily
5-hour exposures to visual environments dominated by high contrast
vertical or horizontal stripes. At the age of 5 months, these animals behaved
as if blind to contours perpendicular to the orientation they had experienced
previously. Examination of striate cortex neurons in two such cats at age
7.5 months revealed a marked anisotropy of receptive field preferred orientations. The distribution of preferred axes clearly reflected the exposure

experience and no fields showed optimal orientations perpendicular to the stripe orientation experienced during development.

The imbalance of visual stimulation experienced by cortical cells during monocular occlusion is an important factor in the resultant functional derangement. After binocular lid closure, Wiesel & Hubel (140) found that about 41% of the cells recorded in the cortex had normal response properties. Abnormal cells (32%) could be driven, but had lost much of their orientation preference. Only about 27% of cells could not be driven, but this estimate may be low (140). Nonetheless, this contrasts markedly with the virtually total failure of cells to respond to stimulation of the previously occluded eye after monocular deprivation. The seeing eye appears to exert a "suppressive" effect on the central connections of the occluded eye. Guillery & Stelzner (50) presented morphological evidence for such an effect at the level of the lateral geniculate body, where marked changes in cell staining were also noted by Wiesel & Hubel (139, 140, see also 39–42). They found that regions of the geniculate receiving fibers from monocular parts of the visual field are not affected cytologically by deprivation, whereas cells in areas representing the binocular field are smaller, more closely packed, and paler staining in laminae from the deprived eye. This suggests that one should look for differential effects of deprivation on cortical neurons representing binocular and monocular parts of the visual field.

Guillery & Stelzner (50) proposed that cell size and dendritic spread of a geniculate unit are a function of the extent of cortical synaptic surface occupied by that unit's axonal terminals. According to this view, inactive geniculate cells, related to the occluded eye, cannot compete effectively with active cells for synaptic space in the cortical projection, and therefore undergo morphological changes. An additional factor is suggested by recent evidence that the majority of monocularly activated cells in the main geniculate laminae receive inhibitory inputs from the nondominant eye (114). The neural pathways mediating this inhibition are not yet established, but the overall effect would be to enhance the imbalance caused by monocular deprivation. Visual input to the seeing eye would produce virtually unopposed inhibition of cells normally activated by the occluded eye.

Receptive fields and stereoscopic vision.—Since Pettigrew (100) first noted irreducible position disparities in the binocular receptive fields of neurons in the cat's visual cortex, a sizeable body of evidence has accumulated to support the view that these disparities are the key to stereoscopic vision. The details of this work are ably reviewed elsewhere (7, 8) and will not be treated here. The resultant theory begins with the observation that, since many neurons in the cortex receive inputs from both eyes, these cells have two monocular receptive field projections in visual space. For the neuron to be maximally excited, these two receptive fields must be stimulated simultaneously by objects of appropriate shape, size, orientation, and motion. This

is achieved normally when the two receptive fields are in correspondence—
i.e., when a single appropriate stimulus is located in both fields at the same
time. Potent inhibitory effects diminish the response of the cell to stimuli
which do not impinge simultaneously on activating zones of the receptive
fields (vida supra). The great majority of receptive fields are presumably
in correspondence at the plane of fixation so that maximum effective stimulation is achieved by objects in this plane. Binocular receptive fields not in
correspondence at the plane of fixation are, however, exactly superimposed
at some distance in front of or behind the fixation plane. The neuron pos-
sessing a pair of these fields is best stimulated by a single appropriate
stimulus in front of or behind the fixation plane, depending on whether the
fields show crossed (convergent) or uncrossed (divergent) disparity. The
nervous system thus provides a population of neurons with binocular receptive fields exactly in correspondence at some position in a block of space
containing the fixation plane. A stimulus at any locus in this block of space
will excite those members of the neuronal population with receptive fields in
correspondence at that point.

Joshua & Bishop (73) have extended the theory to accord with classical
psychophysical measures of stereoscopic vision. They define the physiological horopter as "that surface in space which contains the fixation point
and for which, irrespective of retinal eccentricity, the greatest number of
receptive fields are in correspondence." Panum's fusional area, which is the
region of binocular single vision on either side of the horopter, is defined
arbitrarily as that zone for which one standard deviation, or about 68%, of
the binocular receptive fields are in perfect correspondence. (For a recent
comprehensive review of these psychophysical concepts, see reference 118).
Joshua & Bishop (73) as well as Blakemore (11) found that, as one moves
away from the area of central vision, receptive field disparity increases in
absolute magnitude and in the range of disparities measured. The magnitude
shift favors convergent disparities, which causes the horopter to curve inward, away from the Vieth-Muller circle. The increased spread of disparities
forces an expansion of Panum's fusional area. Both of these phenomena
parallel psychophysical findings in the human.

Studies in the cat have concentrated on area *17* (striate cortex) and it is
not known at present if receptive fields in area *18* of this species also show the
same type of disparity. Area *18* of the monkey does contain neurons with
binocular receptive fields of varying disparity, whereas area *17* appears to be
devoid of such cells (66). Hubel & Wiesel (66) have presented evidence that
these depth sensitive neurons cluster in columns which encompass many sub-
columns of cells with specific orientation selectivities. In parallel behavioral
studies, Bough (21) has established that the monkey can discriminate stereoscopic images which are devoid of monocular cues to depth.

Blakemore's analysis (14, 19) leaves little doubt that there is a columnar
arrangement of depth sensitive cells in the cat's striate cortex and that there
are at least two classes of columns. One type, the constant depth column, is

formed of cells with virtually identical disparity, indicating that they "see best" at a particular locus in Panum's zone. Because of the finite dimensions of the receptive fields, Blakemore has conceived of these columns as "viewing a thin sheet of space." The other type of column contains cells with widely varying disparities, indicating that their fields are in correspondence at different distances from the eye. These fields, when in exact correspondence, fall on a straight line drawn from the eye contralateral to the recorded neurons. Such cells comprise a constant direction column, and Blakemore has proposed that they view a cylinder of visual space directed away from the contralateral eye. The columnar organization of the visual cortex therefore appears to code not only the contrast geometry and motion of a stimulus feature, but also its direction and distance from the eye, the last two quantities specifying the location of the stimulus in polar coordinates. A polar mapping of visual space in the nervous system has been suggested by Leibovic and his colleagues on theoretical grounds (81, 82).

Midline Stereopsis.— Although man's greatest stereoscopic acuity is in the region of the fixation point (97), this area of the binocular visual field poses a knotty problem for neurological analysis. Objects immediately in front of or behind this region are imaged either bitemporally or binasally, i.e. on hemiretinae which project to separate hemispheres. The neural activity aroused by these images is not combined by the normal overlap of temporal and nasal projections which results from the decussation of nasal fibers in the optic chiasm. Yet, the activity must be brought together in some way for these images to fuse. Neurophysiological and anatomical evidence in the cat indicate that this is done, in large part, via a transcallosal projection which connects cortical areas representing the midline of the visual field (6, 62). In addition, the cat appears to possess a strip of retina at the vertical midline which projects to both hemispheres due to imperfect decussation in the chiasm (125). Either or both of these arrangements may account for the existence in one hemisphere of binocular depth sensitive neurons with receptive fields near the midline in the ipsilateral visual hemifield (5, 7, 8, 11, 73, 95).

Blakemore (11) has argued from geometric considerations that, if the nasotemporal overlap is to account for midline stereopsis in the cat, the range of horizontal disparities of binocular cortical cells must be twice the angular width of the vertical retinal strip which is represented in both hemispheres. His data tend to support the hypothesis. Receptive field centers overlap in the midline of the visual field an average of 1.5° and the distribution of overlap has a standard deviation of about 0.5°. The range of horizontal disparities for these midline fields is about 2.3° and the distribution has a standard deviation of 0.9°. Thus, on measurements of range and distribution width, overall field disparity is about twice overall field center overlap. Nikara et al (95) have reported, however, that the distribution of midline overlap has a standard deviation of 1.3° whereas the disparity distribution has standard deviation of 0.61°. Joshua & Bishop (73) gave standard deviation values of 1.2° and 0.5° for the same distributions respectively. These findings indicate that the average nasotemporal overlap is twice the average disparity, just the converse of what was predicted by Blakemore's geometric model. This need not imply, however, that the extent of naso-temporal overlap is unrelated to the requirements of midline stereopsis. Blakemore's prediction was based on the special case of symmetric conver-gence and does not consider the aniseikonia resulting from asymmetric con-vergence. This relative image magnification in the eye nearest the viewed object occurs for all points in Panum's area, including those with crossed and uncrossed midline disparities. Midline stereopsis during strong asymmetric convergence may require a significantly larger nasotemporal overlap (in the near eye) than is necessary in symmetric convergence.

Decussation of retinal fibers in the human appears to split the retina perfectly into temporal and nasal halves. Combining bitemporal and binasal images for vertical midline stereopsis must therefore involve some central cross connection between the hemispheres. Mitchell & Blakemore (93) have determined that a human with section of the corpus callosum, as well as anterior and hippocampal commissures, does not report stereoscopic per-ception of midline stimuli, and Westheimer & Mitchell (134) have shown that disparate images projected to separate hemispheres in the same subject do not elicit disjunctive eye movements. Section of the optic chiasm in man results in loss of vision for divergent disparity, but leaves convergent stereop-sis intact (12). Were stereoscopic vision dependent on the imperfect decussa-tion of nasal and temporal retinal fibers, it should not survive chiasm section. Mitchell & Blakemore (93) concluded from this that nasotemporal overlap at the retinal level cannot be important in human stereoscopic vision (cf 8).

Thorson et al (131) have described a phenomenon which could prove of considerable value in determining the extent of retinal nasotemporal overlap in the human, if this exists. They found that an illusion of movement is created by sequential flashing of two tiny lights separated by about 0°6'–0°7' of arc. The movement illusion enabled the observer to report the se-quence of illumination at above chance levels for temporal separations of 2.5–200 msec, with best performance occurring at intervals of 25–100 msec. The illusion could occasionally be obtained with dichoptic presentation of the stimuli. However, when the two dots were positioned near the vertical midline, several degrees below the fixation point in their study, all three sub-jects found a small range of positions in which the illusion was abolished. Thorson et al (131) have suggested this may occur when the presentation is "dichogeniculate"—i.e., when the neural activity associated with each spot goes to different hemispheres. If this is true, then the illusion is sustained only by signals reaching a single hemisphere via direct retino-geniculo-striate projections and not by signals which must traverse the corpus cal-losum in one direction or another. On this basis, the data of Thorson et al (131) suggest that the nasotemporal overlap in the human retina does not exceed 0°6'–0°7' of arc.

Richards (104, 105) has presented evidence that anomalous stereoscopic vision is rather more common in humans than generally appreciated. He shows that about 30% of a sample population, composed largely of university students, exhibit defective detection of crossed, uncrossed or near-zero disparities. About 20% of the observers were unable to detect two of the three disparity conditions. Richards concluded that human stereopsis depends on the presence of three classes of disparity detectors, corresponding to the categories of defects which he observed. One or more of these classes can be absent from one or both hemispheres. The data indicate that if one of the classes is absent from one hemisphere, midline stereopsis for that class is lost completely.

Receptive fields as spatial filters.— Another link between the coding properties of visual cortical neurons and psychophysical phenomena has been explored in an extensive series of studies by Campbell and his associates (23–27). Central to this work is the concept that pattern analysis in the visual system is achieved by mechanisms which behave like spatial filters exhibiting angular selectivity and limited bandwidth. This notion is important because it raises the possibility that Fourier methods, which have been applied previously to temporal processes in vision (see 44), may also be used to study mechanisms of spatial analysis.

The human visual system perceives a grating pattern when the contrast reaches a certain value which varies with the spatial frequency of the pattern. The curve describing this is the threshold contrast function and the reciprocals of its ordinate values form the contrast sensitivity function (23, 27, 112, 113). The latter curve gives the sensitivity of the visual system in the spatial frequency domain, and its Fourier transform, the line spread function, describes visual sensitivity in the spatial "distance" domain. By convoluting the line spread function with equations describing certain aperiodic patterns, Campbell et al (23) were able to predict the contrast sensitivity functions for the aperiodic patterns, at least over certain frequency ranges. This result, plus earlier observations by Campbell & Robson (27) using square, rectangular, and saw-tooth patterns, suggests that the visual system may exhibit linear behavior at threshold for relatively simple types of stimulus configurations and under well controlled conditions. It is important to note that the pivotal function, the contrast sensitivity curve, is itself dependent on several parameters of the viewing situation, including the field size, the average field luminance and the stability of the grating (27, 113). If the grating is stationary, for instance, the contrast sensitivity peaks at about 4–6 c/deg[1] (27), whereas, when the grating is changed in phase at 8 c/sec, sensitivity continues to rise for spatial frequencies below 4–6 c/deg (26, 112). This suggests that the generality of the Fourier approach may depend very much on the development of a contrast sensitivity function which reflects a wide range of dynamic and static viewing conditions.

[1] The spatial frequency of a grating is expressed as the number of complete cycles of the dark-light bar pattern per degree of visual angle (c/deg).

Blakemore & Campbell (15) have shown that the threshold sensitivity curve may be markedly depressed by adaptation to high contrast sinusoidal gratings and that the threshold elevation is limited to a narrow spectrum of frequencies centered on the adapting frequency. Adaptation to a high contrast square wave grating affects the sensitivity in the regions of the fundamental and the third harmonic components of the square wave, as predicted by theory. The adaptational effects show orientation selectivity and interocular transfer, pointing to the visual cortex as the site of interaction. Visual illusions resulting from such a frequency specific adaptation have been described (18, 20).

Evoked potentials, recorded from the occipital region of the human scalp are very sensitive to the contrast of a grating which is alternating in phase (15, 26, 43, 86, 103). The amplitude of a highly filtered time-locked cortical potential is linearly related to the log contrast and, from this relationship, the psychophysical threshold can be predicted (26). Adaptation experiments indicate a high degree of orientation specificity, such that evoked activity of a stimulus grating is little affected by an adapting grating differing in orientation by 15°. These experiments support the hypothesis that there are neurons in the human visual system which are highly selective for orientation and spatial frequency. Extending this hypothesis, Blakemore (13) argued that some binocular cortical cells may be sensitive to depth because their component monocular receptive fields are tuned to slightly different spatial frequencies. Such cells could respond preferentially to parallax induced size disparities in the retinal images of a solid object. Evidence is presented that vertical gratings of different spatial frequency, projected separately to each eye, produce the illusion of a single grating which slants away from the observer.

Angular and spatial selectivity of visual cells in the cat have been investigated with grating patterns similar to those used in the psychophysical work described above (24, 25). Lateral geniculate and cortical cells clearly exhibit preferences for certain spatial frequencies and orientations, as is predictable from the findings of Hubel & Wiesel (60, 61). Quantitative differences between orientation selectivity of cortical cells in the cat and psychophysical data in the human are interpreted as indicating fundamental differences in the orientation selective mechanisms of cat and human (24). It is not clear, though, how much such differences may have resulted from the use of stationary patterns in the human studies and moving gratings in the neurophysiological experiments. It is also somewhat puzzling that lateral geniculate cells exhibit higher cutoff frequencies than do cortical neurons (25). If fine pattern analysis is a cortical function, one would expect the neural mechanisms there to discriminate the higher harmonic content of the geniculo-striate input.

OPTIC TECTUM

An extensive review of work done prior to 1969 on the anatomy, physiology and function of the optic tectum and pretectum has been provided by

Sprague et al (123). Current thinking in this area is reflected in a symposium held in 1969 on subcortical visual systems (70), which dealt extensively with tectum and pretectum and other midbrain and thalamic regions. Two issues, which have received considerable attention in recent years, will be reviewed briefly here. These are (a) the possible role of specialized receptive fields in orienting movements and (b) the influence of the visual cortex on the superior colliculus.

Directional selectivity and orienting behavior.— Orienting movements aim teloreceptors at provocative stimuli. Since in most vertebrate species the primary teloreceptors are located on the head, movements of the head or of organs attached thereto constitute the principal orienting movements. It is well established that in many species electrical and chemical stimulation of the superior colliculus or optic tectum elicits behavior which resembles normal orienting responses (1, 3, 32, 36, 37, 111, 115, 117, 123). Conversely, destruction of these mesencephalic structures can lead to profound deficits in orienting behavior in certain animals (34, 36, 123, cf 2).

Movement is the stimulus *par excellence* for evoking visual orienting behavior. It is therefore not surprising to find in the visual system, and particularly in the tectum, neurons which are very sensitive to movement. A subclass of these movement sensitive neurons often respond best to stimuli moving in a particular direction and are said to be directional or directionally selective. The direction of motion giving the most vigorous response is called the preferred direction. The angular selectivity of directionally selective units varies considerably, such that some units have quite narrow directional requirements whereas others show only a general preference for movements with a given directional component. Although directional units represent a general response class, it is not known if they subserve the same function in all animals, or, indeed, if all directional units in a given species are part of a single functional system.

Clues to their role in certain animals may be found in the distribution of preferred directions with respect to the center of gaze or to areas of retina specialized for acute vision. The preferred directions of collicular receptive fields in the cat are, in general, directed away from the area centralis, such that the units are maximally excited by stimuli moving centrifugally with respect to the center of gaze (123, 126). Electrical stimulation of the collicular surface causes the eyes to deflect in the preferred direction of the majority of cells at the stimulus site (126). Thus, a target moving away from the center of gaze will trigger activity in a given collicular region and the same region, stimulated electrically, produces a movement which would swing the visual axis toward the moving object. Such responses strongly suggest that the system mediates a visual fixation reflex (1, 31).

Robinson (111) finds that collicular stimulation in unanesthetized rhesus monkeys produces conjugate contralateral saccades of direction and amplitude dependent solely on the stimulus site and independent of the initial position of the eyes. Continued stimulation elicits repeated saccades of the same direction and amplitude, separated by pauses of about 150 msec. Stimulation elicits the largest saccades from the caudal part of the colliculus and the smallest from the rostral part. Medial stimulus sites yield movements with upward components; lateral sites yield movements with downward components. Robinson suggests that the stimulation creates a phosphene in the monkey's visual field and triggers an oculomotor fixation response, which aims the fovea at the apparent location of the phosphene. The motor responses demonstrated in these experiments correlate very well with the retinotopic sensory maps described in the colliculi of the squirrel monkey (76) and owl monkey (79). Moreover, directionally selective cells in the colliculus of the squirrel monkey tend to have their preferred directions oriented away from the fovea, toward the periphery of the countralateral hemifield (76). The situation in the monkey would thus appear to parallel that in the cat.

Although a correlation does exist between electrically elicited eye movements and the distribution of preferred directions of directional fields in cat and monkey, important differences are reported for the character of the evoked eye movements. The stimulus site in the monkey is said to determine only the direction and amplitude of the saccadic movement (111), whereas the stimulus site in the cat appears to dictate the terminal position of the eye (67, 126). The latter observation has led some investigators to characterize the movements in the cat as "goal directed", implying that the motor map on the collicular surface is fixed with respect to the body (somatocentric) or head (craniocentric) and is independent of the visual axis (67, 126, 133). The motor responses in the monkey, on the other hand, appear to be based on a foveocentric map whose coordinates shift as the eyes move. Yet the retinotopic sensory maps on the colliculi of both cat and monkey are clearly determined by fixed anatomical projections. Movement of the eyes alone must shift the coordinates of this map relative to the body axis and head. If electrical or chemical stimulation of the superior colliculus produces the equivalent of a phosphene in the animal's visual field, this phosphene will always appear at a fixed distance from the center of vision, regardless of the position of the eyes. Continued stimulation should thus provoke successive orienting movements, as found by Robinson (111). However, Hyde & Eliasson (67) who studied eye movements evoked from the cat's tectum stated that "when the eyes had reached this [their terminal] position, they remained there as long as the stimulus continued" (67, p. 667). Results in the cat differed also in that the eye movements were slow and smooth, rather than ballistic. Virtually identical movements were produced by electrical stimulation of the midbrain tegmentum and the medulla oblongata. These differences suggest that Hyde & Eliasson were not stimulating the same system as Robinson, or were perhaps injecting their electrical stimuli at another point in the oculomotor command pathway, a point from which a fixed pattern of contraction was called forth in the extraocular muscles. These workers found their best stimulus points deep in the superior colliculus and, indeed, reported that only one in five collicular points yielded eye movements, and then only with long lasting stimuli (67). This contrasts markedly with Robinson's findings of ballistic eye movements at latencies of 20–30 msec from onset of stimulation (111).

Any discussion of this problem must consider the results of Apter (3), who combined local strychninization of the collicular surface with light stimulation to elicit oculomotor responses in the cat. After a crystal of strychnine was placed on the collicular surface, a flash of light provoked a deflection of the eyes to that point in the visual field related retinotopically to the treated collicular site. This lead Apter to the conclusion that "each small area of the superior colliculus is, therefore, responsible for movement of the eyes to a particular point in the visual field" (3, p. 76). Although this appears to support a cranio- or somatocentric motor map on the collicular surface, the results are in fact equally compatible with the findings and interpretations of Robinson (111). The cat's eyes, in Apter's study, always moved to the same position after a flash, but they did so each time from the position of rest. Thus, the movements were of the same amplitude and direction with each stimulation. Furthermore, when repeated flashes were given after the eyes had deflected to their "terminal position", the eyes deflected still further in the same direction. Although the displacements were small compared to the original movements, the phenomenon is qualitatively the same as that seen by Robinson (111).

So-called "goal directed" eye movements are also produced by electrical stimulation of the inferior colliculus in the cat (130). No correlation of final eye position and stimulus locus has been reported. The effective points in the inferior colliculus also excite cells in the deep layers of the superior colliculus (stratum intermedium and stratum profundum). These units respond to acoustic and visual stimulation and may show directional selectivity. Syka & Straschill (130) proposed that the eye movements accompanying orientation to auditory stimuli may be mediated by fibers from the inferior colliculus to the deep layers of the superior colliculus. A preliminary report by Wickelgren (136) also suggests close correlation between the auditory and visual responses of bimodal neurons of the deep strata of the superior colliculus.

The rabbit, which possesses directional retinal ganglion cells, presents a picture somewhat different from cat and monkey. The preferred axes of directionally selective neurons in the superior colliculi of this animal do not appear to be grouped according to location in the visual field (56, 87). One report, that preferred axes tend to point toward the center of the retina (116), has not been corroborated in other studies (56, 87). The retinal area specialized for acute vision, the "horizontal streak", is less circumscribed than the cat's area centralis and the monkey's fovea. The rabbit is said to exhibit poorly developed fixation reflexes (99), but stimulation of the superior colliculus elicits fixation-like deflections of head and eyes toward that part of the visual field corresponding to the stimulus site (115, 117). In addition, the ears are observed to turn toward the same region in predictable fashion.

Oyster & Barlow (98) have demonstrated that the preferred directions of on-off type directional units in the rabbit retina, while appearing to be scattered randomly over the visual field, are actually highly correlated with the directions of pull of the extraocular muscles. They suggest that these cells provide error signals via the superior colliculus to the extraocular muscles, whenever there is motion of a stimulus image with respect to the retina. Corrective eye movements then nullify the relative motion and fix the image somewhere on the extensive visual streak. The result is a slow pursuit or following motion of the eye (98, 99). Hoffman & Straschill (59) have proposed an analogous function for directionally selective units of the cat's superior colliculus.

A difficulty with this interpretation is that large numbers of directionally selective units have their receptive fields outside the cat's area centralis and the rabbit's visual streak. Indeed, Oyster (99) found a higher proportion of on-off type directional units in the peripheral retina than in the visual streak. If these units subserve an image stabilizing reflex, they would immobilize images in the peripheral retina as well as in the visual streak. This is clearly inconsistent with the organism's need to examine the provocative image with a retinal region specialized for acute vision. This consideration reinforces the suggestion, made earlier, that collicular directional units in the cat subserve fixation rather than following reflexes. The inconsistency is avoided in the rabbit if the following movements mediated by on-off type directional units are concerned not with stabilization of provocative stimuli, but with stabilization of the background. This mechanism would cooperate with vestibular reflexes to keep the retinal image of the visual background relatively stationary during movements of the head, which occur during hopping, chewing, etc. Under such conditions, the vital stimulus quality of movement would be reserved to objects actually moving relative to the background. Of course, background stabilization could never be perfect, because images of nearby objects sustain greater angular displacements during translatory head movements than do images of distant objects. It is reasonable to suppose that the nervous system could adjust for this, perhaps by stabilizing only that part of the background which is in focus and presumably under constant surveillance by the animal.

Directionally selective cells have been studied in the retinae and midbrains of several other species (49, 72, 92, 129, 149), but there are few reports of correlation between the disposition of preferred directions and visual function. One report linked directionally selective units in the pike retina to the maintenance of forward motion in a flowing stream (149). No directionally selective units have been found in the tectum of the frog (37, 47) and an earlier report (88) of directional units in the frog's optic nerve has not been confirmed (49). Nonetheless, the frog exhibits definite visual orienting responses (69), and Ewert's elegant experiments demonstrate that these behaviors may be evoked by electrical stimulation of points in the optic tectum (32–36). Such stimulation may elicit the entire sequence of prey-catching behavior in this animal. The direction of the orientation and snapping is again predictable from the retinotopic map on the collicular surface. The orienting component of the evoked behavior serves to bring the prey into the binocular region of the frog's visual field (32, 33, 36). Tectal areas representing this region receive inputs from both eyes, although only certain cells in the deeper layers are binocularly excited (45, 77). Binocular fixation appears to be important, since eliminating one eye may seriously hinder the attack sequence of the prey-catching behavior (32, cf 69).

This brief survey suggests that directionally selective units in the brainstem visual areas may have quite different functions in different animals. Those which do function in orienting behavior may mediate various types of responses. Visual orienting behavior may be prominent in certain animals, like the frog, in which the presence of directional units in optic nerve or tectum is in doubt.

Special properties of pretectal neurons.— The pretectal region of the midbrain receives a significant projection from the optic tract, and certain subdivisions of the area show a retinotopic organization (38, 58). Pretectal neurons in the cat may exhibit sustained responses to diffuse illumination, but the majority prefer moving stimuli and are often directionally selective (52, 127). Some of these cells, particularly those located in the deep pretectal nuclei and the nucleus of the posterior commissure, appear to respond selectively to objects moving toward or away from the animal (127). This "looming" or "receding" selectivity is not a function of the luminance or contrast of the target and does not require binocular viewing. Neurons responding to looming targets are also excited by expansion of a circular bright disc focused on the tangent screen, suggesting that the trigger feature for these cells is a centrifugal movement of borders or edges relative to the center of the receptive field. From this it follows that a true looming detector would exhibit different preferred directions of directional selectivity in different parts of its receptive field and that these would be oriented away from the field center. An analogous situation would exist for neurons signaling receding targets, except that the preferred directions would point toward the receptive field center. The receptive fields described by Straschill & Hoffmann (127) do not appear to fit this picture, but are reported to exhibit the same directional selectivity to movements in the frontal plane in all subunits of the receptive field, or they are not directional at all. The demonstration of different preferred directions within the receptive field is crucial to the argument that the cells are looming or receding object detectors, because there are conditions under which an ordinary directionally selective unit can behave as though it were performing these functions. Consider a unit selective for upward movement. An expanding disc, aligned so that only its upper border moves across the field, will cause the unit to discharge. A contracting disc, similarly situated, will cause a border to move in the null direction of the unit, resulting in inhibition or no response. Furthermore, since directional selectivity is often stronger in the central regions of the field than near the edges, slight misalignment of the disc and field could produce apparent selectivity for looming and receding figures, even when the disc image is entirely within the receptive field. The edge moving near the center would have a greater effect than the edge moving at the border of the field and the response to the central edge would dominate the total response. These considerations suggest that further experiments are needed to establish that a class of pretectal neurons unequivocally signal the approach or withdrawal of a stimulus object. It is evident that the discovery of such neurons would have important consequences for theories concerning the neural organization of vergence movements of the eyes, escape and pursuit behavior, and visually guided locomotion in general.

Unit responses and eye movements.— Wurtz & Goldberg (147) have identified a population of cells in the deeper layers of the monkey's superior colliculus which begin to discharge 10–150 msec in advance of saccadic eye movements, even when the animal is in the dark. Activity is most intense for movement toward the contralateral hemifield or for up and down movements. A most surprising finding is that these cells appear to be unresponsive to retinal stimulation. Certain neurons in the cat's superior colliculus also discharge during and sometimes slightly before spontaneous eye movements in light and darkness, but, in contrast to findings in the monkey, these units may be activated by patterned stimulation of the retina (128). The location of these cells in the cat's colliculus is not reported. Cells in the superior colliculus which discharge prior to or during saccades may lie in a motor pathway for eye movements of this type. However, as Wurtz & Goldberg have pointed out (147), a motor pathway from colliculus to oculomotor nuclei would necessarily involve intermediate stations because there appear to be no direct projections between these structures. In addition, the collicular cells often fire 150 msec ahead of eye movement, whereas cells of the third and sixth cranial nerves begin to fire only about 7 msec before detectable displacement of the eyes (46, 110, 119).

The origin of the presaccadic discharge in deep collicular cells is presently as mysterious as its destination. Two cortical regions with visual function, the frontal oculomotor areas and the occipital cortex, project to the superior colliculus (4, 48, 59, 75, 78, 83, 90–92, 123, 124), but do not appear from present evidence to be likely sources of the presaccadic discharge. Striate neurons do not fire prior to eye movements or during such movements made in the dark (145, 146). Cells in the frontal eye fields do discharge with eye movements executed in darkness, but the discharge never precedes the eye movement (9, 10). Other cortical visual areas also project to the superior colliculus (29, 30, 64, 148) but nothing is known about unit behavior in these regions during eye movement. It may be anticipated that continued application of single unit recording techniques in alert freely moving animals will reveal much more about the collicular presaccadic discharge and the role that it plays in oculomotor behavior.[2]

CORTICOTECTAL INTERACTIONS

It has long been recognized that mesencephalic and cortical visual areas are bound together by a prominent corticofugal projection. Anatomical studies indicate that the projection is retinotopic (123) and recent physiological analyses have confirmed this for area 17 of the squirrel monkey (75) and area 18 of the cat (90). The cells of origin of the projection fibers lie in cortical layers V and VI (48, 120, 132). Many neurons in the cat's superior colliculus respond to cortical shock with a short latency excitation followed by inhibition (59, 90, 91). The latencies of excitatory responses are comparable to those for antidromic invasion of cortical neurons from superior colliculus (53, 132), suggesting that the excitatory drive may be monosynaptic. The corticotectal excitatory influence summates with excitatory input from the optic tract (91, cf 59). The inhibitory effect, which is capable of blocking light evoked responses, responses to optic tract shock, or a second volley in the corticofugal projection, is also retinotopically organized and is best elicited from the cortical locus giving the largest excitatory response (91). These effects have not been demonstrated conclusively from area 17 of the cat.

Cells in superior colliculus which are driven or inhibited from area 18 of the cat are also responsive to retinal stimulation (59, 90, 91). This is not so for collicular cells driven from area 17 of the squirrel monkey (75). These neurons, which are located in the deeper layers of the colliculus, do not exhibit visual receptive fields and thus resemble collicular units in *Macaca mulatta*, described by Wurtz & Goldberg (147), which fire prior to saccadic eye movements. A possible anatomical basis for these findings is the observation that the retina projects weakly, if at all, to the anterior third of the superior colliculus in *Macaca mulatta*, whereas the corticotectal projection to this region is strong (54, 142). It is not clear, however, why retinal input would not be relayed effectively to the colliculus by the corticotectal projection.

Two functions have been suggested, so far, for the corticotectal projections. The descending axons may have a role in the oculomotor activity

[2] Wurtz and Goldberg (147) relate this presaccadic collicular activity to the "corollary discharge" theory of perceptual constancy during eye movements. It may also be involved in the phenomenon of saccadic suppression, which has received intense study in the past several years. A discussion of these issues is beyond the scope of the present review but the area is touched on in several articles listed in the bibliography (9, 10, 84, 106, 143, 146, 147).

produced by electrical stimulation of visual cortex and may thus participate in central control of eye movement (135). Circumstantial evidence for this is good, in that electrical stimulation of the collicular surface produces eye movements (111, 115, 117, 126) and stimulation of the cortex produces intense excitation of collicular neurons (56, 75, 90, 91). Studies by Spiegel & Scala (121) suggested that collicular ablation markedly reduced or abolished eye movements induced by occipital lobe stimulation, but these workers cautioned that the cortex may have suffered trauma during surgery. It is important to recognize, however, that demonstration of cortically induced eye movements after collicular ablation does not exclude participation of the corticotectal system in normal oculomotor function.

Since many neurons of the visual cortex are directionally selective, it has been suggested that the corticotectal projection mediates directional selectivity of neurons in the cat's superior colliculus (51, 137, 138). Ablation of the visual area, in the experiments of Wickelgren & Sterling (137, 138), markedly reduced the number of directionally selective units in the colliculus and also essentially abolished collicular excitation from the ipsilateral eye. Early studies bearing on this hypothesis have been reviewed elsewhere (89). Rizzolatti et al (108), in recent experiments which avoided the use of general anesthesia, did not find marked reduction of directionality and binocular activation following ablation of the visual cortex. Similar results were reported by Hoffmann & Straschill (59). These findings do not support the hypothesis that the cat's superior colliculus is totally dependent on cortical mechanisms for the elaboration of its directionally selective receptive fields.

Ablation of visual cortex does not abolish directionality of cells in the superior colliculi of rabbits (87) or ground squirrels (92). Because these animals possess directional units in the retina, there is no need to invoke central mechanisms in the organization of the directionally selective fields of the colliculi. Cortical ablation does, however, abolish hypercomplex responses in the colliculus of the ground squirrel (92), but not in the colliculus of the rabbit (87). This may not be as clear a difference as it first appears because different criteria were used in the two laboratories for the classification of hypercomplex units. Michael (92), following the usage of Hubel & Wiesel (61), described hypercomplex fields as those with excitatory and inhibitory zones having pronounced orientation and directional selectivities. The selectivity criterion for the inhibitory flanks is relaxed in the definition applied by Masland et al (87). A field is called hypercomplex if an inhibitory surround restricts the length of effective stimuli (see also 137). This generalization of the adjective "hypercomplex" clearly makes it applicable to many receptive fields which do not fit the original description of Hubel & Wiesel. It may be noted that collicular receptive fields, with the exception of those described by Michael in the ground squirrel (92), have little in common with cortical hypercomplex fields apart from directional selectivity and inhibitory surrounds. These so-called "hypercomplex" features are also found in retinal ganglion cells of the rabbit (49, 98, 99), pigeon (72), pike

(149) and ground squirrel (92), and at least one of the features is demonstrable in retinal ganglion cells of the goldfish (129) and frog (49, 88). The most prominent general characteristic of cortical hypercomplex cells, that of orientation specificity, has been demonstrated in collicular receptive fields of only one animal, the ground squirrel (92).

The prominence of the corticotectal projection in mammals strongly implies that cortical and tectal visual mechanisms do not function independently. This notion is reinforced by the finding that the central part of the visual field in the macaque monkey influences the superior colliculus largely through the corticotectal connection (54, 142). It is not yet clear what sorts of information flow from the visual cortex to the superior colliculus and what features of collicular unit activity reflect this influence. Limited evidence suggests that both retinotectal and corticotectal afferents have comparable effects on intrinsic collicular mechanisms in the cat (91), but the functional significance of these findings awaits discovery. The corticofugal system clearly provides the cortex with access to brainstem mechanisms implicated in the execution of oculomotor and other orienting behaviors. The system thus presents to the physiologist a splendid opportunity to study control functions of cortical areas customarily regarded as sensory in character.

LITERATURE CITED

1. Akert, K. 1949. Der visuelle Greifreflex. *Helv. Physiol. Pharmacol. Acta* 7:112–34

2. Anderson, K. V., Symmes, D. 1969. The superior colliculus and higher visual function in the monkey. *Brain Res.* 13:37–52

3. Apter, J. T. 1945. Eye movements following strychinization of the superior colliculus in cats. *J. Neurophysiol.* 8:73–78

4. Astruc, J. 1971. Corticofugal connections of area 8 (frontal eye field) in *Macaca mulatta. Brain Res.* In press

5. Berlucchi, G., Rizzolatti, G. 1968. Binocularly driven neurons in visual cortex of split chiasm cats. *Science* 159:308–10

6. Berlucchi, G., Gazzaniga, M. S., Rizzolatti, G. 1967. Microelectrode analysis of transfer of visual information by the corpus callosum. *Arch. Ital. Biol.* 105:583–596

7. Bishop, P. O. 1971. Neurophysiology of binocular single vision and stereopsis. In *Handbook of Sensory Physiology*, 7, ed. R. Jung, Berlin Heidelberg, New York: Springer. In press

8. Bishop, P. O., Henry, G. H. 1971. Spatial vision. *Ann. Rev. Psychol.* 22:119–60

9. Bizzi, E. 1968. Discharge of frontal eye field neurons during saccadic and following eye movements in unanesthetized monkeys. *Exp. Brain Res.* 6:69–80

10. Bizzi, E., Schiller, P. H. 1970. Single unit activity in the frontal eye fields of unanesthetized monkeys during eye and head movement. *Exp. Brain Res.* 10:151–58

11. Blakemore, C. 1969. Binocular depth discrimination and the nasotemporal division. *J. Physiol. London* 205:471–97

12. Blakemore, C. 1970. Binocular depth perception and the optic chiasm. *Vision Res.* 10:43–47

13. Blakemore, C. 1970. A new kind of stereoscopic vision. *Vision Res.* 10:1189–99

14. Blakemore, C. 1970. The representation of three-dimensional space in the cat's striate cortex. *J. Physiol. London* 209:155–78

15. Blakemore, C., Campbell, F. W. 1969. On the existence of neurons in the human visual system selectively sensitive to the orientation and size of retinal images. *J. Physiol. London* 203:237–60

16. Blakemore, C., Carpenter, R. H. S., Georgeson, M. A. 1970. Lateral

inhibition between orientation detectors in the human visual system. *Nature* 228:37–39

17. Blakemore, C., Cooper, G. F. 1970. Development of the brain depends on the visual environment. *Nature* 228:447–48

18. Blakemore, C., Nachmias, J. 1971. The orientation specificity of two visual after-effects. *J. Physiol. London* 213:157–74

19. Blakemore, C., Pettigrew, J. D. 1970. Eye dominance in the visual cortex. *Nature* 225:426–29

20. Blakemore, C., Sutton, P. 1969. Size adaptation: a new after-effect. *Science* 166:245–47

21. Bough, E. W. 1970. Steroscopic vision in the macaque monkey: a behavioral demonstration. *Nature* 225:42–44

22. Burns, B. D., Pritchard, R. 1971. Geometrical illusions and the responses of neurons in the cat's visual cortex to angle patterns. *J. Physiol. London* 213:599–616

23. Campbell, F. W., Carpenter, R. H. S., Levinson, J. Z. 1969. Visibility of aperiodic patterns compared with that of sinusoidal gratings. *J. Physiol. London* 204:283–98

24. Campbell, F. W., Cleland, B. G., Cooper, G. F., Enroth-Cugell, C. 1968. The angular selectivity of visual cortical cells to moving gratings. *J. Physiol. London* 198:237–50

25. Campbell, F. W., Cooper, G. F., Enroth-Cugell, C. 1969. The spatial selectivity of the visual cells of the cat. *J. Physiol. London* 203:223–35

26. Campbell, F. W., Maffei, L. 1970. Electrophysiological evidence for the existence of orientation and size detectors in the human visual system. *J. Physiol. London* 207:635–52

27. Campbell, F. W., Robson, J. G. 1968. Application of Fourier analysis to the visibility of gratings. *J. Physiol. London* 197:551–66

28. Dews, P. B., Wiesel, T. N. 1970. Consequences of monocular deprivation on visual behavior in kittens. *J. Physiol. London* 206:437–55

29. Dow, B. M., Dubner, R. 1969. Visual receptive fields and responses to movement in an association area of cat cerebral cortex. *J. Neurophysiol.* 32:773–84

30. Dow, B. M., Dubner, R. 1971. Single unit responses to moving visual stimuli in the middle suprasylvian gyrus of the cat. *J. Neurophysiol.* 34:47–55

31. Dreher, B., Zernicki, B. 1968. Visual fixation reflex: behavioral properties and neural mechanisms. *Acta Biol. Exp.* 29:359–83

32. Ewert, J.-P. 1967. Aktivierung der Verhaltensfolge beim Beutefang der Erdkröte (*Bufo bufo L.*) durch Elektrische Mittlehirnreizung. *Z. Vergleich. Physiol.* 54:455–81

33. Ewert, J.-P. 1967. Elektrische Reizung des retinalen Projektionsfeldes im Mittlehirn der Erdkröte (*Bufo bufo L.*). *Pfluegers Arch.* 295:90–98

34. Ewert, J.-P. 1968. Der Einfluss von Zwischenhirndefekten auf die Visuomotorik in Beute- und Fluchtverhalten der Erdkröte (*Bufo bufo L.*). *Z. Vergleich. Physiol.* 61:47–70

35. Ewert, J.-P. 1969. Das Beuteverhalten Zwischenhirndefekter Erdkröten (*Bufo bufo L.*) gegenüber bewegten und ruhenden visuellen Mustern. *Pfluegers Arch.* 306:210–18

36. Ewert, J.-P. 1970. Neural mechanisms of prey-catching and avoidance behavior in the toad (*Bufo bufo L.*). *Brain Behav. Evol.* 3:36–56

37. Ewert, J.-P., Borchers, H.-W. 1971. Reaktionscharakteristik von Neuronen aus dem Tectum opticum und Subtectum der Erdkröte *Bufo bufo* (L). *Z. Vergleich. Physiol.* 71:165–89

38. Feldon, S., Feldon, P., Kruger, L. 1970. Topography of the retinal projection upon the superior colliculus of the cat. *Vision Res.* 10:135–44

39. Fifkova, E. 1969. The effect of monocular deprivation on the synaptic contacts of the visual cortex. *J. Neurobiol.* 1:285–94

40. Fifkova, E. 1970. Changes in axosomatic synapses in the visual cortex of monocularly deprived rats. *J. Neurobiol.* 2:61–67

41. Fifkova, E. 1970. The effect of unilateral deprivation on visual centers in rats. *J. Comp. Neurol.* 140:431–38

42. Fifkova, E., Hassler, R. 1969. Quantitative morphological changes in visual centers in rats after unilateral deprivation. *J. Comp. Neurol.* 135:167–78

43. Fiorentini, A., Maffei, L. 1970. Electrophysiological evidence for disparity detectors in human visual system. *Science* 169:208–9

44. Fiorentini, A., Maffei, L. 1970. Transfer characteristics of excitation and inhibition in the human visual system. *J. Neurophysiol.* 33:285–92

45. Fite, K. 1969. Single unit analysis of

binocular neurons in the frog optic tectum. *Exp. Neurol.* 24:475–86

46. Fuchs, A. F., Luschei, E. S. 1970. Firing patterns of abducens neurons of alert monkeys in relationship to horizontal eye movements. *J. Neurophysiol.* 33:382–92

47. Gaze, R. M., Keating, M. J. 1970. Receptive field properties of single units from the visual projection to the ipsilateral tectum in the frog. *Quart. J. Exp. Physiol.* 55:143–52

48. Giolli, R. A., Guthrie, M. D. 1967. Organization of projections of visual areas I and II upon the superior colliculus and pretectal nuclei in the rabbit. *Brain Res.* 6:388–90

49. Grüsser, O.-J., Grüsser-Cornehls, U. 1969. Neurophysiologie des Bewegungsehens. *Ergeb. Physiol.* 61:178–265

50. Guillery, R. W., Stelzner, D. J. 1970. The differential effects of unilateral lid closure upon the monocular and binocular segments of the dorsal lateral geniculate nucleus in the cat. *J. Comp. Neurol.* 139:413–22

51. Harutiunian-Kozak, B., Kozak, W., Dec, K. 1970. Visually evoked potentials and single unit activity in the superior colliculus of the cat. *Acta Neurobiol. Exp.* 30:211–32

52. Harutiunian-Kozak, B., Kozak, W., Dec, K. 1970. Analysis of visually evoked activity in the pretectal region of the cat. *Acta Neurobiol. Exp.* 30:233–62

53. Hayashi, Y. 1969. Recurrent collateral inhibition of visual cortical cells projecting to superior colliculus in cats. *Vision Res.* 9:1367–80

54. Hendrickson, A., Wilson, M. E., Toyne, M. J. 1970. The distribution of optic nerve fibers in *Macaca mulatta*. *Brain Res.* 23:425–27

55. Henry, G. H., Bishop, P. O., Coombs, J. S. 1969. Inhibitory and subliminal excitatory receptive fields of simple units in cat striate cortex. *Vision Res.* 9:1289–96

56. Hill, R. M. 1966. Receptive field properties of the superior colliculus of the rabbit. *Nature* 211:1407–9

57. Hirsch, H. V. B., Spinelli, D. N. 1970. Visual experience modifies distribution of horizontally and vertically oriented receptive fields in cats. *Science* 168:869–71

58. Hoffmann, K.-P. 1970. Retinotopische Beziehungen und Struktur rezeptiver Felder im Tectum opticum und Praetectum der Katze. *Z. Vergleich. Physiol.* 67:26–57

59. Hoffmann, K.-P., Straschill, M. 1971. Influences of cortico-tectal and intertectal connections on visual responses in the cat's superior colliculus. *Exp. Brain Res.* 12:120–31

60. Hubel, D. H., Wiesel, T. N. 1962. Receptive fields, binocular interaction and functional architecture in cat's visual cortex. *J. Physiol. London* 160:106–54

61. Hubel, D. H., Wiesel, T. N. 1965. Receptive fields and functional architecture in two non-striate visual areas (18 and 19) of the cat. *J. Neurophysiol.* 28:229–89

62. Hubel, D. H., Wiesel, T. N. 1967. Cortical and callosal connections concerned with the vertical meridian of visual fields in the cat. *J. Neurophysiol.* 30:1561–73

63. Hubel, D. H., Wiesel, T. N. 1968. Receptive fields and functional architecture of monkey striate cortex. *J. Physiol. London* 195:215–43

64. Hubel, D. H., Wiesel, T. N. 1969. Visual area of the lateral suprasylvian gyrus (Clare-Bishop Area) of the cat. *J. Physiol. London* 202:251–60

65. Hubel, D. H., Wiesel, T. N. 1970. The period of susceptibility to the physiological effects of unilateral eye closure in kittens. *J. Physiol. London* 206:419–36

66. Hubel, D. H., Wiesel, T. N. 1970. Cells sensitive to binocular depth in area 18 of the macaque monkey cortex. *Nature* 225:41–42

67. Hyde, J. E., Eliasson, S. E. 1957. Brainstem induced eye movements in cats. *J. Comp. Neurol.* 108:139–72

68. Imbert, M. 1970. Aspects récents de la physiologie des voies visuelles primaires chez les vertébrés. *J. Physiol. Paris* 62:Suppl. 1, 3–59

69. Ingle, D. 1970. Visuomotor functions of the frog optic tectum. *Brain Behav. Evol.* 3:57–71

70. Ingle, D., Schneider, G. E. Eds. 1970. Subcortical Visual Systems. *Brain Behav. Evol.* 3:1–352

71. Jacobs, G. H. 1969. Receptive fields in visual systems. *Brain Res.* 14:553–73

72. Jassik-Gerschenfeld, D., Minois, F. Condé-Courtine, F. 1970. Receptive field properties of directionally selective units in the pigeon's tectum opticum. *Brain Res.* 24:407–21

73. Joshua, D. E., Bishop, P. O. 1970. Binocular single vision and depth

discrimination. Receptive field disparities for central and peripheral vision and binocular interactions on peripheral single units in cat striate cortex. *Exp. Brain Res.* 10: 389–416

74. Jones, B. H. 1970. Responses of single neurons in cat visual cortex to a simple and a more complex stimulus. *Am. J. Physiol.* 218:1102–7

75. Kadoya, S., Massopust, L. C., Jr., Wolin, L. R. 1971. Striate cortex-superior colliculus projection in squirrel monkey. *Exp. Neurol.* 32: 98–110

76. Kadoya, S., Wolin, L. R., Massopust, L. C., Jr. 1971. Photically evoked unit activity in the tectum opticum of the squirrel monkey. *J. Comp. Neurol.* 142:495–508

77. Keating, M. J., Gaze, R. M. 1970. The ipsilateral retinotectal pathway in the frog. *Quart. J. Exp. Physiol.* 55:284–92

78. Kuypers, H. G. J. M., Lawrence, D. G. 1967. Cortical projections to the red nucleus and the brainstem in the rhesus monkey. *Brain Res.* 4: 151–88

79. Lane, R. H., Allman, J. M., Kaas, J. H., Miezeu, F. M., Woolsey, C. N. 1971. The representation of the visual field in the superior colliculus of the owl monkey (*Aotus trivirgatus*). *Fed. Proc.* 30:615

80. Lee, B. B. 1970. Effect of anaesthetics upon visual responses of neurons in the cat's striate cortex. *J. Physiol. London* 207:74–75P

81. Leibovic, K. N., Balslev, E., Mathieson, T. 1970. Binocular space and its representation by cellular assemblies in the brain. *J. Theor. Biol.* 28:513–30

82. Leibovic, K. N., Balslev, E., Mathieson, T. A. 1971. Binocular vision and pattern recognition. *Kybernetik* 8:14–23

83. Lund, R. D. 1969. Synaptic patterns of the superficial layers of the superior colliculus of the rat. *J. Comp. Neurol.* 135:179–208

84. MacKay, D. M. 1970. Elevation of visual threshold by displacement of retinal image. *Nature* 225:90–92

85. MacKay, D. M. 1970. Interocular transfer of suppressive effects of retinal image displacement. *Nature* 225:872–73

86. Maffei, L., Campbell, F. W. 1970. Neurophysiological localization of the vertical and horizontal visual

coordinates in man. *Science* 167: 386–87

87. Masland, R. H., Chow, K. L., Stewart, D. L. 1971. Receptive field characteristics of superior colliculus neurons in the rabbit. *J. Neurophysiol.* 34:148–56

88. Maturana, H. R., Lettvin, J. Y., McCulloch, W. S., Pitts, W. H. 1960. Anatomy and physiology of vision in the frog. *J. Gen. Physiol.* 43 (part 2):129–75

89. McIlwain, J. T. 1970. Cortical origin of collicular directional selectivity in the cat. A review of the evidence. *Brain Behav. Evol.* 3:129–221

90. McIlwain, J. T., Fields, H. L. 1970. Superior colliculus: single unit responses to stimulation of visual cortex in the cat. *Science* 170:1426–28

91. McIlwain, J. T., Fields, H. L. 1971. Interaction of cortical and retinal projections on single neurons of the cats superior colliculus. *J. Neurophysiol.* In press

92. Michael, C. R. 1970. Integration of retinal and cortical information in the superior colliculus of the ground squirrel. *Brain Behav. Evol.* 3:205–9

93. Mitchell, D. E., Blakemore, C. 1970. Binocular depth perception and the corpus callosum. *Vision Res.* 10: 49–54

94. Motokawa, K. 1970. *Physiology of Color and Pattern Vision.* Tokyo: Igaku Shoin, Ltd. and Berlin, Heidelberg, New York: Springer. 283 pp.

95. Nikara, T., Bishop, P. O., Pettigrew, J. D. 1968. Analysis of retinal correspondence by studying receptive fields of binocular single units in cat striate cortex. *Exp. Brain Res.* 6:353–72

96. von Noorden, G. K., Dowling, J. E., Ferguson, D. C. 1970. Experimental amblyopia in monkeys. I. Behavioral studies of stimulus deprivation amblyopia. *Arch. Opthalmol.* 84: 206–14

97. Ogle, K. N. 1950. *Binocular Vision.* Philadelphia & London: Saunders. 345 pp.

98. Oyster, C. W., Barlow, H. B. 1967. Direction-selective units in rabbit retina: distribution of preferred directions. *Science* 155:841–42

99. Oyster, C. W. 1968. The analysis of image motion by the rabbit retina. *J. Physiol. London* 199:613–35

100. Pettigrew, J. D. 1965. *Binocular Interaction on Single Units of the*

Striate Cortex of the Cat. B.Sc. (Med.) thesis. University of Sydney, Australia

101. Pettigrew, J. D., Nikara, T., Bishop, P. O. 1968. Responses to moving slits by single units in cat striate cortex. *Exp. Brain Res.* 6:373–90

102. Pettigrew, J. D., Nikara, T., Bishop, P. O. 1968. Binocular interaction on single units in cat striate cortex: simultaneous stimulation by single moving slit with receptive fields in correspondence. *Exp. Brain Res.* 6:391–410

103. Regan, D., Spekreijse, H. 1970. Electrophysiological correlates of binocular depth perception in man. *Nature* 225:92–94

104. Richards, W. 1970. Stereopsis and stereoblindness. *Exp. Brain Res.* 10:380–88

105. Richards, W. 1971. Anomalous stereoscopic depth perception. *J. Opt. Soc. Amer.* 61:410–14

106. Riggs, L. A., Wooten, B. L. 1971. Electrical measures and psychophysical data on human vision. In *Handbook of Sensory Physiology*, 7, ed. L. M. Hurvich and D. Jameson. Berlin, Heidelberg, New York: Springer. In press

107. Ripps, H., Weale, R. A. 1969. Color vision. *Ann. Rev. Psychol.* 20:193–216

108. Rizzolatti, G., Tradardi, V., Camarda, R. 1970. Unit responses to visual stimuli in the cat's superior colliculus after removal of the visual cortex. *Brain Res.* 24:336–39

109. Robertson, A. D. J. 1965. Anaesthesia and receptive fields. *Nature* 205:80

110. Robinson, D. A. 1970. Oculomotor unit behavior in the monkey. *J. Neurophysiol.* 33:393–404

111. Robinson, D. A. 1971. *Eye Movements Evoked by Superior Colliculus Stimulation in the Alert Monkey.* Presented before the Association for Research in Vision and Opthalmology, Sarasota, Florida

112. Robson, J. G. 1966. Spatial and temporal contrast sensitivity functions of the visual system. *J. Opt. Soc. Amer.* 56:1141–42

113. Robson, J. G., Campbell, F. W. 1964. A threshold contrast function for the visual system. *Symposium on the Physiological Basis of Form Discrimination*, 44–48. Providence: Hunter Laboratory of Psychology, Brown University

114. Sanderson, K. J., Darian-Smith, I.,

115. Schaefer, K.-P. 1970. Unit analysis and electrical stimulation in the optic tectum of rabbits and cats. *Brain, Behav. Evol.* 3:222–40

116. Schaefer, K.-P. 1966. Mikroableitungen in Tectum opticum des freibeweglichen Kaninchens. *Arch. Psychiat. Nervenkr.* 208:120–46

117. Schaefer, K.-P., Schneider, H. 1968. Reizversuche im Tectum opticum des Kaninchens. *Arch. Psychiat. Nervenkr.* 211:118–37

118. Shipley, T., Rawlings, S. C. 1970. The nonius horopter. I. History and theory. *Vision Res.* 10:1225–62

119. Schiller, P. H. 1970. The discharge characteristics of single units in the oculomotor and abducens nuclei of the unanesthetized monkey. *Exp. Brain Res.* 10:347–62

120. Spatz, W. B., Tigges, J., Tigges, M. 1970. Subcortical projections, cortical associations and some intrinsic interlaminar connections of the striate cortex in the squirrel monkey (*Saimiri*). *J. Comp. Neurol.* 140:155–74

121. Spiegel, E. A., Scala, N. P. 1937. Ocular disturbances associated with experimental lesions of the mesencephalic gray matter. *Arch. Ophthalmol.* 18:614–32

122. Spinelli. D. N., Barrett, T. W. 1969. Visual receptive field organization of single units in the cat's visual cortex. *Exp. Neurol.* 24:76–98

123. Sprague, J. M., Berlucchi, G., Rizzolatti, G. 1971. The role of the superior colliculus and pretectum in vision and visually guided behavior. In *Handbook of Sensory Physiology*, 7, ed. R. Jung. Berlin, Heidelberg, New York: Springer. In press

124. Sterling, P. 1971. Receptive fields and synaptic organization of the superficial gray layer of the cat superior colliculus. *Vision Res.* In press

125. Stone, J. 1966. The nasotemporal division of the cat's retina. *J. Comp. Neurol.* 126:595–99

126. Straschill, M., Hoffmann, K.-P. 1968. Functional aspects of localization in the cat's tectum opticum. *Brain Res.* 13:274–83

127. Straschill, M., Hoffmann, K.-P. 1969. Response characteristics of movement detecting neurons in the

pretectal region of the cat. *Exp. Neurol.* 25:165–76

128. Straschill, M., Hoffmann, K.-P. 1970. Activity of movement sensitive neurons of the cat's tectum opticum during spontaneous eye movements. *Exp. Brain Res.* 11:318–26

129. Sutterlin, A. M., Prosser, C. L. 1970. Electrical properties of goldfish optic tectum. *J. Neurophysiol.* 33:36–45

130. Syka, J., Straschill, M. 1970. Activation of superior colliculus neurons and motor responses after electrical stimulation of the inferior colliculus. *Exp. Neurol.* 28:384–92

131. Thorson, J., Lange, G. D., Biederman-Thorson, M. 1969. Objective measurement of the dynamics of a visual movement illusion. *Science* 164:1087–88

132. Toyama, K., Matsunami, K., Ohno, T. 1969. Antidromic identification of association, commissural and corticofugal efferent cells in cat visual cortex. *Brain Res.* 14:513–17

133. Trevarthen, C. B. 1968. Two mechanisms of vision in primates. *Psychol. Forsch.* 31:299–337

134. Westheimer, G., Mitchell, D. E. 1969. The sensory stimulus for disjunctive eye movements. *Vision Res.* 9:749–55

135. Whitteridge, D. 1960. Central control of eye movements. In *Handbook of Physiology*, ed. J. Field, Vol. 2, 1089–1109, Washington, DC: American Physiological Society

136. Wickelgren, B. G. 1971. Bimodal responses of cells in the cat superior colliculus. *Fed. Proc.* 30:615

137. Wickelgren, B. G., Sterling, P. 1969. Influence of visual cortex on receptive fields in the superior colliculus of the cat. *J. Neurophysiol.* 32:16–23

138. Wickelgren, B. G., Sterling, P. 1969. Effect on the superior colliculus of cortical removal in visually deprived cats. *Nature* 224:1032–33

139. Wiesel, T. N., Hubel, D. H. 1965. Effects of visual deprivation on morphology and physiology of cells in the cat's lateral geniculate body. *J. Neurophysiol.* 26:978–93

140. Wiesel, T. N., Hubel, D. H. 1965. Comparison of the effects of unilateral and bilateral eye closure on cortical unit responses in kittens. *J. Neurophysiol.* 28:1029–40

141. Wiesel, T. N., Hubel, D. H. 1965. Extent of recovery from the effects of visual deprivation in kittens. *J. Neurophysiol.* 28:1060–72

142. Wilson, M. E., Toyne, M. J. 1970. Retinotectal and corticotectal projections in *Macaca mulatta*. *Brain Res.* 24:395–406

143. Wurtz, R. H. 1968. Visual cortex neurons: response to stimuli during rapid eye movements. *Science* 162:1148–50

144. Wurtz, R. H. 1969. Visual receptive fields of striate cortex neurons in awake monkeys. *J. Neurophysiol.* 32:727–42

145. Wurtz, R. H. 1969. Response of striate cortex neurons to stimuli during rapid eye movements in the monkey. *J. Neurophysiol.* 32:975–86

146. Wurtz, R. H. 1969. Comparison of effects of eye movements and stimulus movements on striate cortex neurons of the monkey. *J. Neurophysiol.* 32:987–94

147. Wurtz, R. H., Goldberg, M. E. 1971. Superior colliculus cell responses related to eye movements in awake monkey. *Science* 171:82–84

148. Wright, M. J. 1969. Visual receptive fields of cells in a cortical area remote from the striate cortex of the cat. *Nature* 223:973–75

149. Zenkin, G. M., Pigarev, I. N. 1969. Detector properties of ganglion cells of the pike retina. *Biophysics* 14:763–72

SOMATOSENSORY PATHWAYS

Patrick D. Wall

M.R.C. Cerebral Functions Research Group, University College, London

Ronald Dubner

*Neural Mechanisms Section, National Institute of Dental Research,
Bethesda, Maryland*

All reviews are selective: here, we have chosen to concentrate on some of the recent points of interest in somatosensory afferent systems. The reader is warned that one of the authors is naturally biased in favor of his own survey on the dorsal columns (111). However a more traditional and comprehensive review on this subject is available (85).

GENERAL SCHEMES FOR AFFERENT SYSTEMS

Each succeeding *Annual Review* tends to define the nervous system in terms of more and more specific subdivisions. The intention of this progression is to identify and study the ultimate and indivisible particles whose reconstitution forms the entire system. This search for elementary particles is the most respectable of scientific analytic tactics; final success nevertheless depends on selecting the correct elemental categories. The history of science shows many examples of considerable progress in analysis based on categories which eventually became non-productive. Generations of men at least as clever as we are developed an elaborate technology and, in that sense, an understanding of materials based on the categories of earth, air, fire, and water. Generations of neurophysiologists have also developed categories, each based on a model of the way the system is assumed to operate; the justification and usefulness of these categories, stated or implicit in previous work, are now being questioned.

What are these categories in which the organization and function of afferent systems are described? First, there are the categories of origin, as implied in the names of the cutaneous, proprioceptive, and visceral afferent systems. Within these there are subdivisions which may depend either on morphologically recognizable end organs such as muscle spindles, Golgi tendon organs, and Pacinian corpuscles, or on physiologically recognizable axons such as nociceptors, heat detectors, and cold detectors. No one now doubts the existence of these structures and functions as described, although there remain the questions whether all the morphological types are fundamentally different from each other—especially, whether the physiological

315

groups are genuinely separate or artificially separated from a continuum by stimulus selection. For example, Burgess & Perl have described nociceptive afferents (15) and Christensen & Perl have described dorsal horn cells in lamina I, which respond only to these nociceptive afferents (25). There is, however, no evidence whether these afferent and first central cells are an inherently separate group or whether they are simply the highest threshold members of a continuous spectrum separated from their lower threshold mates by the arbitrary choice of particular stimuli. This can be decided by experiment with graded rather than stepped variations of stimulus intensity.

A much more fundamental question is whether subsequent transmission through the CNS should be studied on the basis of origin of the afferent impulse. This is in fact the classical approach (79). The greatest encouragement for this approach is the existence of the lemniscal pathways which contain elements transmitting information from single types of peripheral receptors. All the other pathways carry mixed information, with greater or lesser deviation from the extreme specificity of the dorsal column medial lemniscus system $(DCMLS)$. There are basically three theories concerning these convergent pathways. One is that they feed information to destinations which are not concerned with highly discriminative sensation (38). Another theory is that these pathways can be ordered back into the role of transmitting some relatively specific information by the action of descending control (13, 51, 110). The third is that specific information is still present in the pathways but recorded within the spatial and temporal pattern of impulses (74). The question is whether the brain receives identical or equivalent information over the multiple parallel pathways.

The second set of categories into which models of afferent systems are subdivided are those of the destination of the afferent fibers. Here we speak of flexor reflex afferents, cerebellar afferents, cortical projection pathways, etc. Sometimes such a label is given simply for experimental convenience; no implication is intended, for example, that a pathway directed toward the cerebellum does not also feed into other systems. However, the textbooks continue to separate the systems by destination, often without a trace of evidence. A special model of the destination category even links the origin and destination category types of model: this is specificity theory in full bloom. Here, the origin is in modality specific groups of afferent fibers, and the destination is in the cortex with cells triggering particular sensations.

Recent spectacular demonstrations of the outcome of this way of thinking have come from Mountcastle's group (103), who equate the actual perception of vibration with the consequences of activity in two sets of peripheral afferents and in thalamic and cortical neurons. It is important when considering this type of demonstration to dissect the stages of the argument. First, it is obvious that whatever may be the central mechanisms of perception, they will be dependent on information received from the periphery and therefore cannot begin to operate until the threshold of the peripheral detectors is overcome. Therefore, the psychophysical threshold must be subservient to the threshold of the end organs.

Next, the demonstration of a correlation between the stimulus intensity, the activity in one system, and the psychological response does not prove the existence of a causally linked chain, especially when a number of parallel systems are known to exist. This statement in no way denies the truth of the elegant observations. A start has to be made somewhere, and a single, simple threshold stimulus affecting known detectors and a known pathway has been fully justified by their work—provided no one concludes that the results establish the unique origin of the nervous activity on which conscious sensation is based.

This brings us to the last area of consideration for these experiments. No one doubts that the relation between the stimulus and the psychological response is grossly shifted by the presence of other external stimuli and shifts in attention. There is now an open question about the mechanism producing this change in stimulus-response relationship. It might be that unadulterated information continues to arrive at the cortex and then flows to some unidentified structure where decisions are made about the relevant perceptual response in the face of all stimuli. An alternative to this straight line model (which is first specific and then mixed) would be a model in which sensation depends on information from those pathways where mixing and control begin at the first synapse. The function of the DCMLS would then be to control the action of convergent pathways rather than to feed directly into conscious sensory mechanisms. The reason for stressing the alternatives is that experiments must continue both to obtain information about the specific inputs and about convergence and control, for there is no evidence that either system monopolizes the information which leads to discriminating perception.

Beyond the fixed action models, various dynamic systems have been suggested which take into account both the excitatory and inhibitory interactions of arriving afferents and also the action of descending controls. The gate control theory (74) is an example. Another is the system developed by Lundberg and his co-workers (67). They first described chains of interneurons that connect afferents to motoneurons to generate segmental reflexes. They next showed how these interneurons are influenced both by arriving afferent impulses and by descending controls. Finally, they proposed afferent systems that report to the brain the firing pattern of each stage of the neuronal chain connecting segmental inputs and outputs.

Dynamic models in which the properties of afferent systems shift under different circumstances will develop inevitably in two directions. In one model, the qualitative nature of the input and output will remain fixed but the gain will vary under the effect of facilitation or inhibition. In a nonlinear system, gain variation can lead to quite complex results. If a cell which is bombarded by several different types of afferents is inhibited, it may become responsive only to the most powerful type of afferent (13), and thereby adopt a specific role. Similarly, general inhibition may restrict receptive field size (110), or may bring out the existence of an inhibitory surround (51), or may allow the demonstration of habituation (52). In the other dynamic model, the emphasis will be on switching systems in which selectivity is achieved by independent control of different components in convergent systems. An example has been shown in lamina VI of the spinal cord, where a cell responds best to a proprioceptive input in the decerebrate state, but in the spinal state the same cell will respond preferentially to a cutaneous input (110). If such switching controls are widespread then the possibility emerges that the so-called nonspecific afferent systems may on occasion be ordered to transmit only specified information. These schemes suggest the controlled and variable origin of information in afferent systems. To complete the symmetry, schemes are also being developed in which the destination is also under control. As with origin control, the simplest method of destination control would be overall threshold control of selected destinations. This is the suggestion of the gate control theory (74), in which it is proposed that firing in a particular pathway above a selected frequency will overcome the threshold of a receptor system that triggers pain reactions. Subtler signs of destination control appear in the work of Freeman (42) on cerebellar cells; these respond to all types of afferents, but if somatosensory cortex is made active they respond preferentially to somatic inputs, and if auditory cortex is made active they respond best to auditory inputs.

We have presented a family of general schemes for afferent systems. Let us now see how they apply to certain particular examples.

DORSAL ROOTS

Dermatomes are the sensory behavioral reflection of the collection of afferent fibers into segmental root bundles—an origin categorization. Perhaps the most startling and certainly the simplest experiments of the year have been the repetition of the Turck-Sherringtonian method of defining a dermatome by leaving one dorsal root intact while cutting two roots rostral and two roots caudal, and then testing the cutaneous area of sensitivity (32, 58). The expected results were observed, but when the rhizotomies were extended further and further from the intact root, it was found that, with each additional root sectioned, the dermatome shrank further. This surprising result could mean that the edges of the dermatome are defined by the activity of afferent fibers that pass into the cord over roots far removed from the main root of that dermatome. Alternatively, the result could mean that neighboring roots carry impulses that maintain the excitatory state of cord cells at a level sufficiently high to allow them to respond to impulses arriving over one particular root. This latter explanation seems to be the case because it was shown that the restricted dermatome expanded to its full extent when the lateral Lissauer tract was sectioned immediately caudal to the intact root. Other work (32, 97) suggests that there may be similar excitability control mechanisms within the trigeminal nucleus and these may explain the facial analgesia which follows section of the descending trigeminal tract. This Sjoqvist operation was not understandable on the basis of section of any known afferent fibers (113).

The lateral Lissauer tract interconnects parts of the substantia gelatinosa (102). Its section has been shown to eliminate the intersegmental spread of primary afferent depolarization and dorsal root potentials (109). Therefore, part of the dermatome control may be through presynaptic mechanisms. Much work continues on this subject. Glia have been suggested as origins of certain prolonged electrical disturbances in cord (7, 101). A new type of cell has been described which projects from lamina III to lamina II (91). A lively debate continues concerning the existence of positive dorsal root potentials and the presumed consequence of presynaptic facilitation. A number of papers have appeared showing that under specific experimental conditions, when small fibers afferent barrages were generated, either by selective blockade of peripheral nerves or by selective stimulation, negative dorsal root potentials (DRPs) were produced, (17, 41, 119). The suggestion that these findings denied the gate control theory of pain (119) was incorrect, since this theory does not depend on the existence of presynaptic rather than postsynaptic control (74). Despite these negative results, others have since found that selective block did lead to positive DRPs (31), that group III muscle produced positive DRPs (75), that certain A delta trigeminal afferents became hyperpolarized after the arrival of volleys over other trigeminal fibers (99), and that brain stem stimulation produced positive DRPs (20, 21, 24). The mechanism for this hyperpolarization remains unknown, but the simplest suggestion is that it is the inhibition of a tonic depolarization of terminals. This tonic depolarization would, in turn, depend on the tonic activity of cord cells and would therefore require for its appearance cord firing levels which may not be achieved in many preparations. Clearly this issue, with its implications for positive as well as negative influences on arriving afferent impulses, will continue to be of interest.

DORSAL COLUMNS

The generally accepted view of discriminative somatosensory mechanisms is based upon the dorsal columns. Sherrington's (100) early cautions about the sensory role of dorsal columns do not appear in more recent literature (85). In the present questioning mood, it is not surprising that the foundations of the classical columned edifice need further inspection. Descriptions of the Acropolis are still published without questioning its role in Athenian society. Similarly, descriptions of the DCMLS continue to appear. Although they are correct in architectural detail and in historical analysis, questions arise concerning functional domination. The great bulk af the DCMLS is characterised by three factors: evolutionary growth, maps, and specificity. We can take one set of examples from the year's literature concerned with mapping this system. Whitsel et al (116) have shown by both anatomical and physiological techniques in the squirrel monkey that lumbar dorsal roots project into the fasciculus gracilis and gradually rearrange themselves —so that by the time they reach cervical levels they resemble the map of the hind limb areas in cortical areas SI and SII.

In the thalamus, Cabral & Johnson (19) have continued their beautiful comparative studies of mammals from rat to primates and have shown for various species the details of mapping in the ventral posterior lateral nucleus (*VPL*). In the raccoon, for example, individual fingers monopolize special areas of *VPL* (114). This analysis has been extended to the mouse cortex, where Woolsey and van der Loos (117) showed that anatomically recognizable "barrels" of cells exist in SI cortex, each barrel concerned with a single whisker. This spectacular spatial separation within the DCMLS is matched by equally convincing physiological separation (103). Little wonder that all this mass of evolutionary, anatomical, and physiological data should reinforce the view that discriminative sensation depends on the DCMLS. The clinicians therefore teach the signs and symptoms of dorsal column disease, i.e. loss of vibration sensitivity, weight discrimination, touch sensitivity, two point discrimination, roughness discrimination, and stereognosis. In spite of this dogma, we find Sherrington writing in 1900, "Observations . . . find special difficulty in regard to the quality of the long dorsal column path. Its severance has in various hands, and practised at various levels, made no striking alterations at all either in movement or in signs interpretable of sensation" (100).

SECTION OF DORSAL COLUMNS

Sensory effects.—A review of the recent literature (111) shows that Sherrington's "special difficulty" has been greatly amplified in this century. Studies on various species from rat to man report the effects of the section dorsal column at various levels. The following sensory tasks have been tested: weight discrimination in monkeys (33, 34), conditioned forelimb flexion on touch to dogs' hind limbs (83), tactile placing in monkey hind limbs (26), cutaneous stimulus location in cats (35), limb position in monkeys (108), two point discrimination in monkeys (64), vibration in monkeys (96) and standard neurological tests in man (27, 90). All these reports agree that the ability to perform these various tasks survives dorsal column section.

Two particularly interesting papers have recently appeared on the subject. Tapper (104) has trained cats to respond by forelimb movement to graded pressure stimuli applied to a single touch corpuscle on the hind limb. In this way the behavioral threshold of the animal can be compared with the known physiological threshold of axons innervating touch corpuscles. Having established the threshold, Tapper then cut dorsal columns and showed that the animal's behavioral threshold, if anything, improved. In this particular case, the explanation may be that this type of afferent fiber does not travel in dorsal columns (85). In a most important experiment,

Dobrey & Casey (37) first showed, as in previous work (59), that pretrained cats with extensive (67–100%) lesions of dorsal columns failed to show any deficit in discrimination for roughness. They next showed that cats with up to 85% of their dorsal columns destroyed learned the most difficult discrimination just as fast as did controls. However, two cats—one with 97% destruction and the other with 100% destruction—failed to meet the performance criterion on more difficult discrimination tests when trained only postoperatively, although it had been shown that such tasks could be performed by animals who had been trained preoperatively.

This long list of negative findings is particularly surprising when one considers the nature of the fibers sectioned in the operations. The largest component, which increases in size with increasing evolutionary complexity, are the collaterals of large myelinated peripheral afferents that terminate on the dorsal column nuclei. In addition, column section will carry out a partial rhizotomy of roots close to the section. Propriospinal fibers will be cut (81). Depending on the level of section, muscle afferents destined for either Clarke's column or the external cuneate nucleus may be cut. The dorsal columns also contain afferents to the brain which originate in spinal grey matter (81, 107). Structures other than dorsal column nuclei receive afferents over dorsal columns (77). Finally, it should not be forgotten that descending fibers also run in dorsal columns (39, 57) and in some species even the pyramidal tract is contained in them (118).

A further problem has been noted by Levitt & Levitt (63). Complete destruction of the dorsal columns is likely to damage fibers in the dorsolateral fasciculus which certainly contains important afferent pathways. Clearly the completeness of the dorsal column section is of great importance in assessing the results. Since the fibers in the dorsal column have a striking spatial pattern (116), partial sections may completely deafferent certain regions, but the behavioral consequences of this might require very special tests just as a visual scotoma can easily be missed by both patient and examiner.

Can redundancy explain the negative results of dorsal column section?— Redundancy is a powerful word thrown rather carelessly into biological arguments to "explain" the lack of effect of partial destruction of a system. Here the word can have a number of entirely different meanings:

A. *Multiplicity of cues in the stimulus.* The stimulus may contain a multiplicity of cues which allow its identification by different tactics. The identification of coins is a common test in the clinic. The patient may adopt a passive attitude to the stimulus of a coin placed in his hand, trying to identify it without exploration, in which case he may measure weight, area, or temperature change. Or, he may actively ask questions of the object by exploratory movements to measure inertia, texture, pattern, etc. One patient with severe astereognosis was seen to identify coins by running his finger nail around the edges while listening for the noise. At the extreme, one can always take the coin to the Mint and ask an official. Although the different tactics adopted towards the same stimulus should concern us all, they are of particular interest to the psychologist. For example, some visual illusions—such as the Muller Lyer distortion of apparent length—are evident when the object is felt as well as when it is viewed. Recent work has shown the effect of experience and bias when moving from a task solved by visual inspection to an identical task solved haptically by palpation (43). Much of the skill in designing experiments consists of selecting stimuli so that the multiplication of alternative cues is either excluded or controlled. Multiple cues, which permit a switch in discrimination tactics, might be invoked to explain away some of the negative results reported, but they represent a highly unlikely explanation of carefully controlled single stimulus experiments such as Tapper's (104).

B. *Duplication of identical components within the system.* The second use of the word "redundancy" implies that there is a multiplication of identical components within the system such that the destruction of a fraction leaves the remainder with sufficient capacity to handle the task. In its strictest sense this type of redundancy cannot be invoked because no system other than the DCMLS receives peripheral afferents, preserves its separate spatial and physiological identity, and shows a similar evolutionary progress.

C. *Functionally equivalent systems.* Here, "redundancy" means that the same solution to a problem may be reached by different systems operating on different principles. We discuss below in the section "Other Afferent Pathways" the routes which might contain the functional equivalents of dorsal columns. In brief, all these alternative pathways differ from the DCMLS proper by having larger receptive fields, a higher degree of convergence of different types of afferent fibers, more interaction between arriving afferents, and more elaborate descending control. A special version of this theory is that equivalent information by alternative pathways converges onto the DCMLS. Dart & Gordon show afferents to dorsal column nuclei running in the dorsolateral fasciculus (30). Nucleus ventralis posterior lateralis (VPL) in thalamus receives many inputs other than from the dorsal column nucleus: these include afferents from lateral cervical nucleus, (50), the spinothalamic tract (71, 72), the reticular formation (8, 95), midbrain tegmentum (82), the opposite VPL (2), cortex (56), and the inferior colliculus (55). A number of studies have been made of the physiological properties of cells in thalamus or cortex following destruction of either dorsal columns or dorsal column nuclei or the lemniscal decussation (2, 10, 60, 63, 84, 89, 105, 115). All agree that there is a considerable loss of cells with small receptive fields, low thresholds, and high specificity, but it is still debated whether any are left when the lateral cervical nucleus projections are intact. All agree that many cells in the lateral edge of VPL continue their activity. Tomasuolo & Emmers (105) have defined this convergent lateral region, which receives from pathways other than dorsal columns, as the input to SII cortex, but others disagree (84). In a study of the VPL in rats under urethane following acute and chronic destruction of the nucleus gracilis, Wall & Egger (112) found a disappearance of the typical units from the bulk of the leg region, an appearance of slightly higher threshold and larger receptive field cells, and an increase in the number of cells in the lateral zone responding with wide, often bilateral, fields. Evidently the impulses arriving from dorsal column nuclei inhibit the excitatory effects of other convergent inputs (2, 112). In their study (112), there was the interesting complication that after three days the afferents from the intact cuneate nucleus appeared to sprout and innervate cells denervated by the gracilis lesion. Evidently information about events on the skin does arrive both in the remnants of the DCMLS and in other systems after dorsal column section. The question remains: is this information alternative and equivalent to that delivered by the dorsal columns?

In either explanation of redundancy, whether duplication or equivalence, there will be an equal lack of effect—regardless of which part of the system is destroyed. To test this symmetry, Wall transected all white matter in rat thoracic cord except the dorsal columns (111). Stimuli to the hind legs evoked segmental reflexes and cortical evoked potentials but did not change the behavior of the intact part of the animal. In spite of evoked cortical activity and normal activity of head and forelimbs, stimuli to hind limbs failed to produce alerting, waking, orientation, or any other observed response. Although unknown to the author at the time, this experiment had, according to Sherrington (100), been performed in the 19th century by Schiff and by Herzen, who report alerting by stimuli below the level of the lesion in animals in a near convulsive state. One must question the completeness of their lesions because Wall (111) saw such reactions in the normally active rat only when fragments of ventral columns had been spared.

Perhaps the most likely explanation for the apparent lack of effect of a lesion is not that its supposed function is shared with another system but that the wrong question has been asked. In the land of the deaf, the audiocircuit of a television receiver would be proved functionless or redundant. Perhaps instead of hammering on with an insistence that DCMLS allows somatosensory discrimination, we should be asking different questions. To follow this course we should turn to look at the relation of movement to dorsal columns.

Movement, descending control, and the dorsal columns.—Sherrington said of the dorsal columns: "The function of the long path must be considered still unproven; my own opinion inclines to relate it to muscular rather than to tactual sense" (100). Monkeys have been reported to have a very severe eye to hand coordination disorder but to be capable of delicate grooming after cervical dorsal column section (46). Personal communications from three laboratories suggest that others have not yet been able to reproduce this deficit with dorsal column lesions. In dogs it is reported that dorsal column section "slightly degrades" fine rapid control of body position during quiet stance and during response to postural disturbance (92). Cats with cervical dorsal column lesions (73) make frequent errors in walking and turning on a narrow beam and in jumping to a moving platform. Rats with similar lesions sitting quietly on a narrow beam allow legs to slip off but return to normal posture if alerted (44). Just after bilateral thoracic column lesions, rats fail to orient towards a cutaneous stimulus (111) but this deficit was not obvious in animals with more chronic lesions (44).

An assessment of the movement disorder is complicated by the fact that many lesions section proprioceptive afferents from muscle. Upper thoracic lesions produced only transient effects on monkey hind limbs (46). Movement disorder in cats was less marked with dorsal column nucleus lesions or lemniscal decussation lesions than with the cervical dorsal column lesion (73). Disorder of posture in rats at rest was apparent even with lesions limited to nucleus gracilis (44). One may conclude tentatively that some disorders of motor response to novel stimuli are apparent which cannot be entirely explained away by the section of proprioceptive afferents.

This suggestion that the DCMLS is in some way connected with movement is reinforced by three studies of the conditions under which descending controls operate on dorsal column nuclei. Recordings in these nuclei from single cells of the rat have shown that transmission is unaffected by sleep, alerting, arousal, orientation, or a fixed action pattern behaviour such as eating and grooming, but is inhibited during the initiation of changes in "voluntary" motor behaviour (86). In cats, two independent experiments were reported in which medial lemniscus responses were recorded following a fixed intensity stimulus to a radial nerve (29, 45). Inhibition of transmission through the nucleus preceded the initiation of a trained movement and continued until the goal was reached. The effect was specific to the limb moved and was not produced by passive movement. Inhibition was also observed following orientation to a novel auditory stimulus in one report (29) but not in others (45, 86).

Alternative hypotheses.—Recently, there have been attempts to suggest models which will reconcile the negative and positive findings. Some still support the classical view by adding the dorsolateral white matter to lateral cervical nucleus to thalamus system as an alternative and equivalent pathway to dorsal columns. In another proposal (73) it was suggested that information in the dorsal columns is used to evaluate the outcome of alternative response strategies. This suggestion depends on the author's analysis of the motor deficits that follow lesions. A third and related theory (111) has retained an indirect role for dorsal columns in discriminative analysis, suggesting that its function is to monitor and explore the somatosensory world so that instructions may be issued to the other sensory systems on the tactics to adopt to handle arriving information.

OTHER AFFERENT PATHWAYS

Having challenged the exclusive role of the dorsal columns in defining the location, shape and intensity of cutaneous stimuli, we must now examine other pathways that may possibly contribute to the discrimination of cutaneous sensation. The number of long ascending fiber systems other than the dorsal columns that relay somatosensory information is considerable. A brief description of the known anatomical and functional organization of these pathways follows.

THE SPINOCERVICAL TRACT

This pathway was originally described in 1955 (78) and its occurrence in the cat (5) and the dog (50) has been well documented. There have also been recent reports of its presence in the human (106), the monkey (76), and the rat (49). The tract arises from dorsal horn cells (110) and projects to the ipsilateral cervical nucleus located at upper cervical levels (66). Spinocervical neurons are distinguished on the basis of their response to mechanical stimuli: in spinal cats they are excited by (a) hair movement, (b) hair movement and skin pressure, or (c) pressure and pinch of the skin (14). The properties of cells are different in the decerebrate state where, in addition, some cells are excited by only one type of hair (tylotrichs) while others are weakly excited by strong pinch and exhibit no spontaneous activity or excitatory receptive field (14). It appears that these neurons are under descending control in the decerebrate animal and that section of block of the spinal cord makes cells more responsive to both excitatory and inhibitory stimuli (13, 110). Of further interest is the finding that descending control mechanisms inhibit the excitatory action of high threshold mechanoreceptors (13). Thus, in contrast to dorsal column neurons, spinocervical tract neurons are extremely sensitive to tonic descending input. They also differ from dorsal columns in that (a) they carry information from receptors innervated by small fibers, and (b) they are not responsive to input from slowly adapting mechanoreceptors (14). In summary, the spinocervical tract appears capable of transmitting information about cutaneous sensation, and its functional characteristics are distinct from those of dorsal column fibers.

Neurons in the lateral cervical nucleus respond to stimuli similar to those in the spinocervical tract (53). Recent evidence indicates that the axons of these cells form a prominent bundle that crosses via the ventral white commissure to the contralateral ventral white matter, and after maintaining a pathway lateral to the medial lemniscus, terminate in the nucleus ventralis posterior lateralis, the medial part of the posterior nuclear complex, and the medial part of the magnocellular part of the medial geniculate body (5, 50).

THE SPINOTHALAMIC TRACT

The difficulty in defining the spinothalamic pathway in lower mammals has been overcome by using the Nauta technique and its modifications. However, even in primates, only a small number of the anterolateral column fibers of the spinal cord constitute the classical spinothalamic tract which projects directly to the thalamus (71). Anatomical studies based on the fiber and preterminal degeneration that occurs after stuitable survival periods following anterolateral sections have revealed that there are medial and lateral tracts of degeneration in the brainstem (1, 71, 82); the spinothalamic pathway travels in the lateral tract which distributes terminal fibers to various parts of the brainstem (see below). There is reasonable agreement in the literature (see 6, 71, for references) on some of the terminations of the spinothalamic tract regardless of the species. Terminal degeneration usually was found in the nucleus ventralis posterior lateralis, nucleus parafascicularis and nucleus centralis lateralis, and in the magnocellular part of the medial geniculate nucleus. Disagreement exists as to possible terminations in the zona incerta, nucleus centrum medianum, nucleus reticularis and nucleus ventralis lateralis.

Spinothalamic axons originate from dorsal horn cells (mainly laminae V and VI) which have expanded cutaneous fields and respond over a wide range of mechanical stimuli from light brush to heavy pinch (36). The proportion of cells sending axons to the thalamus was found to be small and conduction velocities slow, consistent with findings that the spinothalamic fibers are of small diameter (36, 65).

THE SPINORETICULAR PATHS

It is now apparent that a large proportion of fibers ascending in the anterolateral quadrant terminate in the brainstem of the reticular nuclei. There is a major area of preterminal degeneration in the medulla which includes the nucleus gigantocellularis rostrally, and the paramedian reticular nucleus caudally (1, 54, 71, 82, 93). Recent physiological studies of these areas have produced inconsistent results, presumably because of differences in experimental preparations, anesthetics used, and recording sites. It does appear, however, that the more rostral locations (mainly the nucleus gigantocellularis) receive inputs almost entirely from the anterolateral spinal cord, since cell responses are markedly reduced after section of this region (11, 22). In the decerebrate cat, a large proportion of the neurons in this region responded to heavy mechanical or noxious stimuli over at least part of their receptive fields—which were large and included at least one limb (23). Responses improved when cutaneous volleys included A delta fibers (23). Under chloralose anesthesia, or in the waking state, light tapping and touch were the most effective stimuli (11, 98). According to Segundo et al (98), receptive fields varied in size; highly restricted (mainly involving the face) and widespread fields (at least one half of the body surface) were most common. Bowsher et al (11), however, found mainly total body receptive fields, and, in addition, many cells exhibited responses to visual and auditory stimuli.

There is considerable anatomical evidence that these rostral medial reticular neurons project via the central tegmental fascicle to midbrain and thalamic structures (12, 82, 94). However, Casey (22) stimulated the region of the central tegmental fascicle in cats and was not able to excite antidromically any medial reticular units.

In a study of the caudal medullary medial reticular zone, Bowsher (9) reported that most units responded to sharp taps on all four limbs, although some also responded to phasic hair movement. In addition, he observed some heterosensory convergence.

Unfortunately, none of the above studies offers any clear clues as to the role of the medial reticular area in sensory function. Nor do they suggest which cells in the spinal cord provide the ascending input to these reticular areas. It is not known whether the large receptive fields are due to convergence on brainstem neurons or on the spinal cord neurons that project to them. In an attempt to answer the latter question, Fields et al (40) studied the receptive fields of single units located in the ventral white quadrant of spinal cats. Units projecting at least to the upper cervical cord had receptive fields of two types: (a) wide receptive fields with a tendency to bilateral symmetry, and (b) smaller receptive fields usually restricted to the ipsilateral hindlimb.

After anterolateral section of the spinal cord, a lateral pathway of degenerating fibers was found along the medial side of the descending trigeminal nucleus (1, 71, 82). Preterminal degeneration was found in the lateral parvocellular region of the medullary reticular formation, designated the lateral tegmental field by Berman (4). At more rostral levels, a lateral system of ascending fibers followed the ventral spinocerebellar tract and was distributed diffusely to the lateral tegmental field (1, 71, 82). This system may be collaterals of the ventral spinocerebellar tract or it might consist of axons running with the ventral spinocerebellar tract. It eventually terminates throughout the cell region, surrounding the brachium conjuctivum, identified as the parabrachial nuclei (71, 82).

There have been few physiological studies on the response properties of cells in the lateral reticular areas of the brainstem. Burton (18) studied the lateral tegmental field of the caudal medulla in cat and found that units responding to high threshold noxious stimuli were most prevalent. Receptive fields were ipsilateral or bilateral, and mainly restricted to the face. In a study of the more rostral lateral reticular areas (Wall & Dubner, unpublished), receptive fields tended to be either contralateral, involving one or both limbs, or to be bilateral; responses to hair movement, brisk tapping, and pressure and pinch were found. A more valid comparison of the response characteristics of rostral and caudal reticular neurons is available from studies performed in the same laboratory under similar anesthetic conditions (3, 98). These data, although on more medial reticular neurons, were similar to the above findings. In the medulla, unilateral fields were usually ipsilateral, large and restricted fields were equally prevalent, and most of the restricted fields were of the face (3). In the midbrain, unilateral receptive fields were mostly contralateral, large receptive fields predominated, and restricted fields occurred on the face or limbs with equal frequency (98). Our own preliminary data (Wall & Dubner, unpublished) on lumbar spinal cord neurons projecting to the lateral reticular areas, indicate that there are two main types of long ascending fibers to this region. One type originated from dorsal horn neurons with restricted ipsilateral hindlimb receptive fields, ascended in the ipsilateral dorsolateral quadrant, and distributed terminals in caudal and rostral lateral reticular areas. Some of these fibers had branches which entered the restiform body. The second type originated from neurons deeper in the lumbar spinal cord, ascended in the contralateral cord, presumably entered the superior cerebellar peduncle, where they crossed to the opposite side, and distributed terminals to the rostral lateral reticular region.

THE SPINOTECTAL PATH

Long ascending fiber connections from the spinal cord to the tectum have been demonstrated in many species (71). There are two main areas of termination of these fibers: (a) Dense terminal degeneration occurs in a region lateral to the rostral pole of the inferior colliculus nucleus (1, 71, 82). Further rostrally degenerating fibers project into the deep grey stratum of the superior colliculus (1, 71). (b) Terminal degeneration occurred in the central grey matter around the cerebral acqueduct (71). The possible role of these pathways in pain mechanisms has been discussed by Mehler et al (72). More recently, Nashold et al (80) have reported some success in the treatment of atypical facial pain in man after stereotaxic lesions in the periaqueductal grey region.

THE SPINOCEREBELLAR PATHS

The cerebellum is not normally considered relevant to perception. Clinical and experimental observations have concluded that cerebellar lesions do not disturb sensory discrimination. However, after reading the extensive list of negative findings associated with dorsal column lesions, one must obviously be cautious of negative reports, especially when the testing methods used only the passive application of an expected stimulus and did not require active exploration. A second reason for reviewing spinocerebellar pathways is that they may send collaterals to the brainstem as well as to the cerebellum and associated structures. The descriptions of the pathways will be limited mainly to various aspects of the cutaneous input from hindlimbs (laterality, receptive field size, effective natural stimuli), to the location of the spinal cord cells of origin and the ascending spinal cord pathway, and to descending influences.

A. The *dorsal spinocerebellar tract* originates from Clarke's column, ascends uncrossed in the dorsolateral quadrant of the spinal cord, and projects to the cerebellum via the restiform body (66, 69). Besides neurons activated monosynaptically by muscle afferents, some neurons in the dorsal spinocerebellar tract are activated monosynaptically by light pressure to foot pads, and others by tactile stimuli applied to restricted skin fields (66, 68). The latter group of cells is responsive also to pressure and pinch applied to a wider area, and in this respect is similar to the group of lamina V cells of the dorsal horn (110). An additional group of neurons is activated from both high threshold muscle and cutaneous afferents—flexor reflex afferents—and is subject to descending inhibitory control (66). All receptive fields are limited to the ipsilateral (in relationship to the ascending tract) hindlimb.

B. The spinal portion of the *dorsolateral spino-olivocerebellar tract* is located in the lateral part of the dorsolateral funiculus and terminates in the inferior olive of the opposite side (61). This is the only spino-olivocerebellar path activated by a specific group of afferents. The most effective input was from cutaneous afferents in nerves innervating the ipsilateral paws. Responses to natural stimuli were weak; tapping of the pad was most effective.

C. The spinal portion of the *dorsal spino-olivocerebellar tract* is activated by flexor reflex afferents, ascends in the dorsal columns, and presumably terminates in the rostral part of the dorsal column nuclei (88). Receptive fields were found to be mainly ipsilateral and limited to one limb, and only 50% responded with weak excitation to pressure or tapping.

D. The *ventral spinocerebellar tract* appears to arise mainly from contralateral spinal border cells of Cooper & Sherrington (28), ascends in the ventrolateral region of the spinal cord, and projects to the cerebellum via the superior cerebellar peduncle, where most fibers cross to the opposite side (16). The cells are activated by numerous peripheral and descending inputs (70). Besides input from group I muscle afferents, these cells responded to high threshold muscle and cutaneous afferents, both ipsilateral and contralateral. Each afferent system, peripheral or descending, evoked either excitation, inhibition, or both. Descending influences were from both the dorsal and ventral quadrants of the spinal cord.

E. The spinal portion of the *ventral spino-olivocerebellar tract* ascends in the ventral funiculus and terminates in the medial accessory and dorsal accessory olive on the same side (71, 87). No connections have been found with the principal olive, and Mehler (71) concluded that no spino-olivary connections exist in chimpanzee or man. In the cat, this tract is activated mainly from contralateral flexor reflex afferents (cutaneous and high threshold muscle afferents). Receptive fields were often found to be large and included more than one limb (87). Responses to natural stimuli were limited to the contralateral hindlimb and were mainly to a moderate or strong pressure against bone or tendons. Descending influences from the dorsolateral funiculus were found (47).

F. The *ventral flexor reflex tracts* are two pathways with axons ascending in the ventral part of the spinal cord (69). One pathway (the bilateral ventral flexor reflex tract) originating from neurons located in the ventromedial part of the spinal cord grey was found to be activated from bilateral receptive fields, and responded with excitation or inhibition to touch, pressure or pinch. This pathway apparently terminates a few millimeters above the obex, although on occasion it was found to project to a level just caudal to the inferior colliculus. Its position in the brainstem corresponds closely with the lateral reticular pathway described in the previous section. The other pathway (contralateral ventral flexor reflex tract) was activated from contralateral receptive fields and only responded to high threshold mechanical stimuli. Both pathways were differentially influenced by descending input. The spinal component of the spino-reticulocerebellar path has been identified with the bilateral ventral flexor reflex tract (48).

G. A *lateral funiculus-climbing fiber-spinocerebellar* path has been described (62) which extends more ventral than the dorsolateral spino-olivo-cerebellar path and may in part overlap with the bilateral ventral flexor reflex tract. The pathway was activated by flexor afferents from all four limbs.

Some general statements can be made about the spinocerebellar tracts if they are contrasted on the basis of their location in the spinal cord. The more dorsally located tracts are mainly activated from restricted receptive fields limited to the ipsilateral hindlimb, and terminate in the more caudal, lateral brainstem regions. Descending influences, other than those acting on flexor reflex afferents, have not been described (66). The ventral tracts, on the other hand, receive their cutaneous input entirely from flexor reflex afferents, exhibit wide bilateral or contralateral receptive fields, distribute to more rostral areas of the brainstem, and show strong descending effects.

It is probable that these spinocerebellar pathways are closely associated with the spinoreticular pathways. The bilateral ventral flexor reflex tract follows a pathway in the lateral brainstem that corresponds to the lateral reticular tract (1, 71, 82) and Lundberg & Oscarsson (69) originally suggested that this was a spinoreticulo-tectal tract. There also is evidence that the ventral spinocerebellar tract distributes collaterals to the more rostral lateral tegmental field (1, 72, 82). Our preliminary data indicate that more dorsally located ascending spinal cord axons terminating in the reticular formation also give off collaterals to the caudal lateral tegmental field (Wall & Dubner, unpublished). If the distribution of spinocerebellar collaterals to the lateral reticular areas is representative of the types of spinoreticular fibers terminating in these regions, then, based on (a) the types of cutaneous input carried by spinocerebellar fibres, and (b) the distribution of terminals of the dorsal and ventral tracts, one would predict the following about the relative organization of the reticular areas: ipsilateral input, and restrictive receptive fields should predominate caudally, and contralateral input and widespread fields should be more prevalent rostrally. This is essentially what was found in these regions and was discussed in more detail in the section on spinoreticular pathways.

The data on spinocerebellar pathways would also suggest that the more rostral component of the lateral reticular formation is concerned with descending control mechanisms. Lundberg (67) recently has suggested that the ventral spinocerebellar tract supplies feedback information in the descending control of inhibitory reflex pathways to motoneurons. Ventral spinocerebellar axons send collaterals to the rostral lateral tegmental field where they could provide feedback information to tegmentospinal and reticulospinal pathways involved in descending control. Thus, the rostral lateral reticular zones appear to be concerned with the control of segmental reflex activity. The caudal lateral reticular zones, on the other hand, receive more specific information about the stimulus and may be involved in the discrimination of cutaneous sensation.

LITERATURE CITED

1. Anderson, F. D., Berry, C. M. 1959. Degeneration studies of long ascending fiber systems in the cat brain stem. *J. Comp. Neurol.* 111: 195–229
2. Bava, A., Fadiga, E., Manzoni, T. 1968. Extralemniscal reactivity and commissural linkages of VPL in cats with chronic cortical lesions. *Arch. Ital. Biol.* 106:204–26
3. Bell, C., Sierra, G., Buendia, N., Segundo, J. P. 1964. Sensory properties of neurons in the mesencephalic reticular formation. *J. Neurophysiol.* 27:961–87
4. Berman, A. L. 1968. *The Brain Stem of the Cat. A Cytoarchitectonic Atlas with Stereotaxic Co-ordinates.* Madison: Univ. Wisc. Press
5. Boivie, J. 1970. The termination of the cervicothalamic tract in cat. An experimental study with silver impregnation methods. *Brain Res.* 19: 333–60
6. Boivie, J. 1971. The termination of the spinothalamic tract in the cat. An experimental study with silver impregnation methods. *Exp. Brain Res.* 12:331–53
7. Borland, R. G., Matthews, B. H. C., Nicholson, A. N. 1970. Spinal cord and root potentials. *J. Physiol. London* 210:116P
8. Bowsher, D. 1967. Etude comparée des projections thalamiques de deux zones localisées des formation reticulées bulbaires et mésencéphaliques. *Compt. Rend. Acad. Sci. Ser.* D 265:340–42
9. Bowsher, D. 1970. Place and modality analysis in caudal reticular formation. *J. Physiol. London* 209:473–86
10. Bowsher, D. 1971. Properties of ventrobasal thalamic neurones in cat following interruption of specific afferent pathways. *Arch. Ital. Biol.* 109:59–74
11. Bowsher, D., Mallart, A., Petit, D., Albe-Fessard, D. 1968. A bulbar relay to the centre median. *J. Neurophysiol.* 31:288–300
12. Brodal, A., Rossi, G. F. 1955. Ascending fibres in brain stem reticular formation of cat. *Arch. Neurol. Psychiat.* 74:68–87
13. Brown, A. G. 1970. Descending control of the spinocervical tract in decerebrate cats. *Brain Res.* 17:152–55
14. Brown, A. G., Franz, D. N. 1969. Responses of spinocervical tract neurones to natural stimulation of identified cutaneous receptors. *Exp. Brain Res.* 7:231–49
15. Burgess, P. R., Perl, E. R. 1967. Myelinated afferents responding specifically to noxious stimulation of the skin. *J. Physiol. London* 190: 541–62
16. Burke, R., Lundberg, A., Weight, F. 1971. Spinal border cell origin of the ventral spinocerebellar tract. *Exp. Brain Res.* 12:283–94
17. Burke, R. E., Rudomin, P., Vyklicky, L., Zajac, F. E. 1971. Primary afferent depolarisation and flexion reflexes produced by radiant heat stimulation of the skin. *J. Physiol. London* 213:185–214
18. Burton, H. 1968. Somatic sensory properties of caudal bulbar reticular neurons in the cat (felis domestica). *Brain Res.* 11:357–72
19. Cabral, R. J., Johnson, J. I. 1971. Organisation of mechanoreceptive projections in the ventrobasal thalamus of sheep. *J. Comp. Neurol.* 141: 17–36
20. Cangiano, A., Cook, W. A., Pompeiano, O. 1969. Cerebellar inhibitory control of the vestibular reflex pathways to primary afferents. *Arch. Ital. Biol.* 107:341–64
21. Carpenter, D., Engberg, I. Funkenstein, H. Lundberg, A. 1963. Decerebrate control of reflexes to primary afferents. *Acta Physiol. Scand.* 59:424–37
22. Casey, K. L. 1969. Somatic stimuli, spinal pathways, and size of cutaneous fibres influencing unit activity in the medial medullary reticular formation. *Exp. Neurol.* 25:35–56
23. Casey, K. L. 1971. Responses of bulboreticular units to somatic stimuli eliciting escape behaviour in the cat. *Int. J. Neurosci.* 2:15–28
24. Chan, S. H-H., Barnes, C. D. 1971. Presynaptic facilitation in positive DRPs evoked from brain stem reticular formation in lumbar cord. *Brain Res.* 28:176–79
25. Christensen, B. R., Perl, E. R. 1970. Spinal neurons specifically excited by noxious or thermal stimuli. Marginal zone of the dorsal horn. *J. Neurophysiol.* 33:293–307
26. Christiansen, J. 1966. Neurological observations of macaques with

spinal cord lesions. *Anat. Rec.* 154: 330

27. Cook, A. W., Browder, E. J. 1965. The function of posterior columns in man. *Arch. Neurol. Chicago* 12:72–79

28. Cooper, S., Sherrington, C. S. 1940. Gower's tract and spinal border cells. *Brain* 63:123–34

29. Coulter, J. D., Thies, R. 1971. Sensory transmission through the lemniscal pathway during movements and arousal in the cat. *Fed. Proc.* 30:664

30. Dart, A. M., Gordon, G. 1970. Excitatory and inhibitory afferent inputs to the dorsal column nuclei not involving the dorsal columns. *J. Physiol. London* 211:36P

31. Dawson, G. D., Merrill, E. G., Wall, P. D. 1970. Dorsal root potentials produced by stimulation of fine afferents. *Science* 167:1385–87

32. Denny-Brown, D., Yanagisawa, N. 1970. The descending trigeminal tract as a mechanism for intersegmental facilitation. *Trans. Am. Neurol. Assoc.*, 95:129–33

33. De Vito, J. L., Ruch, T. C. 1956. Central pathways subserving weight discrimination in monkeys. *Fed. Proc.* 15:152

34. De Vito, J. L., Ruch, T. C., Patton, H. D. 1964. Analysis of residual weight discriminatory ability following section of the dorsal columns in monkeys. *Indian J. Physiol. Pharmacol.* 8:117–26

35. Diamond, I. T., Randall, W., Springer, L. 1964. Tactual localization in cats deprived of cortical areas SI and SII and the dorsal columns. *Psychon. Sci.* 1:261–62

36. Dilly, P. N., Wall, P. D., Webster, K. E. 1968. Cells of origin of the spinothalamic tract in the cat and rat. *Exp. Neurol.* 21:550–62

37. Dobry, P. J. K., Casey, K. L. 1970. Behavioural discriminative capacity and cortical unit responses in cats with dorsal column lesions. *The Physiologist* 13:180

38. Egger, M. D., Wall, P. D. 1971. The plantar cushion reflex circuit: an oligosynaptic cutaneous reflex. *J. Physiol. London* 216:483–501

39. Erulkar, S. D., Sprague, J. M., Whitsel, B. L., Dogan, S., Jannetta, P. J. 1966. Organization of the vestibular projection to spinal cord of the cat. *J. Neurophysiol.* 29:626–64

40. Fields, H. L., Partridge, L. D., Jr., Winter, D. L. 1970. Somatic and visceral receptive field properties of fibers in ventral quadrant white matter of the cat spinal cord. *J. Neurophysiol.* 33:827–37

41. Franz, D. N., Iggo, A. 1968. Dorsal root potentials and ventral root reflexes evoked by non-myelinated fibres. *Science* 162:1140–42

42. Freeman, J. A. 1970. Responses of cat cerebellar Purkinje cells to convergent inputs from cerebral cortex and peripheral sensory systems. *J. Neurophysiol.* 33:697–712

43. Frisby, J. P., Davies, I. R. L. 1971. Is the haptic Muller-Lyer a visual phenomenon? *Nature, London*, 231:463–65

44. Gaffan, D. 1970. Personal communication

45. Ghez, C., Lenzi, G. L. 1971. Modulation of sensory transmission in cat lemniscal system during voluntary movement. *Pfluegers Arch.* 323:273–78

46. Gilman, S., Denny-Brown, D. 1966. Disorders of movement and behaviour following dorsal column lesions. *Brain* 89:397–418

47. Grant, G., Oscarsson, O. 1966. Mass discharges evoked in the olivocerebellar tract on stimulation of muscle and skin nerves. *Exp. Brain Res.* 1:329–37

48. Grant, G., Oscarsson, O., Rosen, I. 1966. Functional organisation of the spino-reticulocerebellar path with identification of its spinal component. *Exp. Brain Res.* 1:306–19

49. Gwyn, D. G., Waldron, H. A. 1968. A nucleus in the dorsolateral funiculus of the spinal cord of the rat. *Brain Res.* 10:342–51

50. Hagg, S., Ha, H. 1970. Cervicothalamic tract in the dog. *J. Comp. Neurol.* 139:357–74

51. Hillman, P., Wall, P. D. 1969. Inhibitory and excitatory factors influencing the receptive fields of lamina 5 spinal cord cells. *Exp. Brain Res.* 9:284–306

52. Horn, G., Hinde, R. A., Eds. 1970. Short term changes in neural activity and behaviour. Cambridge: Cambridge Univ. Press

53. Horrobin, D. F. 1966. The lateral cervical nucleus of the cat; an electrophysiological study. *Quart. J. Physiol.* 51:351–71

54. Jane, J. A., Schroeder, D. M. 1971. A comparison of dorsal column nuclei

and spinal afferents in the European hedgehog. *Exp. Neurol.* 30:1–17

55. Jane, J. A., Yashon, D., Diamond, I. T. 1968. An anatomic basis for multimodel thalamic units. *Exp. Neurol.* 22:464–71

56. Jones, E. G., Powell, T. P. S. 1969. An electron microscope study of the mode of termination of cortico-thalamic fibres within the sensory relay nucleus of the thalamus. *Proc. Roy. Soc. London Ser. B.* 172: 173–85

57. Kerr, F. W. L. 1968. The descending pathway to the lateral cuneate nucleus, the nucleus of Clarke and the ventral horn. *Anat. Rec.* 160:375

58. Kirk, E. J., Denny-Brown, D. 1970. Functional variation in dermatomes in the macaque monkey following dorsal root lesions. *J. Comp. Neurol.* 139:307–20

59. Kitai, S. T., Weinberg, J. 1968. Tactile discrimination study of the dorsal column—medial lemniscus system and spinothalamic tract in cat. *Exp. Brain Res.* 6:234–46

60. Landgren, S., Nordwall, A., Wengstrom, C. 1965. The location of the thalamic relay in the spino-cervico-lemniscal pathway. *Acta Physiol. Scand.* 65:164–75

61. Larson, B., Miller, S., Oscarsson, O. 1969. Termination and functional organisation of the dorsolateral spino-olivocerebellar path. *J. Physiol. London,* 203:611–40

62. Larson, B., Miller, S., Oscarsson, O. 1969. A spinocerebellar climbing fibre path activated by the flexor reflex afferents from all four limbs. *J. Physiol. London,* 203:641–49

63. Levitt, M., Levitt, J. 1968. Sensory hind-limb representation in the SmI cortex of cat after spinal tractotomies. *Exp. Neurol.* 22:276–302

64. Levitt, M., Schwartzman, R. 1966. Spinal sensory tracts and two point tactile sensitivity. *Anat. Rec.* 154: 377

65. Lund, R. D., Webster, K. E. 1967. Thalamic afferents from the spinal cord and trigeminal nuclei. *J. Comp. Neurol.* 130:313–28

66. Lundberg, A. 1964. Ascending spinal hindlimb pathways in the cat. *Progr. Brain Res.* 12:135–63

67. Lundberg, A. 1971. Function of the ventral spinocerebellar tract. A new hypothesis. *Exp. Brain Res.* 12: 317–30

68. Lundberg, A., Oscarsson, O. 1960.

Functional organization of the dorsal spino-cerebellar tract in the cat. VII. Identification of units by antidromic activation from the cerebellar cortex with recognition of five functional subdivisions. *Acta. Physiol. Scand.* 50:356–74

69. Lundberg, A., Oscarsson, O. 1962. Two ascending spinal pathways in the ventral part of the cord. *Acta. Physiol. Scand.* 54:270–86

70. Lundberg, A., Weight, F. 1971. Functional organization of connexions to the ventral spinocerebellar tract. *Exp. Brain Res.* 12:295–316

71. Mehler, W. R. 1969. Some neurological species differences—a posteriori. *Ann. N.Y. Acad. Sci.* 167:424–68

72. Mehler, W. R., Feferman, M. E., Nauta, W. J. H. 1960. Ascending axon degeneration following anterolateral cordotomy. An experimental study in the monkey. *Brain* 83:718–50

73. Melzack, R., Bridges, J. A. 1971. Dorsal column contributions to motor behaviour. *Exp. Neurol.* In press

74. Melzack, R., Wall, P. D. 1965. Pain mechanisms: a new theory. *Science* 150:971–79

75. Mendell, L. M. 1970. Positive dorsal root potentials produced by stimulation of small diameter muscle afferents. *Brain Res.* 18:375–79

76. Mizuno, N., Nakano, K., Imaisumi, M., Okamoto, M. 1967. The lateral cervical nucleus of the japanese monkey (Macaca fuscata). *J. Comp. Neurol.* 129:375–84

77. Morest, D. K. 1967. Experimental study of the projections of the nucleus of the tractus solitarius and the area postrema of the cat. *J. Comp. Neurol.* 130:277–300

78. Morin, F. 1955. A new spinal pathway for cutaneous impulses. *Amer. J. Physiol.* 183:245–52

79. Mountcastle, V. B. 1968. *Medical Physiology,* p. 1415. St. Louis: Mosby 12th ed.

80. Nashold, B. S., Jr., Wilson, W. P., Slaughter, D. G. 1969. Stereotaxic midbrain lesions for central dysesthesia and phantom pain. Preliminary report. *J. Neurosurg.* 30:116–26

81. Nathan, P. W., Smith, M. C. 1959. Fasciculi proprii of the spinal cord in man: Review of present knowledge. *Brain* 82:610–68

82. Nauta, W. J. H., Kuypers, H. G. J. M.

1958. *Some ascending pathways in the brain stem reticular formation.* In *Reticular formation of the Brain*, ed. H. H. Jasper et al 3–30, Boston: Little, Brown

83. Norrsell, U. 1966. The spinal afferent pathways of conditioned reflexes to cutaneous stimuli in the dog. *Exp. Brain Res.* 2:269–82

84. Norrsell, U., Wolpow, E. R. 1966. An evoked potential study of different pathways from hindlimb to somatosensory areas in the cat. *Acta Physiol. Scand.* 66:19–33

85. Norton, A. C. 1968. Cutaneous sensory pathways: dorsal column—medial lemniscus system. *UCLA Brain Inform. Serv.*, Updated Rev. Proj.

86. O'Keefe, J., Gaffan, D. 1971. Response properties of units in dorsal column nuclei of freely moving rat. Changes as a function of behaviour. *Brain Res.* 31:374–75

87. Oscarsson, O. 1968. Termination and functional organization of the ventral spino-olivocerebellar path. *J. Physiol. London*, 196:453–78

88. Oscarsson, O. 1969. Termination and functional organization of the dorsal spino-olivocerebellar path. *J. Physiol. London*, 200:129–49

89. Perl, E. R., Whitlock, D. G. 1961. Somatic stimuli exciting spinothalamic projections to thalamic neurons in cat and monkey. *Exp. Neurol.* 3:256–96

90. Rabiner, A. M., Browder, J. 1948. Concerning the conduction of touch and deep densibilities through the spinal cord. *Trans. Am. Neurol. Assoc.* 73:137–42

91. Rethelyi, M., Szentagothai, J. 1969. The large synaptic complexes of the substantia gelatinosa. *Exp. Brain Res.* 7:258–74

92. Reynolds, P. J., Talbott, R. E., Brookhart, J. M. 1971. Contribution of dorsal columns to postural control in dog. *Fed. Proc.* 30:664

93. Rossi, G. F., Brodal, A. 1957. Terminal distribution of spinoreticular fibres in the cat. *Arch. Neurol. Psychiat.* 78:439–53

94. Scheibel, M. E., Scheibel, A. B. 1958. Structural substrates for integrative patterns in the brain stem reticular core. In *Reticular Formation of the Brain*, ed. H. H. Jasper et al, 31–55. Boston: Little, Brown.

95. Scheibel, M. E., Scheibel, A. B. 1966. Patterns of organization in specific and non-specific thalamic fields. In *The Thalamus* ed. D. P. Purpura, M. D. Yahr, 13–46. New York: Columbia Univ. Press

96. Schwartzman, R. J., Bogdonoff, M. D. 1968. Behavioural and anatomical analysis of vibration sensibility. *Exp. Neurol.* 20:43–51

97. Scibetta, C. J., King, R. B. 1969. Hyperpolarizing influence of trigeminal nucleus caudalis on primary afferent preterminals in trigeminal nucleus oralis. *J. Neurophysiol.* 32:229–38

98. Segundo, J. P., Takenaka, T., Encabo, H. 1967. Somatic sensory properties of bulbar reticular neurons. *J. Neurophysiol.* 30:1221–38

99. Sessle, B. J., Dubner, R. 1970. Presynaptic hyperpolarization of fibres projecting to trigeminal brain stem and thalamic nuclei. *Brain Res.* 22:121–25

100. Sherrington, C. S. 1900. *Textbook of Physiology*, ed. E. A. Schafer 2:862 Edinburgh: Y. J. Pentland

101. Somjen, G. G. 1970. Evoked sustained focal potentials and membrane potentials of neurons and of unresponsive cells of the spinal cord. *J. Neurophysiol.* 23:562–82

102. Szentagothai, J. 1964. Propriospinal pathways and their synapses. *Progr. Brain Res.* 11:155–77

103. Talbot, W. H., Darian-Smith, I., Kornhuber, H. H., Mountcastle, V. B. 1968. The sense of flutter vibration. *J. Neurophysiol.* 31:301–34

104. Tapper, D. N. 1970. Behavioural evaluation of the tactile pad receptor system in hairy skin of the cat. *Exp. Neurol.* 26:447–59

105. Tomasuolo, K. C., Emmers, R. 1970. Spinal afferents to SI and SII of the rat thalamus. *Exp. Neurol.* 26:482–97

106. Truex, R. C., Taylor, M. J., Smythe, M. Q., Gildenberg, P. L. 1970. The lateral cervical nucleus of cat, dog, and man. *J. Comp. Neurol.* 139:93–104

107. Uddenberg, N. 1968. Functional organization of long second order afferents in the dorsal funiculus. *Exp. Brain Res.* 4:377–82

108. Vierck, C. J. 1966. Spinal pathways mediating limb position sense. *Anat. Rec.* 154:437

109. Wall, P. D. 1962. The origin of a spinal cord slow potential. *J. Physiol. London* 164:508–26

110. Wall, P. D. 1967. The laminar organization of dorsal horn and effects of descending impulses. *J. Physiol. London* 188:403–23

111. Wall, P. D. 1970. The sensory and motor role of impulses travelling in the dorsal columns toward cerebral cortex. *Brain* 93:505–24

112. Wall, P. D., Egger, M. D. 1971. Formation of new connections in adult rat brains after partial deafferentation. *Nature London.* 232: 542–545

113. Wall, P. D., Taub, A. 1962. Four aspects of the trigeminal nucleus and a paradox. *J. Neurophysiol.* 25:110–26

114. Welker, W. I., Johnson, J. I., Pubols, B. H. 1964. Some morphological characteristics of the somatic sensory system in racoons. *Am. Zool.* 4:75–94

115. Whitlock, D. G., Perl, E. R. 1961. Thalamic projections of spinothalamic pathways in monkey. *Exp. Neurol.* 3:240–55

116. Whitsel, B. L., Petrucelli, L. M., Sapiro, G., Ha, H., 1970. Fiber sorting in the fasciculus gracilis of squirrel monkeys. *Exp. Neurol.* 29:227–42

117. Woolsey, T. A., van der Loos, H. 1970. The structural organization of layer IV in the somatosensory regions SI of mouse cerebral cortex. *Brain Res.* 17:205–42

118. Zimmerman, E. A., Chambers, W. W., Liu, C. N. 1964. An experimental study of the anatomical organization of the cortico-bulbar systems in the albino rat. *J. Comp. Neurol.* 123:301–32

119. Zimmermann, M. 1968. Dorsal root potentials after C fiber stimulation. *Science* 160:896–98

CNS CELLULAR LEVEL: MEMBRANES

R. WERMAN[1]

*Department of Zoology, The Hebrew University of Jersusalem,
Jerusalem, Israel*

INTRODUCTION

The amount of material on CNS membrane processes published in one year is so large as to preclude even a simple listing of the references in the space allotted for this review. At the onset, I collected titles at the unwieldy rate of more than 100 per month. Therefore I decided to be more selective: this review consists of discussions of a few papers on topics which I feel are of contemporary importance. Even with such paring, space limitations did not allow me to present the entire history of the discussed topics, but further references can be found in the cited works.

After a year's immersion in this work, I feel as if I have been living within a gigantic amoeba (CNS neurophysiology) wherein most scientific activity is represented by seething metabolic activity. The amoeba sends out processes into new directions and incorporates material from without, always growing. I have made trips down some of these pseudopodia but regret not being able to visit others adequately. I look forward to seeing summarized many topics I would like to have been able to review; these include: trophic functions, receptor isolation and identification, the vesicle story, interneurons with long axons, the use of shape-index to characterize neurons, metabolic ionic pumps in resting and synaptic potentials, quantal behavior in CNS synaptic release, the motoneuron EPSP, presynaptic inhibition in the CNS, input-output relationships, and the contributions of the new neurobiologists—the molecular biologists who have already made an impression on the new world they seem intent on conquering.

DENDRITIC SPIKES AND FIELD POTENTIALS

Llinás & Nicholson (100, 116) have recently contributed to the controversy resulting from their original claim (101) that the dendrites of alligator Purkinje cells actively conduct spikes. In two recent papers they supplied, in support of their claim, attractive evidence which included intradendritic recordings confirmed by histological identification of dendrites after intradendritic iontophoretic injection of the dye procion yellow. The field poten-

[1] This review was supported in part by USPHS grant NS 09360-01.

tials of cat, lizard and frog cerebellum, in response to parallel fiber stimulation, uniformly show a superficial slow negative potential which reverses to a positivity in depth, and at greater depths becomes a mirror image of the surface response. These responses are also occasionally found in the alligator cerebellum (116), but apparently in rather unphysiological conditions such as reduced blood flow in the region under study. The usual response to parallel fiber stimulation in the alligator is quite different and provides the basis for recent controversy (see 116 for references): it consists of a slow superficial negativity with a slight positive afterswing. The negativity, however, does not reverse in depth recordings and shows an increasing latency with greater depth and apparent conduction velocities of 7 to 10 cm/sec.

In a series of more than 50 intradendritic penetrations in alligator Purkinje cells, Llinás & Nicholson (100) have shown the uniform presence of spike-like components of approximately 10 msec in duration which behaved essentially like discrete spikes (for similar evidence in rabbit cerebellum, see 57). That is, the "spike" was unitary but could be increased in discrete jumps. With strong stimulation, potential changes which overshoot the zero potential could be obtained; these responses could be resolved into unitary components by hyperpolarization or by graded stimulation and were blocked in degrees by strong hyperpolarization. It is of interest that the larger responses, following strong stimuli, invariably showed an early peak which apparently did not overshoot the zero potential. Moreover, the extradendritic negativity was simultaneous with the rising phase of the early peak, while the larger potentials were not accompanied by inward currents in the nearby extracellular field. These findings suggest: (a) asynchronous activation of excitable sites, (b) diffusely distributed sites of activation, (c) intervening electrically inexcitable membrane making up most of the surface of the dendrite, and (d) a relatively long space constant (λ) for the dendrite. The varying amplitude of the intradendritic spike-like responses may be related to the distance between the activated membrane patch and the site of recording but may also be a function of the size of the shunt provided by the resting conductance of the neighboring electrically inexcitable membrane to the inward currents generated at the active channels.[2]

It is of interest that Hild & Tasaki (70) were able both to stimulate and to record from denderites in tissue cultures of rat and kitten cerebellar neurons. They demonstrated equal somatofugal and somatopetal conduction velocities (about 2–5 cm/sec at 26°C) and did not report discontinuous conduction. On the other hand, antidromic spikes in the alligator Purkinje cell were apparently less well conducted into dendrites than were orthrodromic spikes conducted somatopetally (100). This finding appears reason-

[2] This is comparable to the situation found in arthropod muscles (183, 185). It is worth noting that arthropod muscles in many ways provide interesting and useful analogs for vertebrate dendrites, exhibiting multineuronal innervation, peripheral integration of synaptic inputs, and graded spike electrogenesis.

able in view of the large electrical capacity which the highly ramified adult Purkinje cell dendritic tree presents to a centrifugally approaching spike. Moreover, the patchy quality of spike genesis in the peripheral dendritic tree apparently disappears closer to the soma. Llinás & Nicholson (100) argued for functional independence of the different dendritic branches as a corollary of this centripetal preference, an attractive hypothesis. Thus, activity in any large branch may go on largely undisturbed by a spike generated from activity in other branches. Moreover, the activity of separate branches would be under delicate control by strategically placed inhibitory synapses (see below) near branching points.

Based on the findings already described, the case for an active (i.e. non-electrotonic) transfer of spike-like information from dendrites of the alligator Purkinje cell to the cell soma appears strong. Although the findings of active propagation of spikes in dendrites are apparently not general—a well documented example of an electrically inexcitable dendrite is the Mauthner cell lateral dendrite (58)—such findings are no longer singular; this conclusion has been in the air since the striking simultaneous recording of Terzuolo & Araki (164) from a motoneuron soma and a presumed dendrite, more than 10 years ago (see also 48). There have also been claims for the dendritic origin of spikes in motoneurons following ventral root section (48, 94), and in some normal motoneurons (115), as well as in cells of the reticular formation (14), thalamus (105), and hippocampus (160), and in dendrites of lamina IV spinal neurons (168), inferior olivary neurons (27), red nucleus neurons (106), and "epileptic" (130) and immature (135) cortical neurons. In addition, there is evidence that dendritic spikes may be found in neocortical (134) and hippocampal (133) neurons during weak polarization of the cortex.[3] In addition to the marking of dendrites with dye (100), evidence for intradendritic recording includes an improbably high number of micro-electrode impalements based on anatomical studies in conjunction with electrophysiological recordings (14). Inferential evidence for the origin of spikes in dendrites (cf 131) can also be obtained from the clear occurrence of more than one firing level for action potentials recorded from neuron somata, when this cannot be explained by accommodation or other changes in the membrane properties of the modal spike-generating region. Similar evidence can be obtained as well from evoked depolarizations without apparent reversal potentials [but see (63) for a phenomenological exception] which behave in more or less all or none fashion. At times such depolarizations are capable of generating somatic spikes without prior activation of the initial segment (131).

In addition to the evidence for active responses in dendrites, Nicholson & Llinás (116) have provided an elegant and provocative theoretical analysis of the field potentials produced by these responses. It is of interest to

---

[3] Ochs, on entirely different grounds, has claimed conducted dendritic electrogenesis in mature neocortical neurons (e.g. see 124).

note that the swing towards intracellular recordings in the CNS, which began with Eccles and his collaborators in the early 50s, is in some sense now being reversed. Intracellular recording fails to give adequate information about the flow of currents in the geometrically complex cells often encountered in the CNS, let alone in the external fields derived from multicellular activity. Problems such as localization of synaptic inputs or areas of spike generations can only be inferred from intracellular recordings—while extracellular recordings can often provide this information directly. In the case of invertebrates, cell bodies are generally not innervated; all synaptic activity and, at times, even all spike generation is confined to portions of the axon buried in the neuropile at some distance from the soma.

Intracellular impalements are still necessary to determine changes in membrane conductance, as well as to measure the reversal potential[4] for synaptic processes. They also provide a convenient method for the amplification of subthreshold activity and the integration of all "significant" activity when the soma is electrically "close" to the spike generator whose output determines what the cell "really" sees, and offer the best way to change the local ionic environment in the CNS.

The contribution of dendritic synapses to the generation of field potentials was proposed more than 30 years ago by Adrian (2) and was subsequently reinforced by Purpura & Grundfest (132). A theoretical basis for their contribution was provided by Rall (137) who suggested that dendrites are analogous to leaky core conductors and, since they are long and thin, the transmembrane current in dendrites is almost wholly determined by the internal and membrane properties of the dendrite and is, in general, not influenced by the behavior of the current extracellularly (138). Using these concepts, Nicholson & Llinás (116) have provided a model to explain the extracellular field in the alligator cerebellum. Several interesting postulates were included in the model. The dendrite, following Rall's example, was treated as a uniform leaky cable, while the extracellular field was treated as geometrically equivalent to a cylinder in which all the extracellular current was continuously distributed. This, with the further assumption that the medium was isotropic and homogeneous to a first approximation, allowed the use of Poisson's equation.[5] Finally, the effect of the medium above the pial-cortical interface was taken into account by using a mathematical image technique.

The explicit solution obtained shows that the field potential at any given point is related to the transmembrane current by the distance between the electrode and points at which the current crosses the membrane and thus to the geometry of the synaptically activated areas. With this approach, numerical solutions were determined by using a continuous mathematical

---

[4] An important theoretical contribution to this subject deals with reversal potentials in nonisopotential systems, but it unfortunately only exists in abstract form (11). One would like to urge the authors to publish the entire manuscript.

[5] For another example of use of this equation in explaining extracellular fields, see (127).

function—similar to one I introduced for approximating a frog muscle spike (175)—to approximate the synaptic input for the passive case where superficially activated excitatory synaptic potentials are electronically conducted centripetally.

Curve-fitting techniques yielded some rather reasonable values for the geometrical parameters, including the long λ expected from observations: according to the calculations, the cell is about 2 λ in length with a time constant of 5 msec. A reasonably good fit for the passive case (reversal of the negativity) describing the relation of extracellular potential to depth and time was obtained. When the model was applied to an active situation by adding nine equally spaced, sequentially excited patches in a centripetal direction and then simulating a constant conduction velocity by giving a latency for excitation of each patch proportional to its depth, a reasonably good fit was again obtained to the extracellular field in the active case as a function of depth and time. Only the most drastic and unreasonable changes of parameters in the passive situation were capable of mimicking the progressive decline of the negative wave recorded in the "active" case.

The excellence of fit of the model unfortunately does not prove its validity.[6] The usefulness of such a model appears to be fourfold: (a) ability to explain puzzling phenomena; (b) parsimonious expression of a collection of complex data; (c) predictive value; and (d) ability to suggest definite experiments whose results can negate the validity of the model. The Popperian fourth quality is somewhat masochistic and is unfortunately found but rarely in models. As for predictive properties, the model used has one clear result: it predicts a phenomenon often encountered in superficial recording of evoked potentials, i.e. the greater sensitivity of negative components to shunting, for example by flooding the recording area with saline [for a recent example, see (149)]. This useful result makes the model of more than limited interest, but does not guarantee its validity. Another consequence of the model, in fact also built into the model and supported by the experimental evidence presented, is that it is generally not valid to consider the field potential as a representation of passive decay of the membrane potential in space as though the currents were distributed in space along a leaky cable. Such a hypothesis (18) is valid for the membrane potential but will only be valid for the extracellular potential if it has the same wave shape as the internal potential.[7] In fact, Nicholson & Llinás (116) have shown that the internal and external potentials cannot have the same

---

[6] A parallel worthwhile recording for neurophysiologists is Gasser's comment (transmitted to me by H. Grundfest), "You cannot tell a process from a potential." A contemporary specific reading might be: "All prolonged extracellular negativities are not necessarily examples of primary afferent depolarization."

[7] As Zucker (190) has pointed out, if two identical nerves, separated but parallel, are placed on wet filter paper and stimulated simultaneously, the net transverse current is zero but an electrode midway between the nerves records a triphasic potential, not the monophasic one predicted by cable theory for dendrites where synchrony, symmetry, and zero net current are found (18).

waveform if there is a change of potential with time. The first two qualities, clarification and parsimony, are indeed present and assure further interest in the Nicholson & Llinás model. It should be noted, however, that Zucker (190) has also presented a reasonable model for the findings which share these first two qualities.

Zucker (190) assumed many similarly oriented neurons packed tightly together and activated simultaneously. From considerations of volume conductor theory, the extracellular current from each neuron would then be confined to the immediate region of the neuron and the currents would be almost purely axial. Thus, the extracellular medium can be approximated by a series of resistors. The activated cells would therefore exhibit "closed field" behavior (103) and the field potential gradient in this field would be proportional to the membrane potential gradients. In addition to the simple closed field model, however, a secondary current pathway is invoked to shunt current from the soma to distal dendrites, mimicking the condition where the surface of the cerebellum is not isopotential with an infinitely distant electrode. With the reference electrode on this secondary current pathway, the position of the reference lead can be calculated from the relative amplitude of the passively derived positive and negative peaks. Calculations using this model gave a good fit when λ was taken as 300 μ for the passive case; however, only the introduction of active elements give rise to propagated spatial maximums and reversals of potential in time and space that were found by Llinás et al (101). Thus, the voltage-divider model is not essentially different in its predictions from that of Nicholson & Llinás (116) and somewhat simpler to handle.

The model Zucker used was introduced by Rall & Shepherd (140) in one of the most exciting recent examples of modeling. The work centered on the field potentials of the rabbit olfactory bulb and resulted in an excellent reconstruction of these complex fields. At one stage of the work, the authors were led to postulate the existence of dendrodendritic synaptic interactions and were able to demonstrate the morphological substrate for this postulated interaction (141). Antidromic invasion of olfactory bulb mitral cells was postulated to produce synaptic excitation of granule cell processes which in turn lead to mitral inhibition. Pairs of oppositely oriented synaptic contacts between granule cell gemmules and mitral dendrites were demonstrated and have been confirmed by other investigators (73, 129). Similar morphological findings of reciprocal dendrodendritic synapses have been seen in electron micrographs of the retina (43), the lateral geniculate nucleus (51) and the superior colliculus (104).

An important consideration both for this discussion as well as for the development of the potential divider model of Rall & Shepherd (140) is the evidence for disturbance of symmetry of the external current pathways. In the olfactory bulb, the olfactory tract and the retrobulbar area disturb the spherical symmetry of the bulb by providing a distinct and delimited current pathway to the rest of the brain. This condition also applies in the case of the cerebellum: the cerebellar peduncles are a distinct and delimited pathway for current flow to the rest of the brain. Moreover, the indifferent electrode used by Nicholson & Llinás (116) was located at a distance of more than 10 cm from the recording site, presumably outside of the cerebellum in *Caimon sclerops*. Thus it would appear that the relative usefulness of the Zucker model and the Nicholson & Llinás model is still open to further test.

Llinás & Nicholson (100) have concluded that there is functional significance in the described properties of the alligator Purkinje dendrites. Taking into account the partial independence of spike activation in different dendritic branches, the slow conduction velocity, and the somatopetal tendency for dendritic spike conduction, they have postulated that integration in one branch may go relatively undisturbed by dendritic spike invasion from the rest of the dendritic tree. This would allow for relatively prolonged temporal summation in branches of a dendrite which would not be obliterated by events in other dendrites or even by somatic spike generation. These authors also point out the absence of basket cells in this preparation and note that inhibitory synapses are confined to the dendritic tree. The evidence presented for inhibition are the large hyperpolarizations following the initial EPSP and the reversal of the potential either following the intracellular chloride injection or by depolarizing currents. The later experiments were quite difficult and the results shown (100, Fig. 10) reflect this difficulty.

Perhaps because of this difficulty, the authors have indulged in what appears to me to be an exaggeration. Among other things, they spoke of a characteristic current-voltage relationship for IPSPs in central neurons and stated that a prolonged, graded and chloride-sensitive hyperpolarization is the necessary and sufficient criterion for synaptic inhibition. It should be noted that the illustrated chloride injection apparently damaged the dendrite irreparably and the spike mechanism was eliminated (100, Fig. 10 F–L). Furthermore, it is not clear at this point whether any current-voltage relationship is characteristic of the inhibitory process. The curve shown (100, Fig. 10 M) would appear to illustrate a depolarizing process which resulted from a conductance change whose reversal potential was in the depolarizing direction, i.e. a depolarization produced by an increase in conductance, and nothing more. The marked rectification of the IPSP-current curve is unusual for inhibitory processes but does not rule out such a process. Whether or not rectification of nonsynaptic membrane contributes to the observed rectification is not clear. It should be noted that voltage dependence of a synaptic conductance change has been clearly demonstrated in the eel electroplaque (146) and that such nonlinearity is apparently no longer inconsistent with a synaptic process.

Finally, the finding of a prolonged, graded hyperpolarization sensitive to chloride is neither a necessary nor a sufficient criterion for synaptic inhibition. The prolonged nature of IPSPs arise from factors which are not necessary conditions for inhibition: a long postsynaptic membrane time constant and repetitive or asynchronous presynaptic firing or transmitter release. The graded nature of the synaptic process implies multineuronal innervation as well as the graded electrogenesis characteristic of postsynaptic membrane. Although multineuronal inhibitory innervation has been universally found in chemical inhibition in the CNS, the possibility of a single inhibitory axon innervating a given cell is not ruled out. It is also well known that other ions in addition to Cl^-, such as K^+, may be responsible for synaptic inhibition. Thus, the inhibitory actions of norepinephrine do not appear to be Cl^- sensitive (49, 155). None of the above conditions alone or in combination are sufficient to define an inhibitory input since it is also necessary that the measured effect be the result of chemical activation of the membrane following presynaptic stimulation. Many other processes are prolonged (e.g. the burst activation seen in the somata of the very cells studied), and graded (e.g. EPSPs), and even chloride sensitive (e.g. resting potentials in skeletal muscle). An example of a nonsynaptic, prolonged, graded and chloride-sensitive process is the hyperpolarizing response of *Raia* electroplaques (72).

Taking into account the technical difficulties involved, I accept the evidence as strongly in favor of inhibitory synapses on the dendrites. The authors claim that ". . . the inhibitory terminals seem to be always located proximal to some component of the excitatory input," a point which may be of great significance in understanding dendritic function. As the authors noted, this form of innervation allows selective inhibition of particular dendritic segments, in accord with their idea of independent activation of different branches of the dendritic tree. Thus, we have as properties of this dendritic system a quasi-independent excitation of dendritic branches as well as inhibitory control at vulnerable points.[8] Insight into the problems of dendritic organization is crucial to our understanding of CNS integrative processes; we can look forward to further advances in this direction.

ELECTRICAL INTERACTIONS BETWEEN AFFERENT NERVES AND MOTONEURONS

In a recent series of papers, Decima (39) and Decima & Goldberg (40, 41) have given evidence for electrical coupling between cat motoneurons and presynaptic fibers. Decima's first observations (39) showed that, in a variety of experimental conditions, lumbosacral dorsal root (DR) fibers can be excited by ventral root (VR) stimulation following conditioning stimuli given to different parts of the same or adjacent DR's, as well as following various peripheral stimuli including pressure to the ipsilateral hindpaw. Motoneuron activation did not produce recognizable changes in the dorsal root potential in the absence of a conditioning stimulus (but see below). Conduction velocities measured indicated that group I DR fibers were involved and the latency of the response was always 0.2–0.3 msec longer in the DR–VR direction than in the VR–DR direction. Decima concluded that the normal

---

[8] A further functional significance for dendritic spikes is the observation that axons of CNS neurons may arise directly from dendrites (142). Purpura (personal communication) has noted that in some thalamic regions as many as 25% of the neurons have their axons arising from dendrites.

synaptic delay for the excitatory synapse is short-circuited and the connection is electrotonic.

In subsequent reports (40, 41), these investigators showed: (a) that the DR potential of the conditioning stimulus is not necessary for the interaction and that, in fact, unconditioned VR stimuli were at times capable of evoking DR action potentials; (b) that the DR negativity following the DR discharge shows a phase lag with respect to the increased excitability of DR terminals in the region of the motoneuron pool following a conditioning stimulus; (c) that VR stimuli showed a time course of effectiveness, as measured by the height of the compound DR spike evoked by VR stimulation, similar to that of electrically stimulated DR fibers in the motoneuron pool; (d) that different DR fibers showed different time courses of firing following the same conditioning and test stimuli; (e) that a very small VR filament (about 100 μ) could elicit a DR discharge while all the other VR fibers in that region were incapable of eliciting that same DR spike even when stimulated together; and (f) that a conditioning stimulus which elicited a multi-unit DR reflex would increase the excitability to VR stimulation of a unit which did not fire at all following the conditioning stimulus.

These are an important series of results and the conclusions resulting from them are worthy of discussion. From these findings, the authors concluded that there is electrical coupling between fast afferents and motoneurons in mammals. Thus, it would appear that another example of electrical coupling of CNS neurons in mammals has been demonstrated, in addition to those found in the brainstem (6) and in the retina (42). In addition to the well studied but specialized motoneuron-motoneuron coupling in fish electric motoneurons and their command nuclei neurons (10) and in toadfish swimbladder motoneurons (119), motoneuron-motoneuron and motoneuron-DR terminal coupling have been postulated in other animals. Motoneuron-motoneuron coupling was predicted by Glees (60) in elasmobranchs on the basis of anatomical evidence, was suggested by Washizu (170), and was confirmed by Grinnell (65, 66) in amphibian spinal cord.[9] Furthermore, amphibian motoneuron-DR fiber interactions in the frog have been recognized since the work of Barron & Matthews (7) but some controversy as to whether this interaction is chemically or electrically mediated has ensued [see (65) for references]. Grinnell (66) has helped to resolve the argument by demonstrating that the VR–DR interaction has two components, an early electrical one, rarely seen without potentiation by gallamine or tetraethylammonium (TEA) chloride, and a late chemical one. The latency of the early response is similar to the latency of the electrical interaction between motoneurons and is shorter than in chemical interactions. The early response is not blocked by pharmacological agents and is suppressed by both magnesium (Mg^{++}) and calcium (Ca^{++}) ions without any apparent interaction between the two ion species; Ca^{++} facilitation of synaptic transmission with competi-

---

[9] For evidence of motoneuron-motoneuron interaction in cat spinal cord, see (114), and for anatomical correlations, see (22) and (188).

tive inhibition of the Ca^{2+} action by Mg^{2+} is to be expected at, and is almost diagnostic of, chemical synapses [see (189); but see (84), which shows that iontophoretic doses of Ca^{2+} and Mg^{2+} which do not affect synaptic activity, both reduce electrical excitability of neurons]. In the frog motoneuron, the fast $VR–DR$ interaction shows occlusion to a second stimulus for 10–20 msec, followed by a period of increased excitability. The long period of occlusion and the anatomical findings led the author to conclude that the interaction takes place at remote dendritic sites where gap junctions are seen (159). The augmentation of the weak $VR–DR$ action by drugs suggests that active dendritic invasion by action potentials may be enhanced by these agents.

"Rückmeldung" is a term introduced by Jung (79) to suggest that an electrical feedback between motoneurons and afferent fibers existed. This concept was based on the demonstration of conditioning of DR reflexes by VR stimuli, but was forgotten in the general swing away from the electrical hypothesis in the early fifties. The all too complete rejection of the electrical hypothesis was led by Eccles, formerly one of its leading proponents. The demise of this theory was occasioned by the finding of postsynaptic hyperpolarization relative to a distant electrode in association with inhibitory inputs. It should be noted that this finding is still apparently contradictory to all proposed electrical models of synaptic inhibition, including that of the Golgi type II cell, and has never been observed in the absence of other confirmatory evidence for chemical transmission.[10] However, other forms of electrical transmission have been demonstrated and now, apparently, at the very same cells which were originally involved in the controversy. The nature and extent of the suggested feedback still need to be investigated, including Jung's attractive hypothesis of feedback.

Whether subthreshold presynaptic depolarization produced by motoneuron firing is accompanied by increased or decreased transmitter release (positive or negative feedback) depends on a number of parameters not yet examined. Thus, one would expect an electrically inexcitable presynaptic terminal to show a larger action potential by algebraic addition of depolarization to the spike, thus leading to greater transmitter release; an excitable terminal might show inactivation of inward current-carrying ions as well as activation of potassium conductance, thus producing an attenuated action potential and reduced transmitter release. Proof of activation of a subthreshold EPSP from a retrogradedly activated presynaptic fiber before and after motoneuron discharge would increase our insight into this problem. The finding by Decima & Goldberg (41) of increased excitability of presynaptic terminals after conditioning is unfortunately ambiguous in this respect. Moreover, one would expect that the motor nucleus would not be the best

---

[10] Electrical inhibition in the Mauthner cell is accompanied by an intracellularly recorded depolarization relative to a remote electrode which is smaller than the local extracellular depolarization, producing a *relative* hyperpolarization which can be seen with differential recordings (63).

place to test such interactions and that more remote dendrites would be the expected site of interaction. Finally, Kuno & Llinás (95) reported that strong postsynaptic depolarization often induces an increase of "spontaneous" synaptic responses in cat motoneurons. The currents used (150 μA), however, might be sufficient to produce presynaptic depolarization in the absence of coupling.

The absence of electrotonic conduction of slow potentials into the DR's following VR stimulation (only spikes are seen) may indicate not only a weak or sparse interaction but also a more centrally located site than is responsible for primary afferent depolarization. The problem of presynaptic inhibition in the spinal cord[11] has not yet been resolved. The extent of the phenomenon would suggest a rich axo-axonic innervation of presynaptic terminals to motoneurons. Recent anatomic evidence for axo-axonal synapses (23) does not support the existence of a large population of axo-axonic connections. From the point of view of the physiologist, the remote dendritic location of excitatory synapses (139) would appear to indicate that the inhibition may also be remote. An interesting attempt to confirm this dendritic localization by using blocking agents is presented by Curtis & Felix (32).

If the motoneuron is electrically coupled to the presynaptic fiber, why do we not see evidence for this coupling in recordings from motoneurons? Several explanations exist. For example, it is possible that the coupling is rectified. If it could be demonstrated that hyperpolarization of presynaptic terminals resulted in postsynaptic hyperpolarization while depolarization failed to affect the motoneuron, this hypothesis would be supported. It is also possible that the electrical contacts are too remote from the soma to produce measurable changes, or, as a less likely alternative, that they are relatively close but that impedance mismatching to the large soma-dendritic membrane produces marked attentuation.

Another line of thought suggests that there may indeed be DR–VR coupling. Rall et al (139) have suggested that, since the EPSP is not accompanied by conductance changes experienced in the soma (157), the excitatory synapses must be remotely located on dendrites.[12] They also pointed out a less likely possibility that the excitatory synapse may not be chemical at all, but rather, electrically coupled. Although unlikely, this possibility must be kept in mind and investigated. Another phenomenon which may be of interest is found in the report of the first 60 motoneurons investigated with intracellular electrodes (15). Figure 13 of this classic paper shows an all or

[11] And elsewhere in the CNS (see 44).

[12] The excitatory synapse, predominantly located on portions of the dendrite remote from the soma, may be likened to a constant current source: the voltage change of the EPSP is delivered to the soma, where no conductance change is appreciated, by a high resistence element in series, the dendrite. This arrangement makes the EPSP particularly vulnerable to the conductance changes produced by inhibitory synapses closer to the soma which short-circuit the high resistance of the dendrite.

none early depolarization recorded from a motoneuron with a latency that was too short for a chemical synapse. The depolarization was approximately at threshold. Stimulation of the biceps-semitendinosus nerve produced a typical EPSP with weak stimuli, but with stronger stimulation the early potential appeared with a discrete latency jump. The explanation offered by the authors appears quite naive by current standards, but it is interesting to note that, accompanying the complete theoretical reversal involved in dropping the electrical transmission hypothesis, there is no mention of the possibility of electrical coupling. This possible evidence for electrical coupling should be re-examined in light of recent findings.[13]

The nature of the evidence for electrical coupling between motoneurons and motoneurons in coldblooded animals and between motoneurons and their afferents in both cold- and warmblooded vertebrates is still indirect but strongly suggestive. It is quite likely that these interpretations are correct in view of the available circumstantial evidence and the similar but better studied systems in electric fish (10). Future developments in this area of study should prove interesting. We anticipate strengthening of the case for electrical coupling and a fuller description of the properties and possible functions of these connections.

CRITERIA FOR IDENTIFICATION OF TRANSMITTERS[14]

In spite of recent progress in transmitter identification, there still appear to be misunderstandings about the evidence needed to identify a transmitter. Two topics especially call out for clarification: what are the minimum criteria needed to identify a transmitter, and what is the role of pharmacological identity in the identification of transmitters. [For earlier but more detailed analyses, see (4, 177, 179).]

It is an obvious but ignored fact that only two criteria need be established in order to identify a transmitter: the criteria of identity of action and that of collectibility. All other criteria are of interest only insofar as they elucidate the physiology, pharmacology, and biochemistry of the synapse. Put in another way, if it can be shown that a substance is released into the extracellular space from presynaptic nerves in quantities consistent with the amount and rate of stimulation and the physiology of transmitter release at that junction, and if it can be shown that the material released acts on postsynaptic membranes by using molecular mechanisms identical with

---

[13] It is possible that the reported finding during anoxia (102) of monosynaptic discharges in the absence of EPSPs may indicate increased electrical coupling in the DR-VR direction under these conditions. However, other possibilities also exist, including dendritic origin of spikes, reduction of critical firing level, or initial segment depolarization response to anoxia, in addition to Lloyd's suggestion that the EPSP is an epiphenomenon.

[14] I have recently reviewed the status of amino acids as neurotransmitters (179) and I will not deal with that topic here.

those used by the physiologically evoked transmitter, then that substance is a transmitter. Thus, in order to identify a transmitter, one must satisfy the criteria of collectibility and identity of action. In practice, it is usually extremely difficult to establish one or both of these criteria and, for this reason, much effort has been expended on "proving" that substance A is a transmitter by use of the ancillary criteria. Unfortunately, these ancillary criteria are not sufficiently discriminating to give us more than a reasonable surmise at best whether any substance is a transmitter. On the other hand, I feel rather optimistic about our ability in the near future to resolve many of the technical problems of using the two discriminatory criteria.

Among the technical problems to be faced in satisfying the criterion of collectibility in the CNS are the remoteness of the synapses—often, there are only long and tortuous pathways from synaptic regions to convenient collecting sites—and the existence of effective detoxification mechanisms which include chemical alteration of the transmitter as well as powerful uptake by neighboring cells. Here, study of the pharmacology of the synapse may play an important heuristic role by providing a tool (i.e. inhibition of transmitter detoxification mechanisms) for obtaining measurable quantities of transmitter. One possible direct approach to the collection problem may be the use, in microelectrode conformations, of organic substrate selective electrodes (8) which will register the potential proportional to the local concentration of a given compound. These electrodes are capable of measuring amounts of 10^{-15} moles or less and show great compound specificity as well. Similar electrodes have already been used by electrophysiologists to measure intracellular ionic concentrations (169).

The problem of characterization of the molecular mechanism of postsynaptic action, which is necessary to establish identity of action in the CNS, also appears to be tractable. Since the early days of measuring firing rates—the results of which were limited to a three-category decision: increase, decrease, or no change—much refinement in discriminatory power has followed use of intracellular techniques. These newer measures include recording changes in membrane polarization, changes in conductance, reversal potentials, and determination of the ion species participating in, or capable of participating in, the membrane process initiated by a putative transmitter. As each of these measures, tested with a transmitter candidate, is shown to coincide with the process evoked by the physiologically released transmitter, a greater degree of certitude is obtained in establishing identity of action.

In 1965, I proposed a quantitative procedure for determining whether the molecular mechanism evoked by an agent capable of changing membrane permeability was identical with that produced by another agent, especially a transmitter (176). It was hoped that such a measure would provide a single, highly discriminatory measure, sufficiently powerful to suffice for establishment of identity of action. The test involves comparing reversal potentials in a situation where three or more ion species permeate (if necessary, by addition of nonnative ionic species). The test predicts that, if the reversal potentials for two processes are equal to each other before and after each of $n-2$ separate changes in concentration of a different permeant ion (where n is the number of permeant ion species), the membrane mechanism used by the two activators is identical.[15] This quantitative measure combines all the previously mentioned discriminators. The procedure has already been tested at three synapses whereby glycine was shown to utilize the same molecular mechanism as does the disynaptic reciprocal inhibitory transmitter in spinal motoneurons (182); acetylcholine and weak and strong agonists of that compound were all shown to utilize the same mechanism, as does the frog neuromuscular transmitter (107, 184); and acetylcholine was shown to utilize the same mechanism as does both muscarinic and nicotinic agonists in snail H cells (McCance & Werman, unpublished).

The method described has apparently been challenged, however, by the finding that GABA and glycine produce postsynaptic permeability changes with very similar ionic discrimination in the spinal motoneuron (34) and in the Mauthner cell (145). Moreover, the receptors to GABA and glycine can be differentially blocked by strychnine (33). At first glance, this would appear to invalidate the usefulness of the method. It should be noted, however, that the method itself, which involves the relative permeabilities of three or more ionic species used together, has not yet been used to compare glycine and GABA action at motoneurons or Mauthner cells, and it is clear that this experiment should be done in the near future. Furthermore, even if the method were to fail to distinguish between glycine and GABA action, the experiment would be of importance. A common ionic mechanism for the two compounds would then be indicative of the possible interaction of several types of receptors with a common ionophore, a possibility with important theoretical consequences. For, if ionophores [the part of the membrane responsible for ionic movement; (21)] were common to several receptors, the identity of action criterion would now require two distinct steps: proof of use of identical receptors as well as that of identical ionophores. Only the latter identity appears approachable by the test in question.

Receptor identification, if it becomes vital, could be accomplished by use of blocking agents (see below) or by more direct means. Determination of the stoichiometry and the affinity constants of a transmitter candidate-receptor interaction has been shown feasible (16, 178, 180, 181). It is also probable that a corresponding theory for quantal interactions can be evolved, allowing determination of the stoichiometry and affinity constants of the physiological transmitter-receptor interaction and the results compared with those values obtained from use of externally applied ligands. The use of iontophoretic techniques to obtain dose-response curves for this purpose in the CNS has been shown to be feasible (136, 178, 182).

[15] In practice, permeant ions are increased to three, and only one change in concentration is needed, since more than 90% of synaptic conductance, in all studied cases, involves only one or two permeant ions.

Concerning this point, it has been claimed (35) that iontophoretically activated responses in CNS neurons, like those at neuromuscular junctions, are intense and focal. It is more likely, however, that the CNS responses are, in general, diffusely distributed over the neuron surface. Unlike the situation at neuromuscular junctions, it is usually not possible to place the iontophoretic electrode in close juxtaposition to the CNS neuron where synapses tend to be more or less widely distributed and the chances of placing the electrode close to a desired synapse are even less likely. Several experimental facts appear to support the case of diffuse action. First, it is not difficult to block antidromic invasion of motoneurons by iontophoretic application of inhibitory amino acids, even to the extent of blocking the initial-segment spike and first nodal spike which probably arise from synapse-free regions (see 182, Figs. 1 & 2). It is difficult to conceive of activation of a small somatic membrane patch so intense that it would load down remote membranes so effectively. Similarly, it is difficult to conceive of activation of a small patch of membrane producing increases in effective somadendritic membrane conductances greater than 300% (182). Finally, the iontophoretic application of glycine to motoneurons greatly reduces the apparent IPSP reversal potential in the absence of glycine, while the true reversal potentials for glycine and the IPSP appear to be, in fact, identical (182). This last phenomenon can only be explained by assuming that an appreciable proportion of inhibitory synapses is located at distances electrotonically remote from the motoneuron soma, probably on dendrites. If glycine were to act only locally, one would not expect physiological activation of these remote synapses to exhibit the same reversal potential as does the response to glycine; in fact the reversal potentials are equal (182), as confirmed by Curtis and his collaborators (24, 33) and others.

The role of the criterion of pharmacological identity in transmitter identification is, at best, a controversial one. I have mentioned the possible use of blocking agents in receptor identification. In my earlier review on criteria for transmitter identification (177), I pointed out some of the theoretical difficulties in using this criterion. Apparently, however, I did not emphasize this point enough since I have subsequently been cited as a great proponent of the use of this criterion (69, 123). Moreover, an editorial in *Nature* (1) waxes enthusiastic on the advantages of a blocking agent. It should, however, be pointed out that the very attractiveness claimed for blocking agents is double-edged and that same journal has recently been the scene of intense controversy over the use of strychnine as a glycine blocker (35, 144, 145) and bicuculline as a GABA blocker (30, 31, 62).

In a restricted sense, a blocking agent has great discriminatory power: if it can be shown that the action of substance A is blocked by a given compound which has no effect on synaptic transmission, it can be safely concluded that that compound is not the transmitter at the synapse being studied.[16] Of course, one must worry about technical problems such as ade-

---

[16] I am indebted to Dr. I. J. Kopin for bringing this point to my attention.

quate delivery of the blocking agent to the synaptic region when using this restricted form of the criterion. It should be emphasized that this is not the general use of the criterion. The criterion is almost always used in the inverse sense, where it is not generally valid. Thus, one cannot claim that, if substance A is not blocked by a blocking agent which blocks synaptic action, then substance A is not the transmitter. For example, the blocking agent may act presynaptically, either in the synthesis, storage, mobilization, or release of transmitter. Substances such as botulinium toxin or excess magnesium ions thus block synaptic transmission at peripheral cholinergic junctions without affecting exogeneous ACh action. However, this too is not the most common sense in which blocking action is utilized in transmitter pharmacology. The converse situation, where the action of substance A and synaptic transmission are both blocked by a common agent is usually taken to mean that the agent is a transmitter. A more conservative but also invalid conclusion is that substance A or a cogener of substance A is the transmitter. For example, both depolarizing agents such as excess potassium ions or non-depolarizing agents such as excess calcium ions, diamide (181a), phenol (93) and ethyl alcohol (117) are known to increase transmitter release from cholinergic terminals where their effects would be blocked by curare. Certainly neither group of compounds are transmitters at these junctions.

From this description, it is clear that a major difficulty with the use of blocking agents is the need for ascertaining the site of action of the blocking agent beforehand. Blocking agents which have presynaptic sites of action would not be expected to work against the transmitter. It is not in general feasible, however, to distinguish between pre- and postsynaptic sites of action or a mixture of the two unless the transmitter has already been identified (177, 186).[17] Furthermore, even localization to a postsynaptic site does not guarantee a synaptic action (4, 177). Hence, this use of blocking agents for the identification of transmitters is based on circular reasoning. In other words, once given the transmitter, the site of action of the antagonist is now determinable.

There is, admittedly, a reasonable use for blocking agents as screening agents since both the number of different synaptic inputs and the number of functionally different cell groupings in the CNS are large.[18] Moreover, the techniques for identification of transmitters that are theoretically less objectionable are technically much more difficult than assays of blocking activity. But, the results of blocking studies only provide clues which ultimately must be tested by more discriminating procedures.

Some remarks about the use of blocking agents are worthwhile. There is a certain measure of mystique involved in the use of blocking agents which

---

[17] An outstanding exception is the identification of a presynaptic site of action by change in frequency of spontaneous synaptic activity (e.g. mepps).

[18] An interesting recent use of blocking agents to localize "presynaptic" inhibition to remote dendrites is given by Curtis & Felix (32).

derives from the history of their discovery, their seminal role in early days of describing synaptic phenomena, and the complexity of the molecules. The relative structural complexity of such molecules[19] as d-tubocurarine, strychnine, picrotoxin, and bicuculline at times precludes the possibility of finding chemical similarity to the transmitter. In some cases, such as that of curare, detailed studies of the structure have indicated the nature of relationship of the antagonist to the transmitter in terms of active sites and even steric conformations. But there is yet a sense of mystery because the discovery and even the clinical use of the antagonist preceded the clarification of the mechanism of its action.

The use in well-defined systems of smaller molecules, often designed rationally as structural cogeners of the transmitter, offers us a useful insight into further possible difficulties with use of blocking agents. The crayfish neuromuscular junction contains two interactive cells, the excitatory nerve terminal and the muscle fiber, which both share a common inhibitory transmitter, apparently GABA. β-guanidino-propionic acid, a cogener of GABA, acts as an antagonist at the muscle synapse but, at the nerve terminal synapse, it mimics the action of GABA and is an agonist (45, 55). Thus, the use of this "blockader" at the latter synapse would fail to confirm GABA's transmitter role.

Large molecular blockaders often have lipophilic groupings, giving them the property of high penetrance into biological tissues, as well as highly charged groupings which tend to produce somewhat universal interactions with biological systems. In addition to the example quoted above of multiple actions for propranalol, the other blocking agents are all known to produce convulsive actions. Thus, we find that picrotoxin in convulsive doses (4–10 mg/K) has been recently used to indict GABA as a transmitter in brain stem synapses (76). Even more troublesome is the finding that picrotoxin has, in a number of excitable tissues, an inhibitory effect on nonsynaptic Cl^- conductance (118, 163). Strychnine, too, exhibits multiple actions and operates at multiple sites (5, 36, 53, 121, 128, 144, 145, 162, 166). These findings suggest caution in the use of this compound to identify inhibitory synapses which are physiologically inhibited by glycine. Even that most recent blockader, bicuculline, has been found to have convulsive actions and its value in identifying GABA synapses has been questioned (62). Finally, curare, the father of blocking agents, is operative at sites other than nicotinic synapses (3, 13, 56, 87, 109, 122, 132, 187). The cited references show that curare is capable, under proper circumstances and with proper experimental design, of exhibiting at least five different actions. The clinical usefulness of curare is based at least partly on the masking effect of the neuromuscular action on other actions at the doses used. But clinical use-

[19] I will not deal with the sympatholytic blocking agents but it is worth noting that such powerful β-blocking agents as propanolol are clinically useful local anesthetics (156) and can be shown to have curariform and cholinomimetic properties as well (186).

fulness is quite different from usefulness in the highly magnified situation of examining the physiology and pharmacology of a single synapse.

The use of blocking agents has, therefore, some role in the screening of synaptic transmitter candidates at a given synapse. The action of blocking agents is often complex and the site of action generally unknown before the identification of transmitters. Blockaders are of limited use in showing identity of action and appear to have no important independent role in the precise identification of a transmitter. Transmitters, it would seem, tell us more about blocking agents than the latter tell us about transmitters. This would appear to be a time for great caution in the use of blocking agents and a very promising one for development and use of refined measures of the identity of action and collectibility criteria.

PROLONGED SYNAPTIC ACTIVITY ACCOMPANIED BY INCREASED POSTSYNAPTIC MEMBRANE RESISTANCE

Histochemical evidence (91) as well as collection studies have suggested the presence of two major cholinergic pathways in the mammalian brain. One is the widely distributed reticulocortical system (81), while the other is the more specific sensory pathway from specific thalamic nuclei to the primary cortical sensory areas (111, 113). Ca^{2+} dependence of ACh release from the cortex has also been demonstrated (143). The neurophysiologist has, until now, been baffled by the behavior of cortical neurons to application of ACh. Most cortical neurons[20] respond to acetylcholine by increased rates of firing, or increased sensitivity to iontophoresis of glutamate (86). The onset of the response to ACh, however, is remarkably slow and the apparent excitation greatly outlasts the administration of ACh (86, 89). This is in sharp contrast both to the quick excitation produced on these cells by glutamate and to the rapid excitatory action of ACh on Renshaw cells (see below). Moreover, the cortical responses are primarily muscarinic (87) while those of Renshaw cells are primarily nicotinic (see below).

Intracellular studies (90) showed that ACh produced depolarization without clear changes in membrane resistance. When a selective block of the excitatory action of ACh was shown by 2,4-dinitrophenol (*DNP*), it was concluded that the major action of ACh was metabolic, controlling the activity of an electrogenic ionic pump (82, 90). In a recent series of papers from this laboratory (61, 88, 89), a new explanation for the action of ACh has been offered: ACh reduces resting conductance of K^+ ions.[21]

---

[20] Some more superficial neurons show variable degrees of suppression of firing in response to ACh (86). These will not be discussed here.

[21] One cannot help speculating on the role of mutual intellectual stimulation of neurophysiologists who work on simpler preparations and those who work in the CNS in relation to the problem of identifying the ACh mechanism of action. How much of seeing has to do with knowing what to see? And is it not easier to see a new phenomenon in the periphery, in invertebrates, in simpler systems in general? See (83, 85, 125,

DNP has now been shown to block selectively and reversibly both spontaneous firing of cortical neurons and firing elicited by ACh (61). Spikes elicited by glutamate were facilitated by moderate doses of DNP and blocked only by large amounts. Several other uncouplers or inhibitors of oxidative phosphorylation as well as moderate anoxia had similar effects; others, including azide, cyanide, and oubain had mainly an excitatory effect. Intracellular recording showed that extracellularly applied DNP led to hyperpolarization, a fall in membrane resistance, and a secondary marked reduction in electric excitability of cortical neurons. The hyperpolarization produced by DNP had a mean reversal potential nearly 30 mV more negative than the resting potential and identical to the mean reversal potential for the depolarizing action of ACh in the same cells.[22] Intracellular injection of Cl^-, sufficient to produce depolarizing IPSP's had no effect on the DNP potential. The authors concluded that DNP operates by raising membrane K^+ conductance.

As to the mechanism of the conductance change, they suggested that, as in other tissues, DNP inhibits mitochondrial accumulation of Ca^{2+}. Intracellular accumulation of Ca^{2+} would in turn facilitate membrane K^+ conductance as, for example, after intracellular injection of Ca^{2+} in Aplysia neurones (110). The authors suggested that the mechanism for DNP action may be general and noted that DNP and anoxia accelerate repolarization of atrial muscle fibers (171), while DNP and a lack of glucose hyperpolarize pancreatic islet cells (38). Unfortunately, the authors did not attempt to measure the effects of intracellularly injected DNP or Ca^{2+} nor was any attempt made to see if the same K^+ channels that were opened by DNP are occluded by ACh. The effect of DNP on ACh action could be determined by measuring the conductance change produced by several fixed doses of ACh before and during DNP treatment (see 179).

The authors concluded with a suggestion that effects similar to those of DNP may account for the action of general anesthetic agents. They noted that nembutal blocks excitation in Aplysia neurons by increasing K^+ conductance (150) and that volatile anesthetics produce hyperpolarization and decrease membrane resistance in the same cells (20). Furthermore, volatile anesthetics induce a non-energized conformational state in mitochondria (64). Presumably, the effects of anesthetic agents on cortical neurons will be checked for evidence of hyperpolarization and increased K^+

---

and 173) where a parallel historical development occurs. It appears possible that in frog sympathetic ganglion cells, the slow EPSP may have both a fast component, which is the result of an inactivation of potassium conductance, and a latter component, which is related to electrogenic pump activation (98, 174).

[22] The use of a resistance bridge for potential measurements is not to be recommended for accurate numerical determinations even in such high resistance cells as cortical neurons. When comparing reversal potentials of potential changes of the same order of magnitude in the same cell, however, this criticism is not important and differences in reversal potential would be expected to be significant.

conductance. The synaptic actions of the anesthetic agents (e.g. 20) could also, in fact, be explained by presynaptic hyperpolarization in the presence of a marked increase in conductance. These phenomena would shunt and reduce the overshoot of the terminal action potential, thereby reducing transmitter release. Again, this presumed action can be tested.

Just as DNP antagonized the action of ACh, Ba^{2+} and TEA were found (88) to have some agonistic actions similar to findings in other tissues (cf 183, 185). The authors (88) found that iontophoretically applied Ba^{2+} excited most neurons that are excitable by ACh, while depressing others. The action potentials evoked by Ba^{2+} were longer in duration than those produced by ACh and are characterized by firing in prolonged bursts. The excitatory action of Ba^{2+} was prevented by DNP but was not antagonized by the muscarinic blocking agents which are effective against ACh. Reversal potentials for the action of Ba^{2+} were found to be close to those of ACh and DNP. An unusual effect of Ba^{2+} was a late increase in resistance and hyperpolarization; the authors suggested that the cell was restored to its prepenetration state by the membrane-stabilizing action of Ba^{2+} (88).

It is clear from these results that a reduction in K^+ conductance must play a major role in Ba^{2+} action. The authors claim that the absence of any effect on the Cl^- sensitive IPSP implies an absence of Ba^{2+} effect on Cl^- conductance. This claim is probably not justified since the resting Cl^- conductance may not operate by the same mechanism as does the synaptic Cl^- conductance. Thus, even when a drug like picrotoxin is shown to block Cl^- conductance in synaptic and nonsynaptic membranes of the same cell, the dose ranges for the two actions are entirely different (118). The fact that the resting Cl^- conductance in cortical neurons appears to be very low, however, argues strongly against a major effect on Cl^- conductance. After all, one cannot have a 38% decrease in resting resistance produced by blocking Cl^- conductance when the cell membrane has a transport number of 0.1 or less for Cl^-. The effect of injected Cl^- ions on Ba^{2+} action would provide a more direct test of this point. The blocking action of Ba^{2+} on K^+ conductance is thus similar to its action on other excitable tissues (cf 183, 185).

Krnjević et al (88) claim that the actions of Ba^{2+} and ACh are markedly occlusive. The data offered do not entirely support this view, however. Since there is probably a maximal action produced by blocking all readily available K^+ conductance channels, working at or near maximal effectiveness of the drugs may produce a situation where no further response is obtained (161, 178). It must be appreciated that, in contrast to a process which increases conductance, the reduction of conductance will have a greater "driving force" when the membrane potential is close to the reversal potential. The further the membrane potential is from the reversal potential of the occluded ion (in the direction of the reversal potential of the counter-ions), the more the "driving force" is reduced. The real driving force is, of course, set by the reversal potential for the other ions whose conductance contributes to the resting potential. At all events, conductance measurements are to be preferred to firing rate measurements or even to depolarization (178). Furthermore, Figure 2 of Krnjević et al (88), which illustrates the interaction of Ba^{2+} and ACh, is not very convincing; the fact that glutamate produces a further increase in firing after the "occluded" response may only indicate that another ion is involved in glutamate action, probably Na^+. To test competition by Ba^{2+} and ACh for the same ionophore (see above), it is necessary to show that the conductance changes produced by fixed doses of each agent are not additive (179).

Krnjević et al (88) have also shown that TEA has no effect on resting membrane resistance or potential nor does it produce repetitive firing. TEA, intracellularly or extracellularly applied, however, greatly increases the duration of spikes, showing that its action is probably on the activated K^+ conductance of the action potential alone and not on the resting K^+ conductance, similar to TEA action on other tissues (68, 71, 183). Finally, they have shown that hemicholinium, a presumed specific antagonizer of ACh synthesis, has a strong excitatory action on those cells excited by ACh.

The mechanism of ACh excitation in cortical neurons was discussed in the third paper from Krnjević's laboratory (89). ACh, through muscarinic action, was shown to produce an increase in membrane resistance associated with a depolarization whose reversal potential is close to that of K^+. The authors emphasized the slow onset of excitation, even when the cell showed a brisk discharge; there may have even been an initial decrease in firing. The slow onset of firing cannot be explained by the measured membrane properties of the cell. The authors concluded that the slow onset can be ascribed to a slow interaction between ACh and membrane receptors. Unfortunately, no conductance or membrane potential changes were found during the period of depression and the mechanism of the early depression remains obscure. The after–discharge produced by ACh treatment is usually prolonged and may continue indefinitely. This effect is especially marked in cells that are initially relatively silent.

Intracellular recordings (89) show that ACh, like TEA (88), slows the repolarizating phase of the spike. Moreover, direct stimulation of a cell which has been depolarized by Ach and has still not fired produces a profound after-discharge. It was shown that the depolarization did not return to the baseline after the current pulse but instead returned to a new level, about 10 mV more depolarized than the level expected by extrapolation of the slowly rising ACh depolarization. This would suggest that the inactivation of the potassium conductance during action potential repolarization is greatly prolonged, or more likely, that there is a prolonged state of K^+ inactivation produced by the depolarization of the spike in the presence of ACh. It would have been of interest to see resistance measurements before and after the change in polarization level. Also, it would be of interest to know if the new polarization level can be abolished by a hyperpolarizing current or by an IPSP.

The authors noted that with extracellular recording a subthreshold excitatory effect could sometimes be demonstrated by application of glutamate. Moreover, some cells which were not at all excited by ACh showed enhanced responsivity to glutamate, including after-discharges which are not characteristic for glutamate effects. The possibility arises that physiological ACh action may not or only rarely reach threshold by itself. This would make for an interesting physiological mechanism, whereby ACh input would not only condition subthreshold fast synaptic stimuli (e.g. a glutamate releasing presynaptic neuron) but would also invoke a positive feedback mechanism, manifested by after-discharge.

It would be worthwhile to investigate the K^+ reversal potential directly in these cells. Thus, in frog sympathetic ganglion cells, Weight & Voltava have shown that the hyperpolarizing resistance increase induced by ACh and the after-potential of the spike have the same reversal potential. Such a direct comparison of K^+ and ACh reversal potentials, as well as the effect of intracellular K^+ ions on both processes should be investigated in cortical neurons. A three-ion test (176, also see above) using such ions as Rb^+ and Cs^+ could also be attempted. One important aspect of the ACh story in cerebral cortex unfortunately remains obscure: what is the effect of stimulating a coherent ACh-releasing pathway on these cells (177). It is important to demonstrate identical membrane mechanisms for both a specific physiological stimulus and ACh. One assumes that this data will soon be forthcoming.

Norepinephrine (NE) actions on cerebral cortex neurons were even slower in onset than those of ACh, were inversely and logarithmically related to the "spontaneous" neuronal firing rate and were very sensitive to barbiturate anesthesia (78). These authors also found that both ACh and NE onsets were overcome by stronger currents, suggesting that diffusional delays contribute substantially to the delayed onsets of action. The mechanism of action of NE, however, appears closest to clarification in the cerebellum.

Bloom and his collaborators have investigated the action of NE on Purkinje cells in the rat. Anatomical studies show a sparse localization of NE containing terminals around Purkinje cells (12), although the authors suggest that under different functional conditions the innervation might appear richer. These afferents appear to arise from the brain stem but their precise localization has not been established nor have they been stimulated. The authors have shown (74) that (a) almost all Purkinje cells show decreased firing in response to iontophoresis of NE and related compounds; (b) these responses are blocked by a β-antagonist, MJ-1999; (c) pharmacological blocking by desmethylimipramine of re-uptake of NE by presynaptic terminals markedly potentiates the response to NE; and (d) drug effects are not changed by treatment with 6-hydroxydopamine, which destroys NE terminals (12). The authors concluded that NE operates postsynaptically, probably as an inhibitory transmitter. In the last paper of this sequence (154), the authors showed that (a) cyclic AMP mimics the actions of NE;

(b) methyl xanthines, which inhibit enzymatic breakdown of cyclic AMP, were potentiaters of the depressant effects of both NE and cyclic AMP; (c) compounds reported to reduce cyclic AMP levels in peripheral tissues, including prostaglandins, block the action of NE; and (d) destruction of NE presynaptic terminals did not affect any of these actions. The effects of cyclic AMP have a much briefer onset than those of NE and the characteristic NE aftereffect is not seen with cyclic AMP. The authors concluded that NE effects are mediated by cyclic AMP in the Purkinje cell. The authors noted that in vitro NE increases cyclic AMP (80). This last study also showed increased cyclic AMP after application of histamine, a putative transmitter (165) which was also found to mimic the effects of NE and cyclic AMP but to be somewhat less potent than NE (154).

The story is pharmacologically rich and complex; relative potency of two agents, however, is not by itself a valid discriminant of transmitter function. One wishes that, in addition to evidence for similarity of action, there might be evidence that the various agents operated on the same membrane system, i.e. evidence of occlusion of effects of the compounds. Finally, one wishes that a physiological stimulus could be compared with the pharmacological effects.

The authors, however, have more information for us. After initially concluding that NE may act via an electrogenic pump mechanism (154) similar to that postulated for the slow IPSPs of frog and rabbit sympathetic neurons (97), they presented data showing that both cyclic AMP produced their effects via a membrane hyperpolarization accompanied by decreased membrane ionic conductance (155). The hyperpolarizing responses did not exhibit any reversal potential or consistent changes in magnitude within the membrane potential range of -10 to -80 mV. The responses were also unaffected by Cl^- injections sufficient to reverse IPSPs to depolarizing potentials. Nor were the authors able to find evidence for rectification of non-synaptic membranes in the range examined. The authors concluded that the data may be explained by a decrease in conductance to some ion (presumably Na^+) or by activation of an electrogenic pump. They noted the EPSP was enhanced but whether this can be explained by the hyperpolarization and resistance increase alone is not clear. The authors did not show any effect on action potential size or on interaction of the hyperpolarization with the rising phase of the action potential, nor have they studied effects of known pump uncouplers. It should be pointed out that the effects noted can be explained by pump poisoning as well as by activation, whether pharmacologically (a toxic effect) or physiologically (a synaptic effect). The known relationships of cyclic AMP to Ca^{2+} secretion suggest that the mechanisms discussed for cerebral cortical cell responses to ACh (89) may be of interest here as well. The data are of great interest and exploitation of these beginnings should help us understand at least one mechanism of NE action.

In their discussion of the mechanism of action of ACh, Krnjević et al (89) assumed that the steady-state net current is zero. Although this appears to be a reasonable assumption, it should be questioned in the case of cells which are leaky to ions at rest and which increase their resistance during synaptic activation. In vertebrate retinal receptors, the cells are depolarized in the dark and respond to light with hyperpolarization and a decrease in membrane conductance (cf 9). Hagins et al (67) have recently demonstrated that the leaky visual receptor exhibits a steady current in the dark. The similarity between ionic mechanisms for receptor potentials and synaptic potentials is compelling enough to warrant a search for a similar current in the absence of synaptic input in the leaky Purkinje cells and cerebral cortex cells which respond to synaptic input with decreased ionic conductances.[23]

It has become clear that in addition to synaptic mechanisms of different ionic behavior, including those operating via conductance increases as well as those operating via conductance decreases, one must get used to the idea of synaptic actions of different durations. The prolonged after-action of acetylcholine is quite different from the prolonged synaptic responses seen in the Renshaw cell (see below) and suggests a more or less stable change in membrane conformation lasting seconds. An even more stable synaptic action is predicated by Libet & Tosaka (99) in rabbit sympathetic ganglia where there is a facilitory excitation produced by dopamine which lasts hours. The slow onset of ACh and NE actions are also different from the responses seen with the better studied transmitters that produce brief conductance increases.

We have tended to focus attention on these latter synapses even when considering slower actions. The concept of a modulator, hitherto used to describe slow synaptic actions, ought to be discarded in favor of a mechanistic description of the transmitter actions. Transynaptic trophic activities and postsynaptic "learning" may involve synaptic actions of an extremely long time course even when compared to the action of dopamine. Finally, there may be cells which respond only to slow, prolonged inputs. For example, many hypothalamic cells show only continuous increase or decrease in firing to presynaptic stimuli when measured over periods up to 2.5 or 4.0 seconds (e.g. 52), a finding that suggests synaptic excitation lasting for periods that are long compared to the testing interval. In view of the probable neurosecretory function of these cells, a time course of seconds for synaptic action would be teleologically appropriate. It is further possible that some of these cells are physiologically stimulated only by transmitters exhibiting prolonged activity.

Renshaw Cells

Willis (188) has summarized arguments for and against the existence of the Renshaw cell as a separate entity and has presented a thorough discussion of current knowledge about Renshaw elements. The arguments against

---

[23] In both the NE and ACh stories, one would like to see evidence that these compounds do not inhibit release from atonically active presynaptic fiber of a different type.

the existence of a Renshaw cell are both anatomical and physiological-pharmacological in nature. The anatomical arguments include the failure to find short-axoned interneurons in the ventral horn (151) as well as the results of intracellular dye marking of presumed Renshaw elements (50). Only a few ventral horn interneurons were seen with axons which project ipsilaterally and none of these sent short axons toward motoneurons or their dendrites (151). Moreover, the same authors found that motoneuron recurrent collaterals apparently make synaptic contact with other motoneurons (151). Willis noted that there may be technical objections to the anatomical studies but, more cogently, that there is no reason to assume that Renshaw cells should have short axons. The basis for this assumption is the finding that the greatest recurrent efforts are from adjacent motoneurons. However, as Willis noted, the branching of a Renshaw cell element could easily occur close to its termination rather than close to the cell body.

Erulkar et al (50) attempted to identify physiologically defined Renshaw cells by marking with the dye fast green. The stained structures were generally quite small, 5 to 10 μ (except in one case of 17 μ) and all appeared to lack processes; all were found to be in close proximity to motoneurons. Moreover, these structures stained lightly to moderately for acetylcholinesterase. The authors suggest that these structures might be boutons, specifically the terminals of motoneuron recurrent collaterals. Willis has noted the technical difficulties in dye marking, but the failure to mark even one definite cell clearly remains disturbing. Recent success with procion yellow marking of dendrites (100) suggests that it might be worthwhile to repeat these experiments with that dye. Thus, Jankowska and Lindstrom (76a) have very recently reported Procion yellow marking of eight Renshaw cells. The recordings shown in their paper are not the best but probably do represent Renshaw elements. The cells so marked were small, 10 to 15 μ in diameter, and had dendrites extending 100 to 150 μ from the cell body. The cells were all located near the medial border of the ventral horn. However, in the two cases where axons could be identified and followed for some distance, they projected to the border of the ventro-medial funiculus, instead of towards nearby motoneurons. If these were indeed typical Renshaw cells, one must presume that the axons ascend or descend within the cord some distance before making synaptic contact with motoneurons.

Weight (172) has joined the argument for a motor axon recurrent collateral site for Renshaw activity. Weight has contended that the first spike of the Renshaw response is an all or none antidromic spike, noting that intracellular records show the first spike arose directly from the baseline with no underlying EPSP. The first spike was also shown to have an almost constant latency, slightly longer than that of the motoneuron, over a large range of stimulus strengths. The relatively long latency, contended Weight, could be explained by slower conduction velocity and a more tortuous pathway for the recurrent collateral. Moreover, the first spike could follow repetitive stimulation better than the motoneuron soma, at rates up to 100/sec

(96) and even massive doses of dihydro-β-erythroidin failed to affect the first spike. These facts add to the argument against the synaptic origin of the first spike.

Weight assumed that the latter Renshaw discharges resulted from presynaptic operation of ACh released by the spike on nicotinic receptors of the presynaptic terminals, a mechanism of positive feedback. He explained convergence of Renshaw cell responses as the result of diffusion of ACh from one set of terminals to those of neighboring axons. Finally, Weight claimed that atropine, in doses which do not affect Renshaw cell processes, eliminates recurrent inhibition. Thus, acetylcholine acting on motoneuron muscarinic receptors would be responsible for recurrent inhibition.

Willis (188) has argued that the absence of antidromic firing from Weight's postulated converging terminals presents an insurmountable objection to the latter's hypothesis and has cited examples of antidromic firing from terminals of motor axons in muscles and from DRs in DR reflexes as evidence that antidromic spikes should occur. The fact that antidromic discharge following terminal depolarization can occur, however, does not imply that it must occur, and the geometry of single branches of an arborizing terminal system presents a serious impedence mismatch where antidromic failure of invasion can and does occur. In fact, such terminal arborizations may represent physiologically useful frequency filters even in the orthodromic direction (120). Antidromic invasion from depolarized terminals would appear to be exceptional rather than usual: even in the case of muscles, the cat soleus stands out as an exceptional case. Finally, a second possible site of invasion blockage may exist at the junction of the recurrent collateral with the motor axon.

Weight (172) has argued that only one of many inputs to a Renshaw element gives a brief latency, drug resistant spike. However, Ryall (147) reported that more than one input may have the same very brief latency of 0.7 to 0.9 msec. This would put some strain on Weight's contention that only one axon is responsible for the earliest spike and that all others result from ACh leakage from adjacent terminals. Weight bolstered the argument for adjacent terminal interaction, on the other hand, by reminding us that Golgi studies (151) showed that synaptic boutons of motor axon collaterals often occur in clusters and that acetylcholinesterase-staining synaptic terminals are also often clumped together on spinal neurons (158). Furthermore, there is a great diminution in these cholinesterase-staining terminals on motoneurons 8 to 30 days following ventral root section (158). It should be noted, however, that the presence of acetylcholinesterase in spinal structures is only suggestive and not diagnostic of motoneuron processes.

Willis (188) has contended that the blockade of the first Renshaw spike by dihydro-β-erythroidin when a sub-maximal antidromic volley is given (29) is a valid refutation of Weight's claims. It appears that he misunderstood Weight's point; Weight (172, Fig. 1G-J) had presented even more convincing evidence that the first spike can be blocked than that found in

Willis's study. However, Weight noted that with different inputs only the longer latency first spike, which he admitted is synaptic, is blocked while the earlier one, which he suggested is antidromic, is not. Much more to the point would be to examine the pharmacological behavior in a situation such as that reported by Ryall (147, without documentation), where two separate inputs gave very brief latency responses. Although transmitter blocking studies are often ambiguous (see above), the persistent finding of a qualitative difference between the behavior of the short latency first spike and later, longer latency spikes appears compelling.

It should be pointed out that intracellular records are of two kinds, the first a typical orthodromic activation pattern with a long latency synaptic potential (172, Fig. 1F; 188, Fig. 8B), while the second is a brief latency peaked "EPSP" followed by a more typical but prolonged EPSP (172, Fig. 1E; 188, Fig. 7B; apparently also seen in extracellular records in 148, Fig. 2B). This will be further discussed below. Even more difficult to interpret is the finding (136) that hemicholinium causes block of the first spike. However, the first spike in the illustration shown in that paper was of relatively long latency (1.2 msec) and the drug also produced excitation of the Renshaw element. The actions of this drug are notoriously complex (88, 153).

A particularly intriguing and thus far unconfirmed finding by Weight (172) is that atropine decreased the initial slope of the recurrent IPSP of motoneurons without affecting the initial high frequency Renshaw discharge, both at the single cell level and in recordings from the dorsolateral surface of the spinal cord. Despite the author's unwarranted implication that a reduction of the initial slope of the recurrent EPSP indicated competitive inhibition at postsynaptic receptors, the finding must be taken seriously. The IPSP recordings shown (172, Fig. 2L-O) do not unequivocally support the author's claim. The earliest effects appear to be shortening of the IPSP followed by a general reduction and disappearance of the recurrent inhibitory potential. However, the author showed that dihydro-β-erythroidin can also block the recurrent IPSP while leaving the first three Renshaw spikes intact (172, Fig. 2D-F). This would suggest that the well known atropine effects on later parts of the Renshaw discharge may be sufficient to block the IPSP. It should also be noted that atropine does not appear to interfere significantly with recurrent inhibition as measured by monosynaptic reflex testing (29). It is thus possible that postsynaptic effects other than competitive inhibition of receptors may be produced by atropine. These include hyperpolarization or change in recurrent inhibitory reversal potential level. Resting potential and conductance measurements during the recurrent IPSP before and after atropine would therefore be useful in elucidating the nature of any postsynaptic effect of atropine.

Even more complicated findings reported (172) with the use of prostigmine include prolongation of the IPSP with apparent blockade accompanied by membrane hyperpolarization. Atropine now first restores the recurrent IPSP and then, in higher doses, blocks it anew. Again, conductance measurements and intracellular chloride injection as well as actual testing of inhibition of a known excitatory input might be helpful in elucidating the underlying mechanisms. The use of pharmacological agents is always complicated by the possibility of multiple sites of action of the agent. For further comments on use of pharmacological agents, see the section above on criteria for transmitter identification.

Felpel et al (54) have confirmed earlier reports (92, 126) that morphine markedly reduces recurrent inhibition without producing any change either on the monosynaptic reflex or on "direct" inhibition. In addition, the authors carefully studied the effect of morphine on Renshaw activity and found no changes in Renshaw response either to VR stimulation or to intravenous nicotine.[24] These findings may well be complementary to Weight's (172) findings with atropine. At any rate, they raise a question about the nature of the transmitter at the Renshaw synapse.[25]

It has been assumed that the Renshaw transmitter and the transmitter for direct inhibition are the same, because (a) recurrent and "direct" IPSPs are both blocked by strychnine (17); (b) the two different inhibitory potentials have the same sensitivity to strychnine (26); and (c) both inhibitory potentials have the same reversal potentials and ionic sensitivities (25, 47). Although these findings appear very strongly to favor a common transmitter, it should be noted that this has by no means been proved. Thus, strychnine appears to have a postsynaptic action on motoneurons which is not that of competitive inhibition (5, 36, 144, 145, 162, 166). Furthermore, the ionic sensitivity studies did not include a test as refined as the more recent three-ion test (176, also see above) and are, therefore, probably not conclusive. It is clear, however, that both processes are dominated by an increased permeability to chloride. The three-ion test should be applied to a comparison of recurrent and "direct" inhibitory potentials. Even if the ionic mechanisms are identical, however, we are left with the disturbing, but thus far undemonstrated possibility that more than one receptor share a common ionophore (see above).

Finally, the techniques used for reversal potential measurements have improved somewhat since the above studies of the mid-50s. Thus, we have a recent report of the reversal potential for recurrent inhibition being larger than that for direct inhibition in chromatolyzed motoneurons (95). The

---

[24] A minority report (28) found that morphine antagonizes glycine but not GABA. The authors also claimed that morphine has equal effects on "direct" and recurrent inhibition. The data presented do not support this last claim very strongly: there is certainly a more marked effect on recurrent inhibition than on disynaptic reciprocal inhibition in their figure.

[25] Morphine has been shown, in some situations, to reduce ACh release (77). Weight would presumably interpret this as a differential action of morphine on post-Renshaw release as against pre-Renshaw release. The finding does not support either the presence or absence of a specific Renshaw cell, but adds fuel to the argument concerning whether ACh is released from the Renshaw terminal.

authors attributed this finding to a localization of recurrent inhibitory synapses more remote from the soma than that for "direct" inhibitory synapses. It is also possible, however, that this reflects a different ionic mechanism for the two processes. This finding, as well as the two possible conclusions, should be investigated anew in normal motoneurons. It would be of interest in this connection to see if glycine drives the potential of recurrent inhibition to zero in the same manner as it does that of direct inhibition: (a) reducing the driving force; (b) shunting of the potential; (c) competition for receptors (182).

The study (37) which established the criterion of presence for glycine for "direct" inhibition did not answer any questions about the Renshaw transmitter: the procedure, which extensively destroyed spinal interneurons, did not effect Renshaw discharge (see also 112). It should be pointed out that this procedure, thoracic ligation, if sufficiently prolonged, can eliminate all spinal interneurons in lumbosacral segments while leaving 80% of motoneurons intact (59). The procedure used by van Harreveld (e.g. 167) can bring about the same result. The presence of Renshaw activity in the absence of interneurons would provide sufficient evidence for the validity of the Weight hypothesis; hence this experiment is an absolute must.

The challenge presented by Weight to the Renshaw cell hypothesis has been seminal on two counts.[26] First, it has brought to focus the undecided question as to the nature of the recurrent inhibitory transmitter. Weight's suggestion that this transmitter is ACh acting on motoneuron muscarinic receptors is subject to one obvious and vital criticism: iontophoretically applied ACh or muscarinic analogs have not been shown to have any action on motoneurons. On the other hand, the challenge to the existence of Renshaw cells as entities separate from motoneurons and their processes is another matter. The existence of separate Renshaw cells has not been completely demonstrated at this point. Weight's findings and interpretations suggest a valid, but unproven and unlikely alternative.

It should be pointed out that there are some other possible interpretations of some or all of the data presented. I agree with Weight (172) and Willis (188) that the suggestion (151, 152) that Renshaw effects are mediated through demonstrated dendrodendritic contacts (22, 151, 152, 188) is probably not tenable. The finding that Renshaw cells will follow at frequencies greater than somatic spikes can follow would appear to eliminate this possibility. I would like to offer another possibility which may account for the high frequency following, drug resistant first Renshaw spike as well as for convergence. A rather common result of intracellular recording is the peaked

---

[26] I do not condone iconoclasm for its own sake, but one must bear in mind Caws' (19) statement that ". . . some theories produced under powerful sponsorship may have a longer run than they deserve." It is also worth noting that controversy provides some of the most worthwhile and exciting moments in science. It inspires critical re-evaluation and dramatic experiments. I must agree with others, however, that when prolonged, controversy can become a bore.

early "EPSP" followed by a slower, smaller depolarization (in addition to the figures cited above, similar records can be seen in 46 and 47). We have recorded similar events and in some cases succeeded in hyperpolarizing the cells during these responses (Davidoff & Werman, unpublished observations). The two components of the response behaved quite differently: the late response grew with hyperpolarization, behaving like a conductance change with a reversal potential in the depolarizing direction. The early, peaked response, however, did not increase in amplitude and in one case, decreased in size with strong hyperpolarization. There has also been some published evidence that the first component may be graded (46). This behavior is not at all consistent with an EPSP. Weight (172, Fig. 1B) has pointed out that first spikes often showed extracellular notching. He has suggested that this constitutes evidence for an antidromic nature of the first spike but has not explained why "orthodromic" or direct spikes should not also have this notching as they do in motoneurons (24). These findings may indicate that the first response may really have a composite nature.

Willis (188) spoke of a tight synaptic coupling between recurrent collaterals and Renshaw elements. I would like to extend this by suggesting that the first response is electrically coupled to Renshaw elements, while the later responses are chemically transmitted. A similar situation has been found in ciliary ganglion synapses (108). It should be noted that the possibility of combined electric and chemical transmission does not identify the postsynaptic element (motoneuron collateral terminal or separate Renshaw cell), but it would make the Weight hypothesis a bit superfluous—although not invalid—especially if some of the synapses are located near Renshaw terminals.

CONCLUSION

The topics illustrated in this review give some idea of the ferment in CNS neurophysiology. I am greatly excited by the developments and the vitality of the field and I feel that a critical approach to ongoing problems need not be destructive. The highly critical approach[27] has as its own reward the enhanced satisfaction that an important contribution offers to the critic. In a world without values there may be no failures but, alas, there are also no successes.

[27] As an example of a much more negative temperament than mine, I offer the entire summary of a recent paper: "The author gave his critical remarks and objections against the classical theory of association fields and intracortical connections, against Penfield's concept of a centrencephalic system, against the doctrine of Magoun and Moruzzi about a non-specific activating system of the brain-stem reticular formation and against Jasper's concept of the so-called non-specific thalamic system" (75).

LITERATURE CITED

1. Advantages of an antagonist. 1970. *Nature London* 226:1199–200

2. Adrian, E. D. 1937. The spread of activity in the cerebral cortex. *J. Physiol. London* 88:127–61

3. Altimirano, M., Schleyer, W. L., Coates, C. W., Nachmansohn, D. 1955. Electrical activity in electric tissues. I. The difference between tertiary and quaternary nitrogen compounds in relation to their chemical and electrical activities. *Biochim. Biophys. Acta* 16:268–82

4. Aprison, M. H., Werman, R. 1968. A combined neurochemical and neurophysiological approach to identification of central nervous system transmitters. *Neurosci. Res.* 1:143–74

5. Araki, T. 1965. The effects of strychnine on the postsynaptic inhibitory action. *Abstr. Int. Congr. Physiol. Sci., 23rd*, p. 5.

6. Baker, R., Llinás, R. 1971. Electrotonic coupling between neurons in the rat mesencephalic nucleus. *J. Physiol. London* 212:45–63

7. Barron, D. H., Matthews, B. H. C. 1938. The interpretation of potential changes in the spinal cord. *J. Physiol. London* 92:276–321

8. Baum, G. 1971. Determination of acetylcholinesterase by an organic substrate selective electrode. *Anal. Biochem.* 39:65–72

9. Baylor, D. A., Fuortes, M. G. F. 1970. Electrical responses of single cones in the retina of the turtle. *J. Physiol. London* 207:77–92

10. Bennett. M. V. L. 1970. Comparative physiology: electric organs. *Ann. Rev. Physiol.* 32:471–528

11. Bennett, M. V. L., Freeman, A. R., Thaddeus, P. 1966. "Reversal" of postsynaptic potentials in nonisopotential systems. *Abstr. Biophys. Soc.* 10:142

12. Bloom, F. E., Hoffer, B. J., Siggins, G. R. 1971. Studies on norepinephrine-containing afferents to Purkinje cells of rat cerebellum. I. Localization of the fibers and their synapses. *Brain Res.* 25:501–21

13. Bowman, W. C., Roper, C. 1965. The effects of sympathomimetic amines on chronically denervated skeletal muscles. *Brit. J. Pharmacol. Chemother.* 24:98–109

14. Bowsher, D. 1970. Place and modality analysis in caudal reticular formation. *J. Physiol. London* 209:473–86

15. Brock, L. G., Coombs, J. S., Eccles, J. C. 1952. The recording of potentials from motoneurones with an intracellular electrode. *J. Physiol. London* 117:431–60

16. Brookes, N., Werman, R. 1970. Use of conductance measurements in the study of drug-receptor interactions. *Isr. J. Med. Sci.* 6:322

17. Brooks, V. B., Curtis, D. R., Eccles, J. C. 1957. The action of tetanus toxin on the inhibition of motoneurones. *J. Physiol. London* 135:655–672.

18. Calvin, W. H., Hellerstein, D. 1969. Dendritic spikes versus cable properties. *Science* 163:96–97

19. Caws, P. 1970. The structure of discovery. *Science* 166:1375–80

20. Chalazonitis, N. 1967. Selective actions of volatile anesthetics on synaptic transmission and autorhythmicity in single identifiable neurons. *Anesthesiology.* 28:111–122

21. Changeux, J. P., Podleski, T. R., Meunier, J. C. 1969. On some structural analogies between acetylcholinesterase and the macromolecular receptor of acetylcholine. *J. Gen. Physiol.* 54:225s–244s.

22. Conradi, S. 1969. Ultrastructure and distribution of neuronal and glial elements on the motoneuron surface in the lumbosacral spinal cord of the adult cat. *Acta Physiol. Scand. Suppl.* 332:5–48

23. Conradi, S. 1969. Ultrastructure of dorsal root boutons on lumbosacral motoneurons of the adult cat, as revealed by dorsal root section. *Acta Physiol. Scand. Suppl.* 332:85–115

24. Coombs, J. S., Curtis, D. R., Eccles, J. C. 1957. The generation of impulses in motoneurones. *J. Physiol. London* 139:232–49

25. Coombs, J. S., Eccles, J. C., Fatt, P. 1955. The specific ionic conductances and the ionic movement across the motoneuronal membrane that produce the inhibitory postsynaptic potential. *J. Physiol. London* 130:326–73

26. Coombs, J. S., Eccles, J. C., Fatt, P. 1955. The inhibitory suppression of

reflex discharges from motoneurones. *J. Physiol. London* 130:396–413

27. Crill, W. E. 1970. Unitary multiple-spiked responses in cat inferior olive nucleus. *J. Neurophysiol.* 32: 199–209

28. Curtis, D. R., Duggan, A. W. 1969. The depression of spinal inhibition by morphine. *Agents & Actions* 1: 14–19

29. Curtis, D. R., Duggan, A. W. 1969. On the existence of Renshaw cells. *Brain Res.* 15:597–99

30. Curtis, D. R., Duggan, A. W., Felix, D., Johnston, G. A. R. 1970. GABA, bicuculline and central inhibition. *Nature London* 226:1222–24

31. Curtis, D. R., Duggan, A. W., Felix, D., Johnston, G. A. R. 1970. Bicuculline and central GABA receptors. *Nature London* 228:676–77

32. Curtis, D. R., Felix, D. 1971. GABA and prolonged spinal inhibition. *Nature New Biol.* 231:187–88

33. Curtis, D. R., Hösli, L., Johnston, G. A. R. 1968. A pharmacological study of the depression of spinal neurones by glycine and related amino acids. *Exp. Brain Res.* 6:1–18

34. Curtis, D. R., Hösli, L., Johnston, G. A. R., Johnston, I. H. 1968. The hyperpolarization of spinal motoneurones by glycine and related amino acids. *Exp. Brain Res.* 5: 238–62

35. Curtis, D. R., Johnston, G. A. R. 1970. Strychnine, glycine and vertebrate postsynaptic inhibition. *Nature London* 225:1258–59

36. Davidoff, R. A., Aprison, M. H., Werman, R. 1969. The effects of strychnine on the inhibition of interneurons by glycine and γ-aminobutyric acid. *Int. J. Neuropharmacol.* 8:191–94

37. Davidoff, R. A., Graham, L. T., Shank, R. P., Werman, R., Aprison, M. H. 1968. Changes in amino acid concentrations associated with loss of spinal interneurons. *J. Neurochem.* 14:1025–31

38. Deane, P. M., Matthews, E. K. 1970. Glucose-induced activity in pancreatic islet cells. *J. Physiol.* 210: 255–64

39. Decima, E. E. 1969. An effect of postsynaptic neurons upon presynaptic terminals. *Proc. Nat. Acad. Sci. USA* 63:58–64

40. Decima, E. E., Goldberg, L. J. 1969. Time course of excitability changes of primary afferent terminals as determined by motoneuron-presynaptic interaction. *Brain Res.* 15: 288–90

41. Decima, E. E., Goldberg, L. J. 1970. Centrifugal dorsal root discharges induced by motoneurone activation. *J. Physiol. London* 207:103–18

42. Dowling, J. E., Boycott, B. B. 1965. Neural connections of the retina: fine structure of the inner plexiform layer. *Cold Spring Harbor Symp. Quant. Biol.* 30:393–402

43. Dowling, J. E., Boycott, B. B. 1966. Organization of the primate retina: electron microscopy. *Proc. Roy. Soc. London Ser.* B 166:80–111

44. Dubner, R. 1970. Oral-facial sensory and motor mechanisms. *Science.* 170:1130–32

45. Dudel, J. 1965. Presynaptic and postsynaptic effects of inhibitory drugs on the crayfish neuromuscular junction. *Pfluegers Arch. Gesamte Physiol. Menschen Tiere* 283:104–18

46. Eccles, J. C., Eccles, R. M., Iggo, A., Lundberg, A. 1961. Electrophysiological investigations on Renshaw cells. *J. Physiol. London* 159:461–78

47. Eccles, J. C., Fatt, P., Koketsu, K. 1954. Cholinergic and inhibitory synapses in a pathway from motor-axon collaterals to motoneurones. *J. Physiol. London* 126:524–62

48. Eccles, J. C., Libet, B., Young, R. R. 1958. The behavior of chromatolysed motoneurones studied by intracellular recording. *J. Physiol. London* 143:11–40

49. Engberg, I., Thaller, A. 1970. Hyperpolarizing actions of noradrenaline in spinal motoneurones. *Acta Physiol. Scand.* 80:34A–35A

50. Erulkar, S. D., Nichols, C. W., Popp, M. B., Koelle, G. B. 1968. Renshaw elements: localization and acetylcholinesterase content. *J. Histochem. Cytochem.* 16:128–35

51. Famigliatti, E. V., Jr. 1970. Dendrodendritic synapses in the lateral geniculate nucleus of the cat. *Brain Res.* 20:181–91

52. Feldman, S., Dafny, N. 1970. Effects of cortisol on unit activity in the hypothalamus of the rat. *Exp. Neurol.* 27:375–87

53. Ferguson, R. K., Zablocka-Esplin, B., Esplin, D. W. 1970. Peripheral cholinergic blockade by drugs that block postsynaptic central inhibition. *Arch. Int. Pharmacodyn. Ther.* 185:298–307

54. Felpel, L. P., Sinclair, J. G., Yim,

G. K. W. 1970. Effects of morphine on Renshaw cell activity. *Neuropharmacology* 9:203–10

55. Felz, A. 1971. Competitive interaction of β-guanidino-proprionic acid and γ-aminobutyric acid on the muscle fibre of the crayfish. *J. Physiol. London* In press

56. Fisk-Holmberg, M., Uvnäs, B. 1969. The mechanism of histamine release from isolated rat peritoneal mast cells induced by d-tubocurarine. *Acta Physiol. Scand.* 76:335–39

57. Fujita, Y. 1968. Activity of dendrites of single Purkinje cells and its relationship to so-called inactivation response in rabbit cerebellum. *J. Neurophysiol.* 31:131–41

58. Furukawa, T., Furshpan, E. J. 1963. Two inhibitory mechanisms in the Mauthner neurons of goldfish. *J. Neurophysiol.* 26:140–76

59. Gelfan, S., Tarlov, I. M. 1963. Altered neuron population in L_7 segment of dogs with experimental hind-limb rigidity. *Am. J. Physiol.* 205:606–16

60. Glees, P. 1961. *Experimental Neurology,* p. 169–70. Oxford: Clarendon Press 532 pp.

61. Godfraind, J. M., Kawamura, H., Krnjević, K., Pumain, R. 1971. Actions of dinitrophenol and some other metabolic inhibitors on cortical neurones. *J. Physiol. London* 215:199–222

62. Godfraind, J. M., Krnjević, K., Pumain, R. 1970. Doubtful value of bicuculline as a specific antagonist of GABA. *Nature London* 228:675–76

63. Granit, R., Kernall, D., Smith, R. S. 1963. Delayed depolarization and the repetitive response to intracellular stimulation of mammalian motoneurones. *J. Physiol. London* 168:890–910

64. Green, D. E. 1970., quoted in ref. 61.

65. Grinnell, A. D. 1966. A study of the interaction between motoneurones in the frog spinal cord. *J. Physiol. London* 182:612–48

66. Grinnell, A. D. 1970. Electrical interaction between antidromically stimulated frog motoneurones and dorsal root afferents: enhancement by gallamine and TEA. *J. Physiol. London* 210:17–43

67. Hagins, W. A., Penn. R. D., Yoshikami, S. 1970. Dark current and photocurrent in retinal rods. *Biophys. J.* 10:380–412

68. Hagiwara, S., Saito, N. 1959. Voltage-current relations in nerve membrane of *Onchidium verruculatum. J. Physiol. London* 148:161–79

69. Hebb, C. 1970. CNS at the cellular level: identity of transmitter agents. *Ann. Rev. Physiol.* 32:165–92

70. Hild, W., Tasaki, I. 1962. Morphological and physiological properties of neurons and glial cells in tissue culture. *J. Neurophysiol.* 25:277–304

71. Hille, B. 1967. The inhibition of delayed potassium currents in nerve by tetraethylammonium ion. *J. Gen. Physiol.* 50:1287–302

72. Hille, B., Bennett, M. V. L., Grundfest, H. 1965. Voltage clamp measurements of the Cl-conductance changes in skate electroplaques. *Biol. Bull.* 129:407–8

73. Hinds, J. W. 1970. Reciprocal and serial dendrodendritic synapses in the glomerular layer of the rat olfactory bulb. *Brain Res.* 17:530–34

74. Hoffer, B. J., Siggins, G. R., Bloom, F. E. 1971. Studies on norepinephrine-containing afferents to Purkinje cells of rat cerebellum. II. Sensitivity of Purkinje cells to norepinephrine and related substances administered by microiontophoresis. *Brain Res.* 25:523–34

75. Hrbek, J. 1968. A critique of the hitherto interpretation of nervous integration. *Acta Univ. Palackianae Olomuc., Fac. Med.* 49:5–12

76. Ito, M., Highstein, S. M., Tsuchiya, T. 1970. The postsynaptic inhibition of rabbit oculomotor neurones by secondary vestibular impulses and its blockage by picrotoxin. *Brain Res.* 17:520–23

76a. Jankowska, E., Lindstrom, S. 1971. Morphological identification of Renshaw cells. *Acta Physiol. Scand.* 81:428–30

77. Jhamandas, K., Pinsky, C., Phillis, J. W., 1970. Effects of morphine and its antagonists on release of cerebral cortical acetylcholine. *Nature London* 228:17–77

78. Johnson, E. S., Roberts, M. H. T., Sobieszek, A., Straughan, D. W. 1969; Noradrenaline sensitive cells in cat cerebral cortex. *Int. J. Neuropharmacol.* 8:549–66

79. Jung, R. 1953. Antidromic propagation of impulses into motoneurones. p. 120–31, In: *The Spinal Cord,* ed. J. L. Malcolm, J. A. B. Gray,

G. E. W. Wolstenholme, Boston: Little, Brown. 300 pp.

80. Kakiuchi, S., Rall, T. W. 1968. The influence of chemical agents on the accumulation of adrenosine $3'5'$-phosphate in slices of rabbit cerebellum. *Mol. Pharmacol.* 4:367–78

81. Kanai, T., Szerb, J. C. 1965. Mesencephalic reticular activating system and cortical acetylcholine output. *Nature London* 205:80–82

82. Kawamura, H., Krnjević, K. 1969. Action of acetylcholine on cortical neurones. *Pharmacologist* 11:254

83. Kehoe, J. S., Ascher, P. 1970. Reevaluation of the synaptic activation of an electrogenic sodium pump. *Nature London* 225:820–23

84. Kelly, J. S., Krnjević, K., Somjen, G. G. 1969. Divalent cations and electrical properties of cortical cells. *J. Neurobiol.* 2:197–208

85. Kobayashi, H., Libet, B. 1970. Actions of noradrenaline and acetylcholine on sympathetic ganglion cells. *J. Physiol. London* 208:353–72

86. Krnjević, K., Phillis, J. W. 1963. Acetylcholine-sensitive cells in the cerebral cortex. *J. Physiol. London* 166:296–327

87. Krnjević, K., Phillis, J. W. 1963. Pharmacological properties of acetylcholine sensitive cells in the cerebral cortex. *J. Physiol. London* 166:328–50

88. Krnjević, K., Pumain, R., Renaud, L. 1971. Effect of Ba^{2+} and tetraethylammonium on cortical neurones. *J. Physiol. London* 215:223–45

89. Krnjević, K., Pumain, R., Renaud, L. 1971. The mechanism of excitation by acetylcholine in the cerebral cortex. *J. Physiol. London* 215:247–68

90. Krnjević, K., Schwartz, S. 1967. Some properties of unresponsive cells in the cerebral cortex. *Exp. Brain Res.* 3-306–19

91. Krnjević, K., Silver, A. 1965. A histochemical study of cholinergic fibres in the cerebral cortex. *J. Anat.* 99: 711–59

92. Kruglov, N. A. 1964. Effect of the morphine-group analgesics on the central inhibitory mechanisms. *Int. J. Neuropharmacol.* 3:197–203

93. Kuba, K. 1969. The action of phenol on neuromuscular transmission in the red muscle of fish. *Jap. J. Physiol.* 19:762–74

94. Kuno, M., Llinás, R. 1970. Enhancement of synaptic transmission by

dendritic potentials in chromatolysed motoneurones of the cat. *J. Physiol. London* 210:807–21

95. Kuno, M., Llinás, R. 1970. Alterations of synaptic action in chromatolysed motoneurones of the cat. *J. Physiol. London* 210:823–28

96. Kuno, M., Rudomin, P. 1966. The release of acetylcholine from the spinal cord by antidromic stimulation of motor nerves. *J. Physiol. London* 187:177–93

97. Libet, B. 1970. Generation of slow inhibitory and excitatory postsynaptic potentials. *Fed. Proc.* 29: 1945–55

98. Libet, B. 1971. Inactivation of potassium conductance in slow postsynaptic excitation. *Science* 172:503–4

99. Libet, B., Tosaka, T. 1970. Dopamine as a synaptic transmitter and modulator in sympathetic ganglia: a different mode of synaptic action. *Proc. Nat. Acad. Sci. USA* 67:667–73

100. Llinás, R., Nicholson, C. 1971. Electrophysiological properties of dendrites and somata in alligator Purkinje cells. *J. Neurophysiol.* 34: 532–51

101. Llinás, R. Nicholson, C., Freeman, J. A., Hillman, D. E. 1968. Dendritic spikes and their inhibition in alligator Purkinje cells. *Science* 160:1132–35

102. Lloyd, D. P. C. 1970. Excitatory postsynaptic potential and monosynaptic reflex discharge of spinal motoneurons during anoxic insult. *Proc. Nat. Acad. Sci. USA* 66:626–629.

103. Lorente de Nó, R. 1947. Action potential of the motoneurons of the hypoglossus nucleus. *J. Cell. Comp. Physiol.* 29:207–87

104. Lund, R. D. 1969. Synaptic patterns of the superficial layers of the superior colliculus. *J. Comp. Neurol.* 135:179–208

105. Maekawa, K., Purpura, D. P. 1967. Properties of spontaneous and evoked synaptic activities of thalamic ventrobasal neurons. *J. Neurophysiol.* 30:360–81

106. Maekawa, K., Purpura, D. P. 1969. Quoted in *Electrophysiological Analysis of Synaptic Transmission*, ed. J. I. Hubbard, R. Llinás, D. M. J. Quastel, p. 284–85. London: Edward Arnold 372 pp.

107. Manalis, R. S., Werman, R. 1969. Reversal potentials for iontophore-

tic potentials produced by several cholinomimetics. *Physiologist* 12: 292

108. Martin, A. R., Pilar, G. 1963. Dual mode of synaptic transmission in the avian ciliary ganglion. *J. Physiol. London* 168:443–63

109. McIntyre, A. R., King, R. E., Dunn, A. L. 1945. Electrical activity of denervated mammalian skeletal muscle as influenced by d-tubocurarine. *J. Neurophysiol.* 8:297–307

110. Meech, R. W., Strumwasser, F. 1970. Intracellular calcium injection activates potassium conductance in Aplysia nerve cells. *Fed. Proc.* 29: 834

111. Mitchell, J. F. 1963. The spontaneous and evoked release of acetylcholine from the cerebral cortex. *J. Physiol. London* 165:98–116

112. Murayama, S., Smith, C. H. 1965. Rigidity of hind limbs of cats produced by occlusion of spinal cord blood supply. *Neurology* 15:565–77

113. Neal, M. J., Hemsworth, B. A., Mitchell, J. F. 1968. The excitation of central cholinergic mechanisms by stimulation of the auditory pathway. *Life Sci.* 7:757–63

114. Nelson, P. G. 1966. Interaction between spinal motoneurons of the cat. *J. Neurophysiol.* 29:275–87

115. Nelson, P. G., Burke, R. E. 1967. Delayed depolarization in cat spinal motoneurons. *Exp. Neurol.* 17:16–26

116. Nicholson, R., Llinás, R. 1971. Field potentials in the alligator cerebellum and theory of their relationship to Purkinje cell dendritic spikes. *J. Neurophysiol.* 34:509–31

117. Okada, K. 1970. Effects of divalent cations on the spontaneous transmitter release at the amphibian neuromuscular junction in the presence of ethanol. *Jap. J. Physiol.* 20:97–111

118. Ozeki, M., Freeman, A. R., Grundfest, H. 1966. The membrane components of crustacean neuromuscular systems. II. Analysis of interactions among the electrogenic components. *J. Gen. Physiol.* 49:1335–49

119. Pappas, G. D., Bennett, M. V. L. 1966. Specialized junctions involved in electrical transmission between neurons. *Ann. N Y Acad. Sci.* 137:495–508

120. Parnas, I. 1970. Differences in block-

ing frequency of presynaptic terminals of an axon innervating different crayfish muscles. *Biol. Bull.* 139:432

121. Parnas, I., Atwood, H. L. 1966. Differential effects of strychnine on crustacean slow, fast, and inhibitory neuromuscular systems. *J. Cell. Physiol.* 68:1–12

122. Payne, J. P. 1961. The initial transient stimulating action of neuromuscular blocking agents in the cat. *Brit. J. Anaesth.* 33:285–88

123. Phillis, J. W. 1970. *The Pharmacology of Synapses*, p. 6. Oxford: Pergamon, 358 pp.

124. Phillis, J. W., Ochs, S. 1971. Occlusive behavior of negative-wave direct cortical response (DCR) and single cells in the cortex. *J. Neurophysiol.* 34:374–88

125. Pinsker, H., Kandel, E. R. 1969. Synaptic activation of an electrogenic sodium pump. *Science.* 163: 931–34

126. Pinto Corrado, A., Longo, V. G. 1961. An electrophysiological analysis of the convulsant action of morphine, codeine, and thebaine. *Arch. Int. Pharmacodyn. Ther.* 132:255–69

127. Pollen, D. A. 1969. On the generation of neocortical potentials. p. 411–20 In: *Basic Mechanisms of the Epilepsies*, ed. H. H. Jasper, A. A. Ward, A. Pope Jr. Boston: Little, Brown

128. Pollen, D. A., Lux, H. D. 1966. Conductance changes during inhibitory postsynaptic potentials in normal and strychninized cortical neurons. *J. Neurophysiol.* 29:369–81

129. Price, J. L. 1968. The synaptic vesicles of the reciprocal synapse of the olfactory bulb. *Brain Res.* 11:697–700

130. Prince, D. A. 1969. Electrophysiology of "epileptic" neurons: Spike generation. *Electroencephalog. Clin. Neurophysiol.* 26:476–87

131. Purpura, D. P. 1967. Comparative physiology of dendrites. p. 372–92. In: *The Neurosciences: A Study Program*, ed. G. C. Quarton, T. Melnechuk, F. O. Schmitt, New York: Rockefeller Univ. Press 962 pp.

132. Purpura, D. P., Grundfest, H. 1957. Physiological and pharmacological consequences of different synaptic organization in cerebral and cerebellar cortex of cat. *J. Neurophysiol.* 20:494–522

133. Purpura, D. P., Malliani, A. 1966. Spike generation and propagation initiated in dendrites by transhippocampal polarization. *Brain Res.* 1:403–6

134. Purpura, D. P., McMurtry, J. G. 1965. Intracellular activities and evoked potential changes during polarization of motor cortex. *J. Neurophysiol.* 28:166–85

135. Purpura, D. P., Shofer, R. J., Scarff, T. 1965. Properties of synaptic activities and spike potentials in immature neocortex. *J. Neurophysiol.* 28:925–42

136. Quastel, D. M. J., Curtis, D. R. 1965. A central action of hemicholinium. *Nature London* 208:192–94

137. Rall, W. 1962. Theory of physiological properties of dendrites. *Ann. N Y Acad. Sci.* 96:1071–92

138. Rall, W. 1969. Distributions of potential in cylindrical coordinate and time constants for a membrane cylinder. *Biophys. J.* 9:1509–41

139. Rall, W., Burke, R. E., Smith, T. G., Nelson, P. G., Frank, K. 1967. Dendritic location of synapses and possible mechanisms for the monosynaptic EPSP in motoneurons. *J. Neurophysiol.* 30:1167–93

140. Rall, W., Shepherd, G. M. 1968. Theoretical reconstruction of field potentials and dendrodendritic synaptic interactions in olfactory bulb. *J. Neurophysiol.* 31:884–915

141. Rall, W., Shepherd, G. M., Ruse, T. S., Brightman, M. W. 1966. Dendro-dendritic synaptic pathway for inhibition in the olfactory bulb. *Expt. Neurol.* 14:44–56

142. Ramón y Cajal, S. 1911. Histologie du système nervoux de l'homme et des vertébrés. Paris:Mabine. 2 vols.

143. Randíc, M., Padjen, A. 1967. Effect of calcium ions on the release of acetylcholine from the cerebral cortex. *Nature London* 215:990

144. Roper, S., Diamond, J. 1970. Strychnine antagonism and glycine: a reply. *Nature London* 225:1259

145. Roper, S., Diamond, J., Yasargil, G. M. 1969. Does strychnine block inhibition post-synaptically? *Nature London* 223:1168–69

146. Ruiz-Menresa, F., Grundfest, H. 1971. Synaptic electrogenesis in eel electroplaques. *J. Gen. Physiol.* 57:71–92

147. Ryall, R. W. 1970. Renshaw cell mediated inhibition of Renshaw cells: Patterns of excitation and inhibition from impulses in motor axon collaterals. *J. Neurophysiol.* 33:257–70

148. Ryall, R. W., Piercey, M. F. 1971. Excitation and inhibition of Renshaw cells by impulses in peripheral afferent nerve fibers. *J. Neurophysiol.* 34:242–51

149. Sasaki, K., Shimono, T., Kawaguchi, S., Yoneda, Y. 1969. Field potentials produced by the parallel fibre stimulation in the cerebellar cortex. *Jap. J. Physiol.* 19:80–94

150. Sato, M., Austin, G. M., Yai, H. 1967. Increase in permeability of the postsynaptic membrane to potassium produced by 'Nembutal'. *Nature London* 215:1506–8

151. Scheibel, M. E., Scheibel, A. B. 1966. Spinal motoneurons, interneurons and Renshaw cells. A Golgi study. *Arch. Ital. Biol.* 104:328–53

152. Scheibel, M. E., Scheibel, A. B. 1971. Inhibition and the Renshaw cell: A structural critique. *Brain Behav. Evol.* 4:53–93

153. Scheuler, F. W. 1960. The mechanism of action of the hemicholiniums. *Int. Rev. Neurobiol.* 2:77–97

154. Siggins, G. R., Hoffer, B. J., Bloom, F. E. 1971. Studies on norepinephrine-containing afferents to Purkinje cells of rat cerebellum. III. Evidence for mediation of norepinephrine effects by cyclic $3',5'$-adenosine monophosphate. *Brain Res.* 25:535–53

155. Siggins, G. R., Oliver, A. P., Hoffer, B. J., Bloom, F. E. 1971. Cyclic adenosine monophosphate and norepinephrine: effects on transmembrane properties of cerebellar Purkinje cells. *Science* 171:192–94

156. Sinha, J. N., Jaju, B. P., Misra, U. C., Teufari, I. N., Smiral, R. C. 1967. Clinical efficacy of propranolol as a local anaesthetic. *Brit. J. Anaesth.* 39:887–90

157. Smith, T. G., Wuerker, R. B., Frank, K. 1967. Membrane impedance, changes during synaptic transmission in cat spinal motoneurons. *J. Neurophysiol.* 30:1072–96

158. Söderholm, U. 1965. Histochemical localization of esterases, phosphatases and tetrazolium reductases in the motor neurones of the spinal cord of the rat and the effect of nerve division. *Acta Physiol. Scand.* 65: *Suppl.* 256, 1–60

159. Sotelo, C., Taxi, J. 1970. Ultrastructural aspects of electrotonic junc-

tions in the spinal cord of the frog. *Brain Res.* 17:137–41.

160. Spencer, W. A., Kandel, E. R., 1961. Electrophysiology of hippocampal neurons. IV. Fast prepotentials. *J. Neurophysiol.* 24:272–85

161. Stephenson, R. P. 1956. A modification of receptor theory. *Brit. J. Pharmacol. Chemother.* 11:379–93

162. Stern, P., Hadzović, S. 1970. Effect of glycine on experimental hind-limb rigidity in rats. *Life Sci.* 9(1):955–59

163. Takeda, K., Oomura, Y. 1969. Two component anomalous rectification in frog muscle fibers. *Proc. Japan Acad.* 45:814–19

164. Terzuolo, C. A., Araki, T. 1961. An analysis of intra- versus extracellular potential changes associated with activity of single spinal motoneurones. *Ann. N Y Acad. Sci.* 94:547–58

165. Tebĕcis, A. K. 1970 Effects of histamine on the toad spinal cord. *Nature London* 225:196–97

166. Valdes, F., Orrego, F. 1970. Strychnine inhibits the binding of glycine to rat brain-cortex membrane. *Nature London* 226:761–62

167. van Harreveld, A., Spinelli, D. 1965. Reflex activity in spinal cats with postasphyxial rigidity. *Arch. Int. Physiol. Biochem.* 73:209–30

168. Wall, P. D. 1965. Impulses originating in the region of dendrites. *J. Physiol. London* 180:116–33

169. Walker, J. L., Jr. 1971. Ion specific liquid ion exchanger microelectrodes. *Anal. Chem.* 43:89A–93A

170. Washizu, Y. 1960. Single spinal motoneurons excitable from two different antidromic pathways. *Jap. J. Physiol.* 10:121–31

171. Webb, J. L., Hollander, P. 1956. Metabolic aspects of the relationship between contractility and membrane potentials of the rat atrium. *Cir. Res.* 9:618–26

172. Weight, F. F. 1968. Cholinergic mechanisms in recurrent inhibition of motoneurons In: *Psychopharmacology: A review of progress.* 1957–1967, ed. D. H. Efron, p. 69–75 P.H.S. Publ. No. 1836. Washington:US Govt. Print. Off.

173. Weight, F. F., Votava, J. 1970. Slow synaptic excitation in sympathetic ganglion cells: evidence for synaptic inactivation of potassium conductance. *Science* 170:755–58

174. Weight, F. F., Votava, J. 1971. In-

activation of potassium conductance in slow postsynaptic excitation. *Science* 172:504

175. Werman, R. 1963. Electrical inexcitability of the frog neuromuscular synapse. *J. Gen. Physiol.* 46:517–31

176. Werman, R. 1965. The specificity of molecular processes involved in neural transmission. *J. Theor. Biol.* 9:471–77

177. Werman, R. 1966. Criteria for identification of a central nervous system transmitter. *Comp. Biochem. Physiol.* 18:745–66

178. Werman, R. 1969. An electrophysiological approach to drug-receptor mechanisms. *Comp. Biochem. Physiol.* 30:997–1017

179. Werman, R. 1971. Amino acids as central neurotransmitters. *Res. Publ. Assoc. Res. Nerv. Ment. Dis.* In press

180. Werman, R., Brookes, N. 1969. Interaction of γ-aminobutyric acid with the postsynaptic inhibitory receptor of insect muscle. *Fed. Proc.* 28:831

181. Werman, R., Brookes, N., Blank, M. 1971. The stoichiometry of transmitter-receptor interactions. *Experientia* 27:14

181a. Werman, R., Carlen, P. L., Kushnir, M., Kosower, E. M. 1971. Effect of the thioloxidizing agent, diamide, on acetylcholine release at the frog endplate. *Nature New Biol.* 233:120–1

182. Werman, R., Davidoff, R. A., Aprison, M. H. 1968. The inhibitory action of glycine on spinal neurons in the cat. *J. Neurophysiol.* 31:81–95

183. Werman, R., Grundfest, H. 1961. Graded and all-or-none electrogenesis in arthropod muscle. II. The effects of alkali-earth and onium ions on lobster muscle fibers. *J. Gen. Physiol.* 44:997–1025

184. Werman, R., Manalis, R. S. 1970. Reversal potential measurements for strong and weak agonists of acetylcholine at the frog neuromuscular junction. *Isr. J. Med. Sci.* 6:320–21

185. Werman, R., McCann, F. V., Grundfest, H. 1961. Graded and all-or-none electrogenesis in arthropod muscle. I. The effects of alkali-earth cations on the neuromuscular system of *Romalea microptera. J. Gen. Physiol.* 44:979–95

186. Werman, R., Wislicki, L. 1971. Propranolol, a curariform and cholinomimetric agent at the frog neuro-

muscular junction. *Comp. Gen. Pharmacol.* 2:69–81

187. Whittaker, G. E., Thornton, J. A. 1970. The effect of tubocurarine on ulnar nerve conduction velocity. *Brit. J. Anaesth.* 42:497–500

188. Willis, W. D. 1971. The case for the Renshaw cell. *Brain Behav. Evol.* 4:5–52

189. Yamamoto, C. 1970. Synaptic transmission between mossy fiber and hippocampal neurons studied *in vitro* in thin brain sections. *Proc. Jap. Acad.* 46:1041–45

190. Zucker, R. S. 1969. Field potentials generated by dendritic spikes and synaptic potentials. *Science* 165:409–13

ENDOCRINE REGULATION OF BEHAVIOR 1084

Julian M. Davidson[1] and Seymour Levine[2]

Departments of Physiology and Psychiatry,
Stanford University School of Medicine, Stanford, California

The long history of mankind's obsession with love potions on the one hand, and of the practice of human and animal castration on the other, testifies to the longstanding belief in chemical control of sexual and agressive behavior patterns. It also illustrates the combination of fact and fantasy which has characterized such beliefs. While no scientific justification has yet been found for the reputed aphrodisiac properties of the various drugs which have been used to stimulate libido, there is no question of the efficacy of the gonadal hormones in this respect—androgens in the human, and both androgens and ovarian hormones in animal species. As to aggressive behavior, the ancients had observed that castration of bulls both pacified them and improved the quality of their meat. But only fairly recently has the relationship between testicular hormones and aggressive behavior been systematically studied. Apart from various aspects of reproductive and aggressive behavior, hormones are also involved in regulating a variety of other behavior patterns: we shall devote special attention in this chapter to the relatively new development of interest in adrenocortical hormones and nonreproductive behavior. We will deal primarily with work published in 1970 and the first half of 1971 and will limit our attention in general to mammals. Several reviews on different aspects of the field have appeared (10, 36, 57, 96, 98, 173) and are referred to below; a new quarterly journal entitled *Hormones and Behavior* has recently been founded.

This is the first time that a chapter devoted to behavioral endocrinology has been included in *Annual Review of Physiology*. We take this to reflect an increasing recognition of the interest of this field to physiologists, and welcome it as a manifestation of the progressive breakdown of interdisciplinary barriers.

REPRODUCTIVE BEHAVIOR

For no other behavior complex does the dependence on hormones seem to be so complete as for those behavior patterns related to reproduction.

[1] Dr. Davidson was supported by an NIH Special Fellowship at the Department of Human Anatomy, Oxford. The bibliographic assistance of Dorothy Buckland is warmly acknowledged.

[2] Dr. Levine is supported by USPHS Research Scientist Award 1-KO5-MH-19, 936-01 from the National Institute of Mental Health.

375

Perhaps this is because this relationship has been studied most. Scientific investigation in this area is often thought to date from Brown-Sequard's brave though misguided attempts (35) to stimulate his aging libido with aqueous extracts of testicular tissue. Forty years earlier, however, Berthold's small but classic study on castration and testicular transplantation in fowls included observations on behavioral changes (19). It is also not generally recognized that several of the modern findings in this area were presaged by work of the ancient Chinese alchemists, who not only administered testicular tissue for sexual debility and impotence, but also developed some skill in fractionating human urine to obtain partially purified steroids for this purpose (169).

ACTIVATIONAL EFFECTS OF GONADAL HORMONES

The central problem in relation to activational effects is how to explain inter- and intra-individual variations in sexual behavor—in particular the waxing and waning of receptivity during the female cycle—in terms of variations in circulating hormone levels. With the advent of easy and sensitive steroid saturation analysis assays, it has become feasible to correlate behavioral changes with simultaneous measurements of circulating steroids on a large scale. This possibility has not yet been exploited, although Feder et al (85, 86) have correlated progesterone levels in the guinea pig and rat with sexual receptivity using the chemical methods (with consequently limited numbers of animals).

The demonstration by many investigators of a preovulatory estrogen peak in all mammalian species so far studied [for review see (31)] supports the well established concept that estrogenic hormones are the principal activators of female sexual behavior. In the rat, the latency from estrogen peak to behavioral onset is considerably shorter than that found following estrogen-progesterone administration to ovariectomized animals. However, this discrepancy might be explained by such variables as previous exposure to ovarian hormones and concurrent effects of hormones other than estrogens. The minimum time for appearance of receptivity in ovariectomized rats following a large dose of intravenous estradiol was found to be 16–22 hrs (100), but experiments with intravenous infusion of smaller doses have not yet been reported. Clearly, neither administration of subcutaneous hormones in oil nor single intravenous pulses can duplicate the natural situation.

The question of the precise role of progesterone in activation of lordosis behavior is not yet settled. In the spayed rat, full receptivity may be activated with chronic administration of approximately physiological doses of estrogen (61, 218). This does not mean that progesterone is not involved or even essential under the conditions of the natural estrous cycle. In rats showing four-day cycles, receptivity appears at about the time of the critical period for ovulatory LH secretion (170, 181) which is about the time of the steep rise in circulating progesterone level. Powers (176) found that ovariectomy just before, but not after, the presumed time of the preovulatory progesterone rise eliminates or suppresses mating behavior. These findings in rats with a 4-day cycle indicate that progesterone is the physiological activator of female sexual behavior following estrogen "priming." In the 5-day cycle, however, receptivity was found to appear in 50% of cases before 2 PM (170), i.e. presumably before appreciable progesterone secretion has occurred. Furthermore, an appreciable percentage of rats of certain strains with 5-day cycles show receptivity on the evening before proestrus (8) and it appears that estrogen levels rise earlier in them than in those with 4-day cycles (see 170). In the 5-day cycle, therefore, the role of progesterone seems less prominent.

A high proportion of rats exposed to constant light display receptivity with normal lordosis quotients (104). The percentage of animals which were receptive rose from 40% after 30–60 days exposure to constant light to 73% after 150–183 days exposure; virtually all of these animals would be anovulatory. This suggests that constant, but not very high, levels of estrogen may be sufficient to induce normal receptivity in the absence of a progesterone "surge." A similar situation obtains for female rats treated neonatally with 10 µg testosterone propionate: they become anovulatory but show persistent behavioral estrus. Both situations resemble that of the spayed rat treated chronically with estrogen, which does not require progesterone for estrous behavior (61, 218).

The ability of ACTH (and therefore "stress") to stimulate the secretion of sufficient adrenal progesterone to affect sexual behavior in the rat (87, 172) introduces a possibly important new element into our understanding of the hormonal control of female sexual behavior. That this factor must be considered in relation to experimental manipulations of the cycle follows from the finding that sham ovariectomy advances the onset of receptivity on proestrus (170) and from the work on reserpine (see below). But while adrenal progesterone is important as a complicating factor in experiments on rodents, it remains to be established whether it plays an important role in the conditions of natural estrus. No effects of chronic adrenalectomy, on either natural (118) or estrogen-induced estrous behavior (60) have yet been demonstrated. However, Nequin & Schwartz (170) reported that acute adrenalectomy (at proestrus) was found to delay the onset of receptivity by some hours, while combined adrenalectomy and ovariectomy eliminated it completely; this effect could be reversed by progesterone (170). It should be noted that the diurnal rise in adrenocortical activity (plasma corticosterone) occurs at about the same time as the LH-progesterone rise, i.e. during the late afternoon [see (31)]. It has recently been confirmed that the adrenocortical peak is considerably higher on the day of proestrus (179).

Analogous to its effects on ovulation and other reproductive physiological parameters, progesterone can have inhibitory as well as facilitatory effects on female sexual behavior. It was earlier reported that guinea pigs differed from rats in that inhibitory effects were clearly demonstrable in the former but not in the latter (see references in 57). The concept that progesterone's inhibitory role is minimal in species with short cycles may be incorrect, however. Given the appropriate experimental conditions, the initial facilitatory phase of progesterone action seems to be followed by a later inhibitory phase in rats (167), mice (75), and hamsters (44) as well as in sheep, goats, and pigs (194, 195). The effect was shown to depend both on the amount of the "priming" dose of estrogen as well as on the time following progesterone administration.

In reflex ovulators a role for progesterone seems to be excluded by the fact that progesterone secretion is dependent on LH, which does not surge until mating occurs in these species. Rather small doses of estrogen alone are quite effective in activating receptivity in the rabbit (138). In fact, no clear demonstration of facilitatory effects of progesterone is yet available, although inhibitory effects have been demonstrated (see references in 57). Likewise, in the sow, progesterone is reported to inhibit but not to facilitate receptivity (195).

Heterotypical effects of hormones.—By appropriate manipulation of experimental conditions it can be shown that heterotypical (pertaining to the opposite sex) and homotypical hormones can produce both homotypical and heterotypical behavior in males and females [for a review of early work see (223)]. Recent detailed investigations (174, 218) have shown that testosterone acts much like estrogen in the induction of receptive behavior in the female rat, including its interaction with superimposed progesterone. Since the levels of circulating androgen produced in these experiments were presumably higher than those found normally, this effect is apparently "pharmacological." In the rabbit, however, McDonald et al (138) produced reliable receptive behavior with rather small amounts of testosterone propionate, and speculated that endogenous androgen secretion might suffice to influence estrous behavior in this species. Beyer et al (21) have proposed that the effect of androgen may be due to aromatization of the molecule to estrogenically active compounds. This was supported by the finding that testosterone, androstenedione and its 19-hydroxylated derivative, and dehydroepiandrosterone all stimulated lordosis as well as mounting behavior in the rabbit, whereas androsterone, dihydrotestosterone and chlorotestosterone acetate did not. The former compounds but not the latter are presumably aromatizable to estrogen, although evidence for such metabolic transformations in the rabbit was not available.

The earlier finding (56) that repeated high doses of estrogen elicit high levels of lordosis behavior in male rats, but that progesterone did not facilitate this behavior, has been confirmed (6). Others have found that estrogen treatment was only slightly effective (and not facilitated with progesterone) (222) or ineffective (80). It was suggested that the discrepancy might be due to differences in strain (80) or behavioral criteria (222).

Maternal behavior.—There has been little progress as yet in defining the precise endocrine conditions necessary for maternal behavior. The complex of stimuli which activates this behavior in the postpartum rat seems to include endocrine factors of pituitary and ovarian origin as well as exteroceptive signals from the pups (102, 160). Zarrow and collaborators (4) have provided evidence for the importance of the pituitary in the rabbit, a species in which they had previously demonstrated the involvement of ovarian steroids.

Mechanism of Behavioral Action of Gonadal Hormones

Although virtually nothing is yet known of the molecular mechanism involved, many data relevant to the manner in which gonadal hormones act on behavior are being collected. This information on the characteristics of the behavioral response to hormones and neuroactive agents, on the localization of brain areas involved in sexual behavior and on physicochemical events in the brain which accompany behavioral activation will no doubt contribute to the development of a future molecular psychobiology.

Receptors: location and properties.—The idea that the initial effect of steroid hormones is to bind to specific receptors in the target tissues has motivated a spate of studies on uptake and retention of testicular and ovarian hormones in the brain (e.g. 101, 140–142, 202). Unfortunately, we do not yet know which brain cells are involved in mediating the behavioral effects of hormones. Thus, particular patterns of uptake could reflect any of a variety of behavioral or nonbehavioral effects of the hormone being studied, including particularly feedback effects on neuroendocrine systems.

Further stimulation and lesion studies on the location of brain areas involved in the control of sexual behavior have appeared. In these, the importance of the preoptic region continues to receive confirmation. Recent experiments that are more thorough and convincing than previous ones demonstrate activation of sexual behavior on electrical stimulation of the preoptic region in male rats (17, 39, 134). Stimulation of other parts of the hypothalamus was, however, also effective (17, 39). The effectiveness of preoptic lesions in suppressing homotypical sexual behavior of males has been confirmed in rats (71, 93) and cats (107), and some aspects of the behavior of the female were eliminated by lesions of the medial forebrain bundle (112). Elimination of the olfactory bulbs has different effects depending upon the species and sex (see below). Lesions in the amygdala, and its projection pathway to the hypothalamus, the stria terminalis, reduced homotypical behavior in male rats, although not as effectively as did preoptic lesions (93).

Stimulation or lesion data do not provide definitive evidence on the location of steroid sensitive behavior-influencing regions, even when the inhibiting effect of a lesion cannot be reversed by steroid treatment, since it might remove an area essential for the behavior, but not involved in hormonal influences. More direct evidence comes from work on intracerebral implantation of steroid hormones. In the male barbary dove, Hutchison (116) obtained activation of courtship behavior with testosterone implants not only in the preoptic area, but also in other areas of the hypothalamus. This is consistent with the concept of a "network" of androgen sensitive hypothalamic cells involved in male reproductive behavior (55). Courtship behavior, unlike copulation, is not dependent on peripheral stimulation from the genitalia and this may be why it is more completely restored by hypothalamic testosterone implants (see 57). An interesting development in this area is the rapid (15 min) activation of lordosis in spayed female rats following implantation of crystalline progesterone in the midbrain reticular formation (183). No effects followed progesterone implantation in the lateral preoptic or the anterior or ventromedial hypothalamus.

Assuming the existence of receptors for hormonal effects on behavior, their functional characteristics can be compared to those of well established extracerebral receptors by studying relative thresholds of response to various steroids and their metabolites. Meyerson (149) has compared the relative effectiveness of a variety of estrogenic compounds on lordosis and peripheral reproductive tissues. Using compounds with different stereochemical configurations or other physicochemical properties including some shown to have different affinities for peripheral estrogen receptors, he found that the ratios of activities of different compounds were similar with respect to behavioral and vaginal responses. Thus, in respect to recognition characteristics for different molecules, the putative brain receptor for estrogen seemed to resemble that in the reproductive tract. The threshold of response to estrogen of the vaginal epithelium of the spayed rat and cat is lower than that for the lordosis response (61, 106, 149, 218). In male rats, on the other hand, behavioral responses are relatively more sensitive to androgen than are the accessory sex glands. Full behavioral maintenance in the castrate male could be obtained with lower daily doses of testosterone propionate than are required to maintain the structure of the sexual accessory glands (57). The "behavioral receptor" in the male rat shares with other endocrine target tissues the characteristic that, when deprived of its trophic hormone, its sensitivity to that hormone declined. Thus, more testosterone was required to restore sexual behavior after its disappearance in castrate rats than to maintain it following androgen administration from the day of castration (57). Similarly, in birds, Hutchinson found that intrahypothalamic implants of testosterone were more effective in restoring sexual behavior when implanted close to the time of castration than when a longer postcastration interval ensued (115).

From experiments on intrahypothalamic implantation of testosterone and of the antiandrogen cyproterone in male rats, Bloch & Davidson (23, 58) postulated the existence of two separate hypothalamic receptors for androgen: a behavioral receptor and one (in the medial basal region) for negative feedback regulation of gonadotropin secretion. Although testosterone implants in the anterior hypothalamus had no feedback effects, this was the most consistently effective site for behavioral activation [see references in (58)]. While the feedback receptor seems to respond to cyproterone as an antiandrogen, this steroid acts as a weak androgen in the activation of male sexual behavior (23). Evidence was provided that this dichotomy is not due to different thresholds of the various responses to androgen, since cyproterone is antiandrogenic for the growth of the penile spines, probably the most sensitive known response to androgen. There seems however, to be absolutely no antiandrogenic effect of cyproterone on sexual behavior of male rats (23). The same is true of aggressive behavior in mice (76) and gerbils (187) and spontaneous activity in rats (201), although apparently not for intracranial self-stimulation in rabbits (41).

The demonstration that testosterone action on the male accessory sexual glands seems to depend on its reduction to dihydrotestosterone (DHT) which is bound to the nucleus (37), has motivated several investigations on the effects of this steroid on male sexual behavior. The results from at least four laboratories (59, 84, 139, 221) were uniformly negative. The ineffectiveness of DHT as an activator of behavior is apparently not due to a failure of the steroid to cross the blood brain barrier, since it accumulates in the hypothalamus as much as testosterone (221) and it is effective in the feedback inhibition of gonadotropin secretion in guinea pigs (27) and rats (84), presumably via action on the hypothalamus (58). Intrahypothalamic DHT implants were considerably less effective than testosterone implants in restoring sexual behavior in the male rat (59). Finally, neonatal DHT is also ineffective in producing anovulatory sterility (32, 132).

Amines and sexual behavior.—The current interest among neural scientists in the physiological role of monoamines is reflected in recent attempts to implicate these compounds as neurotransmitters in pathways influencing sexual behavior. Some years ago Meyerson (147) proposed the existence of a serotoninergic central nervous mechanism controlling lordosis behavior. This hypothesis was based on the findings that brain monoamine depletors (reserpine and tetrabenazine) could substitute for progesterone in the activation of lordosis in estrogen primed spayed rats. Similarly, monoamine oxidase inhibitors depressed the lordosis response to estrogen-progesterone treatment (147). Meyerson measured receptivity essentially by a quantal (all or none) method. However, his use of large numbers of animals probably compensated for the loss of quantitative information which could be gained from measurements of lordosis-to-mount ratios.

Recently, this laboratory has extended its pharmacological observations to the hamster. In this species reserpine and tetrabenazine were ineffective in reducing estrous behavior, and the monoamine oxidase inhibitors pargyline and nialimide were less effective than in the rat (148). A synergism was observed between the inhibitory effects of monoamine oxidase inhibitors in rats and those of pilocarpine, suggesting a "relationship between muscarinic and monoaminergic hormone inhibitory mechanisms" (129). Further strengthening the case for a serotoninergic mechanism was the finding that parachlorophenylalanine (PCPA), a tryptophan hydroxylase inhibitor which specifically blocks serotonin synthesis, could replace progesterone in the estrogen primed rat (150). However, these authors could not obtain similar effects with another tryptophan hydroxylase inhibitor, α-propyldopacetamide, and others have been unable to confirm the stimulatory effects of PCPA on female sexual behavior (190).

Meyerson has not implied that the amines are necessarily affected by different levels of ovarian hormones; in fact, estrogen and progesterone had no effect on brain serotonin turnover (150). This negative finding might be due to failure to sample appropriate cells in the brain. Alternatively, the pharmacological treatments may not be related to normal physiological mechanisms of behavioral activation. One possibility is that their effects are mediated by changes in endocrine secretion. In his original experiments, Meyerson (147) attempted to eliminate adrenal activation as possibly mediating the effects of reserpine. However, pituitary-adrenal activation increases blood progesterone levels (87) and from thorough experiments in both the mouse (213) and the rat (172) it now seems that reserpine indeed acts via the adrenal to influence lordosis behavior.

It has been suggested, too, that serotoninergic mechanisms are involved in male copulatory behavior. Thus Dewsbury (67, 68) has confirmed earlier observations of Soulairac (197) that reserpine is stimulatory to the male. The observations of Tagliamonte et al (206), Shillito (192) and Sheard (191) that PCPA stimulates mounting behavior ("hypersexuality") in male and female rats initiated a small flurry of publications on this topic. Similar effects were reported to follow PCPA administration to male cats (88, 113). Whalen & Luttge (219) however, could find no evidence of changes in heterosexual behavior. Subsequently, a group including investigators who had earlier reported positive effects (88) failed to show any changes in sexual or aggressive behavior in male cats (226). This report included a plea for greater methodological care, including "stable and sensitive baseline measurements" in such studies. Compliance with this suggestion might reconcile a number of the inconsistencies between different investigations in this field. It is, for instance, not yet clear whether methodological considerations could explain the discrepancy between the failure to find effects of PCPA in normal male rats (219) and the finding that it stimulated mounting behavior (135). It should be noted, however, that in the latter investigation, effects of PCPA were found only when the castrated male rats were treated with submaximal doses of testosterone.

Triggering action of estrogen.—The behavioral action of estrogen in rats is characterized by a minimum "silent period" of about one day (depending on experimental conditions) before lordosis appears, even when facilitated with progesterone. Circulating estradiol is very rapidly metabolized (62), and lordosis may be activated by a single intravenous dose in the rat (100) or by exposure to estrogen in a removable silastic capsule in the guinea pig (38). Furthermore, estrogen accumulated in the brain disappears before the onset of receptive behavior [see references in (100)]. It thus appears that estrogen has a "triggering" action. The events occurring during the "silent period" following exposure to the hormone have been the object of some attention. Motivated by the observation that estrogen's action on the uterus involves stimulation of DNA-dependent RNA synthesis, Quadagno et al (177) implanted actinomycin-D into the hypothalamus of spayed rats 12 hrs after a priming dose of estrogen. Implants in the medial preoptic area and ventromedial hypothalamus, but not in the caudate nucleus, inhibited the lordosis response to 3 μg estradiol benzoate but not to 15 μg. If conclusive evidence can be obtained that the inhibitory effects were not due to the production of a "chemical lesion" or other nonspecific effects, these experiments will constitute evidence for the involvement of RNA synthesis in estrogen's action on behavior.

DIFFERENTIATION OF SEXUAL BEHAVIOR

Differentiation of behavioral patterns by perinatal administration of steroids is an area of intense interest to investigators in psychoendocrinology today. The basic doctrine in this area is that future masculinization of reproductive behavioral patterns is the result of the action of androgen at critical periods in early development. In the absence of circulating androgen, the brain remains in its neutral state, which is one of potential femaleness. This concept remains acceptable in its general outline, and various investigators have been occupied with extending the basic observations made on rats and guinea pigs to different species and testing the effects of different steroids in various dose regimens. Some of these studies will be considered before passing on to consideration of some general theoretical issues.

Two other short-cycle rodent species have now been shown to respond much as does the rat to neonatal manipulations. Mice underwent marked suppression of estrogen-progesterone induced lordosis following neonatal androgen treatment on the first but not the tenth day of life (78). Female hamsters also showed the expected responses to neonatal androgenization of the female and neonatal castration of the male (73, 205). Normal untreated male hamsters manifested a degree of lordosis behavior which is not found in rats (205, 209). Interestingly, treatment with androgen at the time of neonatal castration eliminated this behavior, thus in a sense producing an organism that is less "feminine" than the normal male hamster (73, 205). Similarly anomalous effects of testosterone treatment in neonatally castrated hamsters serve to illustrate the point that perinatal treatments with androgen may fail to duplicate the events by which endogenous androgen determines the process of behavioral differentiation. This may be due to use of the "wrong" androgen or, more likely, the "wrong" regimen of hormone administration (73).

Recent work on the dog by Beach & Kuehn (11) indicates the pattern of

reproductive behavior differentiation in a species with more complex courtship and mating patterns. Perinatal androgen prevented development of
overt sexual receptivity in the adult female offspring, and inhibited a variety
of "positive social responses" of the female to prospective male suitors
(prancing and barking at the male, etc). In addition, the attractiveness of
the female to the male was impaired. While genital differentiation in dogs is
mostly prenatal, androgen-induced sensitivity to the behavioral effects of
ovarian hormones appears to develop more slowly than in rodents, over the
intrauterine and postnatal phases.

A critical period for differentiation of mating behavior has not yet been
demonstrated for the rabbit. Anderson et al (3) have shown, however, that,
like sexual behavior in monkeys and guinea pigs, maternal behavior (nest
building) in rabbit offspring can be suppressed following adrogen administration to the mother during the gestation period. The observation by Neumann
et al (171) of the appearance of maternal behavior in male rats treated pre-
and postnatally with cyproterone acetate suggests perinatal differentiation
of maternal behavior in this species too.

The slow job of collecting data on the developmental effects of early
androgen on rhesus monkeys continues at the Beaverton Primate Center.
Despite the variety of behavioral changes shown to result from prenatal
exposure to androgen, the anovulatory sterility syndrome has not yet been
demonstrated in primates (96). That syndrome has now been described in
detail for guinea pigs treated prenatally with androgen (34); it would be
desirable to have more information on nonrodent species.

A variety of steroids have now been studied for their ability to affect
sexual differentiation on perinatal adminstration. Compared to the propionate, the free alcohol of testosterone is remarkably ineffective in this system.
Single doses had no observed effect on future reproductive function (33).
Repeated doses of 800 μg/day of free testosterone did produce anovulation
and acyclicity, but no lordosis suppression; in these experiments andro-
stendione and DHT were totally ineffective (132). These data suggest that
the threshold for physiological differentiation is lower than that for behavioral differentiation, a conclusion in keeping with the results of administering low doses of testosterone propionate (9). In mice, testosterone
propionate and androstenedione were both found to suppress ovulation and
sexual receptivity, although the former steroid was more effective (77).

Further reports on neonatal estrogen administration to rats have shown
again that it mimics the effects of androgen on the development of female
behavior patterns (72, 80, 109). Neonatal estradiol had only minor effects on
the behavior of adult mice (40). We still do not know what relationship the
perinatal effects of estrogen have to the normal differentiation process.

Further information on the type of changes in adult behavior resulting
from early androgen has been reported. These include a decrease in sexual
motivation as measured by the tendency to cross barriers and traverse run-
ways to reach males (151) and the "masculinization" of fear-related be-

havior (98, 175), feeding patterns (16), and olfactory preference for estrous odors in rats (180), and of aggression in mice (29, 50) and monkeys (96). Changes in maternal behavior were noted above.

Several issues of basic importance for the development of a theory of sexual differentiation have been admirably discussed in reviews by Goy (96) and Beach (10). The latter author condemned the characterization of the early androgen effect as "organizational," because of the implication that structural changes in the brain are involved. His point that the developmental effects are better viewed as changes in development of brain thresholds of response to hormonal stimulation is certainly valid for sexual and aggressive behavior. Nevertheless, it is not necessarily applicable to certain other perinatally organized behaviors such as various patterns of social behavior in prepuberal monkeys (96) which do not require hormones for their activation in adulthood.

Are thresholds of response to estrogen or progesterone affected by the differentiation process? Neonatal androgenization of the female rat abolishes the behavioral response to progesterone; similarly, neonatal castration makes the male rat subject to progesterone facilitation (see 57). Clemens et al (47) proposed that this effect sufficed to explain the lack of receptivity in the androgen sterilized female, while the estrogen threshold was unaffected by neonatal treatment. However, more extensive testing under different conditions showed the hypothesis to be untenable; in several studies thresholds of response to estrogen were also clearly depressed (80, 92, 175, 222).

The problem of the relationship between differentiation of male and female behavior patterns is still unsettled (see 96). The "organizational" effects of early androgen might conform to a "one anlage" model of differentiation in which a single undifferentiated mechanism in the brain of the foetus is influenced by androgen to develop in the male direction. This is analogous to the genital tubercle which differentiates either to a penis or a clitoris, with intermediate forms, but not dual structures, as possible outcomes of incomplete differentiation. Alternatively, a "two anlage" model might apply, resembling the process of reproductive tract differentiation. In this case, although the development of the male primordium usually parallels the suppression of the female primordium, both are actually retained, albeit vestigially, into adulthood and the possibility exists of simultaneous development of both primordia. In favor of the double anlage hypothesis is the well established fact that normal adults of both sexes can respond to the heterotypical gonadal hormones by showing heterotypical sexual behavior (see above).

Some curious findings have been reported which suggest that one may separate the brain control of homotypical and heterotypical behavior by selective lesions. An earlier report by Singer (196) claimed that anterior hypothalamic lesions in the female rat selectively eliminate lordosis, leaving androgen-induced mounting behavior intact. Preoptic lesions had the opposite effect. Dorner et al (71) have also claimed differential effects of different hypothalamic lesions on male/female sexual behavior patterns in both sexes. Hitt et al (112) have now reported that medial forebrain bundle lesions in the female rat abolish mounting while leaving lordosis behavior unchanged. The apparent support which these observations lend to the two anlage theory is attenuated by the fact that mounting behavior may be regarded as a normal facet of estrous behavior in the female. Possibly more convincing, however, are the results of neonatal administration of androstenedione to female rats or to neonatally castrated males. These animals show parallel development of both male and female behavior patterns (95, 199).

Unfortunately, the problem of differentiation of male sexual behavior is immensely complicated by the facts that (a) normal masculine behavior (including intromissions and ejaculation) is not possible without a normally developed penis, sensory feedback from which plays a presumably important role and (b) penile development is irreversibly influenced ("organized") by perinatal androgen (10). The behavioral bisexuality of the neonatally androstenedione treated female rat may be explained at least as easily by the development in these animals of an hypertrophied clitoris as by a unique action of androstenedione on a postulated male primordium in the brain. The question of whether there is any central differentiation of androgen in relation to male sexual behavior thus remains unsettled, although it is still vigorously supported by some investigators (70).

Even deeper mystery surrounds the question of the cellular mechanism of the differentiating action of androgen on the brain. Certainly the first step is to characterize the physiological or biochemical differences between the brains of males and females, and this can hardly be said to be accomplished. A promising development, however, has emerged from ultrastructure studies by Raisman & Field (178) on projections from the amygdala to the hypothalamus. They found that the ratio of the number of preoptic region synapses ending on dendritic spines to those ending on dendritic shafts was significantly lower in the male than in the female rat.

Several laboratories have sought changes in RNA or protein synthesis in relation to androgenization. Shimada & Gorbman (193) found evidence for synthesis of new species of RNA in the rat forebrain. Clayton, Kogura & Kraemer (46) reported that neonatal testosterone selectively affects synthesis of labelled RNA from tritiated uridine in the amygdala and preoptic areas of the female rat's brain. Using a different autoradiographic method, MacKinnon (133) has found changes in protein synthesis in roughly the same two regions of the mouse brain in relation to puberty and the estrous cycle. No effects of neonatal androgen on brain uptake of testosterone could be demonstrated in the female rat (101, 141). Several investigators have reported lower retention of ^{3}H-estradiol in brain tissue from androgen sterilized females [see references in (220)] but there are dissenters (220). At any rate, any differences in uptake which may exist between males, females, and neonatally manipulated rats seem to be rather small (141).

BEHAVIORAL AND SOCIAL REGULATION OF ENDOCRINE FUNCTION

Hormone-behavior interactions in which the endocrine changes are dependent rather than independent variables are gaining increasing attention. The two currently most prominent classes of such phenomena comprise (a) situations wherein pheromones may be involved [for review see (36)] and (b) situations in which sexual stimuli, particularly copulation, affect hormonal mechanisms essential for fertilization and successful gestation.

Pheromones.—The experimental evidence for mammalian pheromones, until recently largely confined to mice, is being rapidly extended to other species. The relative importance of these phenomena in different species may be reflected in interspecific differences in the effects of olfactory bulb ablation. In the male hamster this operation is reported to eliminate sexual behavior completely (166); but the effects seem to be relatively minor in the male (18) or female (8) rat. In fact a small but significant enhancement of lordosis has been reported (162). In the female mouse, olfactory bulbectomy has now been found to abolish maternal behavior with resulting cannibalization of the young (91).

The Bruce effect (36) has been demonstrated in the meadow vole (*Microtus pennsylvanicus*) (48). This study showed that pregnancy was blocked by exposure to an alien male but did not demonstrate that the effect was pheromonal. However, this is known to be the case for the laboratory mouse. An interesting new twist in relation to the Bruce effect is the finding that exposure to alien male mice actually increases the (usually small) rate of nidation in lactating mice (22). The absence of pregnancy block in lactation is presumed to be due to the low level of pre-existing circulating estrogen. The pheromone is postulated to act by increasing gonadotropin-mediated estrogen secretion. In nonlactaters the resulting high estrogen levels prevent implantation; in lactating mothers, by raising estrogen levels the nidation rate is improved (22). Further evidence for gonadotropin stimulating effects by male mouse pheromone is the demonstration of ovulation facilitation in the PMS or HCG treated immature mouse caused by the presence of (but not contact with) adult males. The effect was preventable by olfactory bulb removal (225). Whether in fact FSH-LH stimulation is the primary mechanism of the Bruce effect rather than prolactin inhibition (if the two are indeed separable) is still problematic, but the same general mechanism may be involved in the Whitten effect (facilitation and synchronization of ovulation and cycling in the mouse by male odor).

Evidence for presumably related phenomena has been reported in rats. Confirming and extending previous findings, McNeilly et al (146) found that the prolongation of estrous cycles in underfed rats could be largely reversed by the proximity of males, although nonolfactory cues were not eliminated in this study. Aron & Chateau (7) observed that exposure to male urine for one or two cycles advanced ovulation by one day in about 50% of five-day cycling rats. Another apparently gonadotropin-mediated pheromonal effect previously demonstrated in mice is the advancement of puberty induced by the odor of alien males. The presence of boars has now been shown to precipitate earlier puberty in the sow and to synchronize estrus. However nonolfactory cues were not eliminated (30) Vandenbergh (214) has interestingly added to the information in this area on mice by providing evidence for a depressed testicular growth rate due to the presence of adult males. This effect seems to represent a mechanism whereby a male can fend off reproductive competitors.

The signaling (e.g. "sex attractant") pheromones share with the primer pheromones (those acting on the endocrine system of the recipient) the property that their production depends on gonadal hormones [see references in (36)]. Further studies have been conducted on the preference shown by male rats for urinary odors of estrous females (42, 180, 200). This effect is not however very strong in rats, as might be expected from the nonessentiality of the olfactory bulbs for sex behavior in that species. More quantitative studies on other species are needed, since there is reason to believe that these effects are very widespread in social mammals (see 49).

While the chemical nature of the mammalian primer pheromones remains unknown, there is quite good evidence for the structure of several signaling pheromones in mammals. Thus the active principle in boar urine which may elicit the "standing reaction" (adoption of the mating stance) is believed to be the steroid 5-α-androst-16-ene-3-one, the source of the boar taint in pork. The active ingredient of the sex attractant material from the tarsal gland of the male blacktailed deer has been reported to be cis-4-hydroxydodeca-6-enoic acid lactone [See references in (49)]. Of particular interest is the recent report by Michael et al (155) of the isolation from the vaginal secretions of the rhesus monkey of substances which stimulate copulation in the male (154). The active ingredients appeared to be a mixture of short chain fatty acids including acetic, propionic, and butyric acids (155).

Finally it should be noted that pheromones participate not only in reproductive behavior but probably also in many other forms of social communication. Mugford & Nowell (163), for example, have adduced evidence for an anti-aggression pheromone. Exposure to urine from nonspayed or spayed estrogen-treated female mice increased the normally aggressive behavior of isolated males. It was suggested that the clitoral glands produce the postulated pheromone. Further evidence for the involvement in aggressive behavior of pheromones produced by male mice has also been presented (145).

Effects of sexual behavior on gonadotropin secretion.—The ubiquity of the endocrine-mediated effects of behavioral stimuli on reproductive function is becoming increasingly recognized. Of course, this is nowhere more obvious than in the numerous avian and occasional mammalian species in which ovulation depends on the mating stimulus. In addition, there are longer latency effects of coital stimuli on endocrine function which result in pseudopregnancy or the fostering of conditions necessary for successful pregnancy. If ovulation is prevented in the rat by various methods which do not block sexual receptivity, mating can induce ovulation. The variety of conditions under which this acute neuroendocrine reflex may be evoked have now been studied fairly extensively [see references in (57)]. Problems of current interest are: (*a*) characterization of the specific stimuli involved in activating the reflex, and (*b*) the pathways which the reflex takes in the central nervous system.

Earlier work in the reflexly ovulating rabbit as well as in rodents has shown that although direct stimulation of the genital tract is not essential for ovulation, such stimulation is considerably more effective than mounting alone [see references in (57)]. Recently, in the reflexly ovulating Alpaca, mounting was found to result in a 33% rate of ovulation while complete mating induced ovulation in 77 to 82% of cases (89). Prevention of mating-induced pseudopregnancy in the rat by pelvic neurotomy has been confirmed (198). In the mouse, several investigators are focusing their efforts on the precise nature of the adequate intravaginal stimulus for the induction of pseudopregnancy. McGill (144) has tested a hypothesis that pseudopregnancy in mice is activated by swelling of the penis during the ejaculatory reflex; the deposition of a vaginal plug is unnecessary in this species (43, 144). In mice and hamsters, Diamond (69) has attempted to work out a code whereby the numbers and spacing of artificial intromissions (using a vibrator) could be related to the efficacy of this stimulus in evoking pseudopregnancy. In both species the optimal combination of these parameters approximated that occurring in normal mating behavior.

The route through the diencephalon traversed by the pathway of these reflexes has been studied by selective deafferentation. Taleisnik et al (207) found that vaginal stimlation-induced psuedoprenancy was not blocked by a section over the preoptic region ("roof cut") which severed descending tracts including the fornix. It was, however, blocked by cutting the connections between the preoptic region and the medial basal hypothalamus. Similarly, Kalra & Sawyer (119) reported inhibition of copulation-induced ovulation in the pentobarbital-blocked rat by a hypothalamic cut, rostral to the suprachiasmatic nucleus, which did not interfere with either the ability of these females to mate or their capacity to ovulate following electrical stimulation of the median eminence. Various other sections were ineffective, and it was concluded that the coital stimulus ascends the brainstem dorsal or lateral to the mammillary body, and then reverses its direction at the preoptic area to enter the hypothalamus proper.

A direct relationship has been demonstrated between numbers of intromissions received by the female rat and probability of successful pregnancy following one ejaculation. That this involves both activation of hormonal change in the recipient female and facilitation of sperm transport (1) has been confirmed, and the intromission frequency threshold for pseudopregnancy induction was higher than that for normal sperm transport (43). It is not yet clear whether a neuroendocrine mechanism (involving oxytocin?)

is involved in the latter process or whether it simply depends on the mechanical state of the vagina or cervix. Increased progesterone levels were observed as early as six hours postcoitum in the rat (2). The experimental conditions reported were not sufficient to conclude when this rise occurred in relation to LH release and ovulation, but the investigators presumed that high intromission rates facilitate a direct neuroendocrine reflex, possibly mediated by ACTH secretion (2). However, nonspecific "stress" was not eliminated as a possibly contributory factor.

If we are to understand the neuroendocrine events following the mating stimulus, it is necessary to study more immediate changes, not in themselves dependent upon luteal activation, such as gonadotropin secretion. In an interesting study, Spies & Niswender (198) measured blood FSH, LH, and prolactin levels in rats at various time intervals following mating early on the morning of estrus; i.e. presumably shortly after ovulation had occurred. Twenty minutes after "mating" (no behavioral details are reported) the levels of all three hormones were significantly elevated in the plasma. They were also found to be elevated 8 hrs postcoitally. Pelvic neurotomy, which prevented pseudopregnancy, inhibited the prolactin rise at 8 hrs but not at 20 min; at neither time interval were the increases in FSH and LH affected. These data may be taken to substantiate the distinction described by Everett (82) between mechanisms involved in reflex ovulation and in induction of pseudopregnancy. They are difficult to reconcile with the finding of Zarrow & Clark (224) that pelvic neurotomy blocks reflex ovulation in rats.

Indications in the literature [see references in (57)] that LH and testosterone secretion in the male may similarly be activated by mating have not yet been sufficiently substantiated. The earlier report that bioassayable plasma LH was elevated in male rats 20 to 30 min after mating could not be confirmed using the more reliable method of radioimmunoassay (198). Although Katongole et al (120) claimed an immediate rise in blood LH following sexual stimulation of the bull, data were presented for only two animals. Convey et al reported briefly (52) the absence of LH changes 5 or 13 minutes after ejaculation in six bulls, although prolactin increased markedly at those times. Despite indications that androgen production may be stimulated by sexual activity in human males (see below) this possibility, too, has not yet been systematically studied.

Finally, two possibly related, albeit mystifying, observations should be mentioned. Wheel running seems to have a "virilizing" effect (stimulation of accessory sex glands) in male rats (108). Also in male rats, copulation was almost invariably found to precipitate some degree of hemolysis (32). Whether the marked increases in plasma hemoglobin were due to some endocrine mechanism is still unknown.

PRIMATE AND HUMAN SEXUAL BEHAVIOR

Further field observations on sexual behavior throughout the menstrual cycle showed two peaks of activity in noncaptive rhesus monkeys; one in midcycle and one perimenstrually (131). In free-ranging chachma baboons, receptivity (numbers of "presentations") and the attractiveness of the female to the male were highest during the follicular phase, i.e. during sexual skin swelling (185). Similarly, under laboratory conditions, the sexual behavior of both males and females was maximal in mid cycle in the talapoin monkey (*Myopithecus talapoin*) (189) as well as in the rhesus (156).

A comparison of the cyclic distribution of sexual activity in rhesus monkeys (frequency of ejaculations) with that in an earlier study on incidence of intercourse in a human population showed similarities in pattern, although the amplitude of the changes in humans were smaller (156). While female monkeys do seem less dependent than "lower" species on ovarian hormones, they are clearly more dependent on them than are human females. Not only does ovariectomy markedly decrease and estrogen markedly increase a variety of sexual invitational behaviors (presentations, hand reaches, head ducks and receptivity) (157, 227), but corresponding changes occur in the female monkey's attractiveness to the male (111 and see below).

Because of the rather widespread, though poorly substantiated (57) view among clinicians that adrenal androgens play an important role in the sexual behavior of women, the recent work by Everitt & Herbert (83, 111) using the female rhesus monkey is of special interest. Those workers found that both adrenalectomy with cortisol replacement and treatment with dexamethasone, the pituitary-adrenal inhibitor, suppressed sexual receptivity in the ovariectomized, estrogen treated rhesus, with consequent decline in male behavior. The effect could be reversed by androstenedione which is produced by the adrenal cortex or by testosterone which may be effectively converted to androstenedione after reaching the circulation. The role of ovarian hormones, in the view of these investigators, differs from that of androgen; the direct effect of the former was believed to be on attractiveness rather than receptivity. Conceivably, estrogen might act to stimulate adrenal androgen production via ACTH and thus affect the behavior of the female, but this mechanism has not yet been substantiated.

Recent work of Michael et al promises to elucidate the action of estrogen on the sexual attractiveness of female rhesus (154, 155). This seems not to be related to estrogen-induced reddening of the sexual skin (111, 154), but rather to depend on olfactory cues reaching the male (153). Michael et al (155) have now reported that intravaginal production of short-chain aliphatic acids is activated by estrogen administration, and these acids act as sexual attractants, stimulating the copulatory behavior of the males. Further substantiation of these briefly reported findings will be awaited with considerable interest since they seem to represent the first isolation of pheromones in primates.

Consideration of our knowledge of endocrine factors in human sexual behavior reveals little if any well established principles beyond the depressing effect of orchidectomy and the generally stimulating effect of testosterone in men. Nevertheless, new evidence continues to appear suggesting that a variety of the phenomena discussed above in the context of animal behavior may have their counterpart in humans.

An entertaining review by Comfort (49) examines the possible role of pheromones in the human species. The production by, and susceptibility to, substances with musk-like odors in humans does suggest that these compounds may function as "signaling" pheromones, even though this function may be suppressed by psychosocial influences during ontogeny. The intriguing findings of McClintock (137) have provided evidence for primer pheromone effects in women. The menstrual periods of girls living in a college dormitory showed significant synchrony among the individuals who had most contact (friends or roommates). Cycle length was found to be shorter among those who "spent more time" with males. The former phenomenon is reminiscent of the Lee-Boot effect, the latter of the Whitten effect; both these phenomena were discovered in mice and both have since been demonstrated in other species.

Most cases of impotence are generally thought to be psychogenic in origin. Cooper et al (53) have reported, however, that the "constitutional" type may be distinguished from "psychogenic" impotence on the basis of urinary testosterone excretion which they found to be higher in the former class of patients. But, as the authors pointed out, the increased testosterone production may be a result rather than a cause of sexual activity, since the "constitutional" patients had sexual outlets, generally masturbation. This suggestion is in keeping with previous animal experiments suggesting copulation induced activation of the pituitary-testicular system (see above). Although the evidence for this is extremely scanty in humans (90, 117), apparently reliable data have now been provided supporting a correlation between sexual activity (both actual and anticipatory) and beard growth in an anonymous investigator (5)! Not surprisingly, the interpretation has been challenged that these data imply stimulation of androgen production as a result of actual or anticipated sexual behavior (103).

It has been reported that cyproterone acetate reduces libido in men, and it is being used by clinicians in Europe and the United States in the treatment of various sexual problems (124, 171). This is somewhat surprising in view of the failure of cyproterone to inhibit sexual behavior in adult rodents (see 23).

From a review of available data Money concurred in the commonly held view that endocrine factors are unimportant in the etiology of homosexuality (161). Loraine et al (130) found urinary testosterone abnormally low in two males with exclusive homosexuality and normal in a third who was "bisexual." Their conclusion that homosexuality may be endocrine related seems only poorly supported by their data (184). A study deserving replication relates homosexuality to androgen metabolism. Margolese (136) found a clearly decreased androsterone to etiocholanolone ratio in homosexual males. There was no overlap between two groups of ten healthy homosexuals and heterosexuals. A much simpler problem, the effect of androgens on penile erections, was studied by Beumant (20) with the appropriate objective and quantitative methods which are all too often absent in this area. The expected stimulatory effect was found, but unfortunately only one subject was studied.

The evidence for copulation-induced ovulation in women has been reviewed by Clark & Zarrow (45). Their conclusion of a strong likelihood for this occurrence seems somewhat overenthusiastic, since the only direct evidence was from clinical reports of questionable value.

The effects of contraceptive steroids on female sexual behavior continue to be an unsettled question whose potential importance gains added credence from the findings that progesterone suppresses sexual behavior in monkeys (152). Another study has appeared pointing to a loss of sexual interest in a certain proportion of a group of selected gynecological patients (114). Udry & Morris (211) have found that various oral contraceptive agents (combined or sequential types) wiped out the luteal phase depression of coital activity which they had previously demonstrated. Since luteal progesterone production is suppressed by these drugs, this constitutes further evidence for endocrine-related variations in libido throughout the menstrual cycle.

One cannot fail to note in current and past literature the impressive dearth of definitive studies on the endocrinology of human sexual behavior. In this vacuum, inadequate clinical impressions and pseudodata often masquerade as well established phenomena. There is a great need for large scale investigations of endocrine-sexual behavior relationships in human males and females using acceptably objective behavioral criteria and the appropriate controls.

NONREPRODUCTIVE BEHAVIOR
GONADAL HORMONES

Although it is apparent that research in the hormone-behavior field continues to emphasize the role of gonadal hormones in the control of sexual behavior, a growing body of evidence indicates that hormones may regulate or modulate many aspects of the organism's behavioral repertoire. Thus, the material we cover in this portion of the review will include behaviors which are influenced by gonadal hormones but are not related directly to reproduction; and the influence of other hormones, in particular ACTH and adrenal corticoids, on various aspects of the organism's behavior.

In recent years we have seen a growing emphasis on the physiological mechanisms regulating aggressive behavior. Aggressive behavior is generally studied in the laboratory by two major methods: first, observation of spontaneous aggression which occurs frequently in laboratory mice and is usually seen when individuals are exposed to each other following a fairly long period of isolation. Spontaneous aggression is sexually dimorphic, occurring predominantly in males and rarely in females. The second laboratory method utilizes a procedure originated by Ulrich & Azrin (212) called shock-induced aggression, and used generally in rats. Pairs of animals are placed in a small compartment and a train of electric shocks is delivered, in response to which the animals take a characteristic fighting posture, strike at each other, and usually show a full pattern of fighting behavior. This is also sexually dimorphic, as it is elicited more easily in male than in female rats.

The role of androgens in the regulation of spontaneous aggression was noted as early as 1947 by Beeman (15). Subsequent studies have all indicated that castration usually inhibits or markedly suppresses this behavior. In contrast to castrated males, which show the full pattern of isolation-induced aggressive behavior following testosterone replacement, females do not show spontaneous or androgen-induced aggression (210). Normally male mice did not show spontaneous aggression against females (188). However, Mugford & Nowell (164) have shown that the tendency for male mice to attack females was increased significantly if the females were given a course of testosterone treatments.

On the basis of previous work, Mugford & Nowell (163) concluded that the change in androgenized female mice was not due directly to some phero-mone which is released as a consequence of androgen, but rather that the female releases a pheromone in her urine which normally inhibits attack and that the treatment with androgen appears to suppress this urinary substance, thus changing the female's stimulus properties.

In view of the highly predictable sexual dimorphism in aggressive behavior in mice, it seems natural that the possible "organizational" role of testosterone in differentiation of aggressive behavior should receive considerable attention. The suggestion by Young (223) and Harris (105) is that one of the major differences between males and females lies in the differential organization of the central nervous system. The data on the influence of early gonadal hormones on reproductive behavior more than amply support this hypothesis. However, inasmuch as the underlying assumption of all biobehavioral scientists is that the brain is in some way concerned with all behavior, it would seem to be a reasonable hypothesis that other sexually dimorphic behaviors should also come under the organizational influence of gonadal hormones.

Conner & Levine (50) have demonstrated that neonatally castrated male rats show all the characteristics of the female when tested for shock-induced aggression. Castration at weaning tends to suppress aggressive behavior, but it is fully restored when testosterone is administered in adulthood. However, testosterone replacement in adulthood does not influence the aggressive behavior of neonatal castrates. Female mice given an injection of testosterone on the day of birth and then given androgen in adulthood show aggressive behavior comparable to that seen in male mice (74). Furthermore, male mice castrated on the day of birth are less aggressive following androgen replacement therapy in adulthood than males castrated on the tenth day of life.

Similar results have been obtained by Bronson & Desjardins (29). These investigators have reported that single injections of testosterone were most effective in facilitating aggressive behavior in adulthood when administered to the female on the day of birth and less effective when given after that time, becoming ineffective some time between the 12th and 24th day. Also, neonatal androgen was effective in enhancing adult aggressiveness only if it was again administered before testing. The implication of both these studies is that early androgen treatment sensitizes appropriate neural elements to androgen encountered in adulthood. The same conclusions can be reached on the basis of studies using shock-induced aggression in rats.

More recently Edwards & Herndon (79) have shown that neonatal estrogen treatments to female mice mimic the effects of neonatal androgen, in terms of facilitating the differentiation of androgen sensitive mechanisms for adult aggressive behavior. Thus, 90% of the pairs of females given neonatal estrogen fought when treated with androgen in adulthood, compared to 25% of oil-treated females and 100% of testosterone-treated females.

Further evidence of the control of sexually dimorphic behaviors by neonatal hormone treatments comes from experiments on the learning of an avoidance response in the rat. The procedure consists usually of presenting a rat with a conditioned signal—a tone, buzzer, light, etc followed closely by electric shock. The animal can usually cross a barrier to another compartment to either escape further shock or avoid it by responding to the signal prior to the onset of the shock. It has been reported (128, 168) that normal females tend to learn the active avoidance response more rapidly than do normal males. Beatty & Beatty (12, 13) found that castrating male rats in adulthood did not influence avoidance conditioning. Testosterone injections to females in infancy, when combined with testosterone treatment in adulthood, produced rats whose avoidance behavior was masculinized in that they showed the same deficit in avoidance learning shown by males.

Further evidence of modification of sexually dimorphic behaviors comes from Pfaff & Zigmond (175) who studied yet another behavior which usually shows sex difference, namely, timidity or emotionality as exhibited by activity and defecation in an open field (a circular arena usually brightly lit). Commonly, females tend to be more active in the open field and to emerge from the home cage faster than males. Neonatally castrated male rats tend to behave more like females and neonatally androgenized females more like males in both the open field test and tests of emergence. Similar findings have been reported by Gray & Levine (99) and by Swanson (203, 204).

Data on the hormonal regulation of other nonreproductive behaviors by gonadal hormones were presented in several other reports during the past year. Rodier (182) showed that progesterone injections resulted in a decrease in wheel running activity and an increase in the rate of body weight gain in intact female rats. However, injections of progesterone into ovariectomized animals had no effect on wheel running activity. On the other hand, progesterone injections caused decreased activity when administered to ovar-

iectomized female rats receiving estradiol. These results were interpreted to
indicate that progesterone can influence wheel running and body weight only
through a direct interaction with estrogen.

Thiessen, Lindzey & Nyby (208) have reported that the tendency for
Mongolian gerbils to mark objects in their environment with a midventral
sebaceous scent gland is androgen dependent. Thus, whereas olfactory bulb
aspiration completely eliminates marking behavior, this behavior can be at
least partly reinstated with large doses of testosterone. Furthermore,
estradiol benzoate given to male rats significantly depresses marking frequency in addition to causing atrophy of the testes and seminal vesicles and
the cessation of spermatogenesis. It would thus appear that territorial marking is another androgen-dependent behavior. Aggressive behavior in this
species is also under the influence of gonadal hormones (187), since a significant decline in aggression in the gerbil was found following castration.
Chronic administration of cyproterone acetate had no significant effect on
aggressive behavior in the gerbil, although the antiandrogen caused regression of the seminal vesicles and the ventral sebaceous glands. It would appear that the use of this antiandrogen for suppression of androgen-dependent behavior has severe limitations (see above); the antiandrogen can
itself have androgenic effects.

THE PITUITARY-ADRENAL SYSTEM AND AGGRESSIVE BEHAVIOR

Although the hormone-behavior field tends to be dominated by studies on
the role of gonadal hormones, evidence is accumulating which increasingly
implicates the pituitary-adrenal system as an important modulator of
behavior. Studies have indicated that the pituitary-adrenal system is involved in sensation and perception; habituation learning and extinction; and,
more recently reported, aggressive behavior (127).

With regard to aggressive behavior, Kostowski, Rewerski & Piechocki
(122) observed that hydrocortisone significantly increased isolation-induced
aggressiveness and also muricide (mouse killing) in rats. Brain, Nowell &
Wouters (28) also report that adrenalectomy suppresses isolation-induced
aggression in both young and old mice, whereas dexamethasone administration enhances isolation-induced aggression in more mature animals and
ACTH injection reduces it.

Although these are the only two reports in which pituitary-adrenal
function was manipulated and the effects on aggressive behavior were measured, other studies have suggested a relationship between aggressive behavior and pituitary-adrenal function.

Conner, Levine & Vernikos-Danellis (51) have demonstrated that in
shock-induced aggression there is a suppression of ACTH release following
fighting when compared with rats that are shocked without fighting.
Sassenrath (186) reported that in monkeys adrenal responsiveness to ACTH
was related to the dominance structure. Although ACTH response levels of
individuals remained relatively constant, there was a three to tenfold

difference between the lowest response to ACTH which was in the dominant male, and the highest response which was found in the most subordinate female cagemate. The response levels to ACTH, however, could be altered when the social stress was changed by transferring subdominant animals to individual cages or removing the dominant male. Conversely, removal of the most subordinate cagemate resulted in elevation of the ACTH response of the remaining subordinates. Sassenrath concluded that the elevated ACTH output in the subdominant animals reflects the characteristic level of stressful stimulation sustained by each member of the social group.

However, Levine et al (125) reported that more highly aggressive monkeys showed a greater increase in urinary 17-hydroxycorticosterone in response to shock than did the least aggressive animals. In this case the more dominant animal in a food competition situation was more responsive to stressful stimuli. It is of course conceivable that the pituitary-adrenal system has little or no direct connection with aggressive behavior but may be related only to the level of arousal which is reflected in changes in pituitary-adrenal activation.

The Pituitary-Adrenal System and Learning

The first demonstration of the effects of the pituitary-adrenal system on learned behavior was presented by Mirsky, Miller & Stein (159) in 1953. Then in 1955, Murphy & Miller (165) found that ACTH delayed extinction of an avoidance response, and subsequently Miller & Ogawa (158) showed that ACTH had a similar effect in adrenalectomized animals. The adrenals themselves appeared not to play a significant role in the maintenance of a conditioned avoidance response when the electric shock was no longer present.

Many studies have indicated the effects of ACTH and adrenocortical hormones on conditioned behavior (63, 126). There are now clearly demonstrable independent action of ACTH, ACTH analogs, and steroids on behavior with regard to the extinction of an avoidance response. ACTH and various other related peptides can apparently inhibit extinction, whereas, in contrast, glucocorticoids appear to facilitate extinction independent of their action on ACTH secretion.

Hypophysectomized animals are deficient in the acquisition of a conditioned avoidance response. De Wied has reported (64) that the deficiency in acquisition in hypophysectomized animals is ameliorated when the animal is given ACTH-replacement therapy. In addition to the naturally occurring ACTH molecule, fragments of the ACTH molecule, $ACTH_{1-10}$, and α-MSH, can also influence the acquisition of the conditioned avoidance response in hypophysectomized animals. Gispen, Van Wimersma Greidanus & De Wied (94) have reported that the threshold for the response to inescapable electric shock was lower in hypophysectomized rats than in intact animals. However, treatment with ACTH and $ACTH_{1-10}$ affected the thresholds in neither hypophysectomized nor intact rats. It was concluded that the stimulating effect of ACTH and ACTH fragments on conditioned avoidance acquisition in hypophysectomized animals is not the result of an influence on sensory capacities, inasmuch as the pain thresholds for electric shock are not changed by these peptides but the learning capacity is markedly enhanced. De Wied and co-workers' examination of fractions of extracts of porcine pituitary has revealed a number of peptide components that are active in restoring the ability of hypophysectomized animals to acquire a conditioned avoidance response. None of these compounds appears to influence hormonal activity as measured by the peripheral effects on adrenals and testes. They have found an active component which has been characterized as deglycin-amide-lysine vasopressin (66, 123).

The role of ACTH in the acquisition of the avoidance response has also been investigated by Beatty et al (14); in intact animals they found that ACTH did not facilitate the acquisition of an avoidance response when the electric shock intensity was high. However, facilitation was observed when the intensity of the unconditioned stimulus was moderate. Adrenalectomy also facilitated the acquisition of an avoidance response, whereas dexameth-asone had no influence on this behavior. They concluded that the action of ACTH on the acquisition of avoidance conditioning is clearly extra-adrenal but that ACTH is not essential to normal performance when the intensity of the fear-inducing stimulus is sufficiently high.

Van Wimersma Greidanus (215) has studied the influence of various steroids on the extinction of an avoidance response in the rat. His results indicated that pregnane-type steroids facilitate extinction of the conditioned avoidance response.

In an attempt to locate the possible site of action of glucocorticoids in the central nervous system Bohus (24, 25) implanted cortisone into various brain sites and determined the influence of these implants on the extinction of a conditioned avoidance response. He concluded that the action of corticoids on avoidance behavior in the rat is localized to several limbic, diencephalic and mesencephalic regions. Implants of hydrocortisone into the medial thalamus, anterior hypothalamus, rostral septum, or amygdala all facilitate the extinction of a conditioned avoidance response. When ACTH was ad-ministered to rats with hydrocortisone implants it was able to maintain conditioned avoidance behavior if the implants were in the anterior hypothalamus or rostral septum. However, ACTH given to animals with implants in the medial thalamus had no effect on the maintenance of the conditioned avoidance response. The involvement of the medial thalamus in the mediation of behavioral effects of α-MSH or ACTH has been demon-strated in rats with bilateral lesions in the thalamic parafascicular region (26). Bohus concluded that the thalamus may be one of the loci of the opposing actions of ACTH and corticoids. He postulated that the influence of ACTH becomes dominant upon forebrain inhibitory systems which are affected by implants of corticosteroids in other brain regions.

Although most of the research in this field has dealt with behaviors under the control of aversive stimuli, recent evidence indicates that pituitary-adrenal hormones may have a more generalized effect on learning and extinction. Coover, Goldman & Levine (54) have demonstrated that the extinction of an appetitive response, i.e. one based on food reward, is accompanied by a marked increase in plasma corticosterone following the first extinction session. Gray (97) has reported that the extinction of the response to food reward is influenced by the administration of exogenous ACTH. The acquisition of appetitive responses also seems to be influenced by the administration of ACTH (see 127).

That hormones of the pituitary-adrenal system influence many aspects of behavior appears to be well established. In some circumstances, however, these effects may be subtle and a number of workers have failed to see what now appear to be well established behavioral effects of these hormones (216). It is apparent from much research that the pituitary-adrenal system is exceedingly labile and responds to a wide variety of environmental stimuli. Furthermore, environmental variables may influence the pituitary-adrenal response to a given stimulus. An animal studied in a behavioral situation may previously have been "stressed" and have had sufficiently high endogenous levels of ACTH and glucocorticoids that any further manipulation may be unable to produce further effects.

We have emphasized the influence of the pituitary-adrenal system on learning and extinction. However, it should be noted that these systems affect other aspects of behavior including sensory processes (110), EEG habituation (81), and activity (121).

There now exists much evidence indicating the influence of hormones on central nervous system processes (65). However we are still unable to postulate any specific mechanisms concerning the actions of hormones on the brain and their relationship to behavior. It is not known whether the influence of hormones is on certain specific central nervous system structures or is related to more generalized excitatory and inhibitory processes as postulated by McEwen & Weiss (143) and by Weiss et al (217). Although we are not yet close to an understanding of the mechanisms of hormonal action on the brain, the role that the pituitary-adrenal system may play in the maintenance and regulation of many adaptive processes is being elucidated.

LITERATURE CITED

1. Adler, N. T. 1969. Effects of the male's copulatory behavior on successful pregnancy of the female rat. *J. Comp. Physiol. Psychol.* 69:613–22
2. Adler, N. T., Resko, J. A., Goy, R. W. 1970. The effect of copulatory behavior on hormonal change in the female rat prior to implantation. *Physiol. Behav.* 5:1003–7
3. Anderson, C. O., Zarrow, M. X., Denenberg, V. H. 1970. Maternal behavior in the rabbit: effects of androgen treatment during gestation upon the nest-building behavior of the mother and her offspring. *Horm. Behav.* 1:337–45
4. Anderson, C., Zarrow, M. X., Fuller, G., Denenberg, V. H. 1971. Pituitary involvement in maternal nest building in rabbit. *Horm. Behav.* 2:183–90
5. Effects of sexual activity on beard growth in man. 1970. *Nature London* 226:869–70

6. Arén-Engelbrektsson, B., Larsson, K., Södersten, P., Wilhelmsson, M. 1970. The female lordosis pattern induced in male rats by estrogen. *Horm. Behav.* 1:181–88

7. Aron, C., Chateau, D. 1971. Pheromones and mating behavior in the rat. *Horm. Behav.* 2:315–24

8. Aron, C., Roos, J., Roos, M. 1970. Effect of removal of the olfactory bulbs on mating behavior and ovulation in the rat. *Neuroendocrinology* 6:109–17

9. Barraclough, C. A., Gorski, R. A. 1962. Studies on mating behavior in the androgen-sterilized rat. *J. Endocrinol.* 25:175–82

10. Beach, F. A. 1971. Hormonal factors controlling the differentiation, development and display of copulatory behavior in the ramstergig and related species. In *Biopsychology of Development*, ed. L. Aronson, E. Tobach. New York: Academic In press

11. Beach, F. A., Kuehn, R. E. 1970. Coital behavior in dogs. X. Effects of androgenic stimulation during development on feminine mating responses in females and males. *Horm. Behav.* 1:347–67

12. Beatty, W. W., Beatty, P. A. 1970. Effects of neonatal testosterone on the acquisition of an active avoidance response in genotypically female rats. *Psychon. Sci.* 19:315–16

13. Beatty, W. W., Beatty, P. A. 1970. Hormonal determinants of sex differences in avoidance behavior and reactivity to electric shock in the rat. *J. Comp. Physiol. Psychol.* 73:446–55

14. Beatty, P. A., Beatty, W. W., Bowman, R. E., Gilchrist, J. C. 1970. The effects of ACTH, adrenalectomy and dexamethasone on the acquisition of an avoidance response in rats. *Physiol. Behav.* 5:939–44

15. Beeman, E. A. 1947. The effect of male hormone on aggressive behavior in mice. *Physiol. Zool.* 20:373–405

16. Bell, D. D., Zucker, I. 1971. Sex differences in body weight and eating: organization by gonadal hormones in the rat. *Physiol. Behav.* 7:27–34

17. Bergquist, E. H. 1970. Output pathways of hypothalamic mechanisms for sexual, aggressive, and other motivated behaviors in opossum. *J. Comp. Physiol. Psychol.* 3:389–98

18. Bermant, G., Taylor, L. 1969. Interactive effects of experience and olfactory bulb lesions in male rat copulation. *Physiol. Behav.* 4:13–17

19. Berthold, A. A. 1849. Transplantation der Hoden. *Arch. Anat. Physiol.* 16:42–46

20. Beumant, P. J. V., Bancroft, J. H. J., Beardwood, C. J., Russell, G. F. M. 1971. Behavioural changes following treatment with testosterone. *Psychol. Med.* In press

21. Beyer, C., Vidal, N., Mijares, A. 1970. Probable role of aromatization in the induction of estrous behavior by androgens in the ovariectomized rabbit. *Endocrinology* 87:1386–89

22. Bloch, S. 1971. Enhancement of ontime nidations in suckling pregnant mice by the proximity of strange males. *J. Endocrinol.* 49:431–36

23. Bloch, G. J., Davidson, J. M. 1971. Behavioral and somatic responses to the antiandrogen cyproterone. *Horm. Behav.* 2:11–25

24. Bohus, B. 1970. Central nervous structures and the effect of ACTH and corticosteroids on avoidance behaviour: a study with intracerebral implantation of corticosteroids in the rat. *Pituitary, Andrenal and the Brain*, ed. D. De Wied, J. A. W. M. Weijnen, p. 171–84. Amsterdam: Elsevier

25. Bohus, B. 1970. The medial thalamus and the opposite effect of corticosteroids and adrenocorticotrophic hormone on avoidance extinction in the rat. *Acta Physiol. Acad. Sci. Hung.* 38:217–23

26. Bohus, B., De Wied, D. 1967. Failure of α-MSH to delay extinction of conditioned avoidance behaviour in rats with lesions in the parafascicular nuclei of the thalamus. *Physiol. Behav.* 2:221–23

27. Bottomley, A. C., Folley, S. J. 1938. The effects of high doses of androgenic substances on the weights of the testes, accessory reproductive organs and endocrine glands of young male guinea pigs. *J. Physiol. London* 94:26–39

28. Brain, P. F., Nowell, N. W., Wouters, A. 1971. Some relationships between adrenal function and the effectiveness of a period of isolation in inducing intermale aggression in albino mice. *Physiol. Behav.* 6:27–29

29. Bronson, F. H., Desjardins, C. 1970. Neonatal androgen administration and adult aggressiveness in female

mice. *Gen. Comp. Endocrinol.* 15: 320–25

30. Brooks, P. H., Cole, D. J. A. 1970. The effect of the presence of a boar on the attainment of puberty in gilts. *J. Reprod. Fert.* 23:435–40

31. Brown-Grant, K. 1971. The role of steroid hormones in the control of gonadotrophin secretion in adult female mammals. *Steroids, Hormones and Brain Function,* ed. C. H. Sawyer, R. A. Gorski. Berkeley: Univ. Calif. Press

32. Brown-Grant, K., Davidson, J. M., Sherwood, M. R., Tapper, C. M. 1971. Haemolysis following copulation in the male rat. *J. Reprod. Fert.* In press

33. Brown-Grant, K., Munck, A., Naftolin, F., Sherwood, M. R. 1971. Effects of administration of TP alone with phenobarbitone and of testosterone metabolites to neonatal female rats. *Horm. Behav.* 2:173–182

34. Brown-Grant, K., Sherwood, M. R. 1971. The early androgen syndrome in the guinea-pig. *J. Endocrinol.* 49: 277–91

35. Brown-Sequard, M. 1889. Des effets produits chez l'homme par des injections souscutanées d'un liquide retivé des testicules frais de cobaye et de chien. *Compt. Rend. Soc. Biol.* Ser. 9, 1:415, 420, 430

36. Bruce, H. M. 1970. Pheromones. *Brit. Med. Bull.* 26:10–13

37. Bruchovsky, N., Wilson, J. D. 1968. The intranuclear binding of testosterone and 5α-androstan-17-β-ol-3-one by rat prostate. *J. Biol. Chem.* 243:5954–60

38. Bullock, D. W. 1970. Induction of heat in ovariectomized guinea pigs by brief exposure to estrogen and progesterone. *Horm. Behav.* 1:137–43

39. Caggiula, A. R. 1970. Analysis of the copulation-reward properties of posterior hypothalamic stimulation in male rats. *J. Comp. Physiol. Psychol.* 70:399–412

40. Campbell, A. B., McGill, T. E. 1970. Neonatal hormone treatment and sexual behavior in male mice. *Horm. Behav.* 1:145–50

41. Campbell, H. J. 1970. The effect of steroid hormones on self stimulation, central and peripheral. *Steroidologia* 1:8–24

42. Carr, W. J., Wylie, N. R., Loeb, L. S. 1970. Responses of adult and immature rats to sex odors. *J. Comp. Physiol. Psychol.* 72:51–59

43. Chester, R. V., Zucker, I. 1970. Influence of male copulatory behavior on sperm transport, pregnancy and pseudopregnancy in female rats. *Physiol. Behav.* 5:35–43

44. Ciaccio, L., Lisk, R. D. 1971. The role of progesterone in regulating the period of sexual receptivity in the female hamster. *J. Endocrinol.* 50: 201–207

45. Clark, J. H., Zarrow, M. X. 1971. Influence of copulation on time of ovulation in women. *Am. J. Obstet. Gynecol.* 109:1083–85

46. Clayton, R. B., Kogura, J., Kraemer, H. C. 1970. Sexual differentiation of the brain: effects of testosterone on brain RNA metabolism in newborn female rats. *Nature London* 226:810–12

47. Clemens, L. G., Shryne, J., Gorski, R. A. 1970. Androgen and development of progesterone responsiveness in male and female rats. *Physiol. Behav.* 5:673–78

48. Clulow, F. V., Langford, P. E. 1971. Pregnancy block in the meadow vole, *Microtus pennsylvanicus.* *J. Reprod. Fert.* 24:275–77

49. Comfort, A. 1971. Likelihood of human pheromones. *Nature London* 230:432–33

50. Conner, R. L., Levine, S. 1969. Hormonal influences on aggressive behaviour. *Aggressive Behaviour,* ed. S. Garattini, E. B. Sigg, p. 150–63. Amsterdam:Excerpta Med.

51. Conner, R. L., Levine, S., Vernikos-Danellis, J. 1970. Shock-induced fighting and pituitary-adrenal activity. *Proc. 78th Ann. Conv. APA,* 201–2

52. Convey, E. M., Breitschneider, E., Hafs, H. D. 1971. Serum hormone levels of bulls before and after ejaculation. *Fed. Proc.* 30:309

53. Cooper, A. J., Ismail, A. A. A., Smith, C. G., Loraine, J. A. 1970. Androgen function in "psychogenic" and "constitutional" types of impotence. *Brit. Med. J.* 3:17–20

54. Coover, G. D., Goldman, L., Levine, S. 1971. Plasma corticosterone increases produced by extinction of operant behavior in rats. *Physiol. Behav.* 6:261–63

55. Davidson, J. M. 1966. Activation of the male rat's sexual behavior by intracerebral implantation of androgen. *Endocrinology* 79:783–94

56. Davidson, J. M. 1969. Effects of estrogen on the sexual behavior of male

rats. *Endocrinology* 84:1365–72
57. Davidson, J. M. 1971. Hormones and reproductive behavior. *Reproductive Biology*, ed. H. Balin, J. Glasser, Amsterdam: Excerpta Med. In press
58. Davidson, J. M., Bloch, G. J. 1969. Neuroendocrine aspects of male reproduction. *Biol. Reprod.* 1:Suppl. 1, 67–92
59. Davidson, J. M., Bloch, G. J., Smith, E. R., Weick, R. F. 1971. Comparative responses to androgen of anatomic, behavioral and other parameters. *Proc. 3rd Int. Congr. on Hormonal Steroids, Hamburg, 1971* In press
60. Davidson, J. M., Rodgers, C. H., Smith, E. R., Bloch, G. J. 1968. Stimulation of female sex behavior in adrenalectomized rats with estrogen alone. *Endocrinology* 82:193–95
61. Davidson, J. M., Smith, E. R., Rodgers, C. H., Bloch, G. J. 1968. Relative thresholds of behavioral and somatic responses to estrogen. *Physiol. Behav.* 3:227–29
62. De Hertogh, R., Ekka, E., Vanderheyden, I., Hoet, J. J. 1970. Metabolic clearance rates and the interconversion factors of estrone and estradiol-17β in the immature and adult female rat. *Endocrinology* 87: 874–80
63. De Wied, D. 1969. Effects of peptide hormones on behavior. *Frontiers in Neuroendocrinology*, ed. W. F. Ganong, L. Martini, p. 97–140. New York:Oxford Univ. Press
64. De Wied, D. 1970. Pituitary control of avoidance behavior. *The Hypothalamus*, ed. L. Martini, M. Motta, F. Fraschini, p. 1–8. New York: Academic
65. De Wied, D., Weijnen, J. A. W. M., Eds. 1970. *Progr. Brain Res.* Vol. 32, *Pituitary, Adrenal and the Brain*. Amsterdam:Elsevier. 357 pp.
66. De Wied, D., Witter, A., Lande, S. 1970. Anterior pituitary peptides and avoidance acquisition of hypophysectomized rats. *Progr. Brain Res.* 32:213–20
67. Dewsbury, D. A. 1971. Copulatory behavior of male rats following reserpine administration. *Psychon. Sci.* 22:177–79
68. Dewsbury, D. A., Davis, H. N. 1970. Effects of reserpine on the copulatory behavior of male rats. *Physiol. Behav.* 5:1331–33
69. Diamond, M. 1971. Intromission pattern and species vaginal code in relation to induction of pseudopregnancy. *Science* 169:995–97
70. Dörner, G. 1970. The influence of sex hormones during the hypothalamic differentiation and maturation phases on gonadal function and sexual behavior during the hypothalamic functional phase. *Endocrinologie* 56:280–91
71. Dörner, G., Döcke, F., Hinz, G. 1969. Homo- and hypersexuality in rats with hypothalamic lesions. *Neuroendocrinology* 4:20–24
72. Dörner, G., Döcke, F., Hinz, G. 1971. Paradoxical effects of estrogen on brain differentiation. *Neuroendocrinology* 7:146–55
73. Eaton, G. 1970. Effect of a single prepuberal injection of testosterone proprionate on adult bisexual behavior of male hamsters castrated at birth. *Endocrinology* 87:934–40
74. Edwards, D. A. 1969. Early androgen stimulation and aggressive behavior in male and female mice. *Physiol. Behav.* 4:333–38
75. Edwards, D. A. 1970. Induction of estrus in female mice: estrogen-progesterone interactions. *Horm. Behav.* 1:299–304
76. Edwards, D. A. 1970. Effects of cyproterone acetate on aggressive behavior and the seminal vesicles of male mice. *J. Endocrinol.* 46:477–81
77. Edwards, D. A. 1971. Neonatal administration of androstenedione, testosterone or testosterone propionate: effects on ovulation, sexual receptivity and aggressive behavior in female mice. *Physiol. Behav.* 6: 223–228
78. Edwards, D. A., Burge, K. G. 1971. Early androgen treatment and male and female sexual behavior in mice. *Horm. Behav.* 2:49–58
79. Edwards, D. A., Herndon, J. 1970. Neonatal estrogen stimulation and aggressive behavior in female mice. *Physiol. Behav.* 5:993–95
80. Edwards, D. A., Thompson, M. L. 1970. Neonatal androgenization and estrogenization and the hormonal induction of sexual receptivity in rats. *Physiol. Behav.* 5:115–19
81. Endroczi, E., Lissak, K., Fekete, T. 1970. Effects of ACTH on EEG habituation in human subjects. *Progr. Brain Res.* 32:254–62
82. Everett, J. W. 1967. Provoked ovulation or long-delayed pseudopreg-

nancy from coital stimuli in barbiturate-blocked rats. *Endocrinology* 80:145–54

83. Everitt, B. J., Herbert, J. 1970. The maintenance of sexual receptivity by adrenal androgens in female rhesus monkeys. *J. Endocrinol.* 48: 38

84. Feder, H. 1971. The comparative actions of testosterone propionate and 5-androstan-17-ol-3-one propionate on the reproductive behavior, physiology and morphology of male rats. *J. Endocrinol.* In press

85. Feder, H. H., Resko, J. A., Goy, R. W. 1968. Progesterone concentrations in the arterial plasma of guinea pigs during the oestrous cycle. *J. Endocrinol.* 40:505–13

86. Feder, H. H., Resko, J. A., Goy, R. W. 1968. Progesterone levels in the arterial plasma of preovulatory and ovariectomized rats. *J. Endocrinol.* 41:563–69

87. Feder, H., Ruf, K. B. 1969. Stimulation of progesterone release and estrous behavior by ACTH in ovariectomized rodents. *Endocrinology* 84:171–74

88. Ferguson, J. et al 1970. "Hypersexuality" and behavioral changes in cats caused by administration of p-chlorophenylalanine. *Science* 168: 499–501

89. Fernandez-Baca, S., Madden, D. H. L., Novoa, C. 1970. Effect of different mating stimuli on induction of ovulation in the alpaca. *J. Reprod. Fert.* 22:261–67

90. Fox, C. A., Ismail, A. A. A., Love, D. N., Loraine, J. A. 1970. Plasma testosterone levels and sexual activity in a male subject. *J. Endocrinol.* 48:41

91. Gandelman, R., Zarrow, M. X., Denenberg, V. H., Myers, M. 1971. Olfactory bulb removal eliminates maternal behavior in the mouse. *Science* 171:210–11

92. Gerall, A. A., Kenney, A. M. 1970. Neonatally androgenized females' responsiveness to estrogen and progesterone. *Endocrinology* 87:560–66

93. Giantonio, G. W., Lund, N. L., Gerall, A. A. 1970. Effect of diencephalic and rhinencephalic lesions on the male rat's sexual behavior. *J. Comp. Physiol. Psychol.* 73:38–46

94. Gispen, W. H., Van Wimersma Greidanus, Tj. B., De Wied, D. 1970. Effects of hypophysectomy and $ACTH_{1-10}$ on responsiveness to

95. Goldfoot, D. A., Feder, H. H., Goy, R. W. 1969. Development of bisexuality in the male rat treated neonatally with androstenedione. *J. Comp. Physiol. Psychol.* 67:41–45

96. Goy, R. W. 1970. Experimental control of psychosexuality. *Phil. Trans. Roy. Soc. Lond. Ser. B.* 259:149–62

97. Gray, J. A. 1971. Effect of ACTH on extinction of rewarded behaviour is blocked by previous administration of ACTH. *Nature London* 229:52–54

98. Gray, J. A. 1971. Sex differences in emotional behaviour in mammals including man: endocrine bases. *Acta Psychol.* 35:29–46

99. Gray, J. A., Levine, S. 1964. Effect of induced oestrus on emotional behaviour in selected strains of rats. *Nature London* 201:1198–200

100. Green, R., Luttge, W. G., Whalen, R. E. 1970. Induction of receptivity in ovariectomized female rats by a single intravenous injection of estradiol 17β. *Physiol. Behav.* 5:137–41

101. Green, R., Luttge, W. G., Whalen, R. E. 1970. Uptake of tritiated testosterone in brain and peripheral tissues of normal and neonatally androgenized female rats. *J. Comp. Physiol. Psychol.* 72:337–40

102. Grosvenor, C. E., Maiweg, H., Mena, F. 1970. A study of factors involved in the development of the exteroceptive release of prolactin in the lactating rat. *Horm. Behav.* 1:111–20

103. Hardisty, R. M. et al 1970. Sexual activity and beard growth. *Nature London* 226:1277–78

104. Hardy, D. F. 1970. The effect of constant light on the estrous cycle and behavior of the female rat. *Physiol. Behav.* 5:421–25

105. Harris, G. W. 1964. Sex hormones, brain development and brain function. *Endocrinology* 75:627–48

106. Harris, G. W., Michael, R. P. 1964. The activation of sexual behavior by hypothalamic implants of oestrogen. *J. Physiol.* 171:275–301

107. Hart, B. L. 1970. Abolition of mating behavior in male cats with lesions in the medial preoptic-anterior hypothalamic region. *Amer. Zool.* 10:36

108. Hayes, K. J. 1970. The virilizing effect of wheel running in male rats. *Horm. Behav.* 1:175–79

electric shock in rats. *Physiol. Behav.* 5:143–46

109. Hendricks, S. E., Gerall, A. A. 1970. Effect of neonatally administered estrogen on development of male and female rats. *Endocrinology* 87:435–39

110. Henkin, R. I. 1970. The effects of corticosteroids and ACTH on sensory systems. *Progr. Brain Res.* 32:270–94

111. Herbert, J. 1970. Hormones and reproductive behaviour in rhesus and talapoin monkeys. *J. Reprod. Fert.* Suppl. 11:119–40

112. Hitt, J. C., Hendricks, S. E., Ginsberg, S.T., Lewis, J. H. 1970. Disruption of male, but not female, sexual behavior by medial forebrain bundle lesions. *J. Comp. Physiol. Psychol.* 73:377–84

113. Hoyland, V. J., Shillito, E. E., Vogt, M. 1970. The effect of parachlorophenylalanine on the behaviour of cats. *Brit. J. Pharmacol.* 40:659–67

114. Huffer, V., Levin, L., Aronson, H. 1970. Oral contraceptives: depression and frigidity. *J. Nerv. Ment. Dis.* 151:35–41

115. Hutchison, J. B. 1969. Changes in hypothalamic responsiveness to testosterone in male Barbary doves (*Streptopelia risoria*). *Nature London* 222:176–77

116. Hutchison, J. B. 1971. Effects of hypothalamic implants of gonadal steroids on courtship behaviour in Barbary doves (*Streptopelia risoria*). *J. Endocrinol.* 50:97–113

117. Ismail, A. A. A., Harkness, R. A. 1967. Urinary testosterone excretion in men in normal and pathological conditions. *Acta Endocrinol. Copenhagen* 56:469–80

118. Jacobel, P., Rodgers, C. H. 1971. Adrenalectomy: effects on mating behavior, ovulation and early gestation in rat. *Horm. Behav.* 2: 201–206

119. Kalra, S. P., Sawyer, C. H. 1970. Blockade of copulation-induced ovulation in the rat by anterior hypothalamic deafferentation. *Endocrinology* 87:1124–28

120. Katongole, C. B., Naftolin, F., Short, R. V. 1971. Relationship between blood levels of luteinizing hormone and testosterone in bulls, and the effects of sexual stimulation. *J. Endocrinol.* 50:457–66.

121. Kendall, J. W. 1970. Dexamethasone stimulation of running activity in the male rat. *Horm. Behav.* 1:327–36

122. Kostowski, W., Rewerski, W., Piechocki, T. 1970. Effects of some steroids on aggressive behaviour in mice and rats. *Neuroendocrinology* 6:311–18

123. Lande, S., Witter, A., De Wied, D. 1971. An octapeptide that stimulates conditioned avoidance acquisition in hypophysectomized rats. *J. Biol. Chem.* 246:2058–62

124. Leach, D. R., Heller, C. G. 1971. Effects of cyproterone acetate on testicular histology, sperm count, and levels of urinary and plasma gonadotropins and testosterone in the normal human male. *Program 53rd Meeting, Endocrine Society, San Francisco*, 145.

125. Levine, M. D., Gordon, T. P., Peterson, R. H., Rose, R. M. 1970. Urinary 17-OHCS response of high- and low-aggressive rhesus monkeys to shock avoidance. *Physiol. Behav.* 5:919–24

126. Levine, S. 1968. Hormones and conditioning. *Neb. Symp. Motiv. 1968*, ed. W. J. Arnold, p. 85–101. Lincoln, Nebr.: Univ. Neb. Press

127. Levine, S. 1971. Stress and behavior. *Sci. Am.* 224:26–31

128. Levine, S., Broadhurst, P. L. 1963. Genetic and ontogenetic determinants of adult behavior in the rat. *J. Comp. Physiol. Psychol.* 56:423–28

129. Lindstrom, L. H. 1970. The effect of pilocarpine in combination with monoamine oxidase inhibitors, imipramine or desmethylimipramine on oestrous behavior in female rats. *Psychopharmacologia* 17:160–68

130. Loraine, J. A., Ismail, A. A. A., Adamopoulos, D. A., Dove, G. A. 1970. Endocrine function in male and female homosexuals. *Brit. J. Med.* 4:406–9

131. Loy, J. 1970. Peri-menstrual sexual behavior among rhesus monkeys. *Folia Primatol.* 13:286–97

132. Luttge, W. G., Whalen, R. E. 1970. Dihydrotestosterone, androstenedione, testosterone: comparative effectiveness in masculinizing and defeminizing reproductive systems in male and female rats. *Horm. Behav.* 1:265–81

133. MacKinnon, P. C. B. 1970. A comparison of protein synthesis in the brains of mice before and after puberty. *J. Physiol. London* 210: 10–11P

134. Madlafousek, J., Freund, K., Grofová, I. 1970. Variables determining the

effect of electrostimulation in the lateral preoptic area on the sexual behavior of male rats. *J. Comp. Physiol. Psychol.* 72:28–44

135. Malmnas, C. O., Meyerson, B. J. 1971. *p*-Chlorophenylalanine and copulatory behaviour in the male rat. *Nature London* 232:398–400

136. Margolese, M. S. 1970. Homosexuality: A new endocrine correlate. *Horm. Behav.* 1:151–55

137. McClintock, M. K. 1971. Menstrual synchrony and suppression. *Nature London* 229:244–45

138. McDonald, P. G., Vidal, N., Beyer, C. 1970. Sexual behavior in the ovariectomized rabbit after treatment with different amounts of gonadal hormones. *Horm. Behav.* 1:161–72

139. McDonald, P. et al 1970. Failure of 5 α-dihydrotestosterone to initiate sexual behaviour in the castrated male rat. *Nature London* 227:964–65

140. McEwen, B. S., Pfaff, D. W. 1970. Factors influencing sex hormone uptake by rat brain regions. I. Effects of neonatal treatment and hypophysectomy, and competing steroid on estradiol uptake. *Brain Res.* 21:1–16

141. McEwen, B. S., Pfaff, D. W., Zigmond, R. E. 1970. Factors influencing sex hormone uptake by rat brain regions. II. Effects of neonatal treatment and hypophysectomy on testosterone uptake. *Brain Res.* 21:17–28

142. McEwen, B. S., Pfaff, D. W., Zigmond, R. E. 1970. Factors influencing sex hormone uptake by rat brain regions. III. Effects of competing steroids on testosterone uptake. *Brain Res.* 21:29–38

143. McEwen, B. S., Weiss, J. M. 1970. The uptake and action of corticosterone: regional and subcellular studies on rat brain. *Progr. Brain Res.* 32:200–12

144. McGill, T. E. 1970. Induction of luteal activity in female house mice. *Horm. Behav.* 1:211–22

145. McKinney, T. D., Christian, J. J. 1970. Effect of preputialectomy on fighting behavior in mice. *Proc. Soc. Exp. Biol. Med.* 134:291–93

146. McNeilly, A. S., Cooper, K. J., Crighton, D. B. 1970. Modification of the oestrous cycle of the underfed rat induced by the proximity of a male. *J. Reprod. Fert.* 22:359–61

147. Meyerson, B. J. 1964. Central nervous monoamines and hormone induced estrous behavior in the spayed rat. *Acta Physiol. Scand.* 63: Suppl. 24, 1–16

148. Meyerson, B. J. 1970. Monoamines and hormone activated oestrus behaviour to the ovariectomized hamster. *Psychopharmacologia* 18: 50–57

149. Meyerson, B. J. 1971. Optical isomers of estrogen and estrogen inhibitors as tools in the investigation of estrogen action on the brain. *Steroid Hormones and Brain Function, UCLA Workshop Conf.* Los Angeles. In press

150. Meyerson, B. J., Lewander, T. 1970. Serotonin synthesis inhibition and estrous behavior in female rats. *Life Sci.* 9:661–71

151. Meyerson, B. J., Lindstrom, L. 1970. Sexual motivation and sex hormones in the female rat. *Int. Congr. Horm. Steroids, 3rd.* Amsterdam.: Excerpta Med. Int. Congr. Ser. No. 210, p. 56

152. Michael, R. P. 1969. Behavioral effects of gonadal hormones and contraceptive steroids in primates. *Metabolic Effects of Gonadal Hormones and Contraceptive Steroids,* ed. H. A. Salhanick, p. 706–21. New York: Plenum Press

153. Michael, R. P., Keverne, E. B. 1968. Pheromones in the communication of sexual status in primates. *Nature London* 218:746–49

154. Michael, R. P., Keverne, E. B. 1970. Primate sex pheromones of vaginal origin. *Nature London* 225:84–85

155. Michael, R. P., Keverne, E. B., Bonsall, R. W. 1971. Pheromones: isolation of male sex attractants from a female primate. *Science* 172:964–66

156. Michael, R. P., Zumpe, D. 1970. Rhythmic changes in the copulatory frequency of rhesus monkeys (*Macaca mulatta*) in relation to the menstrual cycle and a comparison with the human cycle. *J. Reprod. Fert.* 21:199–201

157. Michael, R. P., Zumpe, D. 1970. Sexual initiating behaviour by female rhesus monkeys (*Macaca mulatta*) under laboratory conditions. *Behaviour* 36:168–86

158. Miller, R. E., Ogawa, N. 1962. The effect of adrenocorticotrophic hormone (ACTH) on avoidance conditioning in the adrenalectomized

rat. *J. Comp. Physiol. Psychol.* 55:211-13

159. Mirsky, I. A., Miller, R., Stein, M. 1953. Relation of adrenocortical activity and adaptive behavior. *Psychosom. Med.* 15:574-84

160. Moltz, H., Lubin, M., Veon, M., Numan, M. 1970. Hormonal induction of maternal behavior in the ovariectomized nulliparous rat. *Physiol. Behav.* 5:1373-77

161. Money, J. 1970. Sexual dimorphism and homosexual gender identity. *Psychol. Bull.* 74:425-40

162. Moss, R. L. 1971. Modification of copulatory behavior in the female rat following olfactory bulb removal. *J. Comp. Physiol. Psychol.* 74:374-82

163. Mugford, R. A., Nowell, N. W. 1970. Pheromones and their effect on aggression in mice. *Nature London* 226:967-68

164. Mugford, R. A., Nowell, N. W. 1970. The aggression of male mice against androgenized females. *Psychon. Sci.* 20:191-92

165. Murphy, J. V., Miller, R. E. 1955. The effect of adrenocorticotrophic hormone (ACTH) on avoidance conditioning in the rat. *J. Comp. Physiol. Psychol.* 48:47-49

166. Murphy, M. R., Schneider, G. E. 1970. Olfactory bulb removal eliminates mating behavior in the male golden hamster. *Science* 167:302-4

167. Nadler, R. D. 1970. A biphasic influence of progesterone on sexual receptivity of spayed female rats. *Physiol. Behav.* 5:95-97

168. Nakamura, C. Y., Anderson, N. H. 1962. Avoidance behavior differences within and between strains of rats. *J. Comp. Physiol. Psychol.* 55:740-47

169. Needham, J., Gwei-Djen, L. 1968. Sex hormones in the middle ages. *Endeavour* 27:130-32

170. Nequin, L. G., Schwartz, N. B. 1971. Adrenal participation in the timing of mating and LH release in the cyclic rat. *Endocrinology* 88:325-31

171. Neumann, F. et al 1970. Aspects of androgen-dependent events as studied by antiandrogens. *Rec. Progr. Horm. Res.* 26:337-410

172. Paris, C. A., Resko, J. A., Goy, R. W. 1971. A possible mechanism for the induction of lordosis by reserpine in spayed rats. *Biol. Reprod.* 4:23-30

173. Perry, J. S., Ed. 1970. Reproductive Behaviour. Proc. 6th Symp. Soc.

Study Fert., Bristol, July 1969. *J. Reprod. Fert. Suppl.* 11:1-140

174. Pfaff, D. W. 1970. Nature of sex hormone effects on rat sex behavior: Specificity of effects and individual patterns of response. *J. Comp. Physiol. Psychol.* 73:349-58

175. Pfaff, D. W., Zigmond, R. E. 1971. Neonatal androgen effects on sexual and non-sexual behavior of adult rats tested under various hormone regimes. *Neuroendocrinology* 7:129-45

176. Powers, J. B. 1970. Hormonal control of sexual receptivity during the estrous cycle of the rat. *Physiol. Behav.* 5:831-35

177. Quadagno, D. M., Shryne, J., Gorski, R. A. 1971. The inhibition of steroid-induced sexual behavior by intrahypothalamic actinomycin-D. *Horm. Behav.* 2:1-10

178. Raisman, G., Field, P. M. 1971. Sexual dimorphism in the preoptic area of the rat. *Science* 173:731-33

179. Raps, D., Barthe, P. L., Desaulles, P. A. 1971. Plasma and adrenal corticosterone levels during the different phases of the sexual cycle in normal female rats. *Experientia* 27:339-40

180. Robertson, R. T., Whalen, R. E. 1970, Recent mating experience and olfactory preferences in androgenized female rats. *Psychon. Sci.* 21:266-67

181. Rodgers, C. H. 1970. Timing of sexual behavior in the female rat. *Endocrinology* 86:1181-83

182. Rodier, W. I., III 1971. Progesterone-estrogen interactions in the control of activity-wheel running in the female rat. *J. Comp. Physiol. Psychol.* 74:365-73

183. Ross, J., Claybaugh, C., Clemens, L. G., Gorski, R. A. 1971. Short latency induction of estrous behavior with intracerebral gonadal hormones in ovariectomized rats. *Endocrinology* 89:32-38

184. Ryrie, C. G., Brown, J. C. 1970. Endocrine function in homosexuals. *Brit. Med. J.* 4:685

185. Saayman, G. S. 1970. The menstrual cycle and sexual behaviour in a troop of free ranging chacma baboons (*Papio ursinus*). *Folia Primatol.* 12:81-110

186. Sassenrath, E. N. 1970. Increased adrenal responsiveness related to social stress in rhesus monkeys. *Horm. Behav.* 1:283-98

187. Sayler, A. 1970. The effect of anti-androgens on aggressive behavior in the gerbil. *Physiol. Behav.* 5:667–71

188. Scott, J. P., Fredericson, E. 1951. The causes of fighting in mice and rats. *Physiol. Zool.* 24:273–309

189. Scruton, D. M., Herbert, J. 1970. The menstrual cycle and its effect on behaviour in the talapoin monkey (*Miopithecus talapoin*). *J. Zool.* 162:419–36

190. Segal, D. S., Whalen, R. E. 1970. Effect of chronic administration of p-chlorophenylalanine on sexual receptivity of the female rat. *Psychopharmacologia* 16:434–38

191. Sheard, M. H. 1969. The effect of p-chlorophenylalanine on behavior in rats: relation to brain serotonin and 5-hydroxyindoleacetic acid. *Brain Res.* 15:524–28

192. Shillito, E. E. 1970. The effect of parachlorophenylalanine on social interaction of male rats. *Brit. J. Pharmacol.* 38:305–15

193. Shimada, H., Gorbman, A. 1970. Long-lasting changes in RNA synthesis in the forebrains of female rats treated with testosterone soon after birth. *Biochem. Biophys. Res. Commun.* 38:423–30

194. Signoret, J. P. 1970. Étude de l'equilibre endocrinien de la réceptivité sexuelle chez la truie et la brebis. *Probl. Actuels Endocrinol. Nutr* 14:127–44

195. Signoret, J. P. 1971. Étude de l'action inhibitrice de la progesterone sur l'apparition du comportement sexuel induit par injection d'oestrogenes chez la truie et la brebis ovariectomisées. *Ann. Biol. Biochem. Biophys.* In press

196. Singer, J. J. 1968. Hypothalamic control of male and female sexual behavior in female rats. *J. Comp. Physiol. Psychol.* 66:738–42

197. Soulairac, A., Soulairac, M. L. 1961. Action de la reserpine sur le comportement sexuel du rat male. *C. R. Soc. Biol.* 155:1010–13

198. Spies, H. G., Niswender, G. D. 1971. Levels of prolactin, LH and FSH in the serum of intact and pelvic-neurectomized rats. *Endocrinology* 88:937–43

199. Stern, J. J. 1969. Neonatal castration, androstenedione, and the mating behavior of the male rat. *J. Comp. Physiol. Psychol.* 69:608–12

200. Stern, J. J. 1970. Responses of male rats to sex odors. *Physiol. Behav.* 5:519–24

201. Stern, J. J., Murphy, M. 1971. The effects of cyproterone acetate on the spontaneous activity and seminal vesicle weight of male rats. *J. Endocrinol.* 50:441–43

202. Stumpe, W. E. 1970. Estrogen-neurons and estrogen-neuron systems in the periventricular brain. *Am. J. Anat.* 129:207–18

203. Swanson, H. H. 1966. Sex differences in behaviour of hamsters in open field and emergence tests: effects of pre- and post-pubertal gonadectomy. *Anim. Behav.* 14:522–29

204. Swanson, H. H. 1967. Alteration of sex-typical behaviour of hamsters in open field and emergence tests by neonatal administration of androgen or oestrogen. *Anim. Behav.* 15:209–16

205. Swanson, H. H. 1970. Effects of castration at birth in hamsters of both sexes on luteinization of ovarian implants, oestrous cycles and sexual behavior. *J. Reprod. Fert.* 21:183–86

206. Tagliamonte, A., Tagliamonte, P., Gessa, G. L., Brodie, B. B. 1969. Compulsive sexual activity induced by p-chlorophenylalanine in normal and pinealectomized male rats. *Science* 166:1433–35

207. Taleisnik, S., Velasco, M. E., Astrada, J. J. 1970. Hypothalamic deafferentation and positive feedback effect of progesterone. *J. Endocrinol.* 46:1–7

208. Thiessen, D. D., Lindzey, G., Nyby, J. 1970. The effects of olfactory deprivation and hormones on territorial marking in the male Mongolian gerbil (*Meriones unguiculatus*). *Horm. Behav.* 1:315–25

209. Tiefer, L. 1970. Gonadal hormones and mating behavior in the adult golden hamster. *Horm. Behav.* 1:189–202

210. Tollman, J., King, J. A. 1956. The effects of testosterone propionate on aggression in male and female C57BL/10 mice. *Brit. J. Anim. Behav.* 4:147–49

211. Udry, J. R., Morris, M. N. 1970. Effect of contraceptive pills on the distribution of sexual activity in the menstrual cycle. *Nature London* 227:502–3

212. Ulrich, R. E., Azrin, N. H. 1962. Reflexive fighting in response to aversive stimulation. *J. Exp. Anal. Behav.* 5:511–20

213. Uphouse, L. L., Wilson, J. R., Schlesinger, K. 1970. Induction of estrus in mice: the possible role of adrenal progesterone. *Horm. Behav.* 1:255–64

214. Vandenbergh, J. G. 1971. The influence of the social environment on sexual maturation in male mice. *J. Reprod. Fert.* 24:383–90

215. Van Wimersma Greidanus, Tj. B. 1970. Effects of steroids on extinction of an avoidance response in rats. A. Structure-activity relationship study. *Progr. Brain Res.* 32:185–91

216. Weijnen, J. A. W. M., Slangen, J. L. 1970. Effects of ACTH-analogues on extinction of conditioned behavior. *Progr. Brain Res.* 32:221–35

217. Weiss, J. M., McEwen, B. S., Silva, M. T. A., Kalkut, M. F. 1969. Pituitary-adrenal influences on fear responding. *Science* 163:197–99

218. Whalen, R. E., Hardy, D. F. 1970. Induction of receptivity in female rats and cats with estrogen and testosterone. *Physiol. Behav.* 5:529–33

219. Whalen, R. E., Luttge, W. G. 1970. P-chlorophenylalanine methyl ester: an aphrodisiac? *Science* 169:1000–1

220. Whalen, R. E., Luttge, W. G. 1971. Long-term retention of tritiated estradiol in brain and peripheral tissues of male and female rats. *Neuroendocrinology* 6:255–63

221. Whalen, R. E., Luttge, W. G. 1971. Testosterone, androstenedione and dihydrotestosterone: effects on mating behavior of male rats. *Horm. Behav.* 2:117–25

222. Whalen, R. E., Luttge, W. G., Gorzalka, B. B. 1971. Neonatal androgenization and the development of estrogen responsivity in male and female rats. *Horm. Behav.* 2:83–90

223. Young, W. C. 1961. The hormones and mating behavior. *Sex Intern. Secretions* 2:1173–239

224. Zarrow, M. X., Clark, J. H. 1968. Ovulation following vaginal stimulation in a spontaneous ovulator and its implications. *J. Endocrinol.* 40:343–52

225. Zarrow, M. X., Estes, S. A., Denenberg, V. H., Clark, J. H. 1970. Pheromonal facilitation of ovulation in the immature mouse. *J. Reprod. Fert.* 23:357–60

226. Zitrin, A., Beach, F. A., Barchas, J. D., Dement, W. C. 1970. Sexual behavior of male cats after administration of parachlorophenylalanine. *Science* 170:868–70

227. Zumpe, D., Michael, R. P. 1970. Ovarian hormones and female sexual invitations in captive rhesus monkeys (*Macaca mulatta*). *Anim. Behav.* 18:293–301

THE ADRENAL CORTEX

PATRICK J. MULROW

Professor of Medicine, Yale University School of Medicine
New Haven, Connecticut

INTRODUCTION

A comprehensive review of the adrenal cortex was written by Bransome (14) in 1968. Although progress has been made in understanding the control mechanisms regulating adrenocortical function, no startling new concepts have been developed. Much work has centered on the mechanism of action of ACTH and the cyclic nucleotides. A review of the biology of the cyclic nucleotide recently appeared (Hardman, Robison & Sutherland, 47).

In accordance with advice from the editors, the present review is not meant to be all-inclusive but rather selective and interpretative. It touches upon four topics: (*a*) the actions of ACTH on the adrenal cortex, (*b*) adrenal mitochondrial properties, (*c*) control of aldosterone secretion, and (*d*) the adrenal cortex in hypertension. References were frequently chosen for their recentness and bibliography rather than for any priority in a field.

THE ACTIONS OF ACTH ON THE ADRENAL CORTEX

Although there is a small basal secretion of steroids by the adrenal cortex of hypophysectomized animals (104), the major regulator of glucocortical secretion is ACTH. This anterior pituitary hormone has a profound influence on the entire metabolism of the adrenal gland; ACTH does not appear to enter the adrenal cell but, rather, binds to a specific site on the plasma membrane, possibly to adenyl cyclase, an enzyme activated by ACTH. A solubilized membrane fraction from mouse adrenal tumor binds ACTH-I^{131} with great affinity and has been reported as a specific binding protein for the measurement of ACTH by a displacement analysis technique (67). Studies concerning the intracellular distribution of adenyl cyclase have reported activity in the nuclear, microsomal, and mitochondrial fractions of bovine adrenal glands and of mouse adrenal tumor, (48, 101), but Satre et al (96) recovered adenyl cyclase activity mainly in the microsomal fraction and presented evidence that the mitochondrial activity is due to contamination by microsomal fragments. Adrenal adenyl cyclase has been found to be activated by fluoride and by ACTH but not by other peptide hormones (48, 67, 110) and to be inhibited by phenothiazines (122). Calcium is required for optimal ACTH stimulation of adenyl cyclase activity (4, 53). An exception to the specificity of adrenal adenyl cyclase to stimulation by ACTH has been reported: the adenyl cyclase of a mouse adrenal tumor is stimulated by norepinephrine, epinephrine, and thyroid stimulating hormone (101).

Prostaglandins may also be involved in the action of ACTH. ACTH stimulation of superfused rat adrenal glands results in a rapid release of PGE and PGF compounds and a decrease in the adrenal content of PGE_2, PGF, and $PGF_{2\alpha}$. Several prostaglandins stimulate corticosterone production, with PGE_2 being the most potent. This stimulation is transient and is inhibited by cyclohexamide (35, 90). The prostaglandin story in the adrenal gland is just beginning. As the methods for measuring prostaglandins improve, a better understanding of their role as an intracellular messenger will be achieved.

Cyclic AMP appears to be the intracellular messenger by which ACTH has its effect (102). ACTH stimulates cyclic AMP production within ten seconds and before stimulating steroidogenesis (6, 43). In isolated rat adrenal cells as well as in other adrenal preparations, several different 3'5'-cyclic nucleotides were found to stimulate steroidogenesis (56). It is not known whether ACTH increases the adrenal content of cyclic nucleotides other than cyclic AMP. All actions of ACTH can be duplicated by cyclic AMP, including the effect on adrenal growth (84).

The mechanism of the next step in the action of ACTH on steroidogenesis is not clear. ACTH was found to increase the activity of the rate-limiting reactions conversion of cholesterol to pregnenolone (desmolase) (59). Conversion of cholesterol to 20-hydroxycholesterol may be the rate-limiting step in the overall reaction, and ACTH may enhance this conversion, although the evidence is indirect (45). Koritz & Kumar (59) showed that isolated mitochondria from adrenal glands of rats pretreated with ACTH continued to produce increased quantities of pregnenolone in vitro. This increase was not the result of increased enzyme concentration but was due to increased activity of the enzymes, possibly the result of altered permeability properties of the mitochondria. These authors postulated the extrusion of pregnenolone from the mitochondria relieves feedback inhibition of the reaction, cholesterol to pregnenolone. These experiments do not exclude the possibility that ACTH increases the synthesis of pregnenolone by the mitochondria by increasing the cholesterol content, nor do they explain why cyclohexamide blocks the ACTH stimulation of pregnenolone synthesis by intact mitochondria but not by swollen mitochondria.

Further evidence that ACTH does not change the desmolase content is the failure of hypophysectomy to alter the activity of the desmolase for at least 24 hours (54), and the lack of effect of 3'5'-cyclic AMP on the desmolase when added in vitro (22).

The evidence that ACTH stimulates the synthesis of a protein or proteins which enhances the conversion of cholesterol to pregnenolone has been reviewed by Bransome (14). Most of the evidence was obtained by the use of protein synthesis inhibitors. No protein has been isolated in the intervening years. Indeed, in a murine adrenal tissue culture system Kowal (61) has shown profound inhibition of protein synthesis is necessary before cyclo-hexamide inhibits the steroidogenic action of ACTH, but ACTH can still raise the steroid production to control, non-ACTH stimulated levels. Also, profound inhibition of ATP formation was found to inhibit the ACTH effect (17, 61). When ^{3}H 3′5′-cyclic AMP was found to bind to a microsomal and supernatant fraction (as well as to other fractions) of bovine adrenal glands, Gill & Garren (40) postulated cyclic AMP was binding to a specific microsomal protein. In a subsequent study, this group reported cyclic AMP bound to a protein kinase complex in the microsomal and supernatant fraction of bovine adrenal gland. The cyclic AMP appears to activate the kinase by combining with a repressor protein that is released from the kinase, leaving an activated enzyme which is no longer stimulated by cyclic AMP (113). A similar mechanism for activating kinase has been reported in muscle tissue (94). The specific function of this protein kinase in relation to steroidogenesis is not understood, but one hypothesis is that the kinase catalyzes the phosphorylation of ribosomal proteins and thus stimulates ribosomal protein synthesis (113). This concept implies ACTH stimulates total protein synthesis rather than synthesis of a specific protein. Most studies with ACTH have not demonstrated an acute stimulation of protein synthesis but rather a slight inhibition (14). It has been argued that this inhibition is an artifact of the in vitro system which is due to the accumulation of endogenous steroids which inhibit protein synthesis. When steroidogenesis was blocked by aminoglutethemide and new RNA synthesis by actinomycin, ACTH and cyclic AMP produced a small but inconsistent stimulation of protein synthesis, presumably at the translational level (32). In this study ACTH did not inhibit protein synthesis, but it was also clear that ACTH can stimulate steroidogenesis without stimulating protein synthesis. Although ACTH and cyclohexamide act on the rate limiting step in steroidogenesis, the conversion of cholesterol of pregnenolone, there is no evidence that the concentration of the mitochondrial enzymes involved in the conversion are altered (59). Furthermore, the reports of cyclic AMP enhancing synthesis of pregnenolone by adrenocortical mitochondria must be reinterpreted in view of the fact cyclic AMP inhibits conversion of pregnenolone to progesterone and thereby increases the accumulation of pregnenolone and not its total synthesis (60, 71). This action of cyclic AMP may be pharmacological since unphysiological doses are necessary to demonstrate the effect. The conversion of pregnenolone to progesterone by adrenal mitochondria may be due to contamination with microsomes since the latter is the major site of the conversion, but exhaustive washings of the mitochondria were unable to eliminate the conversion and, moreover, the mitochondrial fraction did not contain 21-hydroxylase activity, another microsomal enzyme (71).

Adrenal cholesterol.—ACTH profoundly influences cholesterol metabolism in the adrenal cortex. In the rat, ACTH was found to stimulate the uptake of ^{3}H cholesterol by the adrenal gland from plasma, (29, 105), but had no effect on the uptake of cholesterol by the liver (29). ACTH induced a marked increase in adrenal cholesterol content when cholesterol utilization was blocked with aminoglutethamide or cyclohexamide (29). Presumably ACTH stimulates cholesterol synthesis as well as uptake. In adrenal tumor in tissue culture, ACTH did not increase cell uptake of cholesterol but stimulated conversion of acetate into cholesterol (61). Furthermore, there is evidence for a feedback inhibition of cholesterol synthesis by cholesterol (62). ACTH also increased hydrolysis of cholesterol esters to free cholesterol, an action which was not dependent upon protein synthesis (39). Free fatty acid release was stimulated, and the adrenal content of free fatty acid was diminished by ACTH, but ^{14}C palmitate utilization was not altered (72). Clofibrate inhibited lipid synthesis by rat adrenal glands and also inhibited 11 β-hydroxylase activity. As a result, corticosterone response to ACTH was diminished (95).

Adrenal glucose metabolism.—ACTH increases the oxidation of glucose by the rat adrenal gland in vitro. Glucose is necessary for the stimulation of steroidogenesis, for cyclic AMP formation, and for the optimal steroidogenic effect of cyclic AMP. Glucose was not found necessary for the stimulation of steroidogenesis by NADPH (50). In contrast, the mouse adrenal tumor in tissue culture did not require glucose for steroidogenic response to ACTH, although ACTH rapidly stimulated glycolysis even in the presence of cyclohexamide (61). In a study of the ACTH activation of glycolysis in the rat adrenal gland, Bell et al (6) measured substrates of glycolysis, the pentose phosphate pathway, the Krebs cycle, and pyridine and adenine nucleotides, including cyclic AMP. Crossovers in substrate concentrations at the level of phosphofructokinase and glyceraldehyde phosphate dehydrogenase were found, indicating an activation of these enzymes. Elevations in cyclic AMP and a decrease in ATP/ADP-AMP ratios were also found, either of which could explain phosphofructokinase activation. No significant changes in the Krebs cycle intermediates or pyridine nucleotides were detected.

Adrenal ascorbic acid.—Both ACTH and cyclic AMP deplete the adrenal gland of ascorbic acid in vivo and in vitro. This depletion was found to be unrelated to the stimulation of steroidogenesis (31). In one study, ACTH inhibited the transport of ascorbic acid into the adrenal gland by a process that is blocked by puromycin, which suggests that ACTH stimulates the synthesis of proteins involved in the transport of ascorbic acid (28). Although a naturally occurring redox couple permitting ascorbate entry into the electron transport system for hydroxylation has not been demonstrated, ascorbate under certain experimental conditions can provide energy to support mitochondrial hydroxylation by reverse electron transport (57).

Adrenal growth and differentiation.—In addition to its acute effects,

ACTH has been found to have a profound influence upon adrenal growth and differentiation (13, 76, 78). Fetal rat adrenal glands in tissue culture did not respond to ACTH immediately, but rather require several days of pretreatment with ACTH before an acute response is observed. This acute response is correlated with morphological changes in the mitochondria and endoplasmic reticulum induced by ACTH. The addition of chloramphenicol, an inhibitor of mitochondrial protein synthesis, prevents the action of ACTH but does not alter the conversion of progesterone to deoxycorticosterone. Presumably, ACTH stimulates the synthesis of mitochondrial proteins involved in the desmolase and 11 β-hydroxylase reactions (78). Kowal et al (63) demonstrated that ACTH increased 11 β-hydroxylase activity of murine adrenal tumor cells in tissue culture by increasing the levels of cytochrome P_{450} and adrenoxin without affecting the levels of the respiratory chain cytochromes. ACTH did not affect total mitochondrial protein synthesis as determined by the incorporation of radioactive amino acids into mitochondrial proteins. In vivo administration of ACTH to rats induced a modest increase in isocitrate dehydrogenase, malic enzyme, and malic dehydrogenase activities in the adrenal mitochondria (65).

Hypophysectomy results in a slow fall in desmolase activity and in several other enzymatic activities. Administration of two units of ACTH per day per rat restored to normal the adrenal weight but not desmolase activity, which required a higher dose (54).

Effects of steroids on the adrenal cortex.—Corticosterone can inhibit protein and RNA synthesis in vitro (18, 33) as well as ATP formation (17). In homogenates addition of ATP overcame steroid inhibition of protein synthesis (17). Dehydroepiandrosterone infused into the blood supply of the dog adrenal inhibited 11 β-hydroxylase activity (36). The effect of gonadal hormones on adrenal function depends upon dose, type of hormone, and experimental preparation (55). These data suggest there is a local feedback loop whereby adrenal steroids inhibit steroidogenesis.

ADRENAL MITOCHONDRIA

A number of laboratories continue to investigate these unusual mitochondria with two separate but connected systems for consuming oxygen, the classical respiratory and the steroid hydroxylating chains. Several stereospecific hydroxylation steps take place in the mitochondria, and all require oxygen, an NADPH flavoprotein, adrenoxin, and a cytochrome P_{450}. The specificity appears to reside in the cytochrome P_{450} or in an enzyme associated with it. Most of the investigations have been conducted on the 11 β-hydroxylase reaction because it is easier to study, but probably the same general principles hold for all mitochondrial hydroxylase reactions.

The 11 β-hydroxylase system and the respiratory chain are located on the inner membrane of the adrenal mitochondria (30). The existence of three NADPH generating reactions, (a) the energy-linked transhydrogenase, (b) the NADPH-linked isocitric dehydrogenase, and (c) malic enzyme, have been shown for both animal and human adrenal cortex mitochondria (19, 99, 100, 105). Furthermore, reducing equivalents may be transferred to the steroid hydroxylating chain by reverse electron transport and by an energy-linked transhydrogenase (57). With certain Kreb cycle intermediates, a competition can be shown between the respiratory chain and steroid hydroxylation for high energy intermediates (97, 98). One molecule of steroid is hydroxylated for each molecule of ATP utilized (98).

Comparison of absorption spectral properties suggests that different forms of cytochrome P_{450} exist for 11 β-hydroxylase and the cholesterol side chain cleavage reactions (108, 121). Jefcoate & Gaylor (49) also interpreted their studies to indicate two forms of cytochrome P_{450} are present in adrenal mitochondria. There appears to be a competition between 11 β-hydroxylation and side chain cleavage. Deoxycorticosterone (DOC) inhibits side chain cleavage of cholesterol, but cholesterol does not inhibit 11 β-hydroxylation of deoxycorticosterone. DOC appears to compete with cholesterol for some site on cytochrome P_{450} or some other factor associated with the cytochrome (124). Metapyrone has been found to inhibit 11 β-hydroxylation to a greater extent than the side chain cleavage of cholesterol, by interfering in a competitive fashion with the binding of deoxycorticosterone to cytochrome P_{450} (120). Dicoumoral has also been found to bind to the cytochrome P_{450} and to be a noncompetitive inhibitor of 11 β-hydroxylation (118). Adrenal mitochondrial phospholipid enhances 11 β-hydroxylation in vitro by stabilizing cytochrome P_{450}. The mitochondrial lipid stabilized the hemoprotein by preventing decomposition of cytochrome P_{450} to P_{420} (119).

ALDOSTERONE

The zona glomerulosa, the site of aldosterone biosynthesis, functions independently from the inner zones, the fasciculata-reticularis (F–R). Histologically these cells are different from the F–R cells, and under the electron microscope the mitochondria appeared to have plate-like cristae in contrast to the vesicular cristae of the inner zones (41, 85). Stimulation of the zona glomerulosa cells by sodium depletion gave these mitochondria vesicular cristae. Prolonged ACTH stimulation of fetal rat adrenal glands in tissue culture caused differentiation in appearance of some zona glomerulosa cells into F–R cells (52). Whether there is also a change in function is not known, but possibly this differentiation is the explanation for the reduced aldosterone secretion following chronic ACTH administration.

Aldosterone is the only unique steroid made by the zona glomerulosa. Although 18-hydroxycorticosterone (18-OH B) is synthesized chiefly by the glomerulosa cells (109), it is also synthesized by the inner zones in both bovine and human adrenal cells (73, 75). Cytochrome P_{450} participated in the conversion of corticosterone to 18-OH B and aldosterone (44). Although an 18-ol-dehydrogenase has been postulated to convert 18-OH B to aldosterone, no studies on it have been reported. Substrate support of steroid hydroxylation in the zona glomerulosa mitochondria is similar to that of the inner zone mitochondria (100). Because of their relatively slow rates, the conversion of cholesterol to pregnenolone and 18-OH B to aldosterone appears to be the rate limiting step in aldosterone biosynthesis. The regulation of aldosterone biosynthesis and secretion is not as simple as the regulation of glucocorticoid secretion by the F–R zones, where one hormone, ACTH, is the sole regulator. The renin-angiotensin system, potassium, ACTH, growth hormone, the plasma Na^+ concentration, and possibly other factors influence aldosterone secretion (81). The renin-angiotensin system has been considered the major physiological control mechanism, but recent reports have questioned its primacy. There seems to be little doubt that the response in aldosterone secretion to postural changes is dependent upon the renin-angiotensin system since nephrectomy abolishes the response (2), but the basal production rate is normal in the anephric human. Infusions of angiotensin into humans resulted in higher angiotensin levels, but lower than those resulting from a low sodium diet (10). In humans, during the early phase of total fasting, plasma aldosterone concentration rose, while plasma renin concentration fell (21). Furthermore, there were a number of clinical situations in which plasma renin levels changed while aldosterone either was unchanged or changed in the opposite direction (80). In view of the evidence that K depletion may increase plasma renin levels while decreasing aldosterone production and that K loading may have the opposite effect, any lack of correlation between renin and aldosterone cannot be construed to indicate another control mechanism, unless K balance is not altered appreciably (103, 111, 112).

In sheep, aldosterone secretion can be altered by sodium depletion or repletion while a constant infusion of renin or angiotensin is maintained. When a sodium-depleted sheep was acutely depleted of sodium, aldosterone secretion declined more rapidly than did plasma renin levels. Furthermore, correction of the low serum sodium concentration by direct infusion of hypertonic $NaHCO_3$ into the adrenal artery without appreciably altering total sodium balance did not correct the increased secretion rate. It was noted during the course of these studies that small changes in serum [K] led to profound decreases in aldosterone secretion (8).

In the rat, a series of experiments have questioned the primary role of the renin-angiotensin system in the response of aldosterone secretion to sodium depletion. Nephrectomy failed to lower the elevated aldosterone levels of sodium depleted rats, while sodium depletion by peritoneal dialysis in nephrectomized rats stimulated aldosterone secretion (88). Sodium depletion did not increase aldosterone levels in hypophysectomized or K-depleted rats despite an increase in plasma renin activity (11, 42, 86, 87, 89).

Prolonged angiotensin infusions produced only a transient increase in aldosterone secretion in hypophysectomized dogs on a high sodium diet (27).

Another argument raised against the renin system is that sodium depletion can stimulate the last steps in aldosterone biosynthesis while angiotensin stimulates only the early steps (3, 9, 74, 80). However, most of the studies of the effect of angiotensin on the biosynthetic pathway have been acute experiments whereas sodium depletion is a chronic stimulus. Recently, Ageulera and Marusic (unpublished observation) found that daily injections of renin for four days into hypophysectomized dogs increased the conversion of corticosterone to aldosterone by the adrenal mitochondria. The renin injections did not cause a natriuresis. Recent in vitro studies (46) with separated adrenal cells indicated a number of aldosterone-stimulating substances increased the conversion of corticosterone to aldosterone. Albumin was necessary in the incubation system to observe this effect. The authors suggested that an increase in glomerulosa cell corticosterone production increased the conversion of corticosterone to aldosterone, possibly by an allosteric effect. However, no evidence of allostery was observed when a series of corticosterone concentrations were used in studying aldosterone formation by isolated mitochondria (74).

The anterior pituitary gland.—It has been known for years that aldosterone secretion is stimulated by injections of ACTH and lowered by hypophysectomy. Evidence is accumulating that another anterior pituitary hormone(s) plays a permissive role in aldosterone production. In the rat, hypophysectomy prevented the increased aldosterone response to sodium depletion even though the zona glomerulosa widened and the plasma renin levels increased (42, 86, 87, 89). Injection of ACTH plus growth hormone maintained the response to sodium depletion, while neither hormone alone can do so (66, 87). Furthermore, anterior pituitary gland extracts also maintained the aldosterone response, although they contain little or no ACTH activity (87). These data suggest some other factor plus growth hormone maintain the biosynthetic capacity of the zona glomerulosa cell. In the chronically hypophysectomized dog, the response of aldosterone secretion to infusions of ACTH and angiotensin was diminished, whereas suppression of ACTH secretion by the chronic administration of a glucocorticoid did not alter the response to the infusions (38). Similar studies in humans with hypopituitarism also indicated that some other pituitary hormone besides ACTH is necessary for optimal aldosterone secretion (117). Hypophysectomy did not reduce the conversion of corticosterone to aldosterone in rat adrenal mitochondria; presumably the lowered secretion rate was due to a decreased rate of an earlier step. (Boyd, Page & Mulrow, unpublished observation).

Potassium.—Recent evidence calls for a re-evaluation of the role of potassium in the regulation of aldosterone secretion. Subtle changes in K concentration can alter aldosterone production in vivo or in vitro. An increase of 0.5 mEq/liter or less in the plasma K perfusing the sheep adrenal gland stimulated aldosterone secretion (37), and an increase of 0.35 mEq/liter in the K concentration of the incubation media increased aldosterone production by rat adrenal quarters (12). Potassium appears to play a critical role in the response of aldosterone secretion to sodium depletion in the rat. Potassium depletion prevents the response and the widening of the zona glomerulosa. Plasma K increased during sodium depletion (11, 79). Chronic K loading resembled Na depletion by increasing aldosterone secretion and the conversion of corticosterone to aldosterone, under conditions in which K loading did not produce a negative Na balance nor increase plasma renin levels (11). This stimulation of the late steps by chronic K loading does not contradict previous studies demonstrating an acute effect of K on earlier steps (27, 80). Potassium depletion inhibited 11 β-hydroxylase activity of capsular adrenal tissue. The stimulating effect of K was limited to the zona glomerulosa cells (80). A number of aldosterone stimulating substances are less effective in vivo or in vitro in the presence of low K (116) and in fact, Baumber et al (5) reported an increase in adrenal cell potassium in the dog following ACTH or angiotensin administration, or with a low sodium diet. These results, although pertinent, are surprising since the zona glomerulosa is only a small part of the adrenal cortex.

The mechanism by which K stimulates aldosterone secretion is slowly being elucidated. Potassium, like ACTH, requires calcium in the media in order to have an effect (80). Inhibition of protein synthesis blocked the stimulation by K, but this inhibition may be a toxic effect of the inhibitors since basal steroid production was diminished (80). Potassium may stimulate Na-K ATPase which is in higher concentration in the outer than the inner zones of the rat adrenal gland (12). Inhibition of Na-K ATPase activity by ouabain or other methods blocked the stimulation of aldosterone production by K (12, 26, 80). Since cell uptake of K was also diminished, intracellular K rather than extracellular K may be important for aldosterone biosynthesis.

Other factors.—Low concentrations of serotonin markedly stimulated steroidogenesis of the zona glomerulosa cell in vitro (80). Whether this effect is important physiologically is not known. Prostaglandins had an inconsistent effect upon aldosterone secretion by the sheep adrenal gland (7).

The previously mentioned experiments in the rat and sheep suggest an unknown factor(s) may be involved in the regulation of aldosterone secretion. The presence of bilateral adrenal hyperplasia in patients with primary aldosteronism and low plasma renin levels also suggests there is an unknown stimulatory factor (1).

ADRENAL CORTEX AND HYPERTENSION

In several types of experimental hypertension, abnormalities in adrenal mitochondrial function are implicated in the pathogenesis of the hypertension. In adrenal regeneration hypertension, the elevated DOC secretion rate has been attributed to a deficient 11 β-hydroxylase activity (106).

Ultrastructural abnormalities have also been observed in the mitochondria of the regenerating cells. The regenerating fasciculata cells appear to stem from the glomerulosa cells. The glomerulosa mitochondria were observed to change into fasciculata mitochondria, presumably under the influence of ACTH. Peripheral blood concentration of 18-hydroxy-deoxycorticosterone (*18-OH-DOC*) was normal (91).

Androgen and metapyrone induced hypertension were also associated with inhibition of 11 β-hydroxylation and in the metapyrone study, peripheral blood concentration of DOC was increased (15, 16, 23, 24). Androgens diminished cytochrome P_{450} content of adrenal mitochondria without changing microsomal cytochrome P_{450}.

Recently, 18-OH-DOC has been implicated in the pathogenesis of human hypertension. In one study of patients with essential hypertension and low plasma renin activity, 18-OH-DOC excretion was elevated in about one third, and in one patient with hypertension and hypokalemia, excessive production seemed to be the cause of the hypertension (77). The available evidence, however, indicates 18-OH-DOC has little mineralocorticoid activity. In rats with either salt-sensitive or spontaneous hypertension, the concentration of 18-OH-DOC in adrenal or peripheral blood was normal. However, rats resistant to the hypertensive effect of salt have a low 18-OH-DOC concentration. When the conversion of DOC to corticosterone and 18-OH-DOC was studied in vitro, the adrenals from salt-sensitive rats converted more DOC to 18-OH-DOC and less to corticosterone than did the adrenals from salt-resistant rats. Apparently, the low 18-OH-DOC/B ratio of the salt-resistant rats is unique and may be a genetic marker for resistance to hypertension (92, 93).

Little progress has been made to resolve the conflict over the incidence of primary aldosteronism in essential hypertension (82). The presence of bilateral adrenal hyperplasia in patients with hyperaldosteronism and low plasma renin levels suggests the presence of a nonrenin mechanism which stimulates adrenal growth and aldosterone production (1, 34). There is disagreement over the beneficial effects of adrenalectomy in these patients (1). "Tertiary" aldosteronism (aldosterone production that has become autonomous from chronic stimulation by renin) has been reported in patients with malignant hypertension (70).

In studies of patients with essential hypertension about 20% had low plasma renin activity and normal or low aldosterone production (20, 51, 68, 114). Evidence is accumulating that the adrenal cortex may play some role in the pathogenesis of the hypertension and the low plasma renin (114, 123). Aminoglutethimide (123) or aldactone treatment alleviated the hypertension in patients with low plasma renin levels but not in those with normal levels. The spontaneously hypertensive rat develops a low plasma renin level and may be a useful model to study the phenomenon (58).

Oral contraceptive agents may cause hypertension, although the incidence is quite low (115). Plasma renin substrate concentration as well as plasma renin activity and angiotensin II levels are uniformly elevated, but plasma renin concentration may be decreased, presumably as a result of feedback inhibition by angiotensin II. Aldosterone excretion is also frequently elevated (64, 69, 83, 107, 114). There appears to be no correlation between the changes in these variables and the development of hypertension (114). The estrogen component of "the pill" stimulates angiotensinogen production which leads to the changes in the renin-angiotensin aldosterone system (25). It is still not understood why only a few women who take oral contraceptive drugs develop hypertension, while most do not.

ACKNOWLEDGMENTS

The preparation of this manuscript was supported in part by grants from the USPHS.

LITERATURE CITED

1. Baer, L. et al 1970. Pseudo-primary aldosteronism. An entity distinct from true primary aldosteronism. *Circ. Res.* 26, 27: Suppl. I, 203–20
2. Balikian, H. M., Brodie, A. H., Dale, S. L., Melby, J. C., Tait, J. F. 1968. Effect of posture on the metabolic clearance rate, plasma concentration and blood production rate of aldosterone in man. *J. Clin. Endocrinol.* 28:1630–40
3. Baniukiewicz, S. et al 1968. *Adrenal biosynthesis of steroids in vitro and in vivo using continuous superfusion and infusion procedures,* ed. K. W. McKerns, p. 153. Amsterdam: Appleton, Century, Crofts
4. Bär, H. P., Hechter, O. 1969. Adenyl cyclase and hormone action III. Calcium requirement for ACTH stimulation of adenyl cyclase. *Biochem. Biophys. Res. Commun.* 34: 681–86
5. Baumber, J. S., David, J. O., Johnson, J. A., Witty, R. T. 1971. Increased adrenocortical potassium in association with increased biosynthesis of aldosterone. *Am. J. Physiol.* 220:1094–99
6. Bell, J., Brooker, G., Harding, B. W. 1970. ACTH activation of glycolysis in rat adrenal gland. *Biochem. Biophys. Res. Commun.* 41:938–43
7. Blair-West, J. R. et al 1971. Effects of prostaglandin E_1 upon the steroid secretion of the adrenal of the sodium deficient sheep. *Endocrinology* 88:367–71
8. Blair-West, J. R. et al 1971. The dissociation of aldosterone secretion and systemic renin and angiotensin II levels during the correction of sodium deficiency. *Acta Endocrinol.* 66:229–47
9. Blair-West, J. R. et al 1970. Studies on the biosynthesis of aldosterone using sheep adrenal transplant: Effect of sodium depletion on the conversion of corticosterone to aldosterone. *J. Endocrinol.* 46:453
10. Boyd, G. W., Adamson, A. R., James, V. H. T., Peart, W. S. 1969. The role of the renin-angiotensin system in the control of aldosterone in man. *Proc. Roy. Soc. London* 62:1253
11. Boyd, J. E., Palmore, W. P., Mulrow, P. J. 1971. Role of potassium in the control of aldosterone secretion in the rat. *Endocrinology* 88:556–65
12. Boyd, J. E., Palmore, W. P., Mulrow, P. J. 1971. Potassium: Is it the adrenal glomerulotrophin? *J. Clin. Invest.* 50:35
13. Bransome, E. D., Jr. 1968. Regulation of adrenal growth. Differences in the effects of ACTH in normal and dexamethasone suppressed guinea pigs. *Endocrinology* 83:956–63
14. Bransome, E. D., Jr. 1968. Adrenal Cortex. *Ann. Rev. Physiol.* 30:171–200
15. Brownie, A. C., Colby, H. D., Gallant, S., Skelton, F. R. 1970. Some studies on the effect of androgens on adrenal cortical function of rats. *Endocrinology* 86:1085–92
16. Brownie, A. C., Skelton, F. R. 1968. Andrenocortical function and structure in adrenal regeneration and methylandrostenediol hypertension. *Funct. Adrenal Cortex* 2:691–718
17. Burrow, G. N. 1969. A steroid inhibitory effect on adrenal mitochondria. *Endocrinology* 84:979–85
18. Burrow, G. N., Morrow, L. B. 1968. Further studies of the steroid inhibition of adrenal protein synthesis. *Endocrinology* 83:18–24
19. Cammer, W., Estabrook, R. W. 1967.

Respiratory activity of adrenal cortex mitochondria during steroid hydroxylation. *Arch. Biochem. Biophys.* 122:721–34

20. Channik, B. J., Adlin, E. V., Marks, A. D. 1969. Suppressed plasma renin activity in hypertension. *Arch. Intern. Med.* 123:131–40

21. Chinn, R. H. et al 1970. The natriuresis of fasting: Relationship to changes in plasma renin and plasma aldosterone concentrations. *Clin. Sci.* 39:437–55

22. Cohen, M. P., Moriwaki, K. 1969. 3′,5′ Cyclic AMP and the adrenal desmolase system. *Proc. Soc. Exp. Biol. Med.* 131:1207–71

23. Colby, H. D., Skelton, F. R., Brownie, A. C. 1970. Testosterone induced hypertension in the rat. *Endocrinology* 86:1093–101

24. Colby, H. D., Skelton, F. R., Brownie, A. C. 1970. Metapyrone induced hypertension in the rat. *Endocrinology* 86:620–28

25. Crane, M. G., Harris, J. J., Windsor, W., III. 1971. Hypertension, oral contraceptive agents and conjugated estrogens. *Ann. Intern. Med.* 74:13–21

26. Cushman, P., Jr. 1969. Inhibition of aldosterone secretion by ouabain in dog adrenal tissue. *Endocrinology* 84:808–13

27. Davis, W. W., Burwell, L. R., Bartter, F. C. 1959. Inhibition of the effects of angiotensin II on adrenal steroid production by dietary sodium. *Proc. Nat. Acad. Sci.* 63:718–23

28. DeNicola, A. F., Clayman, M., Johnstone, R. M. 1968. Hormonal control of ascorbic acid transport in rat adrenal quarters. *Endocrinology* 82:436–46

29. Dexter, R. N., Fishman, L. M., Ney, R. L. 1970. Stimulation of adrenal cholesterol uptake from plasma by adrenocorticotrophin. *Endocrinology* 87:836

30. Dodge, A. H., Christensen, A. K., Clayton, R. B. 1970. Localization of a steroid 11 β-hydroxylase in the inner membrane subfraction of rat adrenal mitochondria. *Endocrinology* 87:254–61

31. Earp, H. S., Watson, B. S., Ney, R. L. 1970. Adenosine 3′,5′-monophosphate as the mediator of ACTH-induced ascorbin acid depletion in the rat adrenal. *Endocrinology* 87:118–23

32. Farese, R. V. 1969. Effects of ACTH and cyclic AMP in vitro and incorporation of ³H-leucine and ¹⁴C-orotic acid into protein and RNA in the presence of an inhibitor of cholesterol side chain cleavage. *Endocrinology* 85:1209–12

33. Ferguson, J. J., Jr., Morita, Y. Mendelsohn, L. 1967. Incorporation in vitro of precursor into protein and RNA of rat adrenal glands. *Endocrinology* 80:521–26

34. Ferriss, J. B. et al 1970. Hypertension with aldosterone excess and low plasma-renin: Preoperative distinction between patients with and without adrenocortical tumor. *Lancet* 2:995–1000

35. Flack, J. D., Jessup, R., Ramwell, P. W. 1969. Protaglandin stimulation of rat corticosteroidogenesis. *Science* 163:691–92

36. Fragachan, F. et al 1969. Evidence of in vivo inhibition of 11 β-hydroxylation of steroids by dehydroepiandrosterone in the dog. *Endocrinology* 84:98–103

37. Funder, J. W. et al 1969. Effect of plasma [K+] on the secretion of aldosterone. *Endocrinology* 85:381–84

38. Ganong, W. F., Pemberton, D. L., VanBrunt, E. E. 1967. Adrenocortical responsiveness of ACTH and angiotensin II in hypophysectomized dogs and dogs treated with large doses of glucocorticoids. *Endocrinology* 81:1147–50

39. Garren, L. D., Gill, G. N., Masui, H., Walton, G. M. 1971. On the mechanism of action of ACTH. *Recent Prog. Horm. Res.* 27:In press

40. Gill, G. N., Garren, L. D. 1969. On the mechanism of action of adrenocorticotropic hormone: The binding of cyclic-3′,5′-adenosine monophosphate to an adrenal cortical protein. *Proc. Nat. Acad. Sci.* 63:512–19

41. Giocomelli, F., Weiner, J., Spiro, D. 1965. Cytological alterations related to stimulation of the zona glomerulosa of the adrenal gland. *J. Cell Biol.* 26:499–521

42. Goodwin, F. J., Kirshman, J. D., Sealey, J. E., Laragh, J. H. 1970. Influence of the pituitary gland on sodium conservation, plasma renin and renin substrate concentrations in the rat. *Endocrinology* 86:824–34

43. Grahame-Smith, D. G., Butcher, R. W., Ney, R. L., Sutherland, E. W. 1967. Adenosine 3′,5′-monophosphate as the intracellular medi-

ator of the action of adrenocorticotropic hormone in the adrenal cortex. *J. Biol. Chem.* 242:5535–41

44. Greengard, P. et al 1967. Aldosterone synthesis by adrenal mitochondria III. Participation of cytochrome P-450. *Arch. Biochem. Biophys.* 121: 298–303

45. Hall, P. F., Young, D. G. 1968. Site of action of trophic hormones upon the biosynthetic pathways to steroid hormones. *Endocrinology* 82: 559–68

46. Haning, R., Tait, S. A. S., Tait, J. F. 1970. In vitro effects of ACTH, angiotensins, serotonin and potassium on steroid output and conversion of corticosterone to aldosterone by isolated adrenal cells. *Endocrinology* 87:1147–67

47. Hardman, J. G., Robison, G. A., Sutherland, E. W. 1971. Cyclic Nucleotides. *Ann. Rev. Physiol.* 33: 311–36

48. Hechter, O., Bär, H. P., Matsuba, M., Soifer, D. 1969. ACTH sensitive adenyl cyclase in bovine adrenal cortex membrane fractions. *Life Sci.* 8:935–42

49. Jefcoate, C. R. E., Gaylor, J. L. 1970. Ligand interactions with hemoprotein P-450. Equilibria between high- and low-spin forms of P-450 in bovine adrenal mitochondria. *Biochemistry* 9:3815–23

50. Jones, D. J., Nicholson, W. E., Liddle, G. W. 1970. Role of glucose in facilitating the acute steroidogenic action of adrenocorticotropic hormone (ACTH). *Proc. Soc. Exp. Biol. Med.* 133:764–69

51. Jose, A., Kaplan, N. M. 1969. Suppressed plasma renin activity in essential hypertension. *Ann. Intern. Med.* 123:141–46

52. Kahri, A. 1966. Histochemical and electron microscopic studies on cells of the rat adrenal cortex in tissue culture. *Acta Endocrinol.* 52: Suppl. 108, 1–96

53. Kelly, L. A., Koritz, S. B. 1971. Bovine adrenal cortical adenyl cyclase and its stimulation by adrenocorticotropic hormone and NaP. *Biochim. Biophys. Acta.* 237:141–55

54. Kimura, T. 1969. Effects of hypophysectomy and ACTH administration on the level of adrenal cholesterol side-chain desmolase. *Endocrinology* 85:492–99

55. Kitay, J. I., Coyne, M. D., Swygert, N. H. 1970. Influence of gonadectomy and replacement with estradiol or testosterone on formation of 5α-reduced metabolites of corticosterone by the adrenal gland of the rat. *Endocrinology* 87:1257

56. Kitabachi, A. E., Sharma, R. K. 1971. Corticoidogenesis in isolated adrenal cells of rats. I. Effect of corticotropins and 3′,5′-cyclic nucleotides on corticosterone production. *Endocrinology* 88:1109–16

57. Klein, K. O., Harding, B. W. 1970. Electron transport reversal and steroid 11 β-hydroxylation in adrenal cortical mitochondria. *Biochemistry* 9:3653–58

58. Koletsky, S., Shook, P., Rivera, J. 1970. Lack of increased renin-angiotensin activity in rats with spontaneous hypertension. *Proc. Soc. Exp. Biol. Med.* 134:1187–90

59. Koritz, S. B., Kumar, A. M. 1970. On the mechanism of action of the adrenocorticotrophic hormone. *J. Biol. Chem.* 245:152–59

60. Koritz, S. B., Yun, J., Ferguson, J. J., Jr. 1968. Inhibition of adrenal progesterone biosynthesis by 3′,5′-cyclic AMP. *Endocrinology* 82:620–22

61. Kowal, J. 1970. ACTH and the metabolism of adrenal cell cultures. *Recent Prog. Horm. Res.* 26:623–76

62. Kowal, J. 1971. Adrenal cells in tissue culture IV. Use of an inhibitor of steroid synthesis for the study of ACTH action. *Endocrinology* 85: 270–79

63. Kowal, J., Simpson, E. R., Estabrook, R. W. 1970. Adrenal cells in tissue culture V on the specificity of the stimulation of 11 β-hydroxylation by adrenocorticotrophin. *J. Biol. Chem* 245:2438–43

64. Laragh, J. H. 1971. The pill, hypertension and the toxemias of pregnancy. *Am. J. Obstet. Gynecol.* 109:210–13

65. Laury, L., McCarthy, J. 1970. In vitro adrenal mitochondrial 11 β-hydroxylation following in vivo adrenal stimulation or inhibition: Enhanced substrate utilization. *Endocrinology* 87:1380–85

66. Lee, T. C., DeWied, D. 1968. Somatotropin as the non-ACTH factor of anterior pituitary origin for the maintenance of enhanced aldosterone secretory responsiveness of dietary sodium restriction of chronically hypophysectomized rats. *Life Sci.* 7:35

422 MULROW

67. Lefkowitz, R. J. et al 1970. ACTH receptors in the adrenal: specific binding of ACTH-^{125}I and its relation to adenyl cyclase. *Proc. Nat. Acad. Sci.* 65:745–52

68. Leutscher, J. A. et al 1969. Effects of sodium loading, sodium depletion and posture on plasma aldosterone concentration and renin activity in hypertensive patients. *J. Clin. Endocrinol.* 29:1310–18

69. Lipsett, M. B., Combs, J. W., Jr., Catt, K., Seigel, D. G. 1971. Problems in contraception. *Ann. Intern. Med.* 74:251–63

70. McAllister, R. G. et al 1971. Malignant hypertension: Effect of therapy on renin and aldosterone. *Circ. Res.* 28, 29: Suppl. II, 160–73

71. McCune, R. W., Roberts, S., Young P. L. 1970. Competitive inhibition of adrenal Δ^5-3β-hydroxysteroid dehydrogenase and Δ^5-3β-ketosteroid isomerase activities by adenosine 3',5'-monophosphate. *J. Biol. Chem.* 245:3859–67

72. Macho, L., Saffran, M. 1967. Metabolism of fatty acids in the rat adrenal gland. *Endocrinology* 81:179–85

73. Marusic, E. T., Mulrow, P. J. 1967. In vitro conversion of corticosterone 4-^{14}C to 18-hydroxycorticosterone by zona fasciculata-reticularis of beef adrenal. *Endocrinology* 80:214–18

74. Marusic, E. T., Mulrow, P. J. 1967. Stimulation of aldosterone biosynthesis in adrenal mitochondria by sodium depletion. *J. Clin. Invest.* 46:2101–8

75. Marusic, E. T., Mulrow, P. J. 1969. 18-hydroxycorticosterone biosynthesis in an aldosterone secreting tumor and in the surrounding nontumorous adrenal gland (33976). *Proc. Soc. Exp. Biol. Med.* 131:778–80

76. Masui, H., Garren, L. D. 1970. On the mechanism of action of adrenocorticotropic hormone. Stimulation of deoxyribonucleic acid polymerase and thymidine kinase activities in adrenal glands. *Biol. Chem.* 245:2627–32

77. Melby, J. C., Dale, S. L., Wilson, T. E. 1971. 18-hydroxy-deoxycorticosterone in human hypertension. *Circ. Res.* 28, 29: Suppl. II, 142–52

78. Milner, A. J. 1971. ACTH and the differentiation of rat adrenal cortical cells grown in primary tissue culture. *Endocrinology* 88:66

79. Muller, J. 1969. Effects of sodium deficiency, potassium deficiency, and uremia upon the steroidogenic response of rat adrenal tissue to serotonin, potassium ions and adrenocorticotrophin. *Endocrinology* 85:43–49

80. Muller, J. 1971. Regulation of aldosterone biosynthesis. *Monographs in Endocrinology*, ed. F. Gross, A. Labhart, T. Mann, L. T. Samuels, J. Zander. 5:1–139, New York, Heidelberg, Berlin: Springer

81. Mulrow, P. J. 1969. Aldosterone in hypertension and edema. In *Duncan's Diseases of Metabolism*. ed. P. K. Bondy. 20:1083–102. Philadelphia: Saunders

82. Mulrow, P. J., Bartter, F. C., Kirkendall, W. M., Peterson, R. E., Tait, J. F. 1969. Adrenal cortex, aldosterone and hypertension. *Circulation* 40:739–744

83. Newton, M. A., Sealey, J. E., Ledingham, J. G. G., Laragh, J. H. 1968. High blood pressure and oral contraceptives. *Am. J. Obstet. Gynecol.* 101:1037–45

84. Ney, R. L. 1969. Effects of dibutyryl cyclic AMP on adrenal growth and steroidogenic capacity. *Endocrinology* 84:168

85. Nickerson, P. A., Brownie, A. C., Skelton, F. R. 1969. An electron microscopic study of the regenerating adrenal gland during the development of adrenal regeneration hypertension. *Am. J. Pathol.* 57:335–64

86. Palkovits, M., DeJong, W., Van Der Wal, B., DeWied, D. 1970. Effect of adrenocorticotrophic and growth hormones on aldosterone production and plasma renin activity in chronically hypophysectomized sodium-deficient rats. *J. Endocrinol.* 47:243–50.

87. Palmore, W. P., Anderson, R., Mulrow, P. J. 1970. Role of the pituitary in controlling aldosterone production in sodium-depleted rats. *Endocrinology* 86:728

88. Palmore, W. P., Marieb, N. J., Mulrow, P. J. 1969. Stimulation of aldosterone secretion by sodium depletion in nephrectomized rats. *Endocrinology* 84:1342

89. Palmore, W. P., Mulrow, P. J. 1967. Control of aldosterone secretion by the pituitary gland. *Science* 158:1482

90. Ramwell, P., Shaw, J. E. 1970. Biological significance of the prosta-

glandins. *Recent Prog. Horm. Res.* 26:139–73

91. Rapp, J. P. 1970. Gas chromatographic measurement of peripheral plasma 18-hydroxycorticosterone in adrenal regeneration hypertension. *Endocrinology* 86:668–77

92. Rapp, J. P., Dahl, L. K. 1971. Adrenal steroidogenesis in rats bred for susceptibility and resistance to the hypertensive effect of salt. *Endocrinology* 88:52–65

93. Rapp, J. P., Dahl, L. K. 1971. 18-hydroxy-deoxycorticosterone secretion in experimental hypertension in rats. *Circ. Res.* 28, 29:153–159

94. Reiman, E. M., Walsh, D. A., Krebs, E. G. 1971. Purification skeletal muscle adenosine 3′,5′-monophosphate dependent protein kinase. *J. Biol. Chem.* 246:1986–95

95. Saffran, J., Saffran, M., Salhanick, H. A. 1970. Clofibrate inhibits lipid synthesis and ACTH-stimulated steroidogenesis by rat adrenal tissue. *Endocrinology* 86:652–53

96. Satre, M., Chambaz, E. M., Vignais, P. V. 1971. Intracellular localization of adenyl cyclase and of binding sites for 3′,5′-adenosine monophosphate in adrenal cortex. *FEBS Lett.* 12:207–13

97. Sauer, L. A. 1970. Steroid hydroxylations in rat adrenal mitochondria. II. Competition between energy-linked transhydrogenase-dependent steroid hydroxylation and oxidative phosphorylation for high-energy intermediates and NADH. *Arch. Biochem. Biophys.* 139:340–50

98. Sauer, L. A. 1971. Steroid hydroxylations in rat adrenal mitochondria. III. The ATP-steroid-oxygen stoichiometry of ATP-dependent steroid hydroxylation. *Biochim. Biophys. Acta.* 234:287–92

99. Sauer, L. A. 1971. Steroid hydroxylation and oxidative phosphorylation in human adrenal cortex mitochondria. *Endocrinology* 88:318–24

100. Sauer, L. A., Mulrow, P. J. 1969. Steroid hydroxylations in rat adrenal mitochondria. I. Some properties of the C-18 and 11-β-hydroxylations in tightly coupled mitochondria. *Arch. Biochem. Biophys.* 134:486–96

101. Schorr, I., Ney, R. L. 1971. Abnormal responses of an adrenocortical cancer adenyl cyclase. *J. Clin. Invest.* 50:1295–300

102. Schulster, D., Tait, S. A. S., Tait, J. F.,

Mrotek, J. 1970. Production of steroids by in vitro superfusion of endocrine tissue. III. Corticosterone output from rat adrenals stimulated by adrenocorticotrophin or cyclic 3′,5′-adenosine monophosphate and the inhibitory effect of cyclohexamide. *Endocrinology* 86: 487–502

103. Sealey, J. E., Clair, I., Bull, M. B., Laragh, J. 1970. Potassium balance and the control of renin secretion. *J. Clin. Invest.* 49:2119–27

104. Shima, S., Pincus, G. 1969. Effects of adrenocorticotropic hormone on rat adrenal corticosteroidogenesis in vivo. *Endocrinology* 84:1048

105. Simpson, E. R., Estabrook, R. W. 1969. Mitochondrial malic enzyme: The source of reduced nicotinamide adenine dinucleotide phosphate for steroid hydroxylation in bovine adrenal cortex mitochondria. *Arch. Biochem.* 129:384

106. Skelton, F. R. et al 1969. Adrenal cortical dysfunction as a basis for experimental hypertensive disease. *Circ. Res.* 24, 25: Suppl. I, 35–74

107. Skinner, S. L., Lumbers, E. R., Symonds, E. M. 1969. Alteration by oral contraceptives of normal menstrual changes in plasma renin activity, concentration and substrate. *Clin. Sci.* 36:67–76

108. Sweat, M. L., Young, R. B., Bryson, M. J. 1970. Two adrenal gland cytochrome P-450 entities evidenced by metyrapone-induced spectra. *Biochim. Biophys. Acta* 223:105–14

109. Tait, S. A. S., Schulster, D., Okamoto, M., Flood, C., Tait, J. F. 1970. Production of steroids by in vitro superfusion of endocrine tissue. II. Steroid output from bisected whole, capsular and decapsulated adrenals of normal intact, hypophysectomized and hypophysectomized-nephrectomized rats as a function of time of superfusion. *Endocrinology* 86:360–82

110. Taunton, O. D., Roth, J., Pastan, I. 1969. Studies on the adrenocorticotrophic hormone-activated adenyl cyclase of a functional adrenal tumor. *J. Biol. Chem.* 244:247–53

111. Vander, A. J. 1970. Direct effects of potassium on renin secretion and renal function. *Am. J. Physiol.* 219:455–59

112. Veyrat, R., Brunner, H. R., Grandchamp, A., Muller, A. F. 1967.

Inhibition of renin by potassium in man. *Acta Endocrinol.*|(Copenhagen) Suppl. 119:86 Abstr.

113. Walton, G. M., Gill, G. N., Abrass, I. B., Garren, L. D. 1971. Phosphorylation of ribosome-associated protein by an adenosine 3′,5′-cyclic monophosphate-dependent protein kinase: Location of the microsomal receptor and protein kinase. *Proc. Nat. Acad. Sci.* 68:880–84

114. Weinberger, M. H., Collins, R. D., Dowdy, A. J., Nokes, G. W., Leutscher, J. A. 1969. Hypertension induced by oral contraceptives containing estrogen and gestagen. *Ann. Intern. Med.* 71:891–902

115. Weir, R. J. et al 1971. Blood pressure in women after one year of oral contraception. *Lancet* 1:467–71

116. Williams, G. H., Dluhy, R. G., Underwood, R. H. 1970. The relationship of dietary potassium intake to the aldosterone stimulating properties of ACTH. *Clin. Sci.* 39:489–96

117. Williams, G. H., Rose, L. I., Dluhy, R. G., Dingman, J. F., Lauler, D. P. 1971. Aldosterone response to sodium restriction and ACTH stimulation in panhypopituitarism. *J. Clin. Endocrinol. Metabol.* 32:27–35

118. Williamson, D. G., O'Donnell, V. J. 1969. The role of cytochrome P-450 in the mechanism of inhibition of steroid 11 β-hydroxylation by dicumarol. *Biochemistry* 8:1300–05

119. Williamson, D. G., O'Donnell, V. J. 1969. Effects of adrenal mitochondrial lipid on the reduced nicotinamide-adenine dinucleotide phosphate supported 11 β-hydroxylation of deoxycorticosterone. Interaction of phospholipid with cytochrome P-450. *Biochemistry* 8:1289–99.

120. Williamson, D. G., O'Donnell, V. J. 1969. The interaction of metapyrone with adrenal mitochondrion cytochrome P-450. A mechanism for the inhibition of adrenal steroid 11 β-hydroxylation. *Biochemistry* 8: 1306–11

121. Wilson, L. D., Harding, B. W. 1970. Studies on adrenal cortical cytochrome P-450 III. Effects of carbon monoxide and light on steroid 11 β-hydroxylation. *Biochemistry* 9: 1615–20

122. Wolff, J. B., Jones, A. B. 1970. Inhibition of hormone-sensitive adenyl cyclase by phenothiazines. *Proc. Nat. Acad. Sci.* 65:454–59

123. Woods, J. W., Liddle, G. W., Michelakis, A. M., Brill, A. B. 1969. Effect of an adrenal inhibitor in hypertensive patients with suppressed renin. *Arch. Intern. Med.* 123:366–70

124. Young, D. G., Hall, P. F. 1971. Steroid hydroxylation in bovine adrenocortical mitochondria. Competition between side-chain cleavage of cholesterol and 11 β-hydroxylation. *Biochemistry* 10:1496–502

REPRODUCTION: GONADAL FUNCTION AND ITS REGULATION

NEENA B. SCHWARTZ

Division of Biological Laboratories, Department of Psychiatry
University of Illinois College of Medicine, Chicago, Illinois

CHARLES E. McCORMACK

Department of Physiology and Biophysics,
The Chicago Medical School, Chicago, Illinois

In writing reviews encompassing reproduction, our immediate predecessors have responded to their mandates from the editors by being individualistic and by emphasizing selected areas within the ever burgeoning field of "reproduction." Everett (63) and Yates et al (270) concentrated on the neuroendocrine aspects of the field, Armstrong (12) on steroidogenesis and related problems, while Williams-Ashman & Reddi (259) discussed the cellular and molecular aspects of sex hormone function. In our turn we should like to emphasize the regulatory or control aspects of gonadal function. In doing so, we shall assume that the elements making up the reproductive system are sequential acceptors and emitters of chemical and neural signals. This approach cuts across the conceptual framework used by the aforementioned reviewers, and leads to a synthetic, rather than an analytic, view of the subject.

With the availability of the excellent *Bibliography of Reproduction* (33a) there is little excuse for writing of bibliographic reviews. This monthly publication is classified into a number of subheadings and is cross-indexed. Additionally, the journal frequently includes excellent small selected bibliographies on highly specific topics. Another useful bibliographic service is the UCLA Brain Information Service bulletin on "Neuroendocrine Control Mechanism: The Hypothalamic-Pituitary-Gonadal System" (57a). Finally, the monthly publication of the International Planned Parenthood Federation called "Research in Reproduction" (57b) should be cited for its excellent short reviews of original research.

During the time encompassed by this review (January 1970 to June, 1971) a number of excellent materials of a general review type were published (26, 40, 71, 85, 87, 166, 173, 209, 243, 250, 264). Because of the timely review of spermatogenesis by Steinberger (237), we shall not devote much space to this topic.

SIGNALS IMPORTANT IN THE REGULATION OF GONADAL FUNCTION

Both male and female gonads are organs of two sets of functions: they secrete steroid hormones and produce gametes. The relationships between these two functions are manifold, and occur intragonadally as well as outside the gonads. The fundamental duality of gonadal function and structure is undoubtedly basic to the extreme complexity of regulation. We would like to provide a brief survey in this section of the signals which are known to participate in the regulation of steroidogenesis and gametogenesis.

Most attention has focused on the pituitary hormones since, in the absence of the anterior pituitary, gonadal morphology and function is extremely retarded. Spermatogenesis proceeds only to the primitive primary spermatocyte stage (237) and oogenesis proceeds only to the initiation of meiosis (71); interstitial cells in the testis, and granulosa and thecal elements in the ovary show no proliferation or steroidogenesis (79, 139).

Of the signals influencing the gonads, the two pituitary hormones, FSH and ICSH or LH have been most investigated and probably constitute the most important regulators of function. Prolactin also certainly constitutes a signal to the ovary in rodents but may not be a gonadotrophic hormone in other species (166).

Cyclic adenosine monophosphate ($cAMP$) functions as an intracellular "secondary messenger" for LH in stimulating progesterone secretion and ovulation and can substitute for LH with respect to these functions (12, 206). Prostaglandins can act as luteolytic agents, being capable of terminating corpus luteum secretion of progesterone (57). Whether prostaglandins serve this function in the intact female mammal, and, if so, what the channel is by which they reach the ovary, are questions not resolved.

In four species (pig, guinea pig, rat, hamster), there is known to be a signal from the nonpregnant uterus which can terminate luteal function, as shown by prolongation of the luteal phase by hysterectomy or decidualization (8, 166, 260). The signal reaches the ovary at least partly via a channel which does not involve the general circulation. This latter conclusion seems inescapable in these species, because removal of one half of the nonpregnant uterus prolongs the lifespan of the corpora lutea ipsilaterally, but not contralaterally (8). Attempts to isolate the uterine substance responsible for termination of luteal function have not been wholly successful (142).

Local steroid synthesis and diffusion within the gonads is apparently also an important regulator of gonadal function. Testosterone has been accepted for many years as a participant in maintenance of tubular spermatogenic function (237). Estrogen (from thecal or interstitial cells) has been implicated as necessary for follicular growth (74), as well as possibly, maintenance of corpus luteum function (166). It is possible that the gonadal steroid hormones originated phylogenetically as intragonadal regulators of production of mature gametes and only secondarily became extracellular signals (hormones) which control changes in accessory duct and secondary sex characteristics. Other factors may also play a role as inputs to the gonads. Temperature is certainly an important parameter for testicular function, particularly for spermatogenesis, but perhaps also for steroidogenesis (237). Blood flow, either to the whole ovary, or fractional blood flow to the structural subunits of the ovary, may also serve to regulate ovarian function (111, 263).

Rates of synthesis and release of the gonadotrophic hormones can be altered by, and indeed are controlled by, levels of releasing or inhibiting factors ("hypophysiotrophic hormones") secreted by neurosecretory cells in the hypothalamus and delivered to the pituitary gland via the hypophysial portal system. Rates of secretion of these factors (prolactin inhibiting factor or *PIF*, follicle stimulating hormone releasing factor or *FRF*, and luteinizing hormone releasing factor or *LRF*) can be altered by neural activity (41, 63). The gonadotrophic hormones themselves can alter synthesis and secretion of the respective hypothalamic releasing factors (41). The latter phenomenon has been called "short loop" or "internal" feedback, although it apparently operates through the general circulation.

Steroid hormone feedbacks of either inhibitory or facilitatory nature, have been shown for testosterone (25, 115), estrogen (63, 221), and progesterone (see 210). Additionally, there may be another feedback signal related to spermatogenesis, which partially controls FSH secretion (208, 242). These feedback signals constitute information to the pituitary gland regarding the functional state of the gonads (221), thus permitting the basis or control of the entire system. The site and mode of action of these steroids is not clear. They may act on neural tissue (63) as well as directly on the anterior pituitary gland itself (23, 257) to inhibit or stimulate hormone release. Additionally, there is evidence that they alter the responsiveness of the cells of the pituitary to releasing or inhibiting factors (10, 11).

Environmental changes provide another set of signals known to influence secretion rates of the gonadotrophic hormones and prolactin. The 24 hour light-dark rhythm has been confirmed to be of primary importance in setting the timing of gonadotrophic hormone secretion in the rat, mouse, and hamster (222). Other species may also demonstrate circadian periodicity, and certainly show seasonal periodicities, in gonadotrophic hormone release (202, 222). Research continues into the question of the possible role of the pineal in reproductive events; such a role may be interrelated with effects of light and darkness (92, 196). Coitus is an important signal for gonadotrophin release, related to ovulation in the rabbit (222) and in the rat (204) and pseudopregnancy in rodents (235). Finally, stress appears to affect release of prolactin (168, 188), and of LH (171); the latter effect may be indirectly related to progestin release by the stimulated adrenal cortex (66, 171).

The regulation of gonadal function is thus seen to be the result of the interactions of cascading systems of signals: the central regulation is at the level of the gonad itself and the most peripheral regulation is at the level of the interaction between the organism and the environment. This review will emphasize those signals which have been most thoroughly studied during the past two years: the relationships between the secretion and action of LH and FSH, and LH and prolactin (in luteinization); the mechanism of ovulation; the chemistry of the gonadotrophic hormones and their subunits; the nature of feedback signals from the gonads; the neuroendocrinological regulation of anterior pituitary function (pathways, transmitters, environmental signals).

PROPERTIES OF THE GONADOTROPHIC HORMONES
BIOLOGICAL AND CHEMICAL SEPARABILITY OF FSH AND LH

A recurring issue in the history of regulation of the gonads has been the question of whether the putative two gonadotrophic hormones from the pituitary-FSH and LH are really two hormones, separately controlled and performing separate functions in regulating gonadal function. A review of earlier controversy and data on this subject was written by Greep in 1961 (79). In spite of, or in some instances because of, increasingly sophisticated technology, the recent literature reveals that many of the same problems discussed by Greep still exist.

Table 1 provides a summary of some recent pertinent literature covering a variety of experimental situations and examining a number of variables. Each observation is classified according to whether it supports or contradicts the concept that these two gonadotrophins are separable.

Bioassay.—Basic to all other considerations is the question of whether two gonadotrophins can be defined on separate bioassay systems (Table 1). The ovarian ascorbic acid depletion assay (*OAAD*) has generally been considered to measure LH and the Steelman-Pohley (*S-P*) or HCG-augmentation test to measure FSH—but in each assay the other hormone must also be present simultaneously or as a primer (207). Reichert has recently observed that FSH, clearly separated from LH by electrofocusing in two different pH ranges, has some OAAD activity; it is not known whether this activity is intrinsic to the FSH molecule or represents LH contamination (191). FSH is not usually considered to exert steroidogenic effects by itself in hypophysectomized recipients (139, 207) in which ventral prostate or uterine weight is measured; however, a purified preparation of FSH has been shown to exert such activity, while showing less immunological reactivity than unpurified FSH (226).

Chemical separation.—In separating LH and FSH from pituitary extracts, separability of potency of different fractions with the standard bioassays has been utilized to judge the final end products (Table 1). This criterion appears justifiable in retrospect, since amino acid and carbohydrate constituents differ for the fractions which have been so separated (187, 226, 227). This observation is a very strong argument for there being two hor-

TABLE 1. ARGUMENTS FOR AND AGAINST BIOLOGICAL AND CHEMICAL SEPARABILITY OF LH AND FSH

Variable examined	Separability		Reference
	For	Against	
BIOASSAY			
1. OAAD	FSH not active	PMSG or FSH priming necessary	207
		FSH sep. by electrofocussing has some OAAD activity	191
2. HCG-Augmentation [Steelman-Pohley (S-P)]	LH not "active"	But LH or HCG must be present	207
3. Steroidogenesis in hypophysectomized rat (ventral prostate or uterine wt.)	FSH not usually considered active	But some "purified" FSH active	207, 226
CHEMICAL SEPARATION			
4. Purified FSH and LH	Bioassay potency separates during purification. Constituents of molecules differ in proportions of amino acids and sugars.	Extraction procedure partially defined by bioassay separation	176, 226, 227
5. Subunits of LH and FSH	Hormone specific subunits differ in composition	FSHβ yields Steelman-Pohley activity when combined with FSHα, LHα or LHβ, and OAAD activity with LHβ	175
6. HCG		May have FSH and LH activities in same molecule	15
IMMUNOLOGICAL SEPARATION			
7. Specific RIA possible	Purified human LH does not cross-react with antiserum to human FSH		187
8. Crossreactions seen	Sheep FSH has an antigenic site (with S-P activity) which does not crossreact with LH, TSH	Antiserum to sheep FSH crossreacts with LH, TSH	36
PITUITARY GONADOTROPHS			
9. Histochemical—electron micrograph	Two types of Periodic acid Schiff (PAS) staining cells have been identified as gonadotrophs	Not always possible to correlate changing LH/FSH in pituitary with different cells	24, 200
10. Immunofluorescence		FSH and LH, localized by immunoenzyme histochemistry, frequently in same pituitary cell	165
11. Cloning of cells	Clones of single pituitary cells secrete either LH or FSH, not both		236
NEUROENDOCRINOLOGICAL ASPECTS			
12. Hypothalamic release-factors		Purified fraction has both LRF and FRF activity	151, 215, 228
		Hypothalamic FRF and LRF content drop at proestrus	167
	FSH, but not LH, implants in hypothalamus alter FRF activity		41

TABLE 1. (*continued*)

Variable examined	Separability		Reference
	For	Against	
		Overlap (but not complete?) of hypothalamic areas containing LRF and FRF	45
		Dopamine causes LRF and FRF release	105, 109, 219
13. Hypothalamic stimulation (electrical)	LH secretion occurs earlier after stimulation than FSH secretion	Several stimulation sites yield either both LH and FSH or neither	39, 100

PITUITARY AND SERUM LEVELS

14. Female cycle	Time course and ratios of pituitary and serum FSH and LH differ during cycle	Surge of serum LH and FSH appear before ovulation in rats and humans	46, 72, 152, 209
15. Gonadectomy	Results in changes in FSH/LH ratios, different in different species		25, 177, 178
16. Cryptorchidism or oligospermia	Partly removes inhibition on FSH secretion rate characteristic of intact testis		6, 208, 242

GONADAL EFFECTS OF FSH AND LH

17. Intact female		Either LH or FSH can cause ovulation in drug-blocked rat with ripe follicles	83
		Either LH, or FSH even in the presence of anti-LH, can increase progesterone secretion	144
		FSH can luteinize follicles	223
	Antiserum to LH blocks estrogen secretion or ovulation in rat cycle but antiserum to FSH does not. Active immunization with LH more deleterious than with FSH in rabbits		159, 223, 224
18. Hypophysectomized female	Both LH and FSH needed for estrogen secretion and follicle growth	Once ovary prepared, either FSH or LH can cause ovulation	139
19. Isolated ovary	Granulosa cells from very small follicles need both LH and FSH to luteinize	Either LH or FSH can luteinize medium follicles	34, 35
	FSH, in absence of LH, did not stimulate estrogen or progesterone secretion from rabbit follicle, or ovarian cell suspensions		136, 157
20. Hypophysectomized male	FSH can increase synthesis of testicular phospholipids, but not after irradiation		272
	LH, but not FSH, increases testicular adenyl cyclase in intact, mature rats	FSH or LH can increase testicular adenyl cyclase in very young, or adult hypophysectomized rats	124

mones, not just one large "prohormone" which is broken apart in the course of extractions. On the other hand, since the extraction procedure is partially empirically determined by bioassay, some degree of circularity of definition is inevitable. Furthermore, Papkoff & Ekblad have made a hybrid molecule from subunits of ovine LH and FSH which possesses both OAAD and S-P activity (FSHβ plus LHβ subunits—see below) (175). This raises the possibility that in the course of the original extractions there might have been dissociation and recombination of hybrid subunits of FSH and LH.

Immunology.—Immunological separability (Table 1) of the two gonadotrophins depends firstly upon the ability to separate the hormones to be used as antigens for eliciting antibodies and secondly on the degree of difference in the chemical constituents in each molecule which act as active sites for antibody formation. Specific radioimmunoassays for the two hormones are possible, so that a good degree of immunological specificity is achievable. Chen & Ely (36) have examined the antigenic sites on sheep FSH. They found a site which had HCG-augmentation activity and did not crossreact with LH and TSH; however, all three hormones shared other sites of crossreaction.

Pituitary gonadotrophs.—A question which has been at issue for many years still appears unresolved—the issue of whether there are separate cells in the pituitary which secrete the two hormones (Table 1). Using morphological criteria, it has not always been possible to correlate the relative numbers of two types of cells with different pituitary contents of FSH and LH (24, 200). Using an immunoenzyme fluorescence technique Nakane (165) has demonstrated that FSH and LH frequently localized to the same cells. The ultimate validity of this finding depends on the specificity of the marker antibodies used, as well as the nondiffusibility of reagents across cell boundaries. On the other hand, Steinberger & Chowdhury (236) have claimed that clones from single pituitary cells, under the influence of hypothalamic tissue, secrete either LH or FSH into the medium, but not both. At issue in such in vitro experiments will undoubtedly be the question of whether a given cell, which might secrete both hormones in vivo, might under in vitro conditions lose this flexibility.

Neuroendocrinology.—If one were able clearly to separate a hypothalamic LH releasing factor from a FSH releasing factor, this would mean that separate signals reached the pituitary gland (Table 1). Under those circumstances it might not matter whether FSH and LH are secreted by one or two types of pituitary cells, because theoretically it would still be possible to control separately secretion rates of the gonadotrophins by having different sites on a given pituitary cell respond to different hypophysiotropic inputs. Unfortunately, however, the most purified factors available at present for LH release appear also to release FSH (215, 228). Schally and coworkers (151) have proposed the following amino acid sequence for LRF/

FRF: (pyro)Glu-His-Trp-Ser-Try-Gly-Leu-Arg-Pro-Gly-NH₂. If these two activities do indeed reside within the same secreted molecule, then a tight coupling would exist at this point in the pituitary-gonadal axis. By itself, this need not mean that parallel release of the two pituitary hormones occurs, since differences in the latency of release, the rate of release, or the duration of response could occur because of differences in response characteristics of the pituitary gonadotrophs. Additionally, a direct feedback action of the steroids at the level of the pituitary cells (10, 11, 89, 255) might determine which of the hormones was released by the same releasing factor.

Most, but not all, of the data on neural control suggests at least some simultaneity of release of the two releasing activities. This is apparent at proestrus in the rat when both LRF and FRF activities in the hypothalamus drop (167), as well as following dopamine injection into the third ventricle (105, 219) when both releasing activities increase in the blood. Furthermore, a considerable overlap has been found between the hypothalamic areas yielding FRF and LRF activities (45), not a surprising finding if both reside in the same molecule. Clemens et al (39) have demonstrated that electrochemical stimulation of various hypothalamic areas increases serum levels of both FSH and LH or neither (39). But Kalra et al (100) found LH release, without FSH release, when the preoptic area was stimulated. In both studies (39, 100) LH always appeared in the plasma earlier than FSH. This could imply either a temporal separation of release of two types of releasing factor or a temporal separation of pituitary secretion in response to the same input at the level of the pituitary. Finally, Corbin et al (41) were able to inhibit FRF secretion by implantation of FSH into the hypothalamus but not by LH implants. This experiment implies that the short feedback loop type of negative feedback is hormone specific.

Hormone concentrations.—If indeed techniques for bioassay and radioimmunoassay of FSH and LH are specific, then measurement of the concentration ratios of the two hormones in the pituitary and blood under various conditions should indicate, as an acid test, whether synthesis and release rates for the two hormones are regulated in a tightly coupled manner (Table 1). The most dramatic increase in release of the gonadotrophic hormones occurs before ovulation, the so-called preovulatory surge. Both FSH and LH are released (46, 72, 152, 209) but the time course for the concentrations of the two hormones differs in both pituitary and blood. Furthermore, blockade of LH release by barbiturates or an antiestrogen blocks the release of FSH as well (46, 152). Following gonadectomy, changes in the ratios of the two hormones occur in both serum and pituitary; the magnitudes of the changes depends on species (25, 177, 178). Recent evidence regarding feedback signals from the testis strongly suggests that damage to the spermatogenic function of the tubules partly removes the inhibition exerted by the intact testis on FSH secretion, more than on LH secretion (6, 208, 242). Thus, the data on hormonal concentrations (Table 1) deny an absolute tight coupling of rates of synthesis and release of the two hormones.

FSH and LH on gonads.—When we finally examine the gonadal effects of FSH and LH (Table 1), we have come full circle, since we started with bioassay separability. The logic of using data on the gonadal effects to argue the separability of the two gonadotrophins is different from the previously presented aspects. If one demonstrates that treatment with FSH yields the same effect as treatment with LH, one cannot argue that they are necessarily biologically separate hormones. If, on the other hand, it can be shown that one, but not the other, of the hormones affects a given variable, then they must be different with respect to that biological action. Finally, if both are necessary, either sequentially or simultaneously, in order to obtain a given response, then they are obviously different *and* complementary in affecting that particular variable.

In the intact female (Table 1) either FSH or LH can cause ovulation in a mature follicle (83). Additionally, either LH or FSH can cause luteinization of follicles and increased progesterone secretion (144, 223). An important aspect of the latter observations is that the FSH had been "immunologically purified" by addition of antiserum to LH. Thus, with respect to these functions, there is a redundancy of information conveyed by the two hormones. On the other hand, by using the technique of interfering with availability of endogenous LH by injecting intact rats with antiserum to sheep LH, it has been possible to block ovulation and estrogen secretion within the cycle of injection. Similar injections of antiserum to sheep FSH block neither variable although this antiserum blocks rat FSH on the S-P assay (223, 224). The implications of these "selective chemical blockade" experiments with respect to the issue at hand are as follows: either the S-P assay does not measure the same active site of FSH as is responsible for the actions of the hormone in the adult rat, or the antiserum is more effective in blocking FSH in immature rats than in intact rats, or FSH is not necessary for estrogen secretion and ovulation within one cycle in the rat. The fact that active immunization with LH is more deleterious to the gonads in the recipient rabbit than active immunization with FSH (159) also suggests that specific antibodies are less able to interfere with endogenously secreted FSH than LH, or that FSH is dispensable for some period of time.

In the hypophysectomized female, both LH and FSH are necessary for optimum estrogen secretion and follicle growth, but either hormone will cause ovulation once the animal has been pretreated with both (139). Granulosa cells taken from monkey or pig ovaries, if removed from very small follicles, will not luteinize in tissue culture unless treated with both FSH and LH; however, cultures of cells from medium size follicles can be luteinized with either hormone (34, 35). Channing has interpreted these data as indicating that FSH must be present in the history of a given set of follicular granulosa cells, but then becomes dispensable. In other in vitro experiments, FSH was unable to replace LH in increasing estrogen secretion or progesterone secretion in rabbit follicles or cell suspensions from rabbit ovaries (136, 157).

In the hypophysectomized male (Table 1) either FSH or LH can increase the synthesis of testicular phospholipids, but FSH is no longer effective after destruction of the seminiferous tubules by irradiation, suggesting a tubular site of action for FSH (272). In an interesting experiment Kuel, et al (124) demonstrated that testicular adenyl cyclase was meaningfully increased by exogenous FSH only in very young (less than 21 days old) intact rats or hypophysectomized adult rats (10 days after surgery), whereas LH was effective in all animal preparations. This the authors interpreted to mean that a period free from exposure to endogenous FSH is needed in order to demonstrate an effect of the exogenous hormone on this variable.

These data on the gonadal effects of FSH and LH support the idea that, when fractions of pituitary extracts are separated by chemical and bioassay criteria into two hormones, the hormones show some redundancies of action. However, they also must be different enough in action for both to be required at some point in the postnatal history of a given set of gonadal cells. The fact that this is so does not, however, necessarily support the concept of separability of control or secretion, since even simultaneity of their appearance in the blood might permit normal gonadal function. FSH might act on those cellular elements destined to mature at some future date, and LH on those cellular elements nearing maturity. Since the gonads do show a temporal progression of elements even in the adult, this concept may have some merit.

PURIFICATION AND CHARACTERIZATION OF THE GONADOTROPHINS

A variety of methodologies has been used for chemical separation of two gonadotrophic fractions from the pituitary glands: differential precipitation, chromatography, gel filtration, countercurrent distribution, etc. The biological separability of the fractions is defined by the "specific" bioassays described above: FSH by HCG-augmentation tests, and LH activity by the OAAD test or the ventral prostate test in hypophysectomized recipients (207). It is usually considered that purified FSH will not induce OAAD or steroidogenesis in a hypophysectomized recipient rat, but some recent reports indicate that purified (by chemical criteria) FSH fractions may show activity on both assay systems (191, 226). Amino acid and carbohydrate compositions differ between LH and FSH, but the composition of a given hormone from different species appears more similar [human, bovine and ovine LH, (176, 187, 193, 227); ovine FSH, (175, 226)]. Prolactin, a third hormone from the pituitary suggested to have gonadotrophic activity, has also been studied. Li and co-workers (130) have published a postulated primary structure for sheep prolactin.

HCG has also been purified (161); it can be separated into two fractions which demonstrate different ratios of FSH and LH activity (15). Treatment of HCG with neurominidase to remove sialic acid causes a greater drop in biological activity than in immunoreactivity (162, 251).

Urea treatment of FSH, frequently employed to reduce the LH activity of contaminating LH in order to ensure administration of "pure" FSH, can also reduce the activity of the FSH in the S-P assay (88), suggesting that caution should be exercised in interpreting results of such treated FSH. Removal of sialic acid from human LH lowers biological activity and increases reactivity on the radioimmunoassay according to Braunstein et al (27), but not according to Mori (163). It has been accepted for some time that desialyation of FSH removes biological activity.

Glycoprotein subunits.—HCG, LH, and FSH, as well as TSH, the third glycoprotein hormone from the anterior pituitary gland, have been shown to dissociate, with mild urea, differential gel filtration, or countercurrent distribution techniques, into two nonidentical subunits, which have approximately half the molecular weight of the parent hormone; the mildness of the separation techniques suggests that the subunits in the hormone are linked noncovalently (131, 132, 175, 176, 180, 192, 193, 212, 241). For each of the hormones, the separated subunits have little potency as biologically active hormones, but when recombined regain a significant fraction of the original activity. However, there does seem to be a "hormone specific" subunit for each hormone (respectively LHβ, FSHβ, TSHβ, HCGβ) conveying the activity of the particular hormone when combined with a subunit which does not carry hormone specificity. For the pituitary hormones the nonspecific units resemble each other in composition more than the hormone specific units: FSHα resembles LHα more than LHβ (175); TSHα and LHα have essentially similar amino acid sequences (131, 180); HCGα resembles LHα (241).

Recent detailed studies of the separated and recombined subunits, either natural or "hybrid," have been instructive but sometimes puzzling. It has been claimed that bovine LHβ has somewhat less OAAD activity than the α subunit (193); neither ovine LHα or β is said to have steroidogenic activity (77); ovine LHβ has been said to react immunologically with antiserum to ovine LH (77) whereas bovine LHβ is said to be immunologically deficient in contrast to bovine LHα (193). Bovine TSHβ and LHα, when reconstituted in a "hybrid" molecule, yielded TSH activity (131). Human LHα and bovine LHβ combine to form a hybrid "hormone" which has OAAD activity greater than seen in the isolated subunits (192). Finally, Papkoff & Ekblad have shown that FSHβ plus either LHα or FSHα partially restored FSH activity (S-P); FSHα plus LHβ did *not* show OAAD activity but FSHβ combined with LHβ showed good restoration of OAAD activity, as well as partial restoration of S-P activity (175)!

The amino acid sequences of ovine LHβ (212), and bovine TSHα and β and LHα (131, 137, 180) have been worked out in the laboratories of Ward, Papkoff & Pierce. TSHα and LHα share essentially identical amino acid sequences, but differ in carbohydrate composition. A start has been made in detecting terminal amino acid sequences in HCG (161).

This survey of recent literature indicates why there continue to be problems concerning specificity of FSH and LH (85) (Table 1). There is, as mentioned above, some circularity in the definition of the hormones, because bioassays are ultimately the criterion of purity and even with highly purified hormones (judged chemically), or recombined subunits, there is some overlap of activity on so-called specific bioassays (15, 77, 175, 226). Discrepancies between biological assays and immunological assays, as well as immunological specificity, is also a problem (162, 193, 226, 251). Immunoelectrophoresis of ovine FSH with an antiserum (absorbed with sheep tissue) to ovine FSH reveals two sets of precipitin lines; the cathodal line is also present in LH and TSH, while the anodal line contains the HCG-augmenting activity (36). These observations may mean that there are two kinds of FSH or may reflect subunits of hormone specific and nonspecific nature, with the nonspecific subunits of the pituitary glycoprotein hormones resembling each other immunologically.

OVULATION AND LUTEINIZATION
MECHANISM OF OVULATION

Nature of the problem.—While luteinization of the follicle invariably follows ovulation, it can be induced without inducing ovulation (94, 97); in fact, the gonadotrophin requirement seems to be less for luteinization than for ovulation. This section will deal with the question of the underlying mechanism of follicular rupture and ovum extrusion; i.e. ovulation.

Visual recognition of follicular rupture and recovery of tubal ova is fairly easy in the rodent. For this reason, the interval (10 to 14 hrs) between an LH surge (endogenous or exogenous) and the time of ovulation is well established in rodents (62). However, in primates it is more difficult to distinguish preovulatory follicles from freshly ruptured follicles or even established corpora lutea (20); thus the time interval between the LH surge and ovulation, though estimated to be 24 hrs (160), remains to be determined definitely.

General description of the mechanism.—Ripe follicles require only about one hour of exposure to LH for ovulation to be induced (147). Protein synthesis is undoubtedly involved, because puromycin can inhibit ovulation when injected into rabbit follicles up to four hours after copulation or LH administration (see 134).

Follicular rupture is not due to increased intrafollicular pressure, since no increase in pressure occurs near the time of ovulation (see 205). In follicles under the influence of an LH surge, the distensibility (strain/stress) of the follicle wall increases (205); as the antrum enlarges, the follicle wall becomes thinner (61), and the breaking strength decreases (205). The increased distensibility and decreased breaking strength are probably produced by the action of a collagenase-like enzyme which interferes with the intrafibrillar bonding of collagen in the follicle wall (205). Extracts of follicular tissue definitely do contain collagenase-like activity, but whether this activity increases at the appropriate place on the follicle at the proper time is not yet certain (205). In this regard, the concentration of microvesicles in fibroblasts of the tunica albuginea and theca externa of rabbit follicles increases shortly before ovulation. These vesicles protrude from the plasma membrane, and the extracellular ground substance appears to be digested around them (61).

Possible importance of the local action of steroids.—The interesting hypothesis (261) that gonadotrophins induce ovulation indirectly by inducing ovarian steroidogenesis, and that the steroids actually induce ovulation by acting locally on the follicle wall, has received recent additional support. Lipner & Greep (134) found that cyanoketone, a drug that inhibits 3β-hydroxy-steroid dehydrogenase, and thereby prevents the conversion of pregnenolone to progesterone, inhibited ovulation (induced by exogenous LH) in PMS-gonadotropin (or *PMSG*)-primed immature rats. Cyanoketone effectively inhibited ovulation when given up to 6 hrs after the LH (134). Lipner & Greep noted that a deficit of other steroids (viz estradiol) further down the synthetic pathway than progesterone could also be responsible for the blockade of ovulation. However, in a different animal preparation (PMSG-primed, but ovulation induced with HCG) administration of an estrogen antagonist (MER-25 or 1-(-p-diethylaminoethoxyphenyl)-1-phenyl-2-p-methoxyphenylethanol) 12 and 6 hrs before HCG suppressed ovulation only slightly (135). Metopirone, which prevents the synthesis of adrenal steroids by inhibiting $11\text{-}\beta$-hydroxylase, did not inhibit LH-induced ovulation (134).

Rondell (206) observed that the distensibility of incubated strips of sow follicles increased if LH, progesterone, or cAMP were added to the incubation media. Estrogen was ineffective. The capacity of LH or cAMP to decrease distensibility could be blocked by the simultaneous addition of cyanoketone to the incubation media, but this blockade could be reversed by the addition of progesterone. Frog ovarian follicles will ovulate in vitro if gonadotrophins, progesterone, or pregnenolone are added to the medium. However, if the frog is treated in vivo with cyanoketone before the ovaries are removed, only progesterone will induce ovulation when added to the ovaries in vitro (262).

In preliminary findings with a small number of animals, Lostroh (138) reported that large doses of progesterone or 20-α-hydroxyprogesterone induced ovulation in FSH-primed, hypophysectomized immature rats. This observation supports an earlier report of Callantine & Humphrey (31) in which progesterone induced some ovulation in PMSG-primed immature rats.

There is also evidence which tends to contradict the hypothesis that the local action of progesterone induces ovulation. Ferin et al (67) were unable to inhibit ovulation by administering antibodies to progesterone on the morning of proestrus, even though the antibody did inactivate circulating progesterone as evidenced by the retention of uterine fluid. Also, Goldman & Mahesh (75) found that when FSH was used to induce ovulation in immature rats, uterine fluid was retained, thus suggesting, by contrast with the effects of LH, that ovulation had occurred with minimal progesterone secretion.

Possible importance of histamine release.—Shortly after LH is injected into rats, the blood flow to the ovary increases (263). This response persists for several hours, and in immature rats after endogenous LH release the entire ovary enlarges and becomes hyperemic (154). It has been hypothesized that these changes are produced locally by histamine release in the ovary (244, 263) and may be essential for ovulation. With this information in mind, Lipner (133) treated immature rats with a mast cell histamine releaser (i.e. a histamine-depleter) or an antihistamine (Benadryl) or both drugs prior to and after administering PMSG. HCG was injected 40 hrs after the PMSG to determine if ovulation could be induced. Neither drug alone nor the combination decreased the percentage of rats ovulating; however, the combination significantly decreased the number of ova per rat. Benadryl alone or the combined drugs prevented ovarian hyperemia, but the histamine-depleter alone did not. Unfortunately, these experiments do not disclose whether or not normal histamine release is important for ovulation itself, because the prolonged course of their administration may have interfered with follicular growth and sensitivity.

Other observations.—When dibenzyline (an alpha adrenergic blocker) was injected into the abdominal aorta just above the ovarian artery 7 or 10 hrs after the administration of an ovulatory dose of HCG, ovulation was partially inhibited. Propranolol (a beta adrenergic blocker) had no effect. These observations are interesting, because they suggest that adrenergic receptors in the ovary may be important quite late in the process of follicular rupture (254).

LUTEAL TISSUE: FORMATION, MAINTENANCE AND TERMINATION OF FUNCTION

The most prominent problems concerning the regulation of luteal tissue have been the following: (*a*) What stimuli transform granulosa and theca cells into luteal cells? Is the process of ovulation, as stimulated by an ovulatory surge of gonadotrophins, sufficient to induce luteinization, or is another contribution from the pituitary necessary? (*b*) Once luteal tissue forms, does it need an additional "luteotrophic" stimulus to maintain integrity of structure and function? (*c*) Is there an "intrinsic life span" characteristic of luteal tissue, or are there luteolytic agents which terminate cellular function? (*d*) What are the relative roles of prolactin and LH in maintaining luteal function? (*e*) What are the species differences in the above regulatory mechanisms? The reader is referred to five extensive reviews of these subjects (12, 56, 78, 166, 210).

Luteinization without ovulation.—Separation of the ovum from the follicular cells can cause luteinization: this has been accomplished by removal of the ovum from the follicle (ovectomy) (58), or by culture of granulosa cells removed from the follicle (34, 35). Since in these situations, the ovulatory signal(s) from the pituitary had not yet been discharged, the surge of gonadotrophins is itself not a necessary event for luteinization. There is the possibility that normally, in the process of causing ovulation, LH (and/or FSH) acts upon the ovum in such a manner as to suppress a signal which is normally emitted by the ovum to prevent luteinization. Thus physical separation of the two elements of the follicle would cause luteinization. Channing's data suggest that, if this is the case, the granulosa cells must reach a certain degree of maturity (stimulation by FSH and LH) to respond in this way (34, 35).

While luteinization (at least the initial morphological signs) always seems to accompany ovulation, luteinization has also been shown to occur in the presence of the enclosed ovum. This is seen after administration of an antiserum to LH, absorbed with an excess of FSH (223); other situations in which abnormal amounts or ratios of LH and FSH are injected or released may also lead to luteinization without ovulation (94, 97, 223). Whole follicles from rat ovaries transplanted into the kidney capsule of intact or hypophysectomized rats also luteinized (if the follicles were mature) in the presence of an entrapped ovum (59). In these latter situations where luteinization occurs with the oocyte present, it is possible that luteinization may be the secondary response to an experimentally induced abnormality in the ovum (59, 97, 223).

Role of LH.—Luteinizing hormone increased progesterone secretion, during the luteal phase of the human (82), sheep (111), and macaque (144), as well as other species (12, 56, 78, 166, 210). LH or FSH (even in combination with antiserum to LH) caused increased progesterone secretion in the monkey, while HCG did so in humans (82, 144). Antiserum to HCG reduced progesterone secretion during the luteal phase in the macaque and caused premature menstruation (164). Prolactin has not been shown to increase progesterone secretion in the monkey (144) nor in most other nonrodent species (56). However, in the estrous ewe, as in the rat, prolactin release accompanied LH release even though the prolactin may not be involved with luteinization (190).

Role of prolactin.—There is little doubt that prolactin is a necessary hormone in the rodent for permitting pseudopregnancy and pregnancy to take place (78). Administration of prolactin to hypophysectomized rats bearing corpora lutea caused prolongation of vaginal diestrus (in the presence of estrogen injections), suggesting progesterone secretion; if heterologous prolactin was used, circulating antibodies appeared and the duration of diestrus was shorter than if rat prolactin was used (145, 146). Prolactin induced enzymes responsible for enhancement of cholesterol turnover, and decreased the activity of 20-α-hydroxysteroid dehydrogenase in PMSG-ovulated ovaries of immature rats (13, 17); both of these effects were associated with increased secretion of progesterone. Serum prolactin levels were elevated during the afternoon of proestrus, even in the unmated rat (72, 170) and during the first three days of pregnancy (7). Pelvic neurectomy (235) to remove afferent signals from the cervix blocked pseudopregnancy and the rise in serum prolactin seen at 8 and 24 hrs after mating. However, the minor copulation-induced rise in FSH and LH was not blocked. These observations suggest that the hormonal stimulus by which mating activates corpora lutea could be prolactin, as assumed for many years. Unfortunately, in this study sham neurectomy (260) was not carried out, and the mating used as the stimulus took place early on the morning of estrus, after ovulation had occurred. It has been demonstrated amply that surgical or other stresses in the course of the cycle can disturb gonadotrophin secretion (168, 171, 188), with stress elevating prolactin secretion in some circumstances.

Antiserum to LH.—While these recent data support earlier literature on the importance of prolactin in maintenance of corpus luteum function in the rat, additional data have emphasized the indispensability of LH as well. Antiserum to LH terminated pregnancy in the rat following a single injection in midpregnancy (8 to 11 days); prolactin did not reverse the effect, but LH did (148). Similarly, antiserum to LH reduced progesterone secretion during lactation (273), a situation accompanied by high rates of prolactin secretion (7).

Ergocornine.—Ergocornine, a drug which has anti-adrenergic properties, has been shown to block the proestrous prolactin surge, without blocking LH release or ovulation, except in high doses (123, 265). A preliminary report by Wuttke & Meites (267) suggests that ergocornine, given at proestrus, causes increased numbers of corpora to survive in the ovary; the authors interpreted this to mean that prolactin release at proestrus is responsible for the luteolysis of the last set of corpora. In the hypophysectomized rat, untreated for seven days and then homotransplanted with a pituitary in the renal capsule, structural luteolysis of remaining luteal tissue in the ovary occurred, presumably due to prolactin secretion from the graft; ergocornine prevented this luteolysis (150).

LH vs prolactin.—When the recent studies of LH and prolactin in the rat are compared with previous studies, some apparent contradictions emerge. LH is luteotrophic when viewed with respect to induction and maintenance of progesterone secretion, but can be luteolytic (210). Prolactin is luteotrophic when presented to a freshly formed rodent corpus luteum (172, 210), but may be luteolytic if the corpora are older (150, 265). Nikitovitch-Winer & Everett (172) demonstrated that, following hypophysectomy, immediate autografting of the pituitary under the renal capsule permitted maintenance of the crop of corpora already present in the ovary, unless the hypophysectomy was carried out on the morning of proestrus, before the release of the afternoon gonadotrophic hormone surge. These data were interpreted to indicate that the corpora from the previous cycle had been rendered incapable of responding to prolactin at some time between diestrus and proestrous morning. However, Wuttke & Meites (267) have suggested that the ergocornine blockade of the afternoon proestrous prolactin release *permits* maintenance (at least morphologic) of the last set of corpora, which according to Nikitovitch-Winer & Everett (172) are already unresponsive to prolactin by the time of ergocornine injection! It is obvious also from the observations of Malven (150) that delayed homotransplantation of the pituitary seven days after hypophysectomy causes luteolysis because of prolactin secretion. It would appear that the effects of LH and prolactin on corpora lutea in the rat depend on the history of the particular set of corpora being studied, and that not only is the amount and kind of hormone administered important but also the sequence of hormone injection.

Two general questions are raised by all of these data: (*a*) In light of the complexities of the relationships between LH and prolactin in regulating corpus luteum function in the rat, can one conclude definitely in other less well studied species that prolactin is not a gonadotrophic hormone (210)? (*b*) Even if prolactin does not play a normal role in corpus luteum maintenance in other species, one may consider the adaptive significance of prolactin to the rodent. These polycyclic species do not have a prolonged "wasteful" luteal phase with each ovulation in the absence of pregnancy. By linking prolongation of luteal function to copulation, instead of to ovulation, the probability of becoming pregnant during a restricted breeding season and a short life span is increased in rodents. In order for luteal maintenance to be separated from follicular growth and ovulation in the rodent, there may have been survival value in "co-opting" prolactin as a gonadotrophin as well as its accepted role as a lactogen.

PITUITARY-GONADAL RELATIONSHIPS: THE QUESTION OF FEEDBACK CONTROL

Historically, simultaneously with the accumulation of data supporting the concept of control of gonadal function by the anterior pituitary, came experiments on the reverse issue— namely, signals from the gonads were shown to control secretion rates of the gonadotrophic hormones. Past reviews helpful in understanding the background of these issues have been published by Everett (62, 63), Rothchild (210), Yates et al (270), Bogdanove (23), and Schwartz (221, 222).

As discussed elsewhere (221), it is not strictly correct to label most of these experiments tests of "positive" and "negative" feedback, since these terms should be reserved for cases when it is known that, because of an action of a gonadal steroid, the secretion rate of that steroid in the intact organism will ultimately be respectively increased or decreased. In many cases it is clear that injection of steroids will suppress gonadotrophic hormone secretion rates, and that when a gonad is present a decreased steroid output will result; this is properly designated negative feedback. However, the instances of facilitation of gonadotrophin secretion by a steroid need not be a positive feedback, unless increases in the endogenous secretion rate of that gonadal hormone would result.

Gonadectomy.—It has been known for many years that gonadectomy in the rat causes an increase in blood levels of FSH and LH; in fact, this observation was basic to our concept of a suppressing ability of gonadal steroids on gonadotrophic hormone secretion rates. Serum levels of LH rise more rapidly in the male rat than in the female (22, 268). The female hamster, however, shows a very rapid rise in serum LH (76).

The human has also been known for many years to show a rise in secretion of both gonadotrophins following castration or after menopause (256). The ovariectomized monkey demonstrated increased LH secretion and had an interesting "circhoral" oscillation of plasma LH—the period length is about an hour, with a "half-time" of fall-off of 72 minutes (51). These data suggest a pulsatile discharge of LH, not seen in the intact monkey.

Recently Parlow (177, 178) has studied serum FSH and LH in guinea pigs and mice. Neither species showed an increase in serum LH (OAAD), and only the mouse demonstrated a rise in serum FSH (S-P). One may speculate how different the field of pituitary and gonadal relationships would have been if these two species, instead of the rat, had been the standard laboratory species for studies of this kind!

Injection of steroids into gonadectomized animals.—The primary purpose of these experiments was to attempt to restore pregonadectomy levels of FSH and LH in animals after removal of gonads. Lest this statement appear simplistic it should be pointed out that hundreds of experiments have been carried out, mostly in the rat, with very little reference back to the intact animal. Part of the problem has been methodological, since bioassays were not always sensitive enough to detect blood levels of the gonadotrophic hormones in intact animals. A question which has rarely been considered is the interval after gonadectomy when treatment is initiated; there is no reason to believe that a normally responding hypothalamic-pituitary axis still exists after long-term castration. At any rate, previous data have indicated that estrogen can lower pituitary and plasma LH and FSH levels in gonadectomized rats, and that progesterone by itself has little effect (210, 221).

Increasing the dose of estrogen administered to ovariectomized rats increased both serum and pituitary levels of prolactin (38). Low doses of progesterone inhibited these effects somewhat; progesterone alone (10 mg) can increase serum and pituitary prolactin. These prolactin data suggest effects in the ovariectomized rat opposite to those found with FSH and LH.

FSH and LH have been found to rise following ovariectomy in women (256). Treatment with mestranol (estrogenic) caused FSH to decline, while LH first declined and then rose. Treatment with a progestogen (ethynodiol diacetate) caused no consistent changes. Combination treatment caused inhibition of both FSH and LH in blood.

More recently, with the demonstrations that estrogen and progesterone can, under some circumstances in the intact animal, elicit increased FSH and LH release from the pituitary (see below) several investigators have designed experiments attempting to detect this phenomenon in the ovariectomized animal. It appears necessary first to treat with estrogen (to lower blood gonadotrophins or to prime some central receptors?), and then test the second steroid for facilitation. In a preliminary report, Karsch et al (110), were able to suppress plasma LH levels in the ovariectomized monkey with chronically implanted estrogen, and found that a single injection of estrogen would then cause a surge of LH. Taleisnik and co-workers have found that preinjection of a large single dose of estrogen into ovariectomized rats could lower plasma LH (30) and FSH (245). (The FSH was measured, without standards, by the mouse HCG-augmentation test, which raises questions of validity.) In both cases, following the estrogen treatment which lowered the levels of gonadotrophin, a second steroid raised it— progesterone in the case of FSH (245) and estrogen or progesterone in the case of LH (30). Of particular interest in the estrogen experiment (30) is that the second dose of estrogen appeared to elicit peaks of LH at the same hour on two consecutive days. This substantiates the theory that estrogen, in conjunction with a time of day signal, stimulates LH release for ovulation in rats (221, 225).

Injection of steroids or steroid antagonists into intact animals.—Chronic injections of high doses of estrogenic or androgenic hormones can suppress synthesis and release of FSH and LH and cause gonadal atrophy in intact animals, revealing the negative feedback properties of these hormones (see 79, 221). Large, chronic doses of progestational hormones can block the surge of LH and ovulation, but may not block folliculogenesis or induce gonadal atrophy (80, 210, 234).

If a single dose of progesterone is administered on the day before proestrus (day of LH release) of the rat four-day cycle, or early on the morning of proestrus, it can block the LH release and ovulation (62, 63, 221). However, when injected a few hours before the normal onset of LH release it advances the release and can overcome barbiturate blockade (62, 63, 221). This effect of progesterone may be considered a positive feedback since it increases endogenous progesterone secretion rate (248).

Injection of hormone antagonists during the normal reproductive cycle has also been useful in determining probable feedback actions of hormones. On the day before proestrus in the rat, injection of peripheral estrogen antagonists, as well as antibodies to estrogen, can mimic the effects of ovariectomy (223) in preventing release of the proestrous surge of LH, FSH and prolactin (67, 125, 169, 229). Estrogen replacement therapy can reverse these effects. Furthermore, estrogen secretion on the day before proestrus can be prevented by antiserum to LH, but not to FSH (223, 224), which reveals the necessity of a small amount of LH secretion for the estrogen secretion to take place.

Clomiphene in the human possesses an antiestrogenic property, since it can counteract the inhibitory effect of exogenous estrogen on the rise in serum FSH during the follicular phase of the cycle (249). The mechanism by which clomiphene induces an ovulatory surge of LH in some otherwise non-ovulating women is unexplained (209). It may be that those women who respond in this manner have a steady state of estrogen and LH secretion such that estrogen levels are too high and constant to allow an LH surge, and that the antiestrogen works by reducing estrogen negative feedback.

Special problems in gonadal feedback signals.—That there may be non-androgen-mediated feedback signals from the gonads to the hypothalamic-pituitary axis controlling FSH secretion is suggested by observations in the male. Experimental cryptorchidism in the rat partially prevented the drop in serum FSH which occurs during maturation, without altering serum LH levels appreciably (242); the rise in FSH and LH following castration, how-ever, is greater than that seen following cryptorchidism. In another study (6) cryptorchid rats failed to show as marked a rise in serum gonadotrophin levels as that induced by castration; however, serum testosterone levels in some of the cryptorchid rats were decreased. In young men with oligo-spermia, serum FSH levels are elevated in the absence of alterations in serum testosterone or LH, whereas men with Klinefelter's syndrome showed both decreased testosterone and elevated LH (208).

Following removal of one gonad, the compensatory hypertrophy of the remaining one continues to raise two questions involving communication between gonads and the pituitary glands. (*a*) What is the signal which in-forms the pituitary that one gonad is missing? (*b*) What is the signal(s) by which the pituitary elicits hypertrophy of the remaining gonad? The sparse recent literature on these subjects has not yet provided definitive answers. Following unilateral ovariectomy in the rat an increase in bioassayable serum FSH has been demonstrated, as measured by a modification of the S-P assay, three days following surgery (18). No sham ovariectomy controls were used. Peppler & Greenwald (179) have repeated earlier studies to determine time when unilateral ovariectomy must be performed within a given cycle to yield doubling of ovulations at the next estrus; follicle counts in various size categories suggested that the doubling which occurs is not de-rived from a decrease of follicular atresia within the first cycle. It is not yet clear whether the suppression of compensatory hypertrophy by administra-tion of gonadal steroids after single ovariectomy (18) is simply the result of the well known negative feedback properties of these hormones, or whether it indicates that a drop in steroid production accompanying ovariectomy is actually responsible for the hypertrophy. Ovarian autografts to the greater omentum of hemi-castrate rats did not grow, even after treatment with exogenous gonadotrophins, until the remaining ovary was removed (19); this suggested to the author that local conditions within the autograft might inhibit growth response to gonadotrophic hormones. Finally, during the anestrus season in the ewe, when serum LH is undetectable in the intact animal (202), compensatory hypertrophy did not occur (149), just as it did not occur in the rat in the presence of certain hypothalamic lesions (121) or following blinding (50, 232).

The distribution of steroid receptors.—The characteristics and distribution of steroid receptors have recently been reviewed by Williams-Ashman & Reddi (259). There appear to be receptors for estradiol and androgens [testosterone and dihydrotestosterone (238)] in the accessory sex tissues, as well as the anterior pituitary gland and areas of the hypothalamus.

Variations in the uptake of labelled estradiol with stages of the rat estrous cycle have been found to occur in uterus (48, 129) and anterior hypothalamus (112), but not in anterior pituitary (112). These alterations could result from changes in the total number of binding sites available or competition with endogenously secreted "cold" estradiol. The three papers just cited used three different experimental situations for measuring uptake of the labelled estradiol and come to three different conclusions about the time of maximum uptake during the cycle. Kato (112) found lowest in vitro uptake by the hypothalamus during proestrus and estrus in four-day cyclic rats. Lee & Jacobson (129), studying rats with four-day cycles, found maximum receptor concentration (determined in vitro) on the day of "estrus," and minimum concentrations at "proestrus;" a puzzling aspect of their data is the high uterine weight seen on both of these days, in contrast with the usual finding of maximum weight at proestrus (221). De Hertogh et al (48), by contrast, found lowest uterine receptor concentration on the day called "estrus," determined by infusion of labelled estradiol in vivo. Unfortunately, cycle stage was assessed in the last experiment by only one vaginal smear, with no information available as to the normal patterning of vaginal changes in these rats throughout the cycle (see 221).

Site of steroid feedback.—The usual way in which the problem of site of steroid feedback has been defined is in terms of whether a given steroid acts on the pituitary gland itself or on the central nervous system. The observation that steroids can be bound to a number of different tissues (259) simply indicates that the particular steroid may act at a particular cell either to impart information concerning facilitatory or negative feedback on gonadotrophic hormone secretion rates, or to alter sexual behavior, or to perform other unsuspected functions.

The earlier literature on pituitary vs neural sites of feedback has been reviewed by Bogdanove (23) and Everett (62, 63). The recent literature has confirmed earlier observations that the gonadal steroids are capable of exerting effects when implanted directly into the anterior pituitary gland. Implantation of androgen into one side of the pituitary altered castration cells and increased FSH content while lowering LH ipsilaterally (115). Using immunoenzyme staining techniques, an implant of estrogen into the pituitary revealed unilateral effects on cell size and intensity of staining (73).

In two interesting experiments Weick and co-workers (257, 258) have shown that the effects of injected estrogen in shortening five-day rat cycles to four days could be mimicked by implants of estrogen into the anterior pituitary, but not by such implants into the hypothalamus. When the implant was carried out two days before the expected proestrus, it not only advanced ovulation but also vaginal cornification and mating behavior. Pentobarbital on the day after the implant has been shown to block the advancement of ovulation, and the effects of the blocking drug shown to be overcome in 50% of the rats by injection of median eminence extract. The authors concluded that the steroid was acting to lower the pituitary threshold to LRF, resulting in increased LH secretion and an earlier rise in endogenous secretion rate of estrogen. The estrogen acted as the facilitatory signal for the ovulatory surge of LH. This theory fits with other data suggesting that estrogen secretion is delayed in the five-day rat (221, 223).

Consistent with the observations of a direct pituitary effect of steroids are some recent data indicating that the effects of LRF on the pituitary are altered by steroid injections. Measurements of the amount of LH released into the medium by LRF addition to pituitaries removed from donor male rats pretreated in vivo by castration or testosterone indicated the following: LH release was greater from pituitaries taken from castrated males and less from pituitaries removed from testosterone treated males than that from intact males (255). Pretreatment of rats or rabbits with progesterone can at least partially block the effects of in vivo injection of LRF in eliciting LH release (10, 89). Pretreatment of intact female rats with estrogen can increase the release of LH resulting from in vivo administration of LRF (11). In the rat parenteral injection of estrogen or progesterone lowered the threshold to electrochemical stimulation in the median-eminence region during pentobarbital blockade (155). The authors concluded that the facilitatory effects of the steroids was at the level of the median eminence or pituitary.

There continue to be observations indicating that implants directly in the central nervous system can influence secretion rates of gonadotrophins (63). Progesterone implanted into the median-eminence arcuate region of the hypothalamus advanced the time of the critical period on the day of proestrus in the rat (119); implants into the anterior hypothalamus or pituitary were ineffective. As noted above, antiestrogens administered on the day before proestrus can prevent release of the ovulatory surge of LH and ovulation (67, 125, 229); Döcke (52) has shown that implants of the antiestrogen clomiphene citrate on this day, into either the anterior pituitary or the medial basal hypothalamus, can inhibit spontaneous ovulation in the rat. Similar implants into immature rats prevented estrogen from inducing ovulation. On the other hand, rats made persistent in estrus by anterior hypothalamic lesions could be made to ovulate by clomiphene citrate implants into the ventromedian hypothalamus, but not by such implants into the pituitary. These observations suggested to the author that the pituitary may be the site of the facilitatory feedback of estrogen, and that the medial basal areas of the hypothalamus could be the site of negative feedback of estrogen.

Thus, the gonadal steroids may act on both hypothalamus and pituitary. The pituitary hormones and releasing factors themselves also may provide feedback information to the hypothalamus (41, 96). At least three interpretations of these observations are possible. First, different receptor sites could represent different functions. Second, a given function, such as negative feedback of estrogen on LH release, might be subsumed by a set of neurons at the low levels of estrogen found normally in the cycle, but might be subsumed by pituitary gonadotrophs under the high concentrations in an implant. Thirdly, what may seem a redundancy of feedback sites, could be a "fail-safe" mechanism, functioning at different thresholds to prevent excess gonadotrophic hormone secretion under extreme conditions of very low steroid levels.

Sequencing of hormone levels in the blood.—The temporal sequence of blood levels of ovarian and pituitary hormones during reproductive cycles should confirm conclusions regarding the effects of pituitary hormones on ovarian secretion rates, and the findings on feedback effects of estrogen and progesterone on pituitary secretion rates. The subject has been reviewed recently (270).

The most obvious change in hormonal levels during a cycle is the abrupt increase in LH concentration (surge) which precedes ovulation. Blood levels of estrogen rise before the peak of LH or ovulation in all species studied: sheep (43, 214), baboon (239), rat (28), monkey (95), and human (1, 247). On the other hand, blood progesterone levels do not rise appreciably until after the appearance of the ovulatory surge of LH or ovulation: mare (230), monkey (95), human (209), hamster (76, 128, 141), cow (86, 231), and baboon (239). This sequence suggests that in the intact mammal the low level of FSH and LH seen before the ovulatory surge is responsible for the secretion of estrogen and that this estrogen is a prerequisite for the release of the LH surge (221, 270). It also suggests that in many species progesterone cannot be the normal signal for the surge, even if it can cause a surge of LH under experimental conditions (63, 221). That estrogen is also exerting a negative feedback effect during the cycle is suggested by the rapidity of increase of blood FSH and LH after ovariectomy (76, 256, 268).

In the rat, the sequence of LH and progesterone secretion is less clear. Some laboratories (221) have reported that, as in the above species, the progesterone rise follows the LH rise. However, recently Barraclough, et al (16) observed that although ovarian progesterone did not rise until after the LH surge, the progesterone in peripheral plasma had already increased slightly but significantly by the onset of the LH surge. This latter finding is substantiated by observations of Feder et al (66). Both of these groups have proposed that progesterone secretion from the adrenal gland may increase prior to the onset of the LH surge. It should be added that adrenalectomized rats do ovulate (66, 171); therefore the adrenal progesterone is not essential for release of the ovulatory surge of LH. It is interesting, however, that in adrenalectomized rats the LH surge may be late (66) and mating behavior delayed (171).

In those species which have been studied, the surge of LH which occurs before ovulation has been accompanied by a surge of FSH (46, 72, 152) and prolactin (72, 170, 190). The role played by these two hormones is not clear. It has been suggested that FSH may elicit growth of the next crop of follicles (152, 224) and prolactin may cause luteolysis (structural) of the last set of corpora (267).

Systems analysis of hormonal interrelationships.—The extreme complexity of relationships among the hormones has been commented upon previously (23, 63, 210). Recent attempts to encompass and summarize these data have employed the techniques of systems analysis: to make models, both diagrammatic and mathematical, of the relationships among the levels of gonadal and pituitary hormones, and to subject the models to computer analysis to verify hypotheses by simulating the wave form of the hormones. These attempts, in both the human menstrual cycle (250, 270) and the rat estrous cycle (221, 225) have been recently discussed (225, 250, 270). It appears to us that such attempts should continue, because they provide an excellent way in which to summarize the literature, as well as a means by which to pretest hypotheses (221).

RELATIONSHIP OF THE CENTRAL NERVOUS SYSTEM TO THE CONTROL OF PITUITARY FSH, LH AND PROLACTIN SECRETION

CONTROL OF RELEASING FACTOR SECRETION

Search for the neurotransmitter.—During the past year considerable interest has focused on the search for "neurotransmitters" that control the secretion of LRF, FRF and PIF. One of the more fruitful experimental approaches utilized has been the injection of alleged neurotransmitters into the third ventricle and observation of the immediate effects on peripheral plasma concentrations of FSH, LH, and prolactin. Kamberi, Mical & Porter have published several studies using this approach. The results of their experiments are summarized in Table 2. Low, but not high, doses of dopamine (DA) increased plasma LH and FSH and decreased plasma prolactin. High, but not low, doses of norepinephrine (NE) and epinephrine (E) increased plasma LH and FSH and decreased plasma prolactin. At all doses tested, serotonin ($5-HT$) and melatonin (M) decreased plasma FSH and LH and increased plasma prolactin.

None of the substances shown in Table 2 influenced LH, FSH, or prolactin secretion when infused for 30 min into the anterior pituitary via a cannulated hypophysial stalk portal vessel (103, 106–108). DA failed to

TABLE 2. The effect of possible neurotransmitters on the plasma levels of FSH, LH, and Prolactin*

Substance	Dose in μg	LH	FSH	Prolactin
Dopamine HCl (DA)	1.25, 2.5	Inc (103)	Inc (106)	Dec (107)
	100	NC (103)	NC (106)	NC (107)
Norepinephrine (NE)	2.5, 5.0	NC (103)	NC (106)	NC (107)
	100	Inc (103)	Inc (106)	Dec (107)
Epinephrine (E) bitartrate	2.5, 5.0	Nc (103)	NC (106)	NC (107)
	100	Inc (103)	Inc (106)	Dec (107)
Serotonin creatinine sulfate (5HT)	1.0–5.0	Dec (103)	Dec (108)	Inc (108)
	50	—	Dec (108)	Inc (108)
Melatonin (M)	1.0, 5.0	Dec (103)	Dec (108)	Inc (108)
	50	Dec (103)	Dec (108)	Inc (108)

Inc = Significant increase
Dec = Significant decrease
NC = No significant change

* Test animals were adult male Sprague Dawley rats; volume injected into third ventricle was 2.5 or 5 μl; FSH, LH and prolactin were measured by specific radioimmunoassay procedures.

alter plasma LH (103), FSH (106), or prolactin (107) when perfused into the median eminence via the local arterial blood supply. Injection of 2.5 μg DA into the third ventricle caused an increased secretion of LRF (102), FRF (105), and PIF (104) into the hypophysial portal blood vessels. Intraventricular injection of 4 μg of DA increased plasma LH in female rats at all stages of the estrous cycle, but was especially effective at proestrus and the day before (218).

Kamberi, Schneider & McCann (109) investigated the effects of biogenic amines on the release of bioassayable FSH from pituitaries incubated in vitro with stalk-median eminence tissue. DA (2.5 or 5.0 μg/ml) significantly increased FSH release into the incubation media; E, NE and 5-HT were ineffective. DA did not increase FSH release if incubated with anterior pituitaries alone; therefore, it probably produced its stimulatory effect by promoting the release of FRF from the median eminence tissue. Furthermore, since DA failed to alter the activity of a partially purified FRF, it seems unlikely that DA increases FSH release by enhancing pituitary sensitivity to FRF. An alpha adrenergic blocker, phentolamine (20 μg/ml), inhibits the ability of DA to increase FSH release; a beta blocker, pronethalol (20 μg/ml), did not. Neither blocking agent influenced FSH release when added to pituitaries incubated in the absence of median eminence tissue. The similarity of these observations with those of an earlier report concerning the stimulatory effect of DA on in vitro release of LRF (216) are quite striking. Schneider & McCann also found that the peripheral plasma levels of LRF in hypophysectomized female rats could be elevated by injecting 4 μg of DA into the third ventricle. NE (4 μg) and E (40 μg) did not cause plasma LRF to increase (217). These observations, along with those of Kamberi, Mical & Porter (Table 2) indicate that FRF and LRF release can be initiated by the same presumed neurotransmitter, i.e. DA.

Epinephrine (11 or 18 μg) induced ovulation, but DA (19 or 38 μg), NE (10 or 17 μg), 5-HT (18 μg), and isoproterenol (1 μg) did not, when administered into the third ventricle of "pentobarbital-blocked" proestrous rats (211). While this observation tends to argue for E, and against DA, as the neurotransmitter for LRF (and FRF?) release, the doses of DA used were found by others to be too high to produce a sustained increase in plasma LH (103) or FSH (106). L-dopa (1–3 μg) or epinephrine (1 μg), but not NE (1 μg) or 5-HT (1 μg), injected into the lateral ventricles at 1230 overrode the ability of pentobarbital (given two hours later) to block ovulation (189).

Microinjection into the arcuate-median eminence of 80 ng of alpha-methyl-dopa (α-MD) (a drug that gives rise to the false transmitter, alpha methyl dopamine, in dopaminergic neurons) markedly suppressed ovulation when given just before the critical period for endogenous LH release in gonadotrophin-primed immature rats (120). Injection of α-MD into the preoptic and suprachiasmatic region, the lateral and dorsal hypothalamus, the premamillary and mamillary region, and the anterior pituitary was ineffective in suppressing ovulation.

A cautionary note (2) has been raised regarding the acceptance of DA (Table 2) as the neurotransmitter for LRF release. DA turnover in the median eminence, as measured by histochemical fluorescence, was lower during the early afternoon of proestrus than during metestrus or diestrus. A similar observation has been made for gonadotrophin-primed immature rats (70). Moreover, it was possible to block ovulation in the latter preparation by administering dopa peripherally, combined with a dopa decarboxylase inhibitor. Treatment with dopa alone did not block ovulation. These workers interpreted their results to mean that the tuberoinfundibular dopaminergic neurons act to inhibit release of LRF, and that removal of this dopaminergic inhibitory input is necessary for ovulation to take place (2).

There is also some support for the notion that NE may promote the release of LRF. Kalra (99) found that in estrogen-primed ovariectomized rats, blockade of a progesterone-induced plasma LH peak was achieved by drugs that presumably decrease brain NE levels without significantly altering DA levels. NE concentration, synthesis, and turnover during the early afternoon was found to be higher in proestrous rats than in estrous rats: NE synthesis was, however, higher on the second day of diestrus than on estrus or proestrus (55).

Evidence for an inhibitory neurotransmitter.—The fact that there appears to be a neurotransmitter which facilitates LRF release has encouraged investigators to look also for an inhibitory neurotransmitter. Kamberi, Mical & Porter (Table 2) found that intraventricular administration of 5-HT or M depressed further the already low plasma LH levels in adult male rats. Labhsetwar (126) found that 50 mg/kg of 5-HT administered subcutaneously to adult female rats at 1700 on the day before proestrus inhibited ovulation. 5-HT did not inhibit ovulation when given at 0930 on the day of proestrus. Other workers (201) found that 5-HT (100 mg/kg) inhibited ovulation when injected during proestrus at 1600, 1700, or 1800 (a two hour period at the end of the critical period!), but did not inhibit ovulation if given at 1400 or 1900. This last observation raises the possibility that high doses of peripherally administered serotonin may block ovulation by interfering with the action of LH on ovarian follicles. It should also be mentioned that Labhsetwar (126) found 50 mg/kg of 5-HT to be sedative. Numerous sedatives block ovulation when administered to proestrous rats (for review see 62, 63); 5-HT in high doses may block ovulation via a nonspecific CNS effect rather than by virtue of being the inhibitory transmitter for control of LRF release.

Drug experiments exploring the nature of the neurotransmitters.—Concerning the nature of the neurotransmitter for the control of PIF release, it has been reported that reserpine, chlorpromazine, alpha-methyl-para-tyrosine (*αMPT*) and alpha-methyl-meta-tyrosine, when given intraperitoneally to adult female rats at 1000 on proestrus, have induced significant elevations in serum prolactin (140). All of these drugs (in one way or another) inhibit catecholamine activity in the hypothalamus, and thereby presumably inhibit PIF release, and thence promote prolactin secretion. None of the tentatively proposed neurotransmitters (DA, E, NE and 5-HT), whether injected intraperitoneally or into the internal carotid, had any effect on serum prolactin (140). In this regard, the reader should be reminded that Kamberi, Mical & Porter found that intraventricular DA increased PIF release (104) and decreased prolactin release (107), but arterial perfusion into the median eminence did not decrease prolactin release. Thus, there seems to be something unique about the third ventricle that makes it an effective site for administration of alleged neurotransmitters. The stimulatory effect of αMPT on prolactin secretion has been confirmed in a preliminary report (54).

It was also found that L-dopa, a precurser for DA synthesis when administered intraperitoneally, causes plasma prolactin to decrease. Several other modifiers of brain monoamine metabolism have been tested; "In every case an expected alteration in brain DA was associated with the converse change in prolactin" (54).

Other aspects of control of releasing factor secretion.—As mentioned previously, DA, when injected into the third ventricle of a hypophysectomized rat, elicits an increase in plasma LRF. This stimulatory action of DA was prevented if 0.1 μg of estradiol was injected into the third ventricle 2 hrs prior to injecting DA (219). The inhibitory action of estradiol on the ability of DA to increase LRF release was also demonstrated in vitro (220). For enthusiasts of the theory that in the intact animal estradiol promotes LH release (see section IV above), it should be added that when estradiol (0.5 or 1.0 μg/ml) was added to incubates of anterior pituitaries alone (i.e. no median-eminence tissue added) LH release was significantly increased (220).

Fink & Harris (68) collected blood from the hypophysial portal vessels of female rats at various stages of the cycle. The LRF concentration in this blood was decreased at estrus as compared to other stages of the cycle. A rise in LRF did not occur during the proestrus critical period. However, since the urethane anesthesia that was used blocked ovulation in their rats, these data do not eliminate the possibility that LRF release normally increases during the critical period. Using the same collection techniques for hypophysial portal blood, Harris & Ruf (84) found that electrical stimulation of the median eminence during proestrus or metestrus elicited increased LRF release, but stimulation during estrus did not.

When lesions were made in the median eminence of ovariectomized rats, plasma LH and FSH were reduced (21) and plasma prolactin was increased (21, 37). Rats with no pituitary had barely "detectable" levels of serum prolactin, whereas hypophysectomized rats with one pituitary transplanted under the kidney capsule had prolactin levels equivalent to the highest levels seen in the estrous cycle of an intact rat (37). Rats with four transplanted pituitaries had very high serum prolactin—equivalent to that of a lactating post-partum rat (37). Administration of estradiol benzoate (1 μg/day for 5 days) increased serum prolactin over pretreatment levels in rats bearing 1, 2, or 4 pituitary transplants (37). These workers were unable to determine from this experiment whether estrogen increased prolactin secretion by decreasing PIF release, or by acting directly on the transplanted pituitary to facilitate prolactin secretion.

The question of whether the releasing factor can cause synthesis as well as release has again been raised. Corbin et al (42) reported that if a median-eminence extract is injected intravenously into an intact male rat, depletion of pituitary FSH is observed. However, if the pituitary FSH content is lowered by a previously placed median eminence lesion, injection of the same extract causes pituitary FSH content to increase.

Anesthetics and stress.—At all times except the afternoon of proestrus, serum prolactin levels were much higher in female rats if blood was taken from the aorta (via laparotomy under ether anesthesia) than if blood was collected by decapitation without anesthesia. Ether plus laparotomy did not increase prolactin levels in male rats, and serum LH was not altered by the collection method in male or female rats (168). Pentobarbital, administered to female rats at proestrus, induced a significant increase in serum prolactin within 10 to 30 min; however, within two hours prolactin levels were depressed (266). In fact, a properly timed injection of pentobarbital can prevent the proestrous surge in prolactin from occurring (100, 266), as well as prevent the surge of proestrous LH (44, 47, 100, 221, 266) and FSH (47, 100, 152). Laparotomy-stress, however, can prevent the barbital blockade of ovulation, apparently by means of early LH secretion induced by adrenal progesterone secretion (171). These data on the effects of barbiturates on hormone release during the proestrous "critical period" confirm by hormone measurements the conclusions based on ovulatory blockade experiments described by Everett (62, 63). They tend to contradict conclusions of Meyer et al (156) that phenobarbital blockade of ovulation is acting importantly at the ovarian level.

AREAS OF THE BRAIN INVOLVED IN GONADOTROPHIN SECRETION

Knife cut and lesion studies.—During the past year the technique of partial deafferentation of the hypothalamus by knife cuts has been increasingly used to determine functional localization. The presumed advantage of this technique over that of electrochemical or electrocoagulative lesions is that the latter techniques undoubtedly destroy cell bodies and nerve tracts, whereas the former destroys mainly nerve tracts. In addition, electrically induced lesions vary in size and effect, according to the size and composition of the electrode, and to the intensity, duration, frequency, and type (AC or DC) of electrical current used. In interpreting data from knife cuts or brain lesions one should remember that "deafferented" neural structures may increase their level of activity due to release of inhibition, or decrease the level of activity due to withdrawal of facilitation. Thus the apparent function of a deafferented hypothalamic region may or may not reflect the normal function of that region. Another cautionary note should be made of the fact that a 10 to 14 day period of diestrus follows certain cuts in the preoptic area (98, 246). This may represent a nonspecific effect of the trauma associated with the procedure; thus evaluation of the specific physiological deficiency produced by the cut must in some instances be delayed two weeks. Even with these limitations, knife cuts have yielded much interesting information.

Koves & Halasz (122) have made bilateral cuts in adult female rats rostral and dorsal to the preoptic area, thus interrupting the anterior and superior connections to the preoptic-anterior hypothalamus (*POAHA*), but leaving the POAHA connected to the medial basal hypothalamus (*MBH*) (*Type I cut*). Survival in these rats was poor, but those which survived showed irregular estrous cycles and ovulation. If the cuts were placed in the caudal suprachiasmatic plane (posterior to the Type I cut) thus separating the POAHA from the MBH (*Type II cut*) survival was more likely, but the rats did not ovulate and the ovaries became "polyfollicular." This Type II cut therefore gives results similar to those of electrolytic lesions in the POAHA (62, 63). In previous work, Halasz & Gorski (81) showed that a cut which consisted of a circle from the suprachiasmatic region backwards totally deafferenting the hypothalamus (*Type III cut*) prevented ovulation, follicular growth and vaginal cornification. A comparison of these three cuts suggests that information relevant to maintenance of follicular growth, but not ovulation, is reaching the MBH in rats with the Type II cut but not the Type III cut. Kaasjager et al (98) obtained similar results in that cuts similar to Type I did not interfere with spontaneous ovulation.

Taleisnik et al (246) also observed that a retrochiasmatic cut [comparable to the Type II cut (122)] caused the production of "polyfollicular" ovaries. They also found that a 4 mm diameter cut made just above the anterior commissure, thus cutting the dorsal connections to the POAHA (presumably limbic input), allowed the continuance of normal ovulatory cycles. Neither of Taleisnik's cuts prevented post-ovariectomy hypersecretion of LH (246). Kalra, Velasco & Sawyer (101) noted that cuts which separated the anterior hypothalamus (AH) from the MBH prevented a postovariectomy increase in FSH, as estimated by observing the ovarian response of an HCG-treated parabiosed rat. If the cut were made far enough rostral to leave most of the AH connected to the MBH, a post-ovariectomy rise in FSH did occur; this increase in FSH could be suppressed by administering 0.5 μg/day of estradiol benzoate to the lesioned rat. A similar frontal cut had previously been reported to allow the post-ovariectomy rise in plasma LH to occur (81).

Observations of Butler & Donovan (29) suggest that the suprachiasmatic nucleus (*Sch*) may be an intermediate control center that is influenced by the preoptic area and which in turn controls the MBH. They found that whereas cuts placed rostral to the Sch resulted in persistent vaginal estrus and follicular ovaries, when cuts were placed just caudal to the Sch, ovulation occurred (as judged by the presence of ovarian corpora lutea) in conjunction with irregular periods of vaginal diestrus. In contrast, Koves & Halasz (121) produced persistent vaginal estrus (no ovulation) with cuts made either rostral or caudal to the Sch, although the rats with the caudal cut did show a decreased capacity to increase gonadotrophin secretion in response to unilateral ovariectomy. Since the negative feedback of gonadal steriods may be partially exerted directly on the anterior pituitary (see above), the problem of localizing the portion of the hypothalamus that monitors steroid levels is difficult.

Printz & Greenwald (181) have shown that in intact hamsters, starvation for longer than one estrous cycle prevented antral follicular development— presumably the result of decreased FSH secretion, and stimulated interstitial hypertrophy—presumably the result of increased LH release. These same authors (182) have reported that bilateral electrocoagulative lesions of the mamillary bodies (*MB*) produces a similar condition, even though loss of body weight did not occur. Lesions of the ventral tegmental nucleus (*VTN*) of the midbrain resulted in normal appearing ovaries even though the hamsters had lost considerable weight. The authors explain their results by suggesting that in the intact, normally fed hamster, information coming from (or through) the MB promotes the cyclic release of FSH. In the starved hamster, information from the VTN inhibits the MB, thereby decreasing the cyclic release of FSH. If, however, the VTN is destroyed, the MB continue to promote cyclic FSH release even though food intake is decreased. These results also indicate that, at least in hamsters, some information essential for normal gonadotrophin secretion is coming from the posterior hypothalamic region. Studies in the rat have primarily emphasized the importance of anterior hypothalamic connections for the normal control of cyclic gonadotrophin secretion (29, 81).

In adult rats, destruction of the corticomedial division of the amygdaloid complex or destruction of the stria terminalis caused the already elevated LH levels of ovariectomized rats to increase further (127). Relkin (198, 199) has found that electrolytic lesions placed in the basal, medial or cortical amygdaloid nuclei of female rats at 4 or 6 days of age caused puberty (day of vaginal opening) to be considerably delayed. This is in marked contrast to the observation of Elwers & Critchlow (60), that lesions placed in similar areas of the amygdaloid complex of female rats at 18 to 20 days of age resulted in precocious puberty. Thus with regard to the amygdala the results of lesioning may also depend on the developmental stage of the animal at the time of surgery.

ELECTRICAL STIMULATION STUDIES

Attempts to determine a preoptic area threshold for ovulation.—The threshold for induction of ovulation with electrochemical stimulation of the preoptic area has been investigated at different stages of the estrous cycle in rats. In both the four- and five-day cycle rat (93) stimulation could induce ovulation earlier in the cycle than the time when LH would normally be released. However, electrochemical stimulation could not induce ovulation as early as injection of LH (94). The times when electrochemical stimulation was effective occurred after the time of significant elevation of estrogen secretion, as indicated by other evidence (28, 223). In four-day cycle Wistar rats, ovulation could be induced by electrical (no iron deposition) stimulation of the preoptic region as early as 1400 to 1600 on the day before proestrus, provided 500 μA was used; 300 μA failed. At 1400 on proestrus only 100 μA were required; thus the threshold was definitely lowered at that time (113).

Proestrous, Charles River-CD rats blocked with pentobarbital required 15 to 20 times as much direct current to induce ovulation than did an inbred strain of Osborne-Mendel rats (65). The ovarian threshold to LH was almost identical in both strains. These observations predict possible pitfalls in using threshold data from one strain of rats for experiments in a second strain.

Quinn (184) found that in guinea pigs the electrical threshold for induction of gonadotrophin secretion by stimulation of the medial preoptic-anterior hypothalamic (*MPOA-AH*) region was higher, on day 12 (i.e. 12 days since the last ovulation), than the threshold in the MBH. This high threshold could be overcome by doubling the applied current. By the fourteenth day, the threshold of the MPOA-AH was reduced to that of the MBH. The author hypothesized that the threshold of the MPOA-AH is kept high by endogenous progesterone until the fourteenth day. It has also been reported that ovulation can be induced in ewes during the last month of anestrus by electrical stimulation of the anterior hypothalamic or ventromedial nuclei. Stimulation of the same areas during the breeding season on the twelfth day of the estrous cycle did not advance ovulation (183).

Measurement of plasma LH and FSH after hypothalamic stimulation.— The availability of sensitive and specific radioimmunoassays for LH and FSH has made it possible to examine the time course of the response of the pituitary to stimulation of the hypothalamus. Bilateral electrical stimulation (iron not deposited) of the preoptic area of pentobarbital-blocked proestrous rats for 40 min caused plasma LH to rise significantly within 40 min after initiation of stimulation; LH was still elevated 120 min poststimulation. The pattern of LH secretion was quite similar to that observed in normal proestrous rats (44). Electrochemical stimulation (iron deposited) of the medial preoptic area also elicited LH release and ovulation in pentobarbital-blocked proestrous rats, even though plasma FSH was not always increased (100); such stimulation in caudal regions of the medial preoptic area and anterior hypothalamic area resulted in increased plasma FSH and LH, and induced ovulation. The authors have concluded that their results "confirm the existence of a rostral-preoptico-tuberal pathway for release of LH," and have suggested that "a distinct but overlapping anterior hypothalamic-tuberal pathway" is involved in the release of FSH (100).

Other CNS structures possibly involved in control of gonadotrophin secretion.—A dual role for mesencephalic structures in the control of gonadotrophin secretion in rats has been postulated (33). Evidence for this contention is that, whereas electrochemical stimulation during proestrus of the ventral tegmentum or medial raphe nucleus significantly decreased the incidence of spontaneous ovulation, electrochemical stimulation of the dorsal tegmentum induced ovulation in rats made persistent estrous by exposure to constant light.

Electrochemical stimulation of the ventral or dorsal hippocampus during proestrus reduced the incidence of spontaneous ovulation in rats (253). However, when the medial corticohypothalamic tract (presumably carrying efferents from the hippocampus to the arcuate nucleus of the hypothalamus) was cut two to three weeks earlier, hippocampal stimulation was no longer able to inhibit spontaneous ovulation. Stimulation of the hippocampus also prevented the ovulation normally observed after stimulation of the arcuate nucleus of the hypothalamus. Velasco & Taleisnik (253) have concluded these results indicate that stimuli arising from the hippocampus are capable of suppressing LH release. The same investigators have also reported that electrochemical stimulation of the medial amygdaloid nucleus induces ovulation in rats made anovulatory by exposure to constant light (252). However, if the stria terminalis (presumably containing efferents from the amygdala) is destroyed, electrochemical stimulation of the medial amygdaloid nucleus no longer induces ovulation.

Rats with only preoptic afferents remaining to the medial basal hypothalamus are still capable of irregular cyclic ovulation [Type I cut (122)]. Thus the contribution of mesencephalic, hippocampal, and amygdaloid inputs to gonadotrophin secretion may be that of adding regularity to the cycle.

Electrophysiological correlates for release of preovulatory gonadotrophins.— If, as seems certain, the brain is involved in the induction of the surge of gonadotrophin that precedes ovulation, it would seem that during this induction, properly placed microelectrodes should detect characteristic changes in the neuronal activity of involved brain regions. Kawakami, Terasawa & Ibuki (114) observed in rats that a characteristic elevated pattern of multiple unit-activity (*MUA*) appeared for 12 to 25 minutes during the afternoon of proestrus both in the MBH and the forebrain-limbic-preoptic-area. However, the association of this elevated MUA pattern with gonadotrophin release is not yet certain, because it was also recorded from the MBH of some rats on the afternoon of estrus, and the second day of diestrus. Injection of progesterone on the morning of proestrus advanced the time of the onset of the elevated MUA. This is an important observation since progesterone when given at that time advances the time of preovulatory LH surge (119). It is not yet possible to state whether the characteristic MUA is associated with (*a*) the release of LRF and FRF, (*b*) the "short loop" negative feedback LH and FSH on the hypothalamic nuclei, or (*c*) the feedback (negative or facilitative) of gonadal steroids on the hypothalamus. Sawyer (213) has recently written a brief, interesting review of this research area, to which we refer the reader.

LOCALIZATION OF HYPOTHALAMIC RELEASING FACTORS

Assay of frozen sections of the hypothalamus for LRF activity revealed that LRF was present in the medial, basal tuberal region (includes the median eminence and arcuate nucleus), and more rostrally in an area including the suprachiasmatic nucleus, and all but the most rostral portions of the preoptic nucleus (45).

PINEAL GLAND

Pinealectomy of adult female rats either produced no impairment of reproductive function (4, 158) or slightly prolonged the estrous cycle (92). When female rats were pinealectomized at four days of age, vaginal opening occurred early (198). When testosterone secretion of male rats was measured four weeks after piealectomy, it was found to be elevated (116). These observations suggest that pinealectomy by itself either fails to influence or else enhances gonadotrophin secretion.

Pinealectomy at the appropriate time prevented the deficiencies in gonadal function which develop in response to light deprivation or blinding in male (196) or female (233) hamsters, or male rats (117). Blinded female rats showed a decreased capacity for ovarian compensatory hypertrophy; this deficiency was prevented by pinealectomy (50, 232). When male rats were blinded and made anosmic (olfactory bulbs removed), the weight of the testes and sex accessories was decreased (197). This dual operation in female rats caused a delay in vaginal opening (194), a decreased gain in body weight (194), and decreased weight of the ovaries and uterine horns (195). Again, all of these gonadal deficiencies were prevented when the rats were also pinealectomized (194, 195, 197).

As shown in Table 2, M or 5-HT, when injected into the third ventricle of male rats, depressed the plasma levels of FSH and LH. However, De Prospo & Hurley report that in female rats (130 to 150 g) daily injection for 10 days into the lateral cerebral ventricles of large quantities (100 μg/day) of M or 5-HT failed to alter the ovarian or uterine weight (49). Daily infusions of M (2 mg/day for 10 days) into the jugular vein of sheep did not inhibit the preovulatory increase in plasma LH, but did partially suppress the increased secretion of LH seen after ovariectomy (203). In young male rats, daily intraperitoneal injections of 20 μg of M for 10 days decreased sex accessory weight and testicular thymidine uptake (117), and 50 μg per day for four weeks caused prostate weight and testosterone secretion (blood taken from testicular vein) to decrease (116). These somewhat divergent responses produced by M (49, 117, 203) make it very difficult to draw a generalization regarding its action on gonadal function. Anton-Tay & Wurtman (9) have demonstrated that 100 times more isotopically labeled melatonin is retained in the brain following injection into the lateral ventricles than after systemic injection. However, differences in the route of administration only partially explain the divergent effects of melatonin.

The significance of the pineal in the normal regulation of gonadal function is uncertain largely because it is not yet possible to measure blood levels (and therefore the secretion rates) of the alleged pineal hormones. Presently, investigators must measure the activity of the melatonin-forming enzyme (hydroxyindole-O-methyltransferase: $HIOMT$) which correlates poorly (143) with the content of bioassayable melatonin (185). Rats exposed to continuous darkness no longer show a rhythm in pineal HIOMT activity, but the circadian rhythm of pineal melatonin persists (143); the melatonin content of the pineal is 10 times higher in rats killed during their peak running period than in rats killed during low activity (186). The question has been raised as to whether HIOMT is rate-limiting in the formation of melatonin (197). It has been suggested that the activity of N-acetyl-transferase (converts serotonin to N-acetylserotonin) may better reflect the melatonin-forming potential of the pineal (118).

For many years, investigators of the pituitary-gonadal relationship did not have assays with sufficient sensitivity to quantitate plasma gonadotrophins. However, because hypophysectomy or administration of pituitary extracts invariably altered gonadal function, they were able to gain some insight as to whether the levels of gonadotrophin in the pituitary (which they *could* measure) were related to secreted gonadotrophin. The investigator of pineal function can measure pineal enzymes and their products, but can only use the gonad as an endpoint when some experimental manipulation (continuous dark, anosmia) presumably increases the output of the pineal or increases the sensitivity of the hypothalamic-pituitary axis to the pineal hormone(s). Under those experimental conditions, the presence of the pineal gland is able to effect an inhibitory action on gonadal function. One of the substances that the pineal synthesizes, melatonin, can inhibit gonadal function when appropriately administered. Whether the pineal is important for the normal physiological regulation of the gonads is still open to question; this question may not be answered until methods are available to measure the output of pineal hormones.

Environmental Influences

In mammals that breed seasonally, the length of the daily photoperiod provides an important environmental signal for alterations in gonadal function (222). The role of the photoperiod is less clear in nonseasonal breeders such as humans, cows, pigs and rats. Hormonal secretion in humans can be influenced by the photoperiod as evidenced by the existence of an endogenous diurnal rhythm of glucocorticoid secretion, and its modification by experimental lighting regimens (174). Controversy still exists as to whether there is a diurnal rhythm of gonadotrophin secretion in man (173). However, an endogenous circadian rhythm which controls the time of preovulatory LH secretion does exist in female rats, mice and hamsters (222); moreover the phase of this rhythm can be shifted by alterations of the photoperiod.

An endogenous rhythm for control of LH secretion.—Before a rhythm is considered endogenous, it must be shown to persist for some time under constant environmental conditions, i.e. with respect to light, continuous light (*LL*) or continuous darkness (*DD*). For a rhythm to be considered circadian, it should in nocturnally active animals (rats and hamsters) have a period in DD very close to 24 hours; in LL, the period should be slightly greater than 24 hours (14).

Carlyle & Carter (32) have shown that in adult rats exposed to DD for four days, the time of ovulation (and presumably the time of preovulatory LH secretion) did not shift noticeably. Strauss (240) saw no change in the time of the critical period for LH secretion in gonadotrophin-primed immature rats after one week of exposure to DD. In adult rats (32) or adult hamsters (3) exposed to LL for three or four days, the time of ovulation was delayed, and in gonadotrophin-primed immature rats, the delay in the time of ovulation was directly proportional to the length of exposure to LL (154). In the latter preparation (154), the period of the circadian rhythm controlling LH release in LL was estimated to be 25.3 to 25.8 hours (light intensity:

130 lux). Daane & Parlow (47) measured serum LH on the afternoon of proestrus in rats exposed to LL. By the first proestrus in LL, only 42% of the rats had elevated serum LH vs 90% of controls kept in alternating light and dark (*LD*). Possibly, exposure to LL had already delayed the LH surge, such that LH was not yet elevated at the time of sampling.

In intact female rats a very low-amplitude but fairly consistent diurnal rhythm in LH secretion was observed with the minimum levels of LH during periods of darkness (72). However, such a diurnal rhythm was not detectable in the plasma of adult male rats (269). Indirect evidence for a diurnal rhythm of LH secretion (under conditions of LD) was seen in four-day cyclic adult female rats. Large doses of pentobarbital (50 mg/kg) reliably delayed ovulation if given at 12:45 on any day of the cycle, but not if given at 0900 or 1700 (53).

Zeitgebers for the endogenous circadian rhythm.—The critical period in rats for preovulatory LH secretion was found to begin at about 1400 on the day of proestrus, provided the midpoint of the photoperiod was defined as 1200. This was true whether the rats were kept under LD 12:12 (4, 90), LD 14:10 (90) or LD 16:8 (90). When the photoperiod was shifted three hours earlier (length of the photoperiod held constant) (64, 90) or five hours earlier or later (240) the time of the critical period shifted accordingly. Thus it seems that the onset of the LH surge is associated with the midpoint of the dark or the midpoint of the light period, rather than the beginning of light or dark.

Another approach to this problem was taken by Strauss (240) who examined the time of the LH surge in gonadotrophin-primed immature rats. In these experiments, the time of the LH surge (after a week of exposure to DD) was shifted two to three hours earlier when the last photoperiod had been shortened by five hours, and four hours later when the last photoperiod had been extended by five hours. Using the same preparation, McCormack (153) found that the delayed time of ovulation (after a week of exposure to LL) had not been altered by advancing or by delaying the onset of LL by six hours. From these experiments (153, 240), it seems likely that the light which falls late in the day influences the rhythm controlling LH secretion more readily than that which falls early in the day.

Parenthetically, it should be added that the administration of sex steroids to rats can also shift the time of ovulation. However, the shift produced is almost always 24 hours. Thus, it seems that sex steroids determine the day of ovulation, while the lighting schedule determines the hour (221). An exception to this generalization is the fact that progesterone, if given on the morning of proestrus, advances the time of ovulation by two hours (119, 221).

Effect of the photoperiod on other reproductive parameters.—The mean length of estrous cycles (measured by the onset of behavioral estrus) of hamsters kept in LL is slightly (but significantly) greater than 96 hrs. This is apparently due to the influence of LL on an endogenous timer with circadian rhymicity which in turn controls the "circa-quadridian" estrous cycle (5). Whether rats have four- or five-day estrous cycles depends on the genetic strain (64, 91), age (older rats tend to have longer cycles) (64) and the length of the photoperiod (long photoperiods tend to cause long cycles) (64, 91). When rats are exposed to continuous light, they eventually display persistent vaginal cornification. The rapidity with which this condition develops varies considerably with the genetic strain (64, 91).

Exposure of pregnant rats to a long photoperiod (LD 22:2) significantly prolonged the length of gestation when compared to a short photoperiod (LD 2:22) or control photoperiod (LD 14:10) (158). In addition, the time period during which the uterus responds to surgical trauma by producing a large deciduomata was delayed by exposure to LD 22:2 (271).

Weight gain as a factor in the attainment of puberty.—The data from three longitudinal studies in girls of growth rate and age of menarche have been carefully analyzed by Frisch & Revelle (69). Whether the girls matured earlier (menarche at 11.9 years or earlier) or late (menarche at 14.0–14.9 years), their mean body weight at menarche was 48 Kg. However, late maturers were significantly taller at menarche than early maturers. These authors have proposed that the "attainment of a body weight in the critical range causes a change in metabolic rate, which, in turn, reduces the sensitivity of the hypothalamus to estrogen, thus altering the ovarian-hypothalamic feedback."

ACKNOWLEDGEMENTS

The preparation of this manuscript was supported in part by PHS grant HD-00440. We would like to thank Dr. Charles Rodgers and Dr. Carol Proudfit for their valuable aid in the preparation of this manuscript.

LITERATURE CITED

1. Abraham, G. E., Klaiber, E. L. 1970. Plasma immunoreactive estrogens and LH during the menstrual cycle. *Am. J. Obstet. Gynecol.* 198:528–31
2. Ahrén, K., Fuxe, K., Hamberger, L., Hökfelt, T. 1971. Turnover changes in the tuberoinfundibular dopamine neurons during the ovarian cycle of the rat. *Endocrinology* 88:1415–24
3. Alleva, J. J., Waleski, M. V., Alleva, F. R. 1968. Synchronizing effect of photoperiodicity on ovulation in hamsters. *Endocrinology* 82:1227–35
4. Alleva, J. J., Waleski, M. V., Alleva, F. R. 1970. The zeitgeber for ovulation in rats: non participation of the pineal gland. *Life Sci.* 9:241–46
5. Alleva, J. J., Waleski, M. V., Alleva, F. R. 1971. A biological clock controlling the estrous cycle of the hamster. *Endocrinology* 88:1368–79
6. Amatayakul, K., Ryan, R., Uozumi, T., Albert, A. 1971. A reinvestigation of testicular-anterior pituitary relationships in the rat: I. Effects of castration and cryptorchidism. *Endocrinology* 88:872–80
7. Amenomori, Y., Chen, C. L. Meites, J. 1970. Serum prolactin levels in rats during different reproductive states. *Endocrinology* 86:506–10
8. Anderson, L. L., Bland, K. P., Melampy, R. M. 1969. Comparative aspects of uterine-luteal relationships. *Recent Prog. Hor. Res.* 25:57–104
9. Anton-Tay, F., Wurtman, R. J. 1969.

Regional uptake of ³H-melatonin from blood and cerebrospinal fluid by rat brain. *Nature London* 221: 474–75

10. Arimura, A., Schally, A. V. 1970. Progesterone suppression of LH-releasing hormone-induced stimulation of LH release in rats. *Endocrinology* 87:653–57

11. Arimura, A., Schally, A. V. 1971. Augmentation of pituitary responsiveness to LH-releasing hormone (LH-RH) by estrogen. *Proc. Soc. Exp. Biol. Med.* 136:290–93

12. Armstrong, D. T. 1970. Reproduction. *Ann. Rev. Physiol.* 32:439–70

13. Armstrong, D. T., Knudsen, K. A., Miller, L. S. 1970. Effects of prolactin upon cholesterol metabolism and progesterone biosynthesis in corpora lutea of rats hypophysectomized during pseudopregnancy. *Endocrinology* 86:634–41

14. Aschoff, J. 1960. Exogenous and endogenous components in circadian rhythms. *Symp. Quant. Biol.* 25: 11–28

15. Ashitaka, Y., Tokura, Y., Tane, M., Mochizuki, M., Tojo, S. 1970. Studies on the biochemical properties of highly purified HCG. *Endocrinology* 87:233–44

16. Barraclough, C. A., Collu, R., Massa, R., Martini, L. 1971. Temporal interrelationships between plasma LH, ovarian secretion rates and peripheral plasma progestin concentrations in the rat: effects of nembutal and exogenous gonadotrophins. *Endocrinology* 88:1437–47

17. Behrman, A. R., Orczyk, G. P., MacDonald, G. J., Greep, R. O. 1970. Prolactin induction of enzymes controlling luteal cholesterol ester turnover. *Endocrinology* 87:1251–56

18. Benson, B., Sorrentino, S., Evans, J. S. 1969. Increase in serum FSH following unilateral ovariectomy in the rat. *Endocrinology* 84:369–74

19. Ber, A. 1971. The effect of gonadotrophins and of growth hormone in the development of ovarian autografts on the greater omentum of hemicastrated rats. *Acta Endocrinol. Copenhagen* 66:99–110

20. Betteridge, K. J., Kelly, W. A., Marston, J. H. 1970. Morphology of the rhesus monkey ovary near the time of ovulation. *J. Reprod. Fert.* 22:453

21. Bishop, W., Krulich, L., Fawcett, C. P., McCann, S. M. 1971. The effect of median eminence (ME) lesions on plasma levels of FSH, LH, and prolactin in the rat. *Proc. Soc. Exp. Biol. Med.* 136:925–27

22. Blackwell, R. E., Amoss, M. S., Jr. 1971. A sex difference in the rate of rise of plasma LH in rats following gonadectomy. *Proc. Soc. Exp. Biol. Med.* 136:11–14

23. Bogdanove, E. M. 1964. The role of the brain in the regulation of pituitary gonadotropin secretion. *Vitam. Horm. New York* 22:205–59

24. Bogdanove, E. M. 1967. Analysis of histophysiologic responses of the rat hypophysis to androgen treatment. *Anat. Rec.* 157:117–36

25. Bogdanove, E. M., Gay, V. L., Midgley, A. R., Jr., Reichert, L. E., Jr. 1970. Use of combined biological and chemical purification procedures in the separation of follicle-stimulating hormone from rat pituitary tissue. *Endocrinology* 87: 201–6

26. "Brain-Endocrine Interactions" 1970. *Symp. Am. Assoc. Anat. 83rd Sess., Am. J. Anat.* 129:193–245

27. Braunstein, G. D., Reichert, L. E., Jr., Van Hall, E. V., Vaitukatis, J. L., Ross, G. T. 1971. The effects of desialylation on the biologic and immunologic activity of human pituitary luteinizing hormone. *Biochem. Biophys. Res. Commun.* 42: 962–67

28. Brown-Grant, K., Exley, D., Naftolin, F. 1970. Peripheral plasma oestradiol and luteinizing hormone concentrations during the oestrous cycle of the rat. *J. Endocrinol.* 48: 295–96

29. Butler, J. E. M., Donovan, B. T. 1971. The effect of surgical isolation of the hypothalamus on reproductive function in the female rat. *J. Endocrinol.* 49:293–304

30. Calagaris, L., Astrada, J. J., Taleisnik, S. 1971. Release of luteinizing hormone induced by estrogen injection into ovariectomized rats. *Endocrinology* 88:810–15

31. Callantine, M. R., Humphrey, P. R., French, P. J. 1962. Induction of ovulation: Effects of norethindrone and progesterone. *Fed. Proc.* 21:214

32. Carlyle, A., Carter, S. B. 1961. The influence of light on the occurrence of ovulation in the rat. *J. Physiol.* 157:44P

33. Carrer, H. F., Taleisnik, S. 1970. Effect of mesencephalic stimula-

REGULATION OF GONADAL FUNCTION 463

tion on the release of gonadotrophins. *J. Endocrinol.* 48:527–39
33a. Casey, D., Ed. *Bibliography of Reproduction* (periodical). Cambridge, England: Reproduction Research Information Service, Ltd.
34. Channing, C. P. 1970. Effects of stage of the menstrual cycle and gonadotrophins on luteinization of rhesus monkey granulosa cells in culture. *Endocrinology* 87:49–60
35. Channing, C. P. 1970. Effect of stage of the estrous cycle and gonadotrophins upon luteinization of porcine granulosa cells in culture. *Endocrinology* 87:156–64
36. Chen, B. L., Ely, C. A. 1971. Immunological studies of the follicle-stimulating hormone. I. Identification of the HCG augmenting principle. *Endocrinology* 88:944–55
37. Chen, C. L., Amenomori, Y., Lu, K. H., Voogt, J. L., Meites, J. 1970. Serum prolactin levels in rats with transplants or hypothalamic lesions. *Neuroendocrinology* 6:220–27
38. Chen, C. L., Meites, J. 1970. Effects of estrogen and progesterone on serum and pituitary prolactin levels in ovariectomized rats. *Endocrinology* 86:503–5
39. Clemens, J. A., Shaar, C. J., Kleber, J. W., Tandy, W. A. 1971. Areas of the brain stimulatory to LH and FSH secretion. *Endocrinology* 88:180–84
40. "Control of Ovulation" 1970. *Physiol. Soc. Symp., FASEB, Fed. Proc.* 29:1875–912
41. Corbin, A., Daniels, E. L., Milmore, J. E. 1970. An "internal" feedback mechanism controlling follicle-stimulating hormone releasing factor. *Endocrinology* 86:735–43
42. Corbin, A., Milmore, J. E., Daniels, E. L. 1970. Further evidence for the existence of a hypothalamic follicle stimulating hormone synthesizing factor. *Experientia* 26:1010–11
43. Cox, R. I., Mattner, P. E., Thorburn, G. D. 1971. Changes in ovarian secretion of oestradiol around oestrus in the sheep. *J. Endocrinol.* 49:345–46
44. Cramer, O. M., Barraclough, C. A. 1971. Effect of stimulation of the preoptic area on plasma LH concentrations in proestrous rats. *Endocrinology* 88:1175–83
45. Crighton, D. B., Schneider, H. P. G., McCann, S. M. 1970. Localization

of LH-releasing factor in the hypothalamus and neurohypophysis as determined by an *in vitro* method. *Endocrinology* 87:323–29
46. Daane, T. A., Parlow, A. F. 1971. Periovulatory patterns of rat serum follicle-stimulating hormone and luteinizing hormone during the normal estrous cycle: effects of pentobarbital. *Endocrinology* 88:653–63
47. Daane, T. A., Parlow, A. F. 1971. Serum FSH and LH in constant light-induced persistent estrus: short-term and long-term studies. *Endocrinology* 88:964–68
48. De Hertogh, R., Ekka, E., Vanderheyden, I., Hoet, J. J. 1971. *In vivo* observation on cyclic variations of estradiol-17β,6,7-³H uptake by the uterus of the adult rat. *Endocrinology* 88:175–79
49. De Prospo, N., Hurley, J. 1971. Effects of injecting melatonin and its precursors into the lateral cerebral ventricles on selected organs in rats. *J. Endocrinol.* 49:545–46
50. Dickson, K., Benson, B., Tate, G., Jr. 1971. The effect of blinding and pinealectomy in unilaterally ovariectomized rats. *Acta Endocrinol.* 66:177–82
51. Dierschke, D. J., Bhattacharya, A. N., Atkinson, L. E., Knobil, E. 1970. Circhoral oscillations of plasma LH levels in the ovariectomized rhesus monkey. *Endocrinology* 87:850–53
52. Döcke, F. 1971. Studies on the antiovulatory and ovulatory action of clomiphene citrate in the rat. *J. Reprod. Fert.* 24:45–54
53. Dominguez, R., Smith, E. R. 1971. Evidence for a daily neural event affecting ovulation in the rat. *Fed. Proc.* 30:310
54. Donoso, A. O., Bishop, W., McCann, S. M., Orias, R. 1971. Effects of alterations in brain monamine concentrations on plasma prolactin. *Endocrine Soc., Program 53rd Meet.* p. A-127
55. Donoso, A. O., Moyano, M. B. D. 1970. Adrenergic activity in hypothalamus and ovulation. *Proc. Soc. Exp. Biol. Med.* 135:633–35
56. Duncan, G. W., Ericsson, R. J., Zimbelman, R. G., Eds. 1966. "Ovarian Regulatory Mechanisms." *J. Reprod. Fert. Suppl.* p. 1–136
57. Duncan, G. W., Pharriss, B. B. 1970. Effect of nonsteroidal compounds on fertility. *Fed. Proc.* 29:1232–39

57a. Dunn, D., Ed. *Neuroendocrine Control Mechanism: The Hypothalamic-Pituitary-Gonadal System* (Periodical). Los Angeles: UCLA Brain Information Service

57b. Edwards, R. G., Ed. *Research in Reproduction* (Periodical). London: International Planned Parenthood Federation

58. El-Fouly, M. A., Cook, B., Nekola, M., Nalbandov, A. V. 1970. Role of the ovum in follicular luteinization. *Endocrinology* 87:288–93

59. Ellsworth, L. R., Armstrong, D. T. 1971. Effect of LH on luteinization of ovarian follicles transplanted under the kidney capsule in rats. *Endocrinology* 88:755–62

60. Elwers, M., Critchlow, V. 1960. Precocious ovarian stimulation following hypothalamic and amygdaloid lesion in rats. *Am. J. Physiol.* 198: 381–85

61. Espey, L. L. 1971. Decomposition of connective tissue in rabbit ovarian follicles by multivesicular structures of thecal fibroblasts. *Endocrinology* 88:437–44

62. Everett, J. W. 1964. Central neural control of reproductive functions of the adenohypophysis. *Physiol. Rev.* 44:374-431

63. Everett, J. W. 1969. Neuroendocrine aspects of mammalian reproduction. *Ann. Rev. Physiol.* 31:383–416

64. Everett, J. W. 1970. Photoregulation of the ovarian cycle in the rat. Conference: La Photoregulation de la Reproduction chez les Oiseaux et les Mammiferes, held in Montpellier, France, July 17–22, 1967. *Colloques internationaux du centre national de la recherche scientifique.* #172, p. 388–408.

65. Everett, J. W., Holsinger, J. W., Jr., Zeilmaker, G. H., Redmond, W. C., Quinn, D. L. 1970. Strain differences for preoptic stimulation of ovulation in cyclic spontaneously persistent-estrous, and androgen-sterilized rats. *Neuroendocrinology* 6:98–108

66. Feder, H. H., Brown-Grant, K., Corker, C. S. 1971. Preovulatory progesterone, the adrenal cortex and the 'critical period' for luteinizing hormone release in rats. *J. Endocrinol.* 50:29–39

67. Ferin, M., Tempone, A., Zimmering, P., Vande Wiele, R. L. 1969. Effect of antibodies to 17β-estradiol and progesterone on the estrous cycle of the rat. *Endocrinology* 85:1070–78

68. Fink, G., Harris, G. W. 1970. The luteinizing hormone releasing activity of extracts of blood from the hypophysial portal vessels of rats. *J. Physiol. London* 208:221–41

69. Frisch, R. E., Revelle, R. 1970. Height and weight at menarche and a hypothesis of critical body weights and adolescent events. *Science* 169: 397–99.

70. Fuxe, K., Hökfelt, T., Sundstedt, C. D. 1971. The tubero-infundibular (TB) dopamine (DA) neurons and ovulation. *Fed. Proc.* 30:309

71. "Gametes and Fertilization" 1970. *Symp. Ann. Meet. Soc. Study Reprod., 2nd. Biol. Reprod.* Suppl. 2

72. Gay, V. L., Midgley, A. R., Jr., Niswender, G. D. 1970. Patterns of gonadotrophin secretion associated with ovulation. *Fed. Proc.* 29:1880–87

73. Gersten, B. E., Baker, B. L. 1970. Local action of intrahypophyseal implants of estrogen as revealed by staining with peroxidase-labelled antibody. *Am. J. Anat.* 128:1–20

74. Goldenberg, R. L., Ross, G. T. 1971. New evidence for a direct effect of estrogen on the Graafian follicle. *Endocrine Soc., Program 53rd Meet.* p. A–116

75. Goldman, B. D., Mahesh, V. B. 1968. Fluctuations in pituitary FSH during the ovulatory cycle in the rat and a possible role of FSH in the induction of ovulation. *Endocrinology* 83:97–106

76. Goldman, B. D., Porter, J. C. 1970. Serum LH levels in intact and castrated golden hamsters. *Endocrinology* 87:676–79

77. Gospodarowicz, D. 1971. Localization of the lipolytic, steroidogenic and immunogenic activity in the ovine luteinizing hormone. *Endocrine Soc., Program 53rd Meet.* p. A–75

78. Greenwald, G. S., Rothchild, I. 1968. Formation and maintenance of corpora lutea in laboratory animals. *J. Anim. Sci.* Suppl. 1, 27:139–62.

79. Greep, R. O. 1961. Physiology of the anterior hypophysis in relation to reproduction. In: *Sex and Internal Secretions*, ed. W. C. Young, 240–301. Baltimore: Williams and Wilkins Co. 3rd ed., vol. 1

80. Hagino, N., Goldzieher, J. W. 1970. Regulation of gonadotrophin release

by the corpus luteum in the baboon. *Endocrinology* 87:413–18

81. Halasz, B., Gorski, R. A. 1967. Gonadotrophic hormone secretion in female rats after partial or total interruption of neural afferents to the medial basal hypothalamus. *Endocrinology* 80:608–22

82. Hanson, F. W., Powell, J. E., Stevens, V. C. 1971. Effects of HCG and human pituitary LH on steroid secretion and functional life of the human corpus luteum. *J. Clin. Endocrinol. Metab.* 32:211–15

83. Harrington, F. E., Bex, F. J., Elton, R. L., Roach, J. B. 1970. The ovulatory effects of follicle-stimulating hormone treated with chymotrypsin in chlorpromazine blocked rats. *Acta Endocrinol. Copenhagen* 65: 222–28

84. Harris, G. W., Ruf, K. B. 1970. Luteinizing hormone releasing factor in rat hypophysial portal blood collected during electrical stimulation of the hypothalamus. *J. Physiol. London* 208:243–50

85. Hellema, M. J. C. 1971. The chameleonic behavior of gonadotrophins: a review of recent results on their physicochemical properties and molecular structure. *J. Endocrinol.* 49: 393–402

86. Hendricks, D. M., Dickey, J. F., Niswender, G. D. 1970. Serum luteinizing hormone and plasma progesterone levels during the estrous cycle and early pregnancy in cows. *Biol. Reprod.* 2:346–51

87. Henzl, M. R., Segre, E. J. 1970. Physiology of human menstrual cycle and early pregnancy. A review of recent investigations. *Contraception* 1:315–38

88. Hermier, C., De La Llosa, P., Jutisz, M. 1970. Effect of urea and guanidine hydrochloride on the biological activity of ovine follicle–stimulating hormone (FSH). *Endocrinology* 87:1364–67

89. Hilliard, J., Schally, A. V., Sawyer, C. H. 1971. Progesterone blockade of the ovulatory response to intrapituitary infusion of LH-RH in rabbits. *Endocrinology* 88:730–36

90. Hoffmann, J. C. 1969. Light and reproduction in the rat: effect of lighting schedule on ovulation blockade. *Biol. Reprod.* 1:185–88

91. Hoffmann, J. C. 1970. Light and reproduction in the rat: effects of photoperiod length on albino rats from two different breeders. *Biol. Reprod.* 2:255–61

92. Hoffmann, J. C., Pomerantz, D. K. 1971. Effect of pinealectomy on photoperiodic control of estrous cycle length in the rat. *Fed. Proc.* 30:363 (Abstr.)

93. Holsinger, J. W., Jr., Everett, J. W. 1970. Thresholds to preoptic stimulation at varying times in the rat estrous cycle. *Endocrinology* 86: 251–56

94. Holsinger, J. W., Jr., Everett, J. W. 1970. Ovarian thresholds to exogenous LH at varying times of the rat estrous cycle. *Endocrinology* 86: 257–60

95. Hopper, B., Tullner, W. W. 1970. Urinary estrone and plasma progesterone levels during the menstrual cycle of the rhesus monkey. *Endocrinology* 86:1225–30

96. Hyyppa, M., Motto, M., Martini, L. 1971. "Ultrashort" feedback control of follicle-stimulating hormone-releasing factor secretion. *Neuroendocrinology* 7:227–35

97. Jones, E. E., Nalbandov, A. V. 1971. Local induction of ovulation and luteinization in the rabbit. *Endocrine Soc., Program 53rd Meet.* p. A–150

98. Kaasjager, W. A., Woodbury, D. M., van Dieten, J. A. M. J., van Rees, G. P. 1971. The role played by the preoptic region and the hypothalamus in spontaneous ovulation and ovulation induced by progesterone. *Neuroendocrinology* 7:54–64

99. Kalra, P. 1971. Involvement of norepinephrine in transmission of the stimulatory influence of progesterone on gonadotropin release. *Endocrine Soc., Program 53rd Meet.* p. A–78

100. Kalra, S. P. et al 1971. Effects of hypothalamic and preoptic electrochemical stimulation on gonadotropin and prolactin release in proestrous rats. *Endocrinology* 88:1150–58

101. Kalra, S. P., Velasco, M. E., Sawyer, C. H. 1970. Influences of hypothalamic deafferentation on pituitary FSH release and estrogen feedback in immature female parabiotic rats. *Neuroendocrinology* 6:228–35

102. Kamberi, I. A., Mical, R. S., Porter, J. C. 1969. LH-releasing activity in hypophysial stalk blood and elevation by dopamine. *Science* 166:388–90

103. Kamberi, I. A., Mical, R. S., Porter, J. C. 1970. Effect of anterior pituitary perfusion and intraventricular injection of catecholamines and indoleamines on LH release. *Endocrinology* 87:1–12

104. Kamberi, I. A., Mical, R. S., Porter, J. C. 1970. Prolactin inhibiting activity in hypophysial stalk blood-elevation by dopamine. *Experientia* 26:1150–51

105. Kamberi, I. A., Mical, R. S., Porter, J. C. 1970. Follicle stimulating hormone releasing activity in hypophysial portal blood and elevation by dopamine. *Nature London* 227:714–15

106. Kamberi, I. A., Mical, R. S., Porter, J. C. 1971. Effect of anterior pituitary perfusion and intraventricular injection of catecholamines on FSH release. *Endocrinology* 88:1003–11

107. Kamberi, I. A., Mical, R. S., Porter, J. C. 1971. Effect of anterior pituitary perfusion and intraventricular injection of catecholamines on prolactin release. *Endocrinology* 88:1012–20

108. Kamberi, I. A., Mical, R. S., Porter, J. C. 1971. Effects of melatonin and serotonin on the release of FSH and prolaction. *Endocrinology* 88:1288–93

109. Kamberi, I. A., Schneider, H. P. G., McCann, S. M. 1970. Action of dopamine to induce release of FSH-releasing factor (FRF) from hypothalamic tissue *in vitro. Endocrinology* 86:278–84

110. Karsch, F. J. et al 1971. Positive and negative feedback control, by estrogen, of luteinizing hormone (LH) secretion in primates. *Fed. Proc.* 30:254

111. Karsch, F. J., Noveroske, J. W., Roche, J. F., Norton, H. W., Nalbandov, A. V. 1970. Maintenance of ovine corpora lutea in the absence of ovarian follicles. *Endocrinology* 87:1228–36

112. Kato, J. 1970. *In vitro* uptake of tritiated oestradiol by the rat anterior hypothalamus during the oestrous cycle. *Acta Endocrinol.* 63:577–84

113. Kawakami, M., Terasawa, E. 1970. Effect of electrical stimulation of the brain on ovulation during estrous cycle in the rats. *Endocrinol. Jap.* 17:7–13

114. Kawakami, M., Terasawa, E., Ibuki, T. 1970. Changes in multiple unit activity of the brain during the estrous cycle *Neuroendocrinology* 6:30–48

115. Kingsley, T. R., Bogdanove, E. M. 1971. Direct androgen-pituitary feedback. *Fed. Proc.* 30:253

116. Kinson, G. A., Peat, F. 1971. The influences of illumination, melatonin and pinealectomy on testicular function in the rat. *Life Sci.* 10:259–70

117. Kinson, G. A., Robinson, S. 1970. Gonadal function of immature male rats subjected to light restriction, melatonin administration and removal of the pineal gland. *J. Endocrinol.* 47:391–92

118. Klein, D. C., Weller, J. L. 1970. Indole metabolism in the pineal gland: a circadian rhythm in N-acetyltransferase. *Science* 169:1093–95

119. Kobayashi, F., Hara, K., Miyake, T. 1970. Facilitation of luteinizing hormone release by progesterone in proestrous rat. *Endocrinol. Jap.* 17:149–55

120. Kordon, C. 1971. Blockade of ovulation in the immature rat by local microinjection of alpha-methyl dopa into the arcuate region of the hypothalamus. *Neuroendocrinology* 7:202–9

121. Koves, K., Halasz, B. 1969. Data on location of the neural structures indispensable for the occurrence of ovarian compensatory hypertrophy. *Neuroendocrinology* 4:1–11

122. Koves, K., Halasz, B. 1970. Location of the neural structures triggering ovulation in the rat. *Neuroendocrinology* 6:180–93

123. Kraicer, P. F., Strauss, J. F., III 1970. Ovulation block produced by an inhibition of luteotrophin, ergocornine. *Acta Endocrinol. Copenhagen* 65:698–706

124. Kuel, F. A., Jr., Patanelli, D. J., Tarnoff, J., Humes, J. L. 1970. Testicular adenyl cyclase: stimulation by the pituitary gonadotrophins. *Biol. Reprod.* 2:154–63

125. Labhsetwar, A. P. 1970. Role of estrogens in ovulation: a study using the estrogen-antagonist, I.C.I. 46,474. *Endocrinology* 87:542–51

126. Labhsetwar, A. P. 1971. Effects of serotonin on spontaneous ovulation in rats. *Nature London* 229:203

127. Lawton, I. E., Sawyer, C. H. 1970. Role of amygdala in regulating LH secretion in the adult female rat. *Am. J. Physiol.* 218:622–26

128. Leavitt, W. W., Blaha, G. C. 1970.

Circulating progesterone levels in the golden hamster during the estrous cycle, pregnancy, and lactation. *Biol. Reprod.* 3:353–61

129. Lee, C., Jacobson, I. 1971. Uterine estrogen receptor in rats during pubescence and the estrous cycle. *Endocrinology* 88:596–601

130. Li, C. H., Dixon, J. S., Lo, T.-B., Schmidt, K. D., Pankov, Y. A. 1970. Studies on pituitary lactogenic hormone. XXX. The primary structure of the sheep hormone. *Arch. Biochem. Biophys.* 141:705–37

131. Liao, T.-H., Pierce, J. G. 1970. The presence of a common type of subunit in bovine thyroid-stimulating and luteinizing hormones. *J. Biol. Chem.* 245:3275–81

132. Liao, T.-H., Pierce, J. G. 1971. The primary structure of bovine thyrotropin. II. The amino acid sequences of the reduced, S-carboxymethyl α and β chains. *J. Biol. Chem.* 246: 850–65

133. Lipner, H. 1971. Ovulation from histamine depleted ovaries. *Proc. Soc. Exp. Biol. Med.* 136:111–14

134. Lipner H., Greep, R. O. 1971. Inhibition of steroidogenesis at various sites in the biosynthetic pathway in relation to induced ovulation. *Endocrinology* 88:602–17

135. Lipner, H., Wendelken, L. 1971. Inhibition of ovulation by inhibition of steroidogenesis in immature rats. *Proc. Soc. Exp. Biol. Med.* 136: 1141–45

136. Liu, T.-C., Gorski, J. 1971. Free cell suspensions from ovarian tissue: preparation and stereoidogenic response to gonadotropins. *Endocrinology* 88:419–26

137. Liu, W.-K., Sweeney, C. M., Nahm, H. S., Holcomb, G. N., Ward, D. N. 1970. The amino acid sequence of the S-carboxymethylated ovine luteinizing hormone A-subunit. *Res. Commun. Chem. Pathol. Pharmacol.* 1:463–70

138. Lostroh, A. J. 1971. Induction of ovulation with 20 α-OH-progesterone in the hypophysectomized rat. *Fed. Proc.* 30:595

139. Lostroh, A. J., Johnson, R. E. 1966. Amounts of interstitial-cell-stimulating hormone and follicle stimulating hormone required for follicular development, uterine growth and ovulation in the hypophysectomized rat. *Endocrinology* 79:991–96

140. Lu, K.-H., Amenomori, Y., Chen, C.-L., Meites, J. 1970. Effects of central acting drugs on serum and pituitary prolactin levels in rats. *Endocrinology* 87:667–72

141. Lukaszewska, J. H., Greenwald, G. S. 1970. Progesterone levels in the cyclic and pregnant hamster. *Endocrinology* 86:1–9

142. Lukaszewska, J. H., Hansel, W. 1970. Extraction and partial purification of luteolytic activity from bovine endometrial tissue. *Endocrinology* 86:261–70

143. Lynch, H. J., Ralph, C. L. 1970. Diurnal variation in pineal melatonin and its non-relationship to HIOMT activity. *Am. Zool.* 10:300

144. Macdonald, G. J. 1971. Effect of FSH, prolactin and LH on serum progesterone levels in the cycling primate. *Fed. Proc.* 30:309

145. Macdonald, G. J., Tashjian, A. H., Jr., Greep, R. O. 1970. Influence of exogenous gonadotropins, antibody formation, and hysterectomy on the duration of luteal function in hypophysectomized rats. *Biol. Reprod.* 2:202–8

146. Macdonald, G. J., Yoshinaga, K., Greep, R. O. 1971. Maintenance of luteal function in rats by rat prolactin. *Proc. Soc. Exp. Biol. Med.* 136:687–88

147. Madhwa Raj, H. G., Moudgal, N. R. 1970. Effect of anti-luteinizing hormone serum on ovulation of rats. *Nature London* 227:1344–45

148. Madhwa Raj, H. G., Moudgal, N. R. 1970. Hormonal control of gestation in the intact rat. *Endocrinology* 86: 874–89

149. Mallampati, R. S., Casida, L. E. 1970. Absence of ovarian compensatory hypertrophy after unilateral ovariectomy during the anestrous season in the ewe. *Proc. Soc. Exp. Biol. Med.* 134:237–40

150. Malven, P. V., Hoge, W. R. 1971. Effect of ergocornine on prolactin secretion by hypophysial homografts. *Endocrinology* 88:445–49

151. Matsuo, H., Baba, Y., Nair, R. M. G., Arimura, A., Schally, A. V. 1971. Structure of the porcine LH- and FSH-releasing hormone. I. The proposed amino acid sequence. *Biochem. Biophys., Res. Commun.* 43: 1334–39

152. McClintock, J. A., Schwartz, N. B. 1968. Changes in pituitary and plasma follicle-stimulating hormone

468   SCHWARTZ & McCORMACK

concentrations during the rat estrous cycle. *Endocrinology* 83:433–41

153. McCormack, C. E. 1971. Timing of ovulation in rats as influenced by the onset of continuous light (LL) or darkness (DD). *Fed. Proc.* 30:310

154. McCormack, C. E., Bennin, B. 1970. Delay of ovulation caused by exposure to continuous light in immature rats treated with pregnant mare's serum gonadotrophin. *Endocrinology* 86:611–19

155. McDonald, P. G., Gilmore, D. P. 1971. The effect of ovarian steroids on hypothalamic thresholds for ovulation in the female rat. *J. Endocrinol.* 49:421–29

156. Meyer, R. K., Karavolas, H. J., Klausing, M., Norgard, D. W. 1971. Blood progesterone and pregnenolone levels during phenobarbital (PB) block of PMS-induced ovulation in immature rats. *Endocrinology* 88:983–90

157. Mills, T. M., Davies, P. J. A., Savard, K. 1971. Stimulation of estrogen synthesis in rabbit follicles by luteinizing hormone. *Endocrinology* 88:857–62

158. Mitchell, J. A., Yochim, J. M. 1970. Influence of environmental lighting on duration of pregnancy in the rat. *Endocrinology* 87:472–80

159. Monastirsky, R., Laurence, K. A., Tovar, E. 1971. The effects of gonadotropin immunization of prepubertal rabbits on gonadal development. *Fert. Steril.* 22:318–24

160. Monroe, S. E., Atkinson, L. E., Knobil, E. 1970. Patterns of circulating luteinizing hormone and their relation to plasma progesterone levels during the menstrual cycle of the rhesus monkey. *Endocrinology* 87:453–55

161. Morgan, F. J., Canfield, R. E. 1971. Nature of the subunits of human chorionic gonadotropin. *Endocrinology* 88:1045–53

162. Mori, K. F. 1970. Antigenic structure of human gonadotropins: importance of protein moiety to the antigenic structure of human chorionic gonadotropin. *Endocrinology* 86:97–106

163. Mori, K. F. 1970. Antigenic structure of human gonadotrophins: pituitary luteinizing hormone. *J. Endocrinol.* 46:517–25

164. Moudgal, N. R., Macdonald, G. J.,

Greep, R. O. 1971. Effect of HCG antiserum on ovulation and corpus luteum formation in the monkey (Macaca fasicularis). *J. Clin. Endocrinol. Metab.* 32:579–81

165. Nakane, P. K. 1970. Classification of anterior pituitary cell types with immunoenzyme histochemistry. *J. Histochem. Cytochem.* 18:9–20

166. Nalbandov, A. V. 1970. First Annual Carl G. Hartmann Lecture: Comparative aspects of corpus luteum function. *Biol. Reprod.* 2:7–13

167. Negro-Vilar, A., Sar, M., Meites, J. 1970. Changes in hypothalamic FSH-RF and pituitary FSH during the estrous cycle of rats. *Endocrinology* 87:1091–93

168. Neill, J. D. 1970. Effect of "stress" on serum prolactin and luteinizing hormone levels during the estrous cycle of the rat. *Endocrinology* 87:1192–97

169. Neill, J. D., Freeman, M. E., Tillson, S. A. 1971. Control of the proestrus "surge" of prolactin and LH secretion by estrogens in the rat. *Fed. Proc.* 30:474

170. Neill, J. D., Reichert, L. E., Jr. 1971. Development of a radioimmunoassay for rat prolactin and evaluation of the NIAMD rat prolactin radioimmunoassay. *Endocrinology* 88:548–55

171. Nequin, L. G., Schwartz, N. B. 1971. Adrenal participation in the timing of mating and LH release in the cyclic rat. *Endocrinology* 88:325–31

172. Nikitovitch-Winer, M., Everett, J. W. 1958. Comparative study of luteotropin secretion by hypophysial autotransplants in the rat. Effects of site and stages of estrus cycle. *Endocrinology* 62:522–32

173. Odell, W. D., Moyer, D. L. 1971. *Physiology of Reproduction*, St. Louis: C. V. Mosby

174. Orth, D. N., Island, D. P. 1969. Light sychronization of the circadian rhythm in plasma cortisol (17-OHCS) concentration in man. *J. Clin. Endocrinol.* 29:479–86

175. Papkoff, H., Ekblad, M. 1970. Ovine follicle-stimulating hormone: preparation and characterization of its subunits. *Biochem. Biophys. Res. Commun.* 40:614–21

176. Papkoff, H., Gan, J. 1970. Bovine interstitial cell-stimulating hormone: purification and properties. *Arch. Biochem. Biophys.* 136:522–28

177. Parlow, A. F. 1970. Biologic detection

of FSH in unconcentrated serum of intact male mice and the unexpected effects of orchidectomy on FSH and LH. *Endocrinology* 87: 271–75

178. Parlow, A. F., Hendrich, C. E. 1970. Peculiar gonadotropin profile of the adult guinea pig pituitary and its response to gonadectomy. *Endocrinology* 87:444–48

179. Peppler, R. D., Greenwald, G. S. 1970. Influence of unilateral ovariectomy on follicular development in cycling rats. *Am. J. Anat.* 127:9–14

180. Pierce, J. G., Liao, T.-H., Carlsen, R. B., Reimo, T. 1971. Comparisons between the α chain of bovine thyrotropin and the CI chain of luteinizing hormone. *J. Biol. Chem.* 246:866–72

181. Printz, R. H., Greenwald, G. S. 1970. Effects of starvation on follicular development in the cyclic hamster. *Endocrinology* 86:290–95

182. Printz, R. H., Greenwald, G. S. 1971. A neural mechanism regulating follicular development in the hamster. *Neuroendocrinology* 7:171–82

183. Przekop, F., Domanski, E. 1970. Induction of ovulation in sheep by electrical stimulation of hypothalamic regions. *J. Endocrinol.* 46:305–11

184. Quinn, D. L. 1970. Hypothalamic mechanisms involved in the control of gonadotropic hormone secretion in the guinea pig: Evidence of elevated brain thresholds to electrical stimulation in the medial preoptic-anterior hypothalamic region during "early" diestrus. *Endocrinology* 87:343–49

185. Ralph, C. L., Lynch, H. J. 1970. A quantitative melatonin bioassay. *Gen. Comp. Endocrinol.* 15:334–38

186. Ralph, C. L., Mull, D., Lynch, H. J. 1970. Locomotor activity rhythms of rats under constant conditions as predictors of melatonin content of their pineals. *Am. Zool.* 10:302

187. Rathnam, P., Saxena, B. B. 1970. Isolation and physicochemical characterization of luteinizing hormone from human pituitary glands. *J. Biol. Chem.* 245:3725–31

188. Raud, H. R., Kiddy, C. A., Odell, W. D. 1971. The effect of stress upon the determination of serum prolactin by radioimmunoassay. *Proc. Soc. Exp. Biol. Med.* 136:689–93

189. Raziano, J., Cowchock, S., Ferin, M., Vande Wiele, R. L. 1971. Estrogen dependency of monamine-induced ovulation. *Endocrinology* 88:1516–18

190. Reeves, J. J., Arimura, A., Schally, A. V. 1970. Serum levels of prolactin and luteinizing hormone (LH) in the ewe at various stages of the estrous cycle. *Proc. Soc. Exp. Biol. Med.* 134:938–42

191. Reichert, L. E., Jr. 1971. Electrophoretic properties of pituitary gonadotropins as studies by electrofocusing. *Endocrinology* 88:1029–44

192. Reichert, L. E., Jr., Midgley, A. R., Jr., Niswender, G. D., Ward, D. N. 1970. Formation of a hybrid molecule from subunits of human and bovine luteinizing hormone. *Endocrinology* 87:534–41

193. Reichert, L. E., Jr., Rasco, M. A., Ward, D. N., Niswender, G. D., Midgley, A. R., Jr. 1969. Isolation and properties of subunits of bovine pituitary luteinizing hormone. *J. Biol Chem.* 244:5110–17

194. Reiter, R. J., Ellison, N. M. 1970. Delayed puberty in blinded anosmic female rats: role of the pineal gland. *Biol. Reprod.* 2:216–22

195. Reiter, R., Sorrentino, S., Jr., Ellison, N. 1970. Interaction of photic and olfactory stimuli in mediating pineal-induced gonadal regression in adult female rats. *Gen. Comp. Endocrinol.* 15:326–33

196. Reiter, R. J., Sorrentino, S., Jr., Hoffman, R. A. 1970. Early photoperiodic conditions and pineal antigonadal function in male hamsters. *Int. J. Fert.* 15:163–70

197. Reiter, R. J., Sorrentino, S., Jr., Ralph, C. L., Lynch, H. J., Mull, D., Jarrow, E. 1971. Some endocrine effects of blinding and anosmia in adult male rats with observations on pineal melatonin. *Endocrinology* 88:895–900

198. Relkin, R. 1971. Relative efficiency of pinealectomy, hypothalamic and amygdaloid lesions in advancing puberty. *Endocrinology* 88:415–18

199. Relkin, R. 1971. Absence of alteration in puberal onset in male rats following amygdaloid lesioning. *Endocrinology* 88:1272–74

200. Rennels, E. G., Bogdanove, E. M., Arimura, A., Saito, M., Schally, A. V. 1971. Ultrastructural observations of rat pituitary gonadotrophs following injection of purified por-

cine LH-RH. *Endocrinology* 88: 1318–26

201. Robson, J. M., Sullivan, F. M., Wilson, C. 1970. The effect of 5-hydroxytryptamine on ovulation in rats. *J. Endocrinol.* 48:1 xiii

202. Roche, J. F., Foster, D. L., Karsch, F. J., Cook, B., Dziuk, P. J. 1970. Levels of luteinizing hormone in sera and pituitaries of ewes during the estrous cycle and anestrus. *Endocrinology* 86:568–72

203. Roche, J. F., Foster, D. L., Karsch, F. J., Dziuk, P. J. 1970. Effect of castration and infusion of melatonin on levels of luteinizing hormone in sera and pituitaries of ewes. *Endocrinology* 87:1205–10

204. Rodgers, C. H. 1971. Influence of copulation on ovulation in the cycling rat. *Endocrinology* 88:433–36

205. Rondell, P. 1970. Biophysical aspects of ovulation. *Biol. Reprod.* Suppl. 2:64–89

206. Rondell, P. 1970. Follicular processes in ovulation. *Fed. Proc.* 29:1875–79

207. Rosemberg, E. (ed.) 1968. *Gonadotropins 1968.* Los Altos, Calif.: Geron-X, Inc.

208. Rosen, S. W., Weintraub, B. D. 1971. Monotropic increase of serum FSH correlated with low sperm count in young men with idiopathic oligospermia and aspermia. *J. Clin. Endocrinol. Metab.* 32:410–16

209. Ross, G. T. et al 1970. Pituitary and gonadal hormones in women during spontaneous and induced ovulatory cycles. *Rec. Progr. Horm. Res.* 26:1–62

210. Rothchild, I. 1965. Interrelations between progesterone and the ovary, pituitary, and central nervous system in the control of ovulation and the regulation of progesterone secretion. *Vitam. Horm. New York* 23: 209–37

211. Rubenstein, L., Sawyer, C. H. 1970. Role of catecholamines in stimulating the release of pituitary ovulating hormones in rats. *Endocrinology* 86:988–95

212. Samy, T. S. A., Papkoff, H., Li, C. H. 1969. The reaction of cyanogen bromide with an ovine ICSH subunit: the sequence of the NH$_2$ terminal forty amino acids. *Arch. Biochem. Biophys.* 132:315–324

213. Sawyer, C. H. 1970. Electrophysiological correlates of release of pituitary ovulating hormones. *Fed. Proc.* 29:1895–99

214. Scaramuzzi, R. J., Caldwell, B. V., Moor, R. M. 1970. Radioimmunoassay of LH and estrogen during the estrous cycle of the ewe. *Biol. Reprod.* 3:110–19

215. Schally, A. V. et al 1971. Purification and properties of the LH and FSH-releasing hormone from porcine hypothalami. *Endocrine Soc., Program 53rd Meet.* p. A–70

216. Schneider, H. P. G., McCann, S. M. 1969. Possible role of dopamine as transmitter to promote discharge of LH-releasing factor. *Endocrinology* 85:121–32

217. Schneider, H. P. G., McCann, S. M. 1970. Luteinizing hormone–releasing factor discharged by dopamine in rats. *J. Endocrinol.* 46:401–2

218. Schneider, H. P. G., McCann, S. M. 1970. Mono- and indolamines and control of LH secretion. *Endocrinology* 86:1127–33

219. Schneider, H. P. G., McCann, S. M. 1970. Evidence of LH-releasing factor (LRF) into the peripheral circulation of hypophysectomized rats by dopamine and its blockage by estradiol. *Endocrinology* 87:249–53

220. Schneider, H. P. G., McCann, S. M. 1970. Estradiol and the neuroendocrine control of LH release *in vitro*. *Endocrinology* 87:330–38

221. Schwartz, N. B. 1969. A model for the regulation of ovulation in the rat. *Rec. Progr. Horm. Res.* 25: 1–55

222. Schwartz, N. B. 1970. Control of rhythmic secretion of gonadotrophins In: *The Hypothalamus*, ed. L. Martini, M. Motta, F. Fraschini, 515–28. New York: Academic

223. Schwartz, N. B., Ely, C. A. 1970. Comparison of effects of hypophysectomy, antiserum to ovine LH, and ovariectomy on estrogen secretion during the rat estrous cycle. *Endocrinology* 86:1420–35

224. Schwartz, N. B., Krone, K., Ely, C. A. 1971. Antiserum to sheep FSH on rat estrous cycle. *Endocrine Soc., Program 53rd Meet.* p. A–79

225. Schwartz, N. B., Waltz, P. 1970. Role of ovulation in the regulation of the estrous cycle. *Fed. Proc.* 29:1907–12

226. Sherwood, O. D., Grimek, H. J., McShan, W. H. 1970. Purification and properties of follicle-stimulating hormone from sheep pituitary glands. *J. Biol. Chem.* 245:2328–36

227. Sherwood, O. D., Grimek, H. J., McShan, W. H. 1971. Purification of luteinizing hormone from sheep

pituitary glands and evidence for several physicochemically distinguishable active components. *Bio-chem. Biophys. Acta* 221:87–106

228. Shin, S., Fawcett, C. P. 1971. Biochemical properties of LRF and FRF. *Endocrine Soc., Program 53rd Meet.* p. A–70

229. Shirley, B., Wolinsky, J., Schwartz, N. B. 1968. Effects of a single injection of an estrogen antagonist on the estrous cycle of the rat. *Endocrinology* 82:959–68

230. Smith, I. D., Bassett, J. M., Williams, T. 1970. Progesterone concentrations in the peripheral plasma of the mare during the estrous cycle. *J. Endocrinol.* 47:523–24

231. Snook, R. B., Saatman, R. R., Hansel, W. 1971. Serum progesterone and luteinizing hormone levels during the bovine estrous cycle. *Endocrinology* 88:678–86

232. Sorrentino, S., Jr., Benson, B. 1970. Effect of blinding and pinealectomy on the reproductive organs of adult male and female rats. *Gen. Comp. Endocrinol.* 15:242–46

233. Sorrentino, S., Jr., Reiter, R. J. 1970. Pineal-induced alteration of estrous cycles in blinded hamsters. *Gen. Comp. Endocrinol.* 15:39–42

234. Spies, H. G., Niswender, G. D. 1971. Blockade of the surge of preovulatory serum luteinizing hormone and ovulation with exogenous progesterone in cycling Rhesus (Macaca mulatta) monkeys. *J. Clin. Endocrinol. Metab.* 32:309–16

235. Spies, H. G., Niswender, G. D. 1971. Levels of prolactin, LH and FSH in the serum of intact and pelvic-neurectomized rats. *Endocrinology* 88:937–43

236. Steinberger, A., Chowdhury, M. 1971. LH and FSH production in clone cultures of rat anterior pituitary cells. *Endocrine Soc., Program 53rd Meet.* p. A–74

237. Steinberger, E. 1971. Hormonal control of mammalian spermatogenesis *Physiol. Rev.* 51:1–22

238. Stern, J. M., Eisenfeld, A. J. 1971. Distribution and metabolism of ³H-testosterone in castrated male rats; effects of cyproterone, progesterone and unlabeled testosterone. *Endocrinology* 88:1117–25

239. Stevens, V. C., Sparks, S. J., Powell, J. E. 1970. Levels of estrogens, progestogens and luteinizing hormone during the menstrual cycle of the baboon. *Endocrinology* 87:658–66

240. Strauss, W. F. 1964. *Neural timing of ovulation in immature rats treated with gonadotrophin.* PhD thesis. Univ. Wisconsin, Madison. 163 pp.

241. Swaminathan, N., Bahl, O. P. 1970. Dissociation and recombination of the subunits of human chorionic gonadotropin. *Biochem. Biophys. Res. Commun.* 40:422–27

242. Swerdloff, R. S., Walsh, P. C., Jacobs, H. S., Odell, W. D. 1971. Serum LH and FSH during sexual maturation in the male rat: effect of castration and cryptorchidism. *Endocrinology* 88:120–28

243. Swyer, G. I. M., Ed. 1970. Control of human fertility. *Brit. Med. Bull.* 26:1

244. Szego, C. M. 1965. Role of histamine in mediation of hormone action. *Fed. Proc.* 24:1343–52

245. Taleisnik, S., Caligaris, L., Astrada, J. J. 1970. Positive feedback of progesterone on the release of FSH and the influence of sex in rats. *J. Reprod. Fert.* 22:89–98

246. Taleisnik, S., Velasco, M. E., Astrada, J. J. 1970. Effect of hypothalamic deafferentation on the control of luteinizing hormone secretion. *J. Endocrinol.* 46:1–7

247. Tulchinsky, D., Korenman, S. G. 1970. A radio-ligand assay for plasma estrone; normal values and variations during the menstrual cycle. *J. Clin. Endocrinol. Metab.* 31:76–80

248. Uchida, K., Kadowaki, M., Miyake, T. 1970. Further studies on the effect of exogenous progesterone and related compounds on the preovulatory progesterone secretion in the rat. *Endocrinol. Jap.* 17:99–106

249. Vaitukaitis, J. L., Bermudez, J. A., Cargille, C. M., Lipsett, M. B., Ross, G. T. 1971. New evidence for an anti-estrogenic action of clomiphene citrate in women. *J. Clin. Endocrinol. Metab.* 32:503

250. Vande Wiele, R. L. et al 1970. Mechanisms regulating the menstrual cycle in women. *Rec. Progr. Horm. Res.* 26:63–103

251. Van Hall, E. V., Vaitukaitis, J. L., Ross, G. T., Hickman, J. W., Ashwell, G. 1971. Immunological and biological activity of HCG following progressive desialylation. *Endocrinology* 88:456–64

252. Velasco, M. E., Taleisnik, S. 1969. Re-

lease of gonadotropins induced by amygdaloid stimulation in the rat. *Endocrinology* 84:132–39

253. Velasco, M. E., Taleisnik, S. 1969. Effect of hippocampal stimulation on the release of gonadotropin. *Endocrinology* 85:1154–59

254. Virutamasen, P., Hickok, R. L., Wallach, E. E. 1971. Local ovarian effects of catecholamines on human chorionic gonadotrophin-induced ovulation in the rabbit. *Fert. Steril.* 22:235–43

255. Wakabayashi, K., McCann, S. M. 1970. *In vitro* responses of anterior pituitary glands from normal, castrated and androgen-treated male rats to LH-releasing factor (LRF) and high potassium medium. *Endocrinology* 87:771–78

256. Wallach, E. E., Root, A. W., Garcia, C. R. 1970. Serum gonadotrophin responses to estrogen and progestogen in recently castrated human females. *J. Clin. Endocrinol. Metab.* 31:376–81

257. Weick, R. F., Davidson, J. M. 1970. Localization of the stimulatory feedback effect of estrogen on ovulation in the rat. *Endocrinology* 87:693–700

258. Weick, R. F., Smith, E. R., Dominguez, R., Dhariwal, A. P. S., Davidson, J. M. 1971. Mechanism of stimulatory feedback effect of estradiol benzoate on the pituitary. *Endocrinology* 88:293–301

259. Williams-Ashman, H. G., Reddi, A. H. 1971. Actions of vertebrate sex hormones. *Ann. Rev. Physiol.* 33:31–82

260. Wilson, L., Jr., Butcher, R. L., Inskeep, E. K. 1970. Studies on the relation of decidual cell response to luteal maintenance in the pseudopregnant rat. *Biol. Reprod.* 3:342–46

261. Wright, P. A. 1961. Induction of ovulation *in vitro* in *Rana pipiens* with steroids. *Gen. Comp. Endocrinol.* 1:20–23

262. Wright, P. A. 1970. Activity of 3β-hydroxysteroid dehydrogenase in *Rana pipiens in vitro. Am. Zool.* 10:493

263. Wurtman, R. J. 1964. An effect of luteinizing hormone on the fractional perfusion of the rat ovary. *Endocrinology* 75:927–933

264. Wurtman, R. J. 1971. Brain monoamines and endocrine function. *Neurosci. Res. Program Bull.* 9:172–297

265. Wuttke, W., Cassell, E., Meites, J. 1971. Effects of ergocornine on serum prolactin and LH, and on hypothalamic content of PIF and LRF. *Endocrinology* 88:737–41

266. Wuttke, W., Meites, J. 1970. Effects of ether and pentobarbital on serum prolactin and LH levels in proestrous rats. *Proc. Soc. Exp. Biol. Med.* 135:648–52

267. Wuttke, W., Meites, J. 1971. Luteolytic role of prolactin during estrous cycle of the rat. *Endocrine Soc., Program 53rd Meet.* p. A–121

268. Yamamoto, M., Diebel, N. D., Bogdanove, E. M. 1970. Analysis of initial and delayed effects of orchidectomy and ovariectomy on pituitary and serum LH levels in adult and immature rats. *Endocrinology* 86:1102–11

269. Yamamoto, M., Diebel, N. D., Bogdanove, E. M. 1970. Radioimmunoassay of serum and pituitary LH and FSH levels in intact male rats and of serum and pituitary LH in castrated rats of both sexes—apparent absence of diurnal rhythms. *Endocrinology* 87:798–806

270. Yates, F. E., Russell, S. M., Maran, J. W. 1971. Brain-adenohypophysial communication in mammals. *Ann. Rev. Physiol.* 33:393–444

271. Yochim, J. M., Mitchell, J. A. 1970. Influence of environmental lighting on decidualization in the rat. *Endocrinology* 87:465–71

272. Yokoe, Y., Irby, D. C., Hall, P. F. 1971. Testicular phospholipids. III: Site of action of ICSH in testis following regression of the germinal epithelium. *Endocrinology* 88:195–205

273. Yoshinaga, K., Moudgal, N. R., Greep, R. O. 1971. Progestin secretion by the ovary in lactating rats: effect of LH-antiserum, LH and prolactin. *Endocrinology* 88:1126–30

SOME RELATED ARTICLES APPEARING
IN OTHER *ANNUAL REVIEWS*

From the *Annual Review of Biochemistry*, Volume 41 (1972)
  Prostaglandins, *J. W. Hinman*
  Membrane Transport, *D. L. Oxender*
  Chemistry of Muscle Contraction, *E. W. Taylor*
  Phospholipid Metabolism, *W. C. McMurray and W. L. Magee*

From the *Annual Review of Biophysics and Bioengineering*, Volume 1 (1972)
  Monitoring of Physiological Data in a Clinical Environment, *R. M. Gardner*
  Active Transport of Calcium Ion in Sarcoplasmic Membranes, *G. Inesi*
  Plasticity of Biological Membranes, *C. Gitler*
  The Mechanism of Signal Transmission in Nerve Axons, *G. Ehrenstein and H. Lecar*
  The Visual Process, *W. A. Hagins*

From the *Annual Review of Entomology*, Volume 17 (1972)
  Learning and Memory in Insects, *Thomas M. Alloway*
  Comparative Anatomy of the Tracheal System, *Joan M. Whitten*
  Environmental and Physiological Control of Sex Determination and Differentiation, *Joseph Bergerard*

From the *Annual Review of Genetics*, Volume 6 (1972)
  Thymic Regulation of Immunological Differentiation, *M. Schlessinger*
  Molecular Basis of Hemoglobin Disease, *G. Stamatoyannopoulos*

From the *Annual Review of Medicine*, Volume 23 (1972)
  Pulmonary Involvement in Hypovolemic Shock, *G. S. Moss*
  Biochemical and Cellular Changes in Cardiac Hypertrophy, *M. Rabinowitz and R. Zak*
  Chemical Mediation of Hormone Action, *M. W. Bitensky and R. E. Gorman*
  Thermal Control in Premature Infants, *J. C. Sinclair*
  Biogenic Amines and Behavior, *R. Baldessarini*

From the *Annual Review of Pharmacology*, Volume 12 (1972)
  Vasoactive Peptides, *C. G. Huggins and G. E. Sander*
  Isolation of Acetylcholine Receptors, *R. D. O'Brien, M. E. Eldefrawi and A. T. Eldefrawi*
  Transport and Storage of Biogenic Amines, *P. A. Shore*
  Adrenergic Receptors, *D. Triggle*
  Prostaglandins, *J. R. Weeks*

AUTHOR INDEX

A

Abbott, B. C., 63, 65
Abbrecht, P. H., 249
Abdelkader, A. B., 124
Abe, K., 197
Abe, Y., 279, 280
Abelmann, W. H., 78
Abraham, G. E., 447
Abrahamsson, H., 271, 272
Abrams, A., 129
Abrass, I. B., 411
Aceves, J., 162
Ackermann, U., 254
Adamopoulos, D. A., 392
Adamson, A. R., 251, 415
Adez, W. R., 222
Adler, N. T., 389, 390
Adlin, E. V., 418
Adomian, G. E., 59
Adrian, E. D., 340
Agostoni, E., 101, 102, 103, 104, 105, 272
Ahrén, K., 450
Akert, K., 301
Akin, A. N., 265
Akiyama, M., 124
Albe-Fessard, D., 326
Albert, A., 430, 432, 444
Albin, R., 122
Alcala, R., 98
Aldred, J. P., 247
Alexander, N., 40
Alexandre, J. M., 249, 250
Alison, S. S., 98
Allen, J. C., 56, 75
Alleva, F. R., 457, 459, 460, 461
Alleva, J. J., 457, 459, 460, 461
Allison, J. L., 40
Allman, J. M., 302
Alpert, J. S., 179
Altimirano, M., 353
Alvarado, R. H., 164
Amakawa, T., 155
Amar-Costesec, A., 127
Amatayakul, K., 430, 432, 444
Ambache, N., 273, 274
Amenomori, Y., 440, 451, 452
Amesz, J., 127
Amoss, M. S., Jr., 442
Anast, C., 247
Andersen, B., 162
Anderson, C. O., 399, 384

Anderson, F. D., 326, 327, 329, 330
Anderson, J. M., 127
Anderson, K. V., 301
Anderson, L. L., 426
Anderson, N. H., 395
Anderson, R., 415, 416
Andersson, B., 35, 239, 244, 248, 252, 253, 254
Anthonisen, N. R., 94
Anton, A. H., 79
Anton-Tay, F., 458
Antunes-Rodrigues, J., 244
Aoki, T., 126
Appelqvist, L. A., 119, 121
Aprison, M. H., 348, 350, 351, 352, 353, 364, 365
Apter, J. T., 301, 303
Araki, T., 339, 353, 364
Aras, M., 37
Arbrecht, P. H., 36
Ardaillou, R., 247
Arén-Engelbrektsson, B., 378
Argaman, M., 126
Argyris, J. H., 104
Arias, I. M., 122
Arimori, M., 264, 265
Arimura, A., 427, 429, 431, 432, 439, 446, 448
Ariyoshi, T., 120
Armett, C. J., 273
Armour, J. A., 60
Armstrong, D. T., 425, 426, 438, 439
Armstrong, J. J., 121
Arnaud, C., 247
Arnold, G., 65
Arntzen, C. J., 127
Aron, C., 377, 387
Aronson, H., 393
Arrighi, M. F., 159
Arsenis, C., 123
Asai, H., 128
Aschenbrenner, V., 48, 122
Ascher, P., 354
Aschoff, J., 459
Ashitaka, Y., 429, 434, 436
Ashwell, G., 434, 436
Assaykeen, T. A., 250
Astrada, J. J., 389, 443, 453, 454
Astruc, J., 306
Atanassova, E., 268, 283
Atkinson, L. E., 436, 442
Atwood, H. L., 353
Auger, R. G., 236

Auliac, P. B., 128
Aurucci, A., 209
Austen, W. G., 52
Austin, G. M., 355
Avasthey, P., 105
Avery, M. E., 99
Axelson, J., 272
Aynedjian, H. S., 37
Ayres, S. M., 29
Aziz, O., 237, 238
Azrin, N. H., 393

B

Baba, Y., 429, 431
Babushkin, V. I., 211
Bacchin, P., 120
Baden, H. P., 197
Baer, L., 36, 249, 417, 418
Baer, P. G., 38
Bahl, O. P., 435
Bailey, E., 122, 123
Bailey, L. E., 56
Bailie, M. D., 250
Bain, T., 102, 104
Bajusz, E., 54
Baker, B. L., 445
Baker, R., 345
Baker, R. D., 261
Balakhovskii, I. S., 224
Baldwin, J., 118
Balikian, H. M., 415
Balint, J. A., 124
Ballard, P. L., 121
Balslev, E., 297
Banchero, N., 29, 71, 212, 216
Bancroft, J. H. J., 393
Baniukiewicz, S., 415
Bank, N., 37
Bär, H. P., 409
Baratz, R. A., 236
Barber, V. C., 92
Barchas, J. D., 382
Barer, A. S., 208, 216, 217, 218, 224
Baretta, L., 123
Barker, J. L., 240, 241
Barlow, H. B., 304, 308
Barlow, N., 7
Barnard, C. N., 29
Barnes, C. D., 319
Baron, C., 129
Barr, L., 279
Barr, M. L., 211
Barr, P. O., 218, 219
Barraclough, C. A., 384, 447, 453, 456
Barrett, T. W., 292, 293, 294

475

AUTHOR INDEX

Garcia, C. R., 442, 447
Garcia-Romeu, F., 141-76; 143, 145, 147, 148, 149, 150, 155, 164, 165, 166, 167
Gargouil, Y. M., 281, 285
Garner, R. C., 123
Garnier, D., 281, 285
Garnier, J., 121
Garrahan, P. J., 150
Garren, L. D., 411, 412, 413
Gauer, O. H., 211, 215, 224, 235, 236, 237, 250
Gault, J. H., 66, 67, 74, 81
Gavrilovich, L., 33
Gay, V. L., 427, 430, 432, 440, 448, 460
Gaylor, J. L., 414
Gaze, R. M., 304, 305
Gazzaniga, M. S., 297
Gear, A. R. L., 119
Geelhaar, A., 92
Geis, W. P., 76
Gelfan, S., 365
Georgeson, M. A., 292
Gerall, A. A., 379, 384, 385
Gerner, E. W., 119
Gershon, M. D., 272, 273
Gersten, B. E., 445
Gertz, E. W., 55
Gessa, G. L., 382
Gest, H., 121
Getz, G. S., 117, 119, 122
Ghez, C., 324
Ghista, D. N., 79
Giannelli, S., Jr., 29
Giantonio, G. W., 379
Giberman, E., 126
Gibson, H., 39
Gilbert, R. D., 28
Gilchrist, J. C., 398
Gildenberg, P. L., 325
Giles, G. R., 265, 266
Gill, G. N., 411, 412
Gill, J. R., Jr., 34
Gillette, J. R., 123
Gilman, S., 323, 324
Gilmore, D. P., 446
Gilmore, J. P., 37, 245, 249
Ginsberg, S. T., 379, 386
Ginsburg, M., 240, 241
Giocomelli, F., 414
Giolli, R. A., 306, 307
Giordan, A., 154
Gispen, W. H., 397
Gisslen, J. L., 180
Gitelman, H. J., 242
Gjurstedt, H., 213
Glaister, D. H., 106, 214, 218, 220
Glaumann, H., 120, 127
Glazier, J. B., 93, 94, 96,

101, 105, 106, 216, 217
Glees, P., 345
Glick, G., 56, 75
Glick, M. C., 119, 121, 122, 123
Glynn, I. M., 150
Godfraind, J. M., 351, 353, 354, 355
Goetz, K. L., 37, 236, 244
Gold, H. K., 55
Goldberg, I., 118, 119
Goldberg, L. J., 344, 345, 346
Goldberg, M. E., 306, 307
Goldenberg, R. L., 426
Goldfien, A., 250
Goldfischer, S., 127
Goldfoot, D. A., 386
Goldman, B. D., 437, 442, 446, 447
Goldman, L., 399
Goldzieher, J. W., 443
Golenhofen, K., 270, 282, 283
Gondaira, T., 35
Gonzalez, N. C., 78
González-Cadavid, N. F., 121
Goodchild, D. J., 127
Goodenough, U. W., 121
Goodkind, M. J., 79
Goodman, A. H., 26
Goodman, J. R., 121
Goodwin, F. J., 415, 416
Gorbman, A., 386
Gordon, A. M., 63
Gordon, G., 322
Gordon, R. D., 250
Gordon, S., 127
Gordon, T. P., 397
Gorecki, D., 155
Gorlin, R., 48, 52
Gorski, J., 430, 433
Gorski, R. A., 380, 383, 384, 385, 453, 454, 455
Gorzalka, B. B., 378, 385
Gospodarowicz, D., 435, 436
Goy, R. W., 375, 376, 377, 382, 384, 385, 386, 390
Grace, W. J., 29
Graf, P. D., 97
Graham, L. T., 365
Graham, T. P., Jr., 81
Grahame-Smith, D. G., 410
Grahn, D., 230
Gram, T. E., 123
Granboulan, P., 127
Grandchamp, A., 415
Granger, H. J., 13-46; 27, 28, 31, 39
Granger, P., 38
Granit, R., 1-12; 1, 339, 346
Granschow, R., 122
Grant, G., 329, 330
Grass, M. F., III, 52

Gravenstein, J. S., 79
Gray, J. A., 375, 385, 395, 399
Gray, J. A. B., 273
Gray, J. L., 123
Gray, R. W., 123
Greaves, M. W., 194
Green, D. E., 117, 355
Green, H. D., 180
Green, H. H., 252
Green, I. D., 104
Green, M., 97
Green, R., 376, 379, 382, 383, 386
Green, W. E., 243
Greene, D. G., 66, 67, 68
Greenfield, A. D. M., 178
Greengard, P., 414
Greenspan, K., 75, 77
Greenwald, G. S., 438, 439, 444, 447, 454
Greep, R. O., 426, 428, 436, 437, 439, 440, 443
Grega, G. J., 180
Gregory, J. E., 270
Gregory, J. J., 29
Gregson, N. A., 122, 123
Grice, H., 194
Griffith, R. W., 153
Grill, G., 38
Grimek, H. J., 428, 429, 434, 436
Grimm, A. F., 48, 59
Grinnell, A. D., 345
Grivel, M. L., 275, 276, 282
Grodner, A. S., 77
Grofová, I., 379
Groot, G. S. P., 119
Gros, F., 127
Grossman, W., 70
Grosvenor, C. E., 379
Grove, D., 48
Grundfest, H., 339, 340, 343, 344, 353, 356, 357
Grüsser, O.-J., 291, 304, 308, 309
Grüsser-Cornehls, U., 291, 304, 308, 309
Guillery, R. W., 295
Guntheroth, W. G., 78
Guthrie, J. P., 121
Guthrie, M. D., 306, 307
Guyton, A. C., 13-46; 13, 20, 27, 28, 29, 30, 31, 32, 33, 34, 35, 36, 39
Gwei-Djen, L., 376
Gwyn, D. G., 325
Gyurjan, I., 121

H

Ha, H., 319, 321, 322, 325
Haber, E., 36, 249
Haberich, F. J., 237, 238
Haddock, J., 119

AUTHOR INDEX

493

Tremblay, G. Y., 127
Trendelenburg, P., 266
Trevarthen, C. B., 302
Trop, D., 98, 101
Truex, R. C., 325
Trump, B. F., 142, 154
Tsakiris, A. G., 29, 64, 65, 66, 71, 74, 212, 216
Tsuchiya, T., 353
Tsukui, R., 285
Tulchinsky, D., 447
Tullner, W. W., 447
Tuppy, H., 119
Turaids, T., 94
Turina, M., 80
Tyberg, J. V., 73
Tyler, W. S., 91

U

Uchida, K., 443
Uchida, Y., 35
Uddenberg, N., 321
Udry, J. R., 393
Ueba, Y., 75
Ueda, H., 33, 35, 250
Ueda, K., 35
Ulrich, R. E., 393
Umberger, F. T., 118
Underwood, R. H., 36, 249, 417
Unkeless, J. C., 126
Uozumi, T., 430, 432, 444
Uphouse, L. L., 382
Urschel, C. W., 68, 69, 70, 73
Usachev, V. V., 211
Ussing, H. H., 141, 148, 158, 160, 161, 162, 163, 165, 166, 167
Uther, J. B., 38
Utida, S., 142, 148, 149, 151, 153, 154, 155, 157
Uvnäs, B., 353

V

Vacca, C., 209
Vaitukaitis, J. L., 434, 435, 436, 444
Valdes, F., 353, 364
Valenca, L. M., 106
Valtin, H., 252
Vanasin, B., 284
Vanatta, J. C., 162
VanBrunt, E. E., 416
van Deenen, L. L. M., 123, 124
Vandenberg, R. A., 220
Vandenbergh, J. G., 388
Van den Bosch, H., 124
Vander, A. J., 35, 36, 248, 249, 250, 253, 254, 415
Vanderheyden, I., 382, 445
van der Loos, H., 320

Van Der Wal, B., 415, 416
Van Der Walt, J. J., 54, 79
Vande Wiele, R. L., 425, 437, 443, 446, 448, 450
van Dieten, J. A. M. J., 453, 454
Vane, J. R., 250, 265
Van Frank, R. M., 127
van Golde, L. M. G., 124
Van Hall, E. V., 434, 435, 436
van Harreveld, A., 365
Vanhoutte, P. M., 180
Van Kooten, W. J., 185
Van Koppen, A. T. J., 247
van Rees, G. P., 453, 454
Vantrappen, G., 262, 263, 264
Van Wimersma Greidanus, Tj. B., 397, 398
Varene, P., 216, 217
Vasil'eva, V. F., 224
Vassaux, C., 36
Vassort, G., 281, 285
Vatner, S. F., 76
Vaz Dias, H., 121, 127
Veer, J. V. S., 247
Velasco, M. E., 389, 453, 454, 456, 457
Velly, J., 248, 249
Veon, M., 379
Veress, A. T., 254
Verney, E. B., 237, 239
Vernikos-Danellis, J., 396
Vernon, L. P., 121, 127
Verrier, R. L., 79
Vetrovec, G. W., 40
Veyrat, R., 415
Vibert, P. J., 286
Vidal, N., 378
Vierck, C. J., 320
Vignais, P. V., 409
Vilallonga, F. A., 160, 161, 163
Vilhardt, H., 246, 252, 255
Villardita, S., 178
Vincent, J. D., 240
Vincent, N. J., 98
Virks, J., 189, 193
Virutamasen, P., 438
Vogel, J. H. K., 56
Vogt, L., 221, 222
Vogt, M., 382
Von Gierke, H. E., 205, 206, 207
von Noorden, G. K., 294
von Wettstein, D., 119, 121
Voogt, J. L., 452
Vorbeck, M. L., 123
Votava, J., 355
Voûte, C. L., 163
Vyklicky, L., 319

W

Wagner, R., 78
Wahl, P., 128
Wahlberg, J. E., 185
Waite, M., 123, 124
Wakabayashi, K., 432, 446
Waldron, H. A., 325
Waleski, M. V., 457, 459, 460, 461
Walker, J. L., Jr., 349
Walker, V., 247
Walker, W. G., 36, 249
Wall, P. D., 315-36; 315, 316, 317, 318, 319, 320, 323, 324, 325, 326, 329, 339
Wallace, P. G., 119
Wallach, E. E., 438, 442, 447
Waller, S. L., 265
Walsh, D. A., 411
Walsh, J. A., 178
Walsh, P. C., 427, 430, 432, 444
Walter, D. O., 222
Walton, G. M., 411
Waltz, P., 443, 448
Wang, N. S., 91, 92, 99
Wangensteen, O. D., 108, 109
Wannemacher, R. W., Jr., 48
Ward, D. B., 118
Ward, D. N., 434, 435, 436
Warren, J. V., 31
Warren, L., 119, 121, 122, 123
Washizu, Y., 345
Watson, B. S., 412
Watson, K., 119
Weale, R. A., 291
Webb, J. L., 355
Webb, J. P. W., 124
Webb, R. L., 181
Weber, J., Jr., 282
Webster, K. E., 326
Wegmann, H. M., 221, 222
Weibel, E. R., 92, 97, 120, 126
Weick, R. F., 381, 427, 446
Weidermann, M. J., 126
Weier, T. E., 127
Weight, F., 329
Weight, F.F., 355, 361, 362, 363, 364, 365, 366
Weijnen, J. A. W. M., 399
Weinbeck, M., 283, 284
Weinberg, J., 321
Weinberger, M. H., 418, 419
Weiner, J., 414
Weinstein, E., 153
Weinstein, G. D., 182

SUBJECT INDEX

CUMULATIVE INDEXES

VOLUMES 30-34

INDEX OF CONTRIBUTING AUTHORS

COMPARATIVE PHYSIOLOGY